Michael S. Greenwood

ADDISON-WESLEY **MATHEMATICS 10**

Brendan Kelly
Professor of Mathematics
University of Toronto
Toronto, Ontario

Bob Alexander
Assistant Co-ordinator
of Mathematics
Toronto Board of Education
Toronto, Ontario

Paul Atkinson
Principal
Cameron Heights
Collegiate Institute
Kitchener, Ontario

Addison-Wesley Publishers Limited

Don Mills, Ontario
Reading, Massachusetts
Menlo Park, California
New York
Wokingham, England
Amsterdam • Bonn
Sydney • Singapore
Tokyo • Madrid
San Juan

Design: John Zehethofer

Editorial:
Dianne Goffin
Bonnie DiMalta

Photo Credits

The publisher wishes to thank the following sources for photographs and other illustrative materials used in this book. We will gladly receive information enabling us to rectify any errors or references in credits.

xiii, British Museum; xviii, ZEFA/Masterfile; xx, Harold M. Lambert/Miller Services; xxii, IBM Canada Ltd.; 1, E. Simonsen/Miller Services; 7, Sherman Hines/Masterfile; 11, Canapress Photo Service; 18, Royal Canadian Mint; 45, H. Armstrong Roberts/Miller Services; 46, Erich Hoyt; 59, Dianne Goffin; 62, H. Armstrong Roberts/Miller Services; 63, Four by Five Inc./W. Woodworth; 64, (1.) Canapress Photo Service; 64, (r.) Richard Harrington/Miller Services; 71, H. Armstrong Roberts/Miller Services; 72, Michael King/Masterfile; 75, Addison-Wesley Photo Library; 84, Gabe Palmer/Masterfile; 109, AM/Keystone Press Agency; 119, H. Armstrong Roberts/Miller Services; 132, Camerique/Miller Services; 139, Ottawa Rough Riders Football Club; 144, Minneapolis Star and Tribune/3M; 150, All-Sport/Masterfile; 155, Camerique/Miller Services; 162, Canapress Photo Service; 163, Australian High Commission, Ottawa; 174, Mike Dobel/Masterfile; 176, Capital Press Service/Miller Services; 189, Camerique/Miller Services; 196, Mike Dobel/Masterfile; 200, H. Armstrong Roberts/Miller Services; 213, H. Armstrong Roberts/Miller Services; 217, Camerique/Miller Services; 223, Canada Steamship Lines; 232, Inco Ltd./Rene T. Dionne Photography ltd.; 238, Eric Hayes/Miller Services; 257, W. Griebeling/Miller Services; 258, Al Harvey/Masterfile; 282 (top), Kroll/Miller Services; 282 (bottom), Truck & Tractor Equipment Limited, Mississauga; 283, David Alexander; 284, All-Sport Photography, USA/Tony Duffy/Masterfile; 288, Outboard Marine Corporation of Canada Ltd.; 294, J. Jacquemain/Miller Services; 296, Tony Stone Worldwide/Masterfile; 301, Canada Steamship Lines; 305, CP Rail; 310, SSC-Photocentre; 315, Fraser Day; 321, Camerique/Miller Services; 341, Peter Christopher/Masterfile; 342, City of Montreal, Public Relations, H. Armstrong Roberts/Miller Services, Camerique/Miller Services, Harold M. Lambert/Miller Services; 343, CP Photos, Camerique/Miller Services, Bob Alexander, Bob Alexander, Ontario Ministry of Industry & Tourism; 344, H. Armstrong Roberts/Miller Services; 348, NASA; 349, Fraser Day; 352, Bill Brooks/Masterfile; 355, J. Jacquemain/Miller Services; 362 (right), J.A. Kraulis/Masterfile; 369, H. Armstrong Roberts/Miller Services; 370, United States Air Force Academy; 377, SSC-Photocentre; 379 (r. & l.), Bob Alexander; 382, Camerique/Miller Services; 387, Bettmann Archives; 398, Bob Alexander; Benjamin Rondel/Masterfile; 401, NASA; 402, Fraser Day; 411 (left), The Westin Peachtree Plaza, Atlanta; 411 (r.), Ontario Ministry of Natural Resources; 416, NASA; 422, Cordon Art; 433, The Toronto Star; 434, Four by Five Inc./E. Cohen; 438, Amazing Horizons/Sygma; 444, Canadian Ladies' Golf Association; 448, Addison-Wesley Photo Library; 455, The Canadian Red Cross Society—Ontario Division; 458, Global Television Network, Fraser Day; 466, Fraser Day; 477, Addison-Wesley Photo Library; 478, Al Harvey/Masterfile; 479, Ontario Ministry of Industry & Tourism; 480, Bob Alexander; 485, Bob Alexander; 504, Travel Alberta.

Written, printed, and bound in Canada

EF— BP —92

ISBN 0-201-18642-X

Features of Mathematics 10

INTRODUCTION

A unique 12-page introductory unit entitled *Perspectives in Mathematics* presents a brief outline of the historical development of the natural numbers. (See pages xiii-xxiv). This unit illustrates that the calculator and the computer are useful tools for exploring some mathematical problems, while other problems are better solved without them.

This material can be studied at any time as a unit, or the individual sections can be studied separately.

APPLICATIONS OF MATHEMATICS

Students can better understand mathematical principles when they are related to their applications. For this reason, applications are integrated throughout *Mathematics 10*.

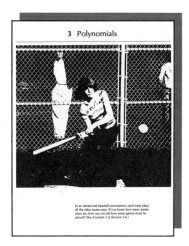

The majority of chapters begin with an illustrated application of the mathematics in the chapter.

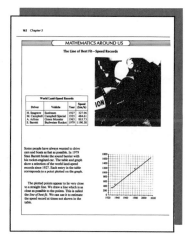

Feature pages entitled *Mathematics Around Us* outline some applications of mathematics in the sciences, the arts, business and industry.

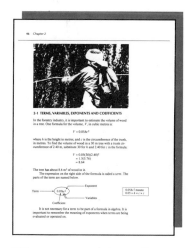

Where appropriate, sections begin with an application which illustrates the necessity for the mathematics that follows. Applications are also included in most of the exercises.

CONCEPT DEVELOPMENT

Mathematics 10 is carefully sequenced to develop concepts in mathematics. Concepts are explained with several examples, each of which has a detailed solution.

REINFORCEMENT

An abundance of exercises is provided to reinforce skills and concepts. These exercises are graded by difficulty with an appropriate balance of A, B, and C exercises. The A exercises may sometimes be completed mentally and the answers given orally or the questions may be used as additional examples when teaching the lesson. The B exercises are intended for the students to consolidate their learning of the concepts that were taught. The C exercises present a challenge and usually involve extensions of the concepts taught in that section.

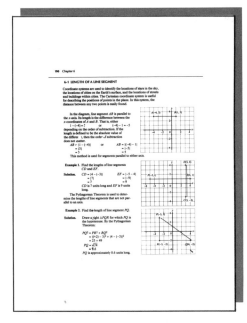

Review Exercises and Cumulative Reviews provide additional practice. Answers to all questions are included in the text.

TECHNOLOGY

A contemporary mathematics program must reflect the impact of calculators and computers on society.

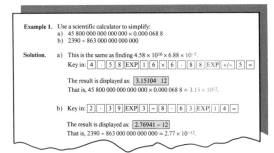

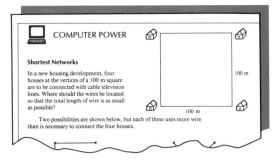

Mathematics 10 assumes that students will use calculators, as needed.

Keying sequences are given for scientific calculators and 4-function calculators, where appropriate.

Computer Power features provide opportunities for students to explore mathematical problems using a computer. It is assumed that students know how to enter a program in BASIC language, but it is not necessary for them to understand the program.

PROBLEM SOLVING

Problem solving is integrated throughout the program, with many of the exercises providing challenging problems for the students to solve. In addition, a variety of special features are included which promote the development of problem solving skills.

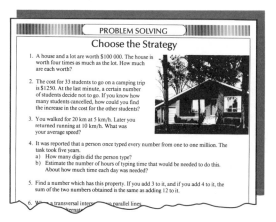

A two page spread in every chapter focuses on the development of problem solving strategies.

Choose the Strategy pages provide students with the opportunity to select and apply the learned strategies.

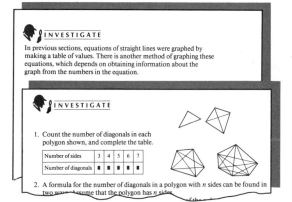

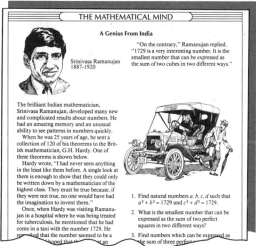

Frequent brief *Investigate* sections are starting points for mathematical investigations. They always relate to the concepts that are developed in the sections in which they occur.

    Longer *Investigate* sections lead students to conclusions which they formulate. Students are more likely to retain knowledge that they discover for themselves.

The Mathematical Mind highlights historical developments in mathematics, and includes anecdotes of human interest that are part of its history. In this context, interesting problems are presented for the students to solve.

Contents

Perspectives In Mathematics: The Natural Numbers

Operations Revisited   *xiv*

The Calculating Prodigies   *xvi*

The Ultimate Prodigy: The Calculator   *xviii*

The Power of Technology   *xx*

The Power of the Mind   *xxii*

A Famous Unsolved Problem   *xxiv*

1 The Real Numbers

1–1 The Natural Numbers   *2*
    COMPUTER POWER: The Euclidean Algorithm   *6*

1–2 The Integers   *7*

1–3 Absolute Value   *9*
    MATHEMATICS AROUND US: The Bermuda Triangle   *11*
    PROBLEM SOLVING: Look for a Pattern   *12*

1–4 The Rational Numbers   *14*

1–5 Radicals   *18*

1–6 The Irrational Numbers   *21*
    THE MATHEMATICAL MIND: A Short History of π *24*

1–7 The Pythagorean Theorem   *25*

1–8 Multiplying Radicals   *30*

1–9 Adding and Subtracting Radicals   *33*

1–10 Combined Operations With Radicals   *37*

1–11 Dividing Radicals   *39*
    MATHEMATICS AROUND US: Simple Interest   *42*
    REVIEW EXERCISES   *43*

2 Exponents

2–1 Terms, Variables, Exponents and Coefficients   *46*
    THE MATHEMATICAL MIND: The Four Squares Problem   *49*
    COMPUTER POWER: Compound Interest   *50*

2–2 Integral Exponents   *52*

2–3 The Exponent Laws   *56*

2–4 Scientific Notation   *59*
    PROBLEM SOLVING: Check for Hidden Assumptions   *62*
    MATHEMATICS AROUND US: Tiny Plants With Shells   *64*

2–5 Fractional Exponents *65*
REVIEW EXERCISES *68*
CUMULATIVE REVIEW *69*

3 Polynomials

3–1 Adding and Subtracting Monomials *72*
MATHEMATICS AROUND US: Gwennap Pit *75*
3–2 Multiplying and Dividing Monomials *76*
3–3 Adding and Subtracting Polynomials *79*
PROBLEM SOLVING: Solve a Simpler Problem *82*
3–4 Multiplying Monomials and Polynomials *84*
3–5 Multiplying Polynomials *88*
INVESTIGATE: Number Patterns *92*
3–6 Common Factors *93*
MATHEMATICS AROUND US: The World's Tallest Building *97*
3–7 Factoring Trinomials of the Form $x^2 + bx + c$ *98*
3–8 Factoring Trinomials of the Form $ax^2 + bx + c$ *101*
3–9 Factoring a Difference of Squares *104*
REVIEW EXERCISES *107*

4 Rational Expressions

4–1 Simplifying Rational Expressions *110*
4–2 Multiplying and Dividing Rational Expressions *116*
MATHEMATICS AROUND US: Meeting the World's Water Needs *119*
4–3 Adding and Subtracting Rational Expressions with Monomial Denominators *120*
4–4 Adding and Subtracting Rational Expressions *124*
THE MATHEMATICAL MIND: A Genius From India *129*
PROBLEM SOLVING: Introduce A Variable *130*
4–5 Applications of Rational Expressions *132*
PROBLEM SOLVING: Choose the Strategy *136*
REVIEW EXERCISES *137*

5 Equations and Inequalities

5–1 Solving Equations in One Variable *140*
5–2 Solving Equations Involving Rational Expressions *144*
5–3 Solving Inequalities *148*

5–4 **Rearranging Formulas** *150*
    MATHEMATICS AROUND US: Typing Speeds *155*
5–5 **Translating Words Into Symbols** *156*
5–6 **Solving Problems Using Equations** *158*
    MATHEMATICS AROUND US: The Line of Best Fit—Speed
                    Records *162*
5–7 **Graphing Linear Equations in Two Variables** *164*
    THE MATHEMATICAL MIND: Diophantine Equations *168*
    COMPUTER POWER: Diophantine Equations *169*
5–8 **Graphing Linear Inequalities** *170*
5–9 **Graphing Non-Linear Relations** *174*
    PROBLEM SOLVING: Work Backwards *178*
5–10 **Solving Quadratic Equations** *180*
    REVIEW EXERCISES *185*
    CUMULATIVE REVIEW *187*

6 Coordinate Geometry: Line Segments

6–1 **Length of a Line Segment** *190*
    COMPUTER POWER: Shortest Networks *194*
6–2 **Midpoint of a Line Segment** *196*
    THE MATHEMATICAL MIND: The Invention of Coordinate
                    Geometry *199*
6–3 **Slope of a Line Segment** *200*
6–4 **Slopes of Parallel Line Segments** *205*
6–5 **Slopes of Perpendicular Line Segments** *208*
    PROBLEM SOLVING: Use a Graph *212*
    MATHEMATICS AROUND US: The Line of Best Fit—Long Distance
                    Telephone Calls *214*
    REVIEW EXERCISES *215*

7 Coordinate Geometry: The Straight Line

7–1 **The Slope of a Line** *218*
7–2 **Direct Variation** *223*
7–3 **Partial Variation** *228*
    MATHEMATICS AROUND US: The Line of Best Fit—Growing
                    Vegetables Underground *232*
    INVESTIGATE: Graphing Equations of the Form $y = mx + b$ *233*
7–4 **The Equation of a Line: Part I** *234*
    PROBLEM SOLVING: Draw a Diagram *238*

7–5 The Equation of a Line: Part II   *240*
7–6 Interpreting the Equation $Ax + By + C = 0$ *245*
7–7 Working With Parallel and Perpendicular Lines   *250*
    REVIEW EXERCISES   *253*
    CUMULATIVE REVIEW   *255*

8 Solving Linear Systems

8–1 Solving Systems of Linear Equations by Graphing   *258*
8–2 Properties of Linear Systems   *261*
8–3 Solving Linear Systems by Addition or Subtraction   *265*
8–4 Solving Linear Systems by Substitution   *269*
8–5 Number of Solutions of a Linear System   *271*
    THE MATHEMATICAL MIND: A Scottish Prodigy   *274*
8–6 Translating Words Into Symbols   *276*
8–7 Solving Problems Using Equations: Part I   *279*
    MATHEMATICS AROUND US: How Fast Do Glaciers Move?   *283*
8–8 Solving Problems Using Equations: Part II   *284*
    PROBLEM SOLVING: Use a Table   *288*
8–9 Solving Problems Using Equations: Part III   *292*
    COMPUTER POWER: A Formula For Linear Systems   *297*
    PROBLEM SOLVING: Choose the Strategy   *298*
    REVIEW EXERCISES   *299*

9 Coordinates and Transformations

9–1 Transformations as Mappings   *302*
9–2 Translations   *305*
9–3 Rotations   *310*
9–4 Reflections   *315*
9–5 Dilatations   *321*
    MATHEMATICS AROUND US: The Pantograph   *327*
9–6 Images of Lines   *328*
    COMPUTER POWER: Images of Lines   *332*
9–7 Applications of Transformations   *333*
    PROBLEM SOLVING: Transform, Solve, Transform   *336*
    REVIEW EXERCISES   *338*
    CUMULATIVE REVIEW   *339*

10 Reasoning and Geometry

MATHEMATICS AROUND US: Recognizing Geometric Figures *342*

10-1 Inductive Reasoning *344*
PROBLEM SOLVING: Look for a Counterexample *346*
THE MATHEMATICAL MIND: A Famous Example of Intuitive
Reasoning *348*

10-2 Deductive Reasoning *349*
10-3 The Opposite Angle Theorem *352*
10-4 The Supplementary Angle Theorem *354*
10-5 Using Deductive Reasoning in Geometry *356*
10-6 The Parallel Lines Theorem *359*
10-7 The Angle Sum Theorem *364*
REVIEW EXERCISES *368*

11 Congruence in Geometry

11-1 Congruent Triangles *370*
11-2 The Isosceles Triangle Theorem *377*
11-3 Properties of a Parallelogram *382*
THE MATHEMATICAL MIND: A Best Seller From Way Back *387*
11-4 Proving the Pythagorean Theorem *388*
PROBLEM SOLVING: Use Indirect Proof *392*
11-5 Proofs using Transformations *394*
MATHEMATICS AROUND US: Geometric Figures and Their
Properties *398*

REVIEW EXERCISES *399*

12 Three-Dimensional Geometry

12-1 Constructing Cylinders and Cones *402*
12-2 Surface Area of Cylinders and Cones *406*
INVESTIGATE: The Volume of a Cone *410*
12-3 Volume of Cylinders and Cones *411*
PROBLEM SOLVING: Use Spatial Visualization *416*
INVESTIGATE: The Surface Area of a Sphere *418*
INVESTIGATE: The Volume of a Sphere *419*
12-4 Surface Area and Volume of a Sphere *420*
THE MATHEMATICAL MIND: Archimedes of Syracuse *424*
COMPUTER POWER: Designing Package Sizes *426*
MATHEMATICS AROUND US: Estimating the Size of a Molecule *428*

REVIEW EXERCISES *429*

CUMULATIVE REVIEW *431*

13 Statistics and Probability

13–1 Interpreting Graphs *434*
13–2 Collecting and Organizing Data *438*
13–3 Measures of Central Tendency *444*
13–4 Scatterplots and Trends *448*
13–5 Manipulating Data: The Median Fit Line *450*
13–6 Manipulating Data: Smoothing Graphs *452*
 COMPUTER POWER: The Median Fit Line *454*
 COMPUTER POWER: Smoothing Data *455*
13–7 Comparing Samples with Populations *456*
 MATHEMATICS AROUND US: Estimating Wildlife Populations *462*
13–8 Sampling and Predicting *463*
13–9 Probability *466*
13–10 The Probability of Two or More Events *470*
 PROBLEM SOLVING: Consider All Cases *474*

 REVIEW EXERCISES *476*

14 Trigonometry

14–1 Similar Triangles *480*
14–2 The Tangent Ratio in Right Triangles *487*
14–3 The Sine and Cosine Ratios in Right Triangles *494*
14–4 Solving Right Triangles *501*
 MATHEMATICS AROUND US: Gondola Lifts in Banff and Jasper National Parks *504*
14–5 Applications of the Trigonometric Ratios *505*
 PROBLEM SOLVING: Use a Model *508*
 PROBLEM SOLVING: Choose the Strategy *510*
 REVIEW EXERCISES *511*
 ANSWERS *515*
 INDEX *543*

Perspectives in Mathematics
The Natural Numbers

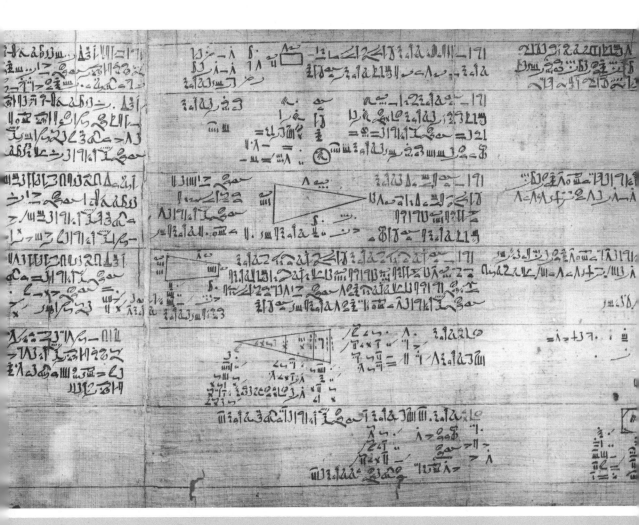

Throughout history, people have used different symbols to represent the natural or counting numbers 1, 2, 3, 4,...Some of these symbols can be found on this illustration from the *Rhind papyrus*, which dates from 1650 B.C. Although mathematicians have studied the natural numbers for hundreds of years, they are still learning more about them.

OPERATIONS REVISITED

Eight hundred years ago, people in Europe did arithmetic using Roman numerals. Although they felt comfortable with this system, they had to keep inventing new symbols for larger numbers, and it was very difficult to do certain arithmetic computations.

Leonardo Fibonacci
(1175 - 1250)

The Hindu-Arabic system was introduced in Europe by Leonardo Fibonacci. He travelled widely in his childhood and learned this system from merchants in the Middle East. He quickly realized that it was far superior to the clumsy Roman numerals still used in Europe.

The central idea of the Hindu-Arabic system is the concept of place value, which assigns meanings to digits written beside each other. Thus 574 means 500 + 70 + 4. This has two great advantages over the Roman system.

- Large numbers can be represented without inventing more symbols. In Roman numerals a certain year would be represented as MCMLXXXVIII. In Hindu-Arabic numerals the year is 1988.

- Arithmetic computations are simplified. In Roman numerals, the product of XXXVIII and VI is CCXXVIII. Using Hindu-Arabic numerals, the product is

$$\begin{array}{r} 38 \\ \times\ 6 \\ \hline 228 \end{array}$$

Example. Find the missing digits.

$$
\begin{array}{r}
\blacksquare 67 \\
\times\, 4 \\
\hline
2\blacksquare 6\blacksquare
\end{array}
$$

Solution. Since $4 \times 7 = 28$, the final digit in the product is 8.
Continuing the multiplication, there are two possibilities for the other digits.

$$
\begin{array}{r}
567 \\
\times\, 4 \\
\hline
2268
\end{array}
\qquad \text{and} \qquad
\begin{array}{r}
667 \\
\times\, 4 \\
\hline
2668
\end{array}
$$

EXERCISES

1. Estimate which products are less than 1000; greater than 2000.

   a) $\begin{array}{r} 22 \\ \times\, 38 \\ \hline \end{array}$
   b) $\begin{array}{r} 43 \\ \times\, 31 \\ \hline \end{array}$
   c) $\begin{array}{r} 84 \\ \times\, 17 \\ \hline \end{array}$
   d) $\begin{array}{r} 53 \\ \times\, 49 \\ \hline \end{array}$
   e) $\begin{array}{r} 28 \\ \times\, 54 \\ \hline \end{array}$
   f) $\begin{array}{r} 64 \\ \times\, 15 \\ \hline \end{array}$

2. Estimate which quotients are less than 10; greater than 20.

   a) $\dfrac{365}{41}$
   b) $\dfrac{646}{29}$
   c) $\dfrac{584}{51}$
   d) $\dfrac{306}{18}$
   e) $\dfrac{1340}{59}$
   f) $\dfrac{520}{72}$

3. From the six numbers in the box, find two
   with a product closest to

   a) 500   b) 1000   c) 2000

15	25	35
45	55	65

4. Find the missing digits.

   a) $\begin{array}{r} 3\blacksquare\blacksquare \\ \times\, 7 \\ \hline \blacksquare 492 \end{array}$
   b) $\begin{array}{r} \blacksquare 17 \\ \times\, 8 \\ \hline 25\blacksquare\blacksquare \end{array}$
   c) $\begin{array}{r} \blacksquare\blacksquare\blacksquare \\ \times\, \blacksquare \\ \hline 36 \end{array}$
   d) $\begin{array}{r} \blacksquare\blacksquare\blacksquare \\ \times\, \blacksquare \\ \hline 80 \end{array}$
   e) $\begin{array}{r} 4\blacksquare \\ \times\, \blacksquare \\ \hline \blacksquare\blacksquare 9 \end{array}$
   f) $\begin{array}{r} \blacksquare 3\blacksquare \\ \times\, 4 \\ \hline \blacksquare\blacksquare 0 \end{array}$

5. Find the path from START to FINISH which passes through each point only once
   and which has the least sum; the greatest sum.

   a)

   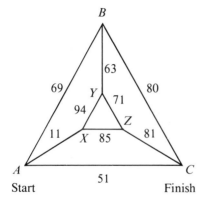

   b)

   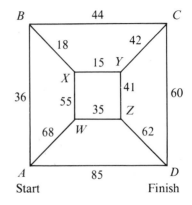

THE CALCULATING PRODIGIES

Would you pay money to watch a child do mental arithmetic? In the nineteenth century this was a popular form of entertainment, for there were a few young children who possessed extraordinary powers of mental calculation. Their parents often made money by taking them on tour to demonstrate their powers publicly.

One of these prodigies was Zerah Colburn (1804-1840), who toured the United States and Europe before he was ten years old. This is one of the questions he did mentally. "What is the product of 21 734 and 543?" Zerah gave the correct answer instantly, 11 801 562.

Zerah and other child prodigies multiplied large numbers by breaking them into parts and multiplying from left to right. Although they worked with much larger numbers, the following examples illustrate their method.

Example 1.   Multiply mentally.

    a) 7×53 b) 8×235 c) 8×38 d) 6×149

Solution.

a) $7 \times 53 = 7(50 + 3)$
              $= 7(50) + 7(3)$
              $= 350 + 21$
              $= 371$

b) $8 \times 235 = 8(200 + 30 + 5)$
                $= 8(200) + 8(30) + 8(5)$
                $= 1600 + 240 + 40$
                $= 1880$

c) $8 \times 38 = 8(40 - 2)$
              $= 320 - 16$
              $= 304$

d) $6 \times 149 = 6(150 - 1)$
                $= 900 - 6$
                $= 894$

Can you multiply products like those in *Example 1* mentally? You may find that with a little practice you can do this more quickly than with paper and pencil.

The child prodigies frequently combined the factors of one number with another number when it was possible, to make the calculations simpler.

Example 2. Multiply mentally.

a) 362×5
b) 25×48

Solution. a) $362 \times 5 = 181 \times 2 \times 5$
$= 181 \times 10$
$= 1810$

b) $25 \times 48 = 25 \times 4 \times 12$
$= 100 \times 12$
$= 1200$

EXERCISES

Do *Exercises 1* to *4* mentally.

1. Simplify.

   a) 8×43 b) 6×52 c) 4×35 d) 4×625
   e) 5×342 f) 5×734 g) 6×825 h) 7×509
   i) 9×79 j) 7×199 k) 12×29 l) 6×498

2. Simplify.

   a) 5×284 b) 5×638 c) 25×412 d) 864×25
   e) $900 \div 5$ f) $1200 \div 25$ g) $900 \div 25$ h) $420 \div 35$

3. How much would you save in one year by getting the subscription instead of buying the magazine at the newsstand?

MAGAZINE SUBSCRIPTIONS
12 issues $27.00
Newsstand price . . . . $ 2.50

4. The average heartbeat pumps 50 mL of blood through the heart.
   a) If a person has 5 L of blood, how many heartbeats are needed to pump it once through the heart?
   b) If the heart beats 75 times per minute, how long would it take?

5. The child prodigies may have been aware of a shortcut for multiplying certain 2-digit numbers. You can discover this shortcut by completing these products.

   a) i) 35×35 ii) 75×75
          36×34 76×74
          37×33 77×73
          38×32 78×72
          39×31 79×71

   b) Examine the results in part (a) and look for a pattern. Can you find the shortcut? If you did, use it to state the following products.

   i) 65×65 ii) 84×86 iii) 52×58 iv) 23×27
   v) 81×89 vi) 67×63 vii) 96×94 viii) 49×41

THE ULTIMATE PRODIGY: THE CALCULATOR

Many years ago people were impressed by the child prodigies who could do difficult computations mentally. Today we take for granted that everyone can do the same kinds of computations with a calculator. Calculators are tools which allow us to think about problems in a different way. For example, the key to the following problem is recognizing that it can be solved by division. The actual computation is of secondary importance, and can be done with a calculator.

Example 1. For economical publication, the total number of pages in a book should be a multiple of 16. A manuscript has 586 pages. Determine if 586 is a multiple of 16.

Solution. Using paper and pencil, this problem could be solved by long division. A more efficient method is to use a calculator.

Key in: $\boxed{5}\ \boxed{8}\ \boxed{6}\ \boxed{\div}\ \boxed{1}\ \boxed{6}\ \boxed{=}$

The result is 36.625.

Since the result is not a whole number, 586 is not a multiple of 16.

As this example indicates, a calculator can be used to test if one number is divisible by another number.

Test for Divisibility

To test if number a is divisible by number b, use a calculator to find $a \div b$. If the result is a whole number, then a is divisible by b.

Example 2. How many pages should be deleted from the manuscript in *Example 1* for the total number of pages to be divisible by 16?

Solution. Since $586 \div 16 = 36.625$, multiply 36 by 16.

Key in: $\boxed{3}\,\boxed{6}\,\boxed{\times}\,\boxed{1}\,\boxed{6}\,\boxed{=}$

The result is 576.

This indicates that the manuscript should have 576 pages. Therefore, 10 pages should be deleted.

Can you solve *Example 2* in a different way?

EXERCISES

Use a calculator.

1. Find which of these numbers are divisible by 16.
   a) 368   b) 512   c) 660   d) 812   e) 1456   f) 1798

2. Find which of these numbers are multiples of 48.
   a) 572   b) 816   c) 1488   d) 1776   e) 2260   f) 3502

3. Determine if the first number in each pair is divisible by the second number.
   a) 5640, 12   b) 2584, 17   c) 2049, 23   d) 1348, 24
   e) 7161, 31   f) 4836, 52   g) 4992, 64   h) 8068, 72

4. A manuscript for a book has 735 pages.
   a) Explain why 735 is not divisible by 16.
   b) How many pages should be deleted from the manuscript for the total number of pages to be divisible by 16?
   c) How many pages could be added to the manuscript to have the total number of pages divisible by 16?

5. a) There is only one number between 700 and 710 which is divisible by 32. Find the number.
   b) Are there any numbers between 710 and 720 which are divisible by 32? Explain.

6. a) Find the greatest 3-digit number which is divisible by 18.
   b) Find the least 4-digit number which is divisible by 18.

7. There is only one number between 500 and 600 which is divisible by both 7 and 11. Find the number.

THE POWER OF TECHNOLOGY

The computer has changed dramatically the kinds of problems that mathematicians and scientists study. For example, we can use a calculator to test if 3 is a factor of 2001. But suppose we wanted to know *all* the factors of 2001. Even with a calculator, it would be time-consuming to discover that the factors of 2001 are 1, 3, 23, 29, 69, 87, 667 and 2001.

The computer program below can be used to find all the factors of any natural number. To enter the program, follow these steps.

- Type NEW and then press $\boxed{\text{RETURN}}$.

- Type each line exactly as it appears.

- Press $\boxed{\text{RETURN}}$ at the end of each line.

```
100 REM *** NUMBER FACTORS ***
110 INPUT "WHAT NUMBER DO YOU WANT TO FACTOR? ";N
120 K=0
130 FOR I=1 TO SQR(N)
140    IF N/I>INT(N/I) THEN 170
150    PRINT I,N/I
160    K=K+1
170 NEXT I
180 IF K=1 THEN 200
190 PRINT "THESE ARE THE FACTORS OF "N:GOTO 210
200 PRINT N" IS A PRIME NUMBER"
210 END
```

Example. Find all the factors of these numbers.
a) 2001   b) 2003

Solution. Use the program. Type RUN and then press $\boxed{\text{RETURN}}$. The computer
will ask for the number to be factored. Enter the number and press
$\boxed{\text{RETURN}}$. The computer will print all the factors of the number. These
are the results for the above numbers.

a) $\begin{array}{ll} 1 & 2001 \\ 3 & 667 \\ 23 & 87 \\ 29 & 69 \end{array}$
THESE ARE THE FACTORS OF 2001

b) $\begin{array}{ll} 1 & 2003 \end{array}$
2003 IS A PRIME NUMBER

Some of the ways in which the computer enhances mathematical
investigations are illustrated in the COMPUTER POWER pages of
this book. These pages contain programs in the BASIC computer language, such as the one above. You can use the programs to explore new
problems using the power of this technology.

EXERCISES

Use the above program.

1. Find all the factors of these numbers.
   a) 36   b) 84   c) 100   d) 331   e) 361   f) 444
   g) 759   h) 797   i) 841   j) 1000   k) 1001   l) 2222

2. Find all the factors of these numbers.
   a) 11 881   b) 104 887   c) 109 319   d) 160 801
   e) 369 389   f) 417 577   g) 1 018 081   h) 3 516 241

3. Examine the results of *Exercises 1* and *2*.
   a) Which numbers have an odd number of factors?
   b) What kind of numbers are they?

4. There are two prime numbers between 400 and 410. Find the numbers.

5. There is only one prime number between 410 and 420. Find the number.

6. a) Find the greatest 3-digit prime number.
   b) Find the least 4-digit prime number.

7. There are four 3-digit prime numbers which have the digits 3, 7 and 9. What are the
   numbers?

THE POWER OF THE MIND

Much research is being done in the field of artificial intelligence. The ultimate goal of this work is to build computers that are capable of thinking. If such a computer can ever be built, it would have to be able to solve a problem such as the one described below.

Suppose we write the natural numbers in a table with six columns. If we circle the prime numbers, it seems that, except for 2 and 3, they appear only in columns 1 and 5. This suggests the following problem.

- If the table is extended, will the prime numbers continue to appear only in columns 1 and 5? Explain why or why not.

1	2	3	4	5	6
1	2	3	4	5	6
7	8	9	10	11	12
13	14	15	16	17	18
19	20	21	22	23	24
25	26	27	28	29	30
31	32	33	34	35	36
37	38	39	40	41	42
43	44	45	46	47	48
49	50	51	52	53	54
55	56	57	58	59	60
61	62	63	64	65	66
67	68	69	70	71	72
73	74	75	76	77	78

We can solve this problem as follows.

- The numbers in columns 2, 4 and 6 are all divisible by 2. Except for 2, none of these is a prime number.
- The numbers in column 3 are all divisible by 3. Except for 3, none of these is a prime number.
- The only remaining columns are columns 1 and 5. Except for 2 and 3, every prime number must appear in these columns.

What is remarkable about this explanation is that it applies to *all* prime numbers, not just those in the table. This illustrates the power of the mind; we have been able to explain something about every prime number without having to examine every one.

Property of Prime Numbers
Except for 2 and 3, every prime number is either 1 less than a multiple of 6, or 1 more than a multiple of 6.

Example. The numbers below are all prime numbers. Which numbers are
a) 1 less than a multiple of 6?   b) 1 more than a multiple of 6?

311   479   1129   4903   7853   11 113

Solution. Use a calculator to divide each number by 6.

$$311 \div 6 = 51.8333\ldots \qquad\qquad 479 \div 6 = 79.8333\ldots$$
$$1129 \div 6 = 188.1666\ldots \qquad\qquad 4903 \div 6 = 817.1666\ldots$$
$$7853 \div 6 = 1308.8333\ldots \qquad\qquad 11\ 113 \div 6 = 1852.1666\ldots$$

a) The numbers 311, 479, and 7853 have decimal parts which are 0.8333....Hence all these numbers are 1 less than a multiple of 6.

b) The numbers 1129, 4903, and 11 113 have decimal parts which are 0.1666....Hence all these numbers are 1 more than a multiple of 6.

EXERCISES

1. These numbers are all prime numbers. Which numbers are
   a) 1 less than a multiple of 6?   b) 1 more than a multiple of 6?
   - i) 317
   - ii) 401
   - iii) 419
   - iv) 787
   - v) 967
   - vi) 1789
   - vii) 2179
   - viii) 3331
   - ix) 3407
   - x) 5693

2. a) Explain why none of these numbers is a prime number.

   142, 154, 376, 498, 610, 1235

   b) What are the only possible final digits that prime numbers can have?

3. Exactly four of these numbers are prime. Which numbers are they?
   - a) 124
   - b) 315
   - c) 593
   - d) 659
   - e) 700
   - f) 701
   - g) 777
   - h) 816
   - i) 865
   - j) 898
   - k) 907
   - l) 955

4. Three prime numbers have a product of 1990. What are the numbers?

5. Three prime numbers have a product of 1 178 510 611 870. What are the numbers?

A FAMOUS UNSOLVED PROBLEM

Despite the best efforts of the world's greatest mathematicians, there are still thousands of problems which have not yet been solved. A famous example of an unsolved problem is known as *Goldbach's Conjecture*.

In 1742 the German mathematician C. Goldbach suggested that every even number greater than 2 is the sum of two primes.

No one has been able to prove that this is true for all even numbers...

$$4 = 2 + 2$$
$$6 = 3 + 3$$
$$8 = 5 + 3$$
$$10 = 7 + 3$$
$$12 = 7 + 5$$
$$14 = 11 + 3$$
$$16 = 13 + 3$$
$$18 = 13 + 5$$

$$76 = 59 + 17$$
$$78 = 71 + 7$$
$$80 = 37 + 43$$
$$82 = 71 + 11$$
$$84 = 79 + 5$$
$$86 = 83 + 3$$
$$88 = 83 + 5$$

...yet no even number has been found which is not the sum of two primes.

As you can see, the conjecture has been verified for even numbers up to 100 000 000.

$$6904 = 2633 + 4271$$
$$6906 = 1907 + 4999$$
$$6908 = 3391 + 3517$$
$$6910 = 6907 + 3$$

$$99\ 999\ 998 =$$
$$99\ 999\ 931 + 67$$

$$100\ 000\ 000 =$$
$$99\ 999\ 989 + 11$$

EXERCISES

1. Express each number as the sum of two prime numbers.
   a) 20   b) 22   c) 24   d) 72   e) 74
   f) 90   g) 92   h) 100   i) 200   j) 300

2. a) Is it possible for an odd number to be the sum of two prime numbers?
   b) Is every odd number the sum of two prime numbers? Give examples to support your answers.

3. a) Is it possible for a prime number to be the sum of two prime numbers?
   b) Is every prime number the sum of two prime numbers? Give examples to support your answers.

1 The Real Numbers

A ground radar unit detects an aircraft at a height of 10 km, 5 km north and 12 km east of the unit. What is the actual distance of the aircraft from the radar unit? (See *Example 4* in Section 1-7.)

1-1 THE NATURAL NUMBERS

Mathematics began with the set of *natural numbers* {1, 2, 3,...}. They have been studied for thousands of years, and are very useful in solving problems.

Example 1. Two speedboats make test runs around a circuit on Lake Winnipeg starting at the same place and time. Boat *A* makes a lap every 40 s, while boat *B* makes a lap every 50 s. When will the two boats cross the starting line together again?

Solution.   Boat *A* returns to the starting point after:
                40 s, 80 s, 120 s, 160 s, 200 s,...
              Boat *B* returns to the starting point after:
                50 s, 100 s, 150 s, 200 s,...
              The two boats will cross the starting line 200 s, or $3\frac{1}{3}$ min after starting.

The numbers 40, 80, 120, 160, 200,...are *multiples* of 40. Similarly, 50, 100, 150, 200,...are *multiples* of 50. The number 200 is the *least common multiple* (l.c.m.) of 40 and 50. It is the least number that is a multiple of both 40 and 50.

Example 2.   Find the l.c.m. of 24 and 32.

Solution.   The multiples of 24 are: 24, 48, 72, 96,...
              The multiples of 32 are: 32, 64, 96,...
              The least common multiple of 24 and 32 is 96.

If *a* is a multiple of *b*, then *b* is a *factor* of *a*. For example: 1, 2, 3, 6, and 9 are factors of 18, because 18 is a multiple of each number.

Example 3.   List all the factors of both 24 and 32.

Solution.   The factors of 24 are: 1 , 2, 3, 4 , 6, 8 , 12, 24.
              The factors of 32 are: 1 , 2 , 4 , 8 , 16, 32.
              The numbers in color are the factors of both 24 and 32:
              1, 2, 4, 8.

To find the *greatest common factor* (g.c.f.) of two numbers, we select the greatest number which is a factor of both. The greatest common factor of 24 and 32 is 8.

Sometimes a natural number has only two factors, itself and 1. Such a number is called a *prime number*. The numbers 2, 3, 5, 7, 11, 13, 17, and 19 are the primes less than 20. A much larger prime number is 149. We can explain why 149 is a prime number as follows.

Use a calculator to divide 149 by the first few primes:

$$149 \div 2 = 74.5$$
$$149 \div 3 \doteq 49.666\ 667$$
$$149 \div 5 = 29.8$$
$$149 \div 7 \doteq 21.285\ 714$$
$$149 \div 11 \doteq 13.545\ 455$$

Since $\sqrt{149} \doteq 12.2$, from here on the quotients will be less than the divisors.

There is no need to continue because the primes less than $\sqrt{149}$ have already been tested. Since none of these is a factor of 149, then 149 is a prime number.

> To test if a given number, n is a prime number, follow these steps:
>
> *Step 1:* Use a calculator to find $\sqrt{n}$.
>
> *Step 2:* Divide n by all the primes less than $\sqrt{n}$.
>
> *Step 3:* If none of the primes in *Step 2* divide evenly, then n is a prime number.

Example 4. Which of the following are prime numbers?

a) 113　　　　　　　　　　　　b) 247

Solution.　a) $\sqrt{113} \doteq 10.63$. The primes less than 10.63 are 2, 3, 5, and 7. None of these is a factor of 113. Therefore, 113 is a prime.

b) $\sqrt{247} \doteq 15.72$. The primes less than 15.72 are 2, 3, 5, 7, 11, and 13. $247 \div 13 = 19$. Therefore, 247 is not a prime.

Example 5. Express as a product of primes.

a)　65　　　　　b)　120　　　　　c)　252

Solution.

a) 65
$= 5 \times 13$

b) 120
$= 12 \times 10$
$= 4 \times 3 \times 2 \times 5$
$= 2^3 \times 3 \times 5$

c) 252
$= 2 \times 126$
$= 2 \times 2 \times 63$
$= 2^2 \times 3^2 \times 7$

In factoring 120 (*Example 5b*), the first step could have been written in other ways, such as 3×40, or 6×20. No matter how 120 is factored into primes, three factors of 2, one factor of 3, and one factor of 5 are always obtained.

> **Prime Factorization Property**
> Every composite number can be expressed as a product of primes in only one way.

The number 1, having only one factor, is neither prime nor composite.

EXERCISES 1-1

(A)

1. Which of the following are prime numbers?
   a) 34   b) 19   c) 71   d) 85   e) 97   f) 109
   g) 129   h) 132   i) 151   j) 152   k) 177   l) 193

2. Express as a product of prime factors.
   a) 18   b) 28   c) 42   d) 56   e) 64   f) 76
   g) 91   h) 110   i) 143   j) 187   k) 200   l) 223

3. Find all the factors of the following numbers.
   a) 12   b) 16   c) 18   d) 25   e) 32   f) 36
   g) 60   h) 84   i) 97   j) 100   k) 144   l) 200

4. Find the g.c.f. of each of these pairs of numbers.
   a) 24, 36   b) 45, 75   c) 42, 70   d) 35, 60   e) 36, 60
   f) 52, 65   g) 96, 144   h) 64, 112   i) 56, 104   j) 54, 90

5. Find the l.c.m. of each of these pairs of numbers.
   a) 24, 36   b) 16, 24   c) 20, 35   d) 32, 40   e) 18, 30
   f) 45, 75   g) 60, 84   h) 72, 120   i) 84, 105   j) 96, 120

(B)

6. Are all the factors of a composite number less than its square root? Illustrate your answer with three examples.

7. Which natural numbers have an odd number of factors? Why?

8. Three primes have a sum of 38. The greatest is equal to the sum of the other two. What are the primes?

9. Write each of the following as the sum of consecutive natural numbers in as many ways as possible.
   a) 9   b) 15   c) 30

10. Some primes can be written in the form $n^2 + 1$, where n is a natural number. Example: $17 = 4^2 + 1$. Find three more primes of the form $n^2 + 1$.

11. Some primes can be written in the form $2^n - 1$, where n is a natural number. Example: $7 = 2^3 - 1$. Find three more primes of the form $2^n - 1$.

12. Find three primes that have a product of
   a) 646   b) 606   c) 2222

13. The lights on one airport tower flash every 16 s. The lights on another tower flash every 20 s. If they started flashing together, what is the time interval between simultaneous flashes?

14. A textbook, having 14 chapters of equal length, is made by sewing together several 32-page booklets. What is the least number of pages that the book may have?

15. When a band marches in rows of 2, 3, 4, 5, or 6, there is always one member left over.
    a) What is the least number of members in the band?
    b) What is the least number of members in the band if there are no members left over when marching in rows of 7?

16. Two gears, A and B, are assembled with the timing arrows in contact. How many rotations does each gear make between successive contacts of the arrows if the numbers of teeth on the gears are
    a) $A:18, B:12$? b) $A:25, B:20$? c) $A:28, B:21$?
    d) $A:25, B:16$? e) $A:32, B:28$? f) $A:35, B:28$?

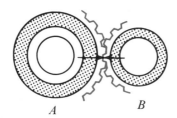

17. Two stock cars race on a 5 km circuit and pass a marker simultaneously. How long will it take the faster car to gain one lap on the slower if their average speeds are
    a) 120 km/h and 100 km/h? b) 150 km/h and 125 km/h?

18. If a certain positive number is doubled, the result is a perfect square. If it is tripled, the result is a perfect cube. Find the number.

19. The number 64 is both a perfect square (since $64 = 8^2$) and a perfect cube (since $64 = 4^3$). Find other integers which are both perfect squares and perfect cubes.

20. Copy and complete the table.

a, b	g.c.f.	l.c.m.	g.c.f. × l.c.m.	ab
9, 12	3	36	108	108
18, 45				
20, 35				
40, 48				

What is the relation between the g.c.f., the l.c.m., and the product of a and b?

21. Find the g.c.f. for each pair of numbers.
    a) 50, 51 b) 189, 190 c) 278, 279
    What conclusion can you make from your answer?

COMPUTER POWER

The Euclidean Algorithm

It is time-consuming to list the factors of two numbers, such as 270 and 84, in order to find their g.c.f. There is a more efficient method known as the *Euclidean algorithm*. It depends on the principle that if x is a factor of both b and $ab + c$, it is also a factor of c.

Example. Find the g.c.f. of 270 and 84.

Solution. Divide 270 by 84:
$$270 = 3(84) + 18$$
The common factors of 270 and 84 are the same as the common factors of 84 and 18. Therefore, the g.c.f. of 270 and 84 is the same as the g.c.f. of 84 and 18. Divide 84 by 18:
$$84 = 4(18) + 12$$
The g.c.f. of 84 and 18 is the same as the g.c.f. of 18 and 12. The division process could be continued further but the g.c.f. of 18 and 12 is easily seen to be 6. Therefore, the g.c.f. of 270 and 84 is 6.

$$\begin{array}{r} 3 \\ 84\overline{)270} \\ 252 \\ \hline 18 \end{array}$$

$$\begin{array}{r} 4 \\ 18\overline{)84} \\ 72 \\ \hline 12 \end{array}$$

Because it involves repeated division, the Euclidean algorithm is ideally suited for computer programming. A simple BASIC program designed to find the g.c.f. of two positive integers follows.

```
100 REM *** EUCLIDEAN ALGORITHM ***
110 INPUT "WHAT ARE THE TWO NUMBERS? ";P,Q
120 R=P-INT(P/Q)*Q
130 IF R>0 THEN P=Q:Q=R:GOTO 120
140 PRINT "THE G.C.F. IS ";Q
150 END
```

When you finish entering the program, type RUN, then press RETURN. Then type one number, a comma, the second number, and press RETURN.

Use the preceding program.

1. Find the g.c.f. of each pair of numbers.
   a) 391, 306 b) 1323, 884 c) 41 992, 30 508

2. Two numbers are said to be *relatively prime* if their g.c.f. is 1. Which of these pairs of numbers are relatively prime?
   a) 27, 16 b) 88, 56 c) 308, 273
   d) 9603, 5841 e) 12 507, 8266 f) 18 886, 10 887

3. Find the g.c.f. of these three numbers.
   a) 432, 288, 243 b) 3584, 3328, 2992

1-2 THE INTEGERS

We know that it can get much colder than freezing, and that a loss is worse than having no profit. Such ideas can be represented by extending the set of natural numbers to include zero and negative numbers. The result is the set of *integers*, I.

$$I = \{\ldots, -3, -2, -1, 0, 1, 2, 3, \ldots\}$$

Just as there is an arithmetic for natural numbers, there is also an arithmetic for integers.

Example 1. Simplify:

a) $(+17) + (-10) - (-3) - (+9)$ b) $(-5)[(+3)(-2) - (-8)(-1)]$

Solution. a) $(+17) + (-10) - (-3) - (+9)$ b) $(-5)[(+3)(-2) - (-8)(-1)]$
                    $= 17 - 10 + 3 - 9$ $= (-5)[(-6) - (+8)]$
                    $= 1$ $= (-5)(-14)$
                                                                                      $= 70$

Example 2. If $x = -3$, $y = -2$, and $z = 5$, find the value of the expression $5x^2y - 3xz^2$.

Solution. $5x^2y - 3xz^2 = 5(-3)^2(-2) - 3(-3)(5)^2$
                              $= 5(9)(-2) + 9(25)$
                              $= -90 + 225$
                              $= 135$

EXERCISES 1-2

Ⓐ

1. Simplify.
   a) $8 - 13$ b) $19 - (-26)$ c) $-9 - 17$ d) $15 - 8 - (-2)$
   e) $-6 + (-4) - (-19)$ f) $14 - (-9) + 5$ g) $2 - (-18) + (-16)$ h) $-23 - 8 - (-11)$

2. Simplify.
   a) $(-3)(-6)$ b) $(+9)(-8)$ c) $(-20)(+15)$ d) $(-12)(+30)$
   e) $(-11)(-7)$ f) $(+80)(-60)$ g) $24 \div (-3) \div 2$ h) $(-15)(-3) \div (-5)$
   i) $(-8)(+5)(-1)$ j) $(-2)(-3)(-4)(-5)$ k) $-(-2)(+3)(-5)(-6)$ l) $(-5)(+13) - (-10)$

Ⓑ

3. Simplify.
   a) $(-2)^2$ b) $-(-2)^2$ c) $(-5)(-2)^2$ d) $(-2)^3$ e) $-(-2)^3$
   f) $(-5)(-2)^3$ g) $-(-4)(-6)$ h) $(-2)(0)(-9)$ i) $(-1)^6$ j) $(-1)^7$

4. Simplify.
   a) $16 - 2(-5)$ b) $3 + 7(-5)$ c) $-23 - 2(-4)$
   d) $(-9)(-12) - 24(3)$ e) $-27 + 6(-9) + 5$ f) $(-7)(3) + (-10) - 12$
   g) $12 \div (-3) + 6(-5)$ h) $-9 + 6(2) - 7$ i) $-25 - 5(-2) - 6$
   j) $54 - 6(-3) + 15$ k) $24 - 3(5) - 4$ l) $45 \div 3 + 3 - 11 \times 2$

5. Simplify.
   a) $(-2)(-5) + (+3)(-4)$ b) $(-8)(+3) - (-2)(-5)$ c) $(+8)(-9) - (-7)(+5)$
   d) $(+6)(-2) + (-7)(-9)$ e) $(+3)^2 + (-4)^2$ f) $(-6)^2 - (-7)^2$
   g) $(-5)^2 + (-8)^2$ h) $(-9)^2 - (+2)^2$ i) $\dfrac{24}{-3} + \dfrac{-20}{-5}$
   j) $\dfrac{-32}{+2} - \dfrac{15}{-3}$ k) $\dfrac{-18}{-9} - \dfrac{12}{-6} + \dfrac{-8}{-4}$ l) $\dfrac{-28}{7} - \dfrac{-48}{-6} + \dfrac{72}{-9}$

6. If $a = -5$ and $b = -3$, find the value of each expression.
   a) $a + b$ b) $a - b$ c) $2a - 5b$ d) $3a + 4b - 6$
   e) $a + ab + b$ f) $(a + b)^2$ g) ab^2 h) a^2b
   i) $(ab)^2$ j) a^2b^2 k) $-(a^2b^3)$ l) $-(a^3b)^2$

7. Simplify.
   a) $-3[5(-2) - 6 + 9]$ b) $6 + 4[12 \div 2 - (-3)(-1)]$
   c) $2[4 + 18 \div (-3) - 2 \times 5]$ d) $[3 - (4 \div 2 \times 10)][2 - 7]$
   e) $2[(-4)(9) - (-12)] \div (7 - 10)$ f) $[-5 - 12 \times 3] - 4(-2)$
   g) $5[-12 \div 3 + (4 - 8) \div (6 - 8)]$ h) $8[3 + 5 - 2(6 - 4) - 1]$

Ⓒ

8. If $x = -2$, $y = 3$, and $z = -1$, evaluate.
   a) $3x^2yz$ b) $5x - 2y + 7z$ c) $2y(-4x) - 3y(-2z)$
   d) $4xyz - 3xy + 7yz$ e) $xy^2 - xz^2 - xyz$ f) $7xyz^2 + 4y^2 - xz^2$
   g) $3y^2z - 2x^2y - xz$ h) $8xyz - 5x^2y^2 + 7xz^3$ i) $\dfrac{5x + 2y}{xz} + \dfrac{xy}{z}$

1-3 ABSOLUTE VALUE

On the number line, the numbers 3 and −3 are each located 3 units from 0. Each is said to have absolute value 3.

$$|3| = 3 \quad \text{and} \quad |-3| = 3 \longleftarrow$$

Read: "absolute value of −3."

The *absolute value* of any number is its distance from 0 on the number line.
The absolute value of a positive number is positive.
The absolute value of a negative number is positive.
The absolute value of zero is zero.

Example 1. Simplify:

    a) $|-17|$ b) $|12 - 22|$ c) $|5| - |-12|$

Solution.
   a) $|-17|$
        $= 17$

   b) $|12 - 22|$
        $= |-10|$
        $= 10$

   c) $|5| - |-12|$
        $= 5 - 12$
        $= -7$

Finding the area of a triangle on a grid is simplified by using absolute value. We assume that the triangle has one vertex at $(0, 0)$.

The area, A, of a triangle with vertices $(0, 0)$, (a, b) and (c, d) is given by the formula:

$$A = \frac{1}{2}|ad - bc|$$

Example 2. Find the area of a triangle with vertices $(0, 0)$, $(-6, 3)$ and $(-2, 5)$.

Solution. Substitute $a = -6$, $b = 3$, $c = -2$ and $d = 5$ in the formula:

$$A = \frac{1}{2}|ad - bc|$$

$$= \frac{1}{2}|(-6)(5) - (3)(-2)|$$

$$= \frac{1}{2}|-30 + 6|$$

$$= \frac{1}{2}|-24|$$

$$= 12$$

The area of the triangle is 12 square units.

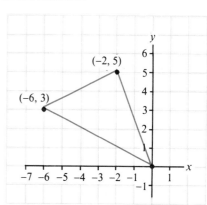

EXERCISES 1-3

(A)

1. Simplify.
   a) $|-29|$ b) $|11|$ c) $|107|$ d) $|-15|$ e) $|6.7|$ f) $|-1.8|$

2. Simplify.
   a) $|3 - 7|$ b) $|-5 + 11|$ c) $|9 - 1|$ d) $|-2 - 5|$
   e) $|14| - |-9|$ f) $|-6| + |-21|$ g) $|-7| + |-3|$ h) $|-2| - |-6|$

3. Simplify.
   a) $5|1 - 7|$ b) $-4|5 - 8|$ c) $-9|-1 - 3|$
   d) $5|-2| + 3|4|$ e) $3|-1| - 2|-6|$ f) $7|-3| - 5|-6|$

4. Find the areas of the triangles with one vertex at the origin and the other vertices having coordinates

   a) $(10, 5)$ and $(2, 8)$ b) $(-6, -3)$ and $(2, 5)$
   c) $(-12, -4)$ and $(10, -3)$ d) $(-3, 9)$ and $(-10, -3)$

(B)

5. Mr. Drake plans to sell a triangular section of his farm for a housing-development project. On a map, the grid references for the three vertices of the section he is selling are $(0, 0)$, $(8, 3)$, and $(2, 12)$, where each number stands for a distance in hecto-metres (hm). What is the area of the section in hectares (ha)?

   | 1 hm = 100 m |
   | 1 ha = 1 hm² |

6. Simplify.
   a) $|-20 - (-37)|$ b) $-|-15 - 9|$ c) $|4 - 9 - 16|$
   d) $2|-19 - (-11)|$ e) $3|4 - 10| + 5|2 - 6|$ f) $5|6 - 2| - 7|-5|$

7. Simplify.
   a) $|12 - 19| - |19 - 12|$ b) $-4|7 - 13| - 2|9 - 14|$ c) $11|2 - 9| - 4|-3|$
   d) $3|-5| + |2(-7) - 4|$ e) $2[5 - |-9| - 3|2 - 4|]$ f) $4[-|6 - 15| - 2|4 - 9|]$

(C)

8. Find the areas of the parallelograms with vertices
   a) $(0, 0), (7, 2), (10, 7), (3, 5)$ b) $(0, 0), (-3, 4), (5, 10), (8, 6)$
   c) $(0, 0), (4, -1), (6, 3), (10, 2)$ d) $(0, 0), (-2, 4), (2, 8), (4, 4)$

9. Find all the values of x which satisfy each equation.
   a) $|x + 1| = 7$ b) $|2x - 1| = 9$ c) $|5x - 7| = -3$
   d) $|x + |x|| = 10$ e) $|x + |x|| = 0$ f) $x + |x| = -2$

MATHEMATICS AROUND US

The Bermuda Triangle

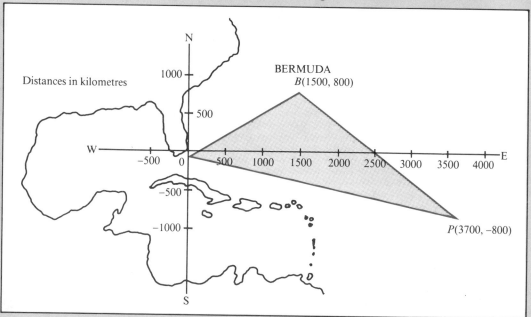

Distances in kilometres

BERMUDA
B(1500, 800)

P(3700, −800)

Over the years, many ships and airplanes have inexplicably disappeared in a region of the Atlantic Ocean. This region has come to be known as the *Bermuda Triangle*. Several books have been written and much research undertaken about this region and the disappearances. The books and the research have done little to solve the mystery of the Bermuda Triangle. To date, no traces of the vanished ships and airplanes have been found.

One side of the Bermuda Triangle is a line segment from Bermuda to the southeast coast of Florida. The other sides extend in a southeasterly direction from Bermuda and Florida to a point in mid-Atlantic. The map shows the approximate location of the Triangle.

QUESTION

- What is the approximate area of the Bermuda Triangle?

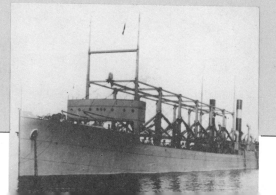

Look for a Pattern

A female-male pair of rabbits produces a new pair of male and female rabbits in their second month, and every month thereafter. Suppose that the new rabbits follow the same pattern. If none of the rabbits dies, how many pairs of rabbits will there be six months later?

Understand the problem

- How long after birth do baby rabbits bear young?
- How many baby rabbits does each pair have when it breeds?
- What sex are the baby rabbits?

Think of a strategy

- Look for a pattern in the number of pairs present after a few months.

Carry out the strategy

- Draw a diagram to show the number of rabbits for each successive month.

- This diagram shows what happens.

- The numbers in the last column form a pattern: 1, 1, 2, 3, 5, 8,...

- Each number after the second number is the sum of the two preceding numbers. By continuing the pattern, we can predict the number of pairs of rabbits at the beginning of any future month.

Month	Pairs of Rabbits	No. of Pairs
1st		1
2nd		1
3rd		2
4th		3
5th		5
6th		8

- After six months there are 8 pairs of rabbits.

Key

Baby rabbits

Adult rabbits

Look back

- This pattern of numbers occurs in many different areas of mathematics, and is known as the *Fibonacci sequence*.

Solve each problem

1. Continue the pattern in the example. How many rabbits will there be at the end of 12 months?

2. Copy and complete each pattern. Continue each pattern for two more lines.

   a)
   $$1^3 = \blacksquare^2$$
   $$1^3 + 2^3 = \blacksquare^2$$
   $$1^3 + 2^3 + 3^3 = \blacksquare^2$$

   b)
   $$6 \times 4 = \blacksquare$$
   $$66 \times 34 = \blacksquare$$
   $$666 \times 334 = \blacksquare$$

   c)
   $$8 \times 7 = \blacksquare$$
   $$98 \times 67 = \blacksquare$$
   $$998 \times 667 = \blacksquare$$

3. The diagram below shows a family tree.
   a) Copy the diagram and continue it, going back at least five generations.
   b) How many people are there in the fifth generation back? the tenth generation back?
   c) How many ancestors do you have in all, going back five generations? ten generations?

Generation Back	Me	Number of People in each Generation
1	M F	2 Parents
2	M F M F	4 Grandparents
3	M F M F M F M F	8 Great-Grandparents

4. A male alien has only one parent, its mother, but a female alien has two parents, its father and its mother.
   a) Construct a family tree for a male alien going back at least five generations.
   b) How many aliens are there in the fifth generation back? the tenth generation back?
   c) How many ancestors does a male alien have in all, going back five generations? ten generations?

5. July 1 is Canada Day each year. The table shows the day of the week on which Canada Day fell from 1968 to 1986.
   a) Copy the table and continue entering the years until you see a pattern develop. Describe the pattern.
   b) Predict the day of the week on which Canada Day will fall in
      i) 1999   ii) 2020

      iii) 2050   iv) 2100

Sun.	Mon.	Tue.	Wed.	Thu.	Fri.	Sat.
	1968	1969	1970	1971		1972
1973	1974	1975		1976	1977	1978
1979		1980	1981	1982	1983	
1984	1985	1986				

1-4 THE RATIONAL NUMBERS

The sum, difference, and product of two integers is an integer. But the quotient of two integers is not necessarily an integer.

$$\frac{7}{+1} = 7 \leftarrow \boxed{\text{integer}} \qquad\qquad \frac{+3}{+4} = 0.75 \leftarrow \boxed{\text{not an integer}}$$

$$\frac{-10}{-2} = 5 \leftarrow \boxed{\text{integer}} \qquad\qquad \frac{+12}{-5} = -2.4 \leftarrow \boxed{\text{not an integer}}$$

All the numbers illustrated above are examples of rational numbers.

> Any number that can be written in the form $\dfrac{m}{n}$, where m and n are integers, and $n \neq 0$, is called a *rational number*.

The rules of arithmetic with integers also apply to rational numbers.

Example 1. Simplify: $\dfrac{2[6 - 3(-4)]}{(+4)(-3)} - \dfrac{(-3)}{4}$

Solution.
$$\frac{2[6 - 3(-4)]}{(+4)(-3)} - \frac{(-3)}{4} = \frac{2(6 + 12)}{-12} + \frac{3}{4}$$
$$= -\frac{36}{12} + \frac{9}{12}$$
$$= -\frac{27}{12}$$
$$= -\frac{9}{4}$$

Example 2. If $x = \dfrac{-2}{3}$ and $y = \dfrac{2}{-5}$, evaluate $\dfrac{3x^2 - xy}{2y}$.

Solution.
$$\frac{3x^2 - xy}{2y} = \frac{3\left(\frac{-2}{3}\right)^2 - \left(\frac{-2}{3}\right)\left(\frac{2}{-5}\right)}{2\left(\frac{2}{-5}\right)}$$
$$= \frac{3\left(\frac{4}{9}\right) - \frac{4}{15}}{-\frac{4}{5}}$$
$$= \left(\frac{4}{3} - \frac{4}{15}\right) \times \left(-\frac{5}{4}\right)$$
$$= \left(\frac{20 - 4}{15}\right) \times \left(-\frac{5}{4}\right)$$
$$= \frac{16}{15} \times \left(-\frac{5}{4}\right)$$
$$= -\frac{4}{3}$$

Rational numbers may be expressed in various forms. The answer to *Example 1* may be written: $-\dfrac{9}{4}$, or $-2\,\dfrac{1}{4}$, or -2.25. The answer to *Example 2* may be written: $-\dfrac{4}{3}$, or $-1\,\dfrac{1}{3}$, or $-1.\overline{3}$.

Any rational number in the form $\dfrac{m}{n}$ can be expressed in decimal form by dividing the numerator by the denominator. The decimal will either terminate or repeat. Conversely, any terminating or repeating decimal can be expressed in the form $\dfrac{m}{n}$.

Example 3. Express these numbers in the form $\dfrac{m}{n}$, where $n \neq 0$:

         a)   5.23   b) $0.\overline{4}$ c) $3.5\,\overline{37}$

Solution.   a)   5.23 means $5\,\dfrac{23}{100}$, or $\dfrac{523}{100}$.

        b)   Let $x = 0.444\ldots$ ①

           Multiply ① by 10 since one digit repeats: Subtract ① from ②

$$10x = 4.444\ldots \quad ②$$
$$\underline{\;\;x = 0.444\ldots \quad ①}$$
$$9x = 4$$
$$x = \dfrac{4}{9}$$

           Therefore, $0.\overline{4} = \dfrac{4}{9}$

        c)   Let $x = 3.5\,37\,37\,37\ldots$ ①

           Multiply ① by 10 to isolate the repeating digits:

$$10x = 35.37\,37\,37\ldots \quad ②$$

           Multiply ② by 100 since two digits repeat: Subtract ② from ③

$$1000x = 3537.37\,37\,37\ldots \quad ③$$
$$\underline{\;\;10x = \;\;\;\;35.37\,37\,37\ldots \quad ②}$$
$$990x = 3502$$
$$x = \dfrac{3502}{990}$$

           Therefore, $3.5\,\overline{37} = \dfrac{3502}{990}$

To eliminate the repeating decimal, multiply by appropriate powers of 10 so that the decimal portions subtract to 0.

EXERCISES 1-4

Ⓐ

1. Simplify.

   a) $-\dfrac{2}{3} \times \dfrac{7}{8}$
   b) $\dfrac{5}{-8} \times \dfrac{-4}{15}$
   c) $\dfrac{3}{5} \times \dfrac{-6}{-11}$
   d) $\dfrac{11}{6} \times (-4)$

   e) $-\dfrac{25}{4} \times \dfrac{5}{2}$
   f) $\dfrac{-15}{8} \times \left(\dfrac{-13}{5}\right)$
   g) $\dfrac{3}{7} \div \left(\dfrac{-9}{14}\right)$
   h) $-\dfrac{13}{4} \div \dfrac{2}{-3}$

2. Simplify.

   a) $\dfrac{-5}{8} - \dfrac{3}{8}$
   b) $\dfrac{13}{-24} + \dfrac{-7}{24}$
   c) $\dfrac{-2}{3} + \dfrac{-4}{9}$
   d) $\dfrac{-7}{8} - \dfrac{-1}{4}$

   e) $\dfrac{-4}{9} + \dfrac{17}{-21}$
   f) $\dfrac{-3}{-4} - \dfrac{-2}{3}$
   g) $-\dfrac{7}{8} - \dfrac{7}{-9}$
   h) $\dfrac{-5}{-7} + \dfrac{-11}{12}$

3. Simplify.

   a) $\dfrac{137}{24} - \left(-\dfrac{19}{8}\right)$
   b) $-\dfrac{32}{15} + \dfrac{19}{6}$
   c) $-\dfrac{110}{9} - \dfrac{29}{6}$
   d) $\dfrac{14}{3} + \left(-\dfrac{31}{4}\right)$

   e) $-\dfrac{14}{3} - \left(\dfrac{31}{4}\right)$
   f) $\dfrac{17}{6} - \dfrac{22}{8}$
   g) $\dfrac{17}{4} - \left(-\dfrac{23}{3}\right)$
   h) $-\dfrac{18}{7} + \left(-\dfrac{15}{2}\right)$

4. If $x = \dfrac{-3}{4}$ and $y = \dfrac{1}{-3}$, evaluate.

   a) $2xy - 6y^2$
   b) $3x - 2y + 5xy$
   c) $4x^2 - 3y^2$
   d) $6x^2y + 2y^2$

   e) $3x^2 - \dfrac{1}{4}xy$
   f) $24xy^2 - 18xy$
   g) $-\dfrac{1}{2}(xy)^2$
   h) $\left(-\dfrac{1}{2}xy\right)^2$

5. Express in decimal form.

   a) $\dfrac{-5}{8}$
   b) $\dfrac{4}{-9}$
   c) $3\dfrac{1}{7}$
   d) $-\dfrac{47}{12}$
   e) $5\dfrac{2}{5}$
   f) $\dfrac{-17}{11}$

Ⓑ

6. Express in the form $\dfrac{m}{n}$.

   a) 1.37
   b) $0.\overline{45}$
   c) $6.\overline{7}$
   d) 2.875
   e) $0.5\overline{17}$

   f) 12.0125
   g) $4.1\overline{32}$
   h) $4.0\overline{12}$
   i) $1.\overline{1}$
   j) $3.1\overline{425}$

   k) $0.5\overline{18}$
   l) $0.312\,\overline{46}$
   m) $0.\overline{9}$
   n) $0.4\overline{9}$
   o) $2.\overline{571\,428}$

7. Simplify.

   a) $\dfrac{5}{2} - \dfrac{11}{3} + \dfrac{5}{4}$
   b) $\dfrac{5}{2} - \dfrac{5}{4} \div \dfrac{4}{5}$
   c) $\dfrac{-6}{5} + \dfrac{10}{-2} \times \left(\dfrac{-3}{5}\right)$

   d) $\left(\dfrac{3}{-4} - \dfrac{-3}{4}\right) \div 2$
   e) $-6\left(\dfrac{4}{5} - \dfrac{1}{2}\right)$
   f) $\dfrac{3}{5}\left(-\dfrac{1}{2}\right)\left(-\dfrac{6}{3}\right) + \dfrac{1}{5}$

8. If $x = \dfrac{-3}{4}$ and $y = \dfrac{1}{-3}$, evaluate.

   a) $\dfrac{2x^2 + 4y}{15y^2}$ b) $\dfrac{12xy + 4y}{5y}$ c) $\dfrac{2x + 7y - xy}{7x^2}$

9. The cost, C, in dollars per hour, of operating a certain type of aircraft is given by the formula: $C = 950 + \dfrac{m}{250} + \dfrac{22\,500\,000}{m}$ where m is the cruise altitude in metres. Find the hourly cost of operating the aircraft at 7500 m; at 9000 m.

10. The power, P, in kilowatts, delivered by a high voltage power line is given by the formula: $P = I\left(132 - \dfrac{1}{10}I\right)$, where I is the current in amperes. What power is available when the current is 440 A (amperes)?

11. The interest rate, r, on a loan is given by the formula: $r = \dfrac{24c}{A(n-1)} \times 100\%$ where c is the interest charged, A is the amount borrowed, and n is the number of monthly payments. Find the interest rate for
    a) $c = \$125$, $A = \$1000$, $n = 16$ b) $c = \$60$, $A = \$900$, $n = 11$

12. If p and q are the distances of an object and its image respectively from a concave mirror of focal length f, the formula relating them is $\dfrac{1}{p} + \dfrac{1}{q} = \dfrac{1}{f}$.

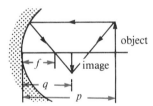 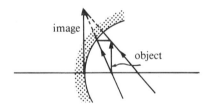

   For a concave mirror with a focal length of 20 cm, find
   a) q when p is: i) 40 cm   ii) 80 cm   iii) 100 cm
   b) p when q is: i) 60 cm   ii) 80 cm   iii) 20 cm
   c) What is the meaning of your answer to b(iii)?

13. Express as a repeating decimal.
    a) $0.\overline{3} + 0.\overline{2}$ b) $0.\overline{3} + 0.\overline{6}$ c) $0.\overline{42} - 0.\overline{20}$
    d) $0.\overline{3} \times 0.25$ e) $0.\overline{3} \times 0.\overline{6}$ f) $0.\overline{6} \times 0.\overline{2}$

🖊 INVESTIGATE

Monica wrote two repeating decimals. When she added, subtracted, multiplied and divided them, the answers were all repeating decimals. Can you find similar examples?

1-5 RADICALS

Gold leaf is so thin that one dollar's worth would cover a square with an area of 3600 cm². The length of a side of the square, in centimetres, is 60, since $60^2 = 3600$. We say that 60 is a square root of 3600, and write $\sqrt{3600} = 60$.

The gold produced in Canada in one day would almost fill a cube with a volume of 8000 cm³. The length of an edge of the cube, in centimetres, is 20, since $20^3 = 8000$. We say that 20 is a cube root of 8000, and write $\sqrt[3]{8000} = 20$.

Expressions such as $\sqrt{3600}$ and $\sqrt[3]{8000}$ are called *radicals*. Radicals occur when we work with square roots and cube roots of numbers.

Square Roots

A number, x, is the *square root* of a number, n, if $x^2 = n$. Positive numbers always have two square roots, one positive, the other negative. The *radical sign*, $\sqrt{}$, always denotes the positive, or *principal*, square root.

$\sqrt{n}$ means the principal square root of n.

Example 1. Find:

a) $\sqrt{1600}$ b) $\sqrt{2.25}$ c) $\sqrt{0.09}$

Solution. a) $\sqrt{1600} = 40$, since $40^2 = 1600$

b) $\sqrt{2.25} = 1.5$, since $1.5^2 = 2.25$

c) $\sqrt{0.09} = 0.3$, since $0.3^2 = 0.09$

In *Example 1*, the square roots were exact. Most numbers do not have exact square roots. The most efficient method of finding the square root of any number is to use a calculator with a $\boxed{\sqrt{}}$ key. Since the calculator can display only a fixed number of digits, the number displayed may not be the exact square root. It may only be an *approximation* of the square root.

Example 2. Use a calculator to find:

    a) $\sqrt{33}$ correct to three decimal places.

    b) $\sqrt{147}$ correct to four decimal places.

Solution.   a) $\sqrt{33} \doteq 5.745$ b) $\sqrt{147} \doteq 12.1244$

Cube Roots

A number, x, is the *cube root* of a number, n, if $x^3 = n$. The cube root of a positive number is positive and the cube root of a negative number is negative.

$$\sqrt[3]{n} \text{ means the cube root of } n.$$

Example 3. Find:

    a) $\sqrt[3]{125}$ b) $\sqrt[3]{-64}$

Solution.   a) $\sqrt[3]{125} = 5$, since   b) $\sqrt[3]{-64} = -4$, since

            $5^3 = 125$. $(-4)^3 = -64$.

Fourth and Fifth Roots

Similarly, the *fourth roots* of 16 are 2 and -2, since $2^4 = 16$, and $(-2)^4 = 16$. We write $\sqrt[4]{16} = 2$ to indicate the principal fourth root of 16.

And, the *fifth root* of -32 is -2, since $(-2)^5 = -32$. We write $\sqrt[5]{-32} = -2$.

An expression of the form $\sqrt[n]{x}$ is called a *radical*. If n is even, the expression represents only the principal root.

EXERCISES 1-5

Ⓐ

1. Find the square roots of these numbers.
    a) 49   b) 81   c) 121   d) 400   e) 529   f) 625

2. Simplify.
    a) $\sqrt{64}$ b) $\sqrt{100}$ c) $\sqrt{144}$ d) $\sqrt{900}$ e) $\sqrt{1600}$
    f) $\sqrt{0.25}$ g) $\sqrt{0.04}$ h) $\sqrt{0.01}$ i) $\sqrt{0.0016}$ j) $\sqrt{0.000\,025}$

3. Use a calculator to find, correct to three decimal places.
    a) $\sqrt{2}$ b) $\sqrt{3}$ c) $\sqrt{52.3}$ d) $\sqrt{128.5}$ e) $\sqrt{471}$
    f) $\sqrt{472}$ g) $\sqrt{473}$ h) $\sqrt{474}$ i) $\sqrt{1.48}$ j) $\sqrt{0.000\,25}$

4. Simplify.
    a) $\sqrt[3]{8}$ b) $\sqrt[3]{-27}$ c) $\sqrt[4]{81}$ d) $\sqrt[5]{32}$ e) $\sqrt[5]{243}$ f) $\sqrt[3]{0.001}$

Ⓑ

5. Find, correct to: i) two decimal places   ii) three decimal places.
   a) $\sqrt{6}$ b) $\sqrt{11}$ c) $\sqrt{13}$ d) $\sqrt{124}$ e) $\sqrt{139}$ f) $\sqrt{154}$

6. From the area of each square, calculate the length of a side and the perimeter.
   a)   b)

   Area 9.61 m²

   Area
   6.4 m²

7. From the volume of each cube, find the length of an edge and the area of a face.
   a)   b)

   Volume
   1000 cm³

   Volume
   125 cm³

8. Simplify.
   a) $\sqrt[3]{64}$ b) $\sqrt[3]{125}$ c) $\sqrt[4]{16}$ d) $\sqrt[5]{-1}$ e) $\sqrt[3]{216}$
   f) $\sqrt[3]{-1000}$ g) $\sqrt[4]{256}$ h) $\sqrt[4]{10\ 000}$ i) $\sqrt[3]{7^3}$ j) $\sqrt[5]{10^5}$

9. One litre of varathane will cover an area of 10 m².
   a) If a square area is covered, how long is its side?
   b) If 2 L of varathane are used to cover a square area, how long is its side?

10. In one day a gold mine produces approximately 1600 cm³ of gold. If five day's gold production is cast into a cube, how long is its edge?

11. Simplify.
    a) $\sqrt{16+9}$ b) $\sqrt{4+9+36}$ c) $\sqrt[3]{27+64+125}$ d) $\sqrt{64}+\sqrt[3]{64}$
    e) $\sqrt[3]{\sqrt{64}}$ f) $\sqrt{6-\sqrt{4}}$ g) $\sqrt{25}+\sqrt[3]{27}-\sqrt[4]{16}$ h) $5\sqrt{9}-4\sqrt[3]{-8}$

Ⓒ

12. Without using the $\boxed{\sqrt{}}$ key, use a calculator to find, correct to two decimals
    a) $\sqrt{6.5}$ b) $\sqrt{65}$ c) $\sqrt[3]{20}$ d) $\sqrt[3]{200}$

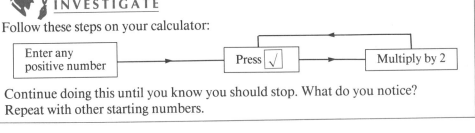

INVESTIGATE

Follow these steps on your calculator:

Enter any positive number → Press $\sqrt{}$ → Multiply by 2

Continue doing this until you know you should stop. What do you notice?
Repeat with other starting numbers.

1-6 THE IRRATIONAL NUMBERS

Many numbers do not have terminating or repeating decimals. The most famous of these is the number π, which occurs in the formulas for the circumference and area of a circle. To twenty decimal places, the value of π is:

$$\pi \doteq 3.141\ 592\ 653\ 589\ 793\ 238\ 46\ldots$$

Mathematicians have always been interested in calculating π. In 1873 William Shanks reported that he had spent more than twenty years finding π to 707 decimal places. For decades this was considered the most impressive calculation ever performed. But in 1945 other mathematicians found that his 528th place, and all following places, were incorrect. π has now been calculated to more than 29 million decimal places using computers.

Mathematicians have proved that no matter how many decimal places are calculated for π, the representation will never terminate or repeat. Therefore, π cannot be expressed in the form $\frac{m}{n}$, where m and n are integers and $n \neq 0$. For this reason, π is called an irrational number.

Any number that cannot be expressed in the form $\frac{m}{n}$, where m and n are integers, and $n \neq 0$, is called an *irrational number*. The decimal representation of an irrational number neither terminates nor repeats.

Example 1. Does each number appear to be rational or irrational?
- a) $x = 0.123456789101112\ldots$
- b) $y = 2.131131131131\ldots$
- c) $\sqrt{2} = 1.414213562373\ldots$

Solution.
- a) Although there is a pattern in the decimal representation of x, there is no sequence of digits that repeats. Therefore, x appears to be irrational.
- b) y appears to be rational since the sequence 131 repeats.
- c) There is no repeating sequence of digits. Therefore, $\sqrt{2}$ appears to be irrational.

In *Example 1c* we cannot be certain that $\sqrt{2}$ is irrational, since a sequence of digits that repeats could occur farther out in the decimal expansion. However, mathematicians have proved that $\sqrt{2}$ is irrational. This example suggests that certain square roots are irrational.

> Any number of the form $\sqrt{x}$, where $x > 0$, and x is not the square of a rational number, is irrational.

Example 2.   Which of the following are irrational?

$$\sqrt{3} \qquad \sqrt{16} \qquad \sqrt{20} \qquad \sqrt{1.44} \qquad \sqrt{\frac{4}{9}} \qquad \sqrt{\frac{4}{5}}$$

Solution. $\sqrt{3}$, $\sqrt{20}$, and $\sqrt{\frac{4}{5}}$ are irrational since 3, 20, and $\frac{4}{5}$ are not perfect squares.

The others are rational since the numbers are perfect squares:

$$\sqrt{16} = 4 \qquad \sqrt{1.44} = 1.2 \qquad \sqrt{\frac{4}{9}} = \frac{2}{3}$$

The numbers that can be expressed as decimals can be grouped into two sets:

Rational Numbers	*Irrational Numbers*
These numbers have decimal representations that terminate or repeat.	These numbers have decimal representations that neither terminate nor repeat.
$\frac{1}{2}$ 0.65 $-\frac{7}{3}$ $5.\overline{21}$	$\sqrt{2}$ $\qquad$ $\sqrt{15}-1$
Integers, I -8 Natural Numbers, N 0 5 144 -51	π $\qquad$ $-\sqrt[3]{10}$ $1.71771777\ldots$

THE REAL NUMBERS

There are no other possibilities. All the numbers represented above are called *real numbers*. The set of real numbers consists of the rational and the irrational numbers. We say that it is the *union* of the set of rational numbers and the set of irrational numbers.

EXERCISES 1-6

Ⓐ

1. Does each number appear to be rational or irrational?
   a) 2.147474747474...
   b) −6.132133134...
   c) 72.04129647....
   d) 0.165165516555...
   e) −2.23606797749....
   f) −4.317495

2. Which of the following are irrational?

   a) $\sqrt{21}$
   b) $\sqrt{16}$
   c) $\sqrt{2\frac{1}{4}}$
   d) $\sqrt{200}$
   e) $\sqrt{2.5}$

3. Which of the following are irrational?
   a) $5\sqrt{2}$
   b) $5 + \sqrt{2}$
   c) $5 - \sqrt{2}$
   d) $2\sqrt{36}$
   e) $7\sqrt{7}$
   f) $\sqrt{5} + \sqrt{2}$
   g) $\sqrt{7+9}$
   h) $\sqrt{7} + \sqrt{9}$
   i) $6\sqrt{21}$
   j) $\sqrt{17+12}$

Ⓑ

4. Give examples of two rational and two irrational numbers between the numbers in each pair.
   a) 3.65,   3.69
   b) −1.476,   −1.47
   c) $0.3\overline{97}$,   0.397 647 28....
   d) $-5.3\overline{76}$, $-5.3\overline{7}$
   e) $\frac{8}{9}$, $\frac{9}{10}$
   f) 2.236 067...,   2.236 071 23......

5. Classify each of the following as a natural number, an integer, a rational, or an irrational number.

   a) $\frac{3}{5}$
   b) $0.2\overline{17}$
   c) −6
   d) 41 275
   e) 6.121 121 112...
   f) $-2\frac{1}{4}$
   g) $\sqrt{27}$
   h) $\sqrt{225}$

Ⓒ

6. On a calculator with a $\boxed{\sqrt{}}$ key, $\sqrt{3} = 1.7320508$.

   1.7320508 is rational, but $\sqrt{3}$ is irrational. Can a number be both rational and irrational? Explain.

7. On a calculator with a $\boxed{\sqrt{}}$ key, $\sqrt{0.1111111} = 0.3333333$.

   a) Write fractions in the form $\frac{m}{n}$ for 0.1111111 and 0.3333333. Use these fractions to explain why the above pattern appeared.
   b) Find another similar result.

8. a) Determine if it is possible for the square root of an irrational number to be rational; irrational.
   b) Give examples to support your conclusions in (a).

9. Mike wrote the formula for the circumference of a circle in the form $\pi = \frac{C}{d}$. He claimed that this proved that π is a rational number. Do you agree?

THE MATHEMATICAL MIND

A Short History of π

1
From ancient times, people have known that the circumference of a circle...

2
...is more than 3 times its diameter.

3
Through the centuries different civilizations have tried to find a fraction which would be exactly equal to the ratio:

$$\frac{\text{circumference}}{\text{diameter}}$$

About 1700 B.C., the Egyptians used the fraction $\frac{256}{81}$ to approximate this ratio.

4
About 220 B.C. the Greeks used the Greek letter π to represent this ratio. And they used the fraction $\frac{22}{7}$ as its approximate value

5
In their search for the elusive rational number equal to π, various other civilizations used these approximations.

Civilization	Date	Value for π
Chinese	470	$\frac{355}{113}$
Hindu	530	$\frac{3927}{1250}$
European	1220	$\frac{864}{275}$

6
Finally, in 1761, Johann Lambert proved that there is no rational number equal to π. That is, the decimal form of π does not repeat.

π = 3.141 592 653 589...

In 1987, mathematicians at the University of Tokyo used a super computer to determine π to 201 326 000 decimal places. As expected, the decimal representation did not repeat.

Use your calculator to determine which civilization up to the year A.D. 1220 had the best approximation for π.

1-7 THE PYTHAGOREAN THEOREM

In the 6th century B.C., the Greek mathematician, Pythagoras, discovered this important theorem which bears his name:

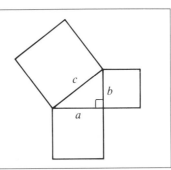

Pythagorean Theorem
In any right triangle, the area of the square on the hypotenuse is equal to the sum of the areas of the squares on the other two sides.

For the triangle at the right,
$$c^2 = a^2 + b^2$$

If the lengths of two sides of a right triangle are known, the Pythagorean Theorem can be used to determine the length of the third side.

Example 1. Calculate the value of x rounded to one decimal place:

a) 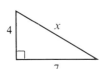   b)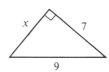

Solution. a)
$$\begin{aligned} x^2 &= 4^2 + 7^2 \\ &= 16 + 49 \\ &= 65 \\ x &= \pm\sqrt{65} \\ &\doteq \pm 8.1 \end{aligned}$$

b)
$$\begin{aligned} 9^2 &= x^2 + 7^2 \\ 81 &= x^2 + 49 \\ 81 - 49 &= x^2 \\ 32 &= x^2 \\ x &= \pm\sqrt{32} \\ &\doteq \pm 5.7 \end{aligned}$$

Since $x > 0$, $x \doteq 8.1$ Since $x > 0$, $x \doteq 5.7$

In *Example 1*, we consider only the principal square roots since we are finding lengths, which are positive.

Example 2. Express the length of side AB of $\triangle ABC$ in terms of x and y.

Solution.
$$\begin{aligned} AC^2 &= AB^2 + BC^2 \\ x^2 &= AB^2 + y^2 \\ AB^2 &= x^2 - y^2 \\ AB &= \sqrt{x^2 - y^2} \end{aligned}$$

Although the ancient Greeks knew that $\sqrt{2}$ was an irrational number, they were able to construct a line segment having a length of $\sqrt{2}$ units. They simply constructed an isosceles right triangle with the equal sides 1 unit in length. The length of the hypotenuse is $\sqrt{2}$ units.

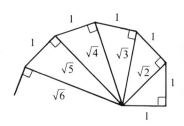

By repeating this process, lengths of $\sqrt{3}, \sqrt{4}, \sqrt{5}, \sqrt{6},\ldots$can be constructed as shown.

Example 3. Construct a line segment of length $\sqrt{11}$ units.

Solution. The procedure illustrated above could be continued until a length of $\sqrt{11}$ is obtained. A faster method is suggested by the diagram below. The length of AB is $\sqrt{11}$ units.

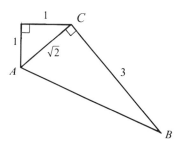

Example 4. A ground radar unit detects an aircraft at a height of 10 km, 5 km north and 12 km east of the unit. What is the actual distance of the aircraft from the radar unit?

Solution. Let R represent the position of the radar unit,
$\quad A$ represent the position of the aircraft,
$\quad P$ represent the point on the ground directly below the aircraft.

N and E are points on the north and east directions through R such that $REPN$ is a rectangle. The required distance is the length of the line segment RA.

Since $\triangle REP$ is a right triangle,

$$\text{length of } RP = \sqrt{12^2 + 5^2}$$
$$= \sqrt{169}$$
$$= 13$$

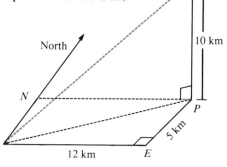

Since $\triangle RPA$ is a right triangle,

$$\text{length of } RA = \sqrt{13^2 + 10^2}$$
$$= \sqrt{269}$$
$$\doteq 16.4$$

The aircraft is approximately 16.4 km from the radar unit.

EXERCISES 1-7

Ⓐ

1. Find x rounded to one decimal place.

   a)

   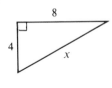

   b)

   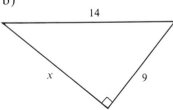

   c)

   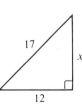

   d)

   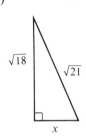

   e)

   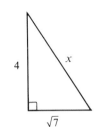

   f)

   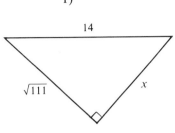

2. Find a.

   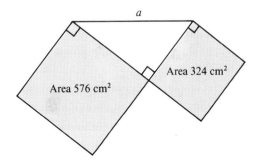

   Area 324 cm²

   Area 576 cm²

Ⓑ

3. Square *ABCD* is divided into 25 small squares each of side length 1 cm. Find the lengths of these line segments shown in the diagram.

   a) *AE*   b) *HF*   c) *DG*   d) *IC*

   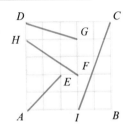

4. Construct a line segment of length
   a) $\sqrt{3}$ units   b) $\sqrt{7}$ units   c) $\sqrt{10}$ units   d) $\sqrt{27}$ units
   e) $\sqrt{41}$ units   f) $\sqrt{21}$ units   g) $\sqrt{12}$ units   h) $\sqrt{19}$ units

5. An equilateral triangle has sides of length 4 cm. Calculate its height and area.

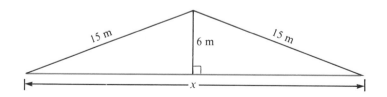

6. Find the length, x, of this roof truss.

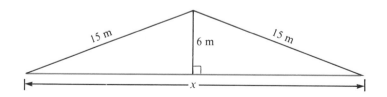

7. The tenth hole at the Silver Dunes Golf Club is a 90° dogleg. The score card shows the distances along the fairway to the circular green. What is the distance across the pond to the edge of the green?

8. How much shorter is it to walk diagonally across a rectangular field than around the sides if the field is 250 m long by 110 m wide?

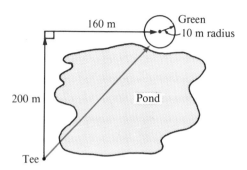

9. The area of $\triangle ABC$ (below, left) is 32 cm². What is the length of BD?

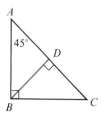

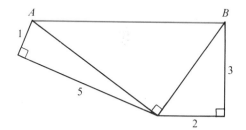

10. In the diagram above (right), find the length of AB.

11. An archaeologist measures a pyramid and finds that the base is square with a side length of 90 m. The slant height is 60 m. Calculate the height of the pyramid to the nearest metre.

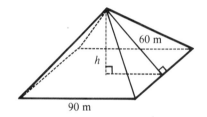

12. A pilot radios her position as 17 km south and 15 km west of an airport's control tower. The altimeter reads 8000 m. How far is the aircraft from the control tower?

13. In the rectangular prism shown, *PQ* is a diagonal.
    a) Find the length of *PQ* if *PR* = 5, *RS* = 3, and *QS* = 2.
    b) Find a formula for the length, *d*, of the diagonal if the dimensions of the prism are *a*, *b*, and *c*.

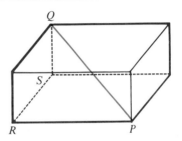

Ⓒ

14. The line segments joining the vertices of a cube are of three different lengths.

edge

face diagonal

body diagonal

   a) If the edge length of the cube is 1, find the lengths of the other two segments joining the vertices.

   b) How many line segments of each length can be drawn joining the vertices?

15. a) How many line segments of different lengths can be drawn to join the midpoints of the edges of a cube?

   b) If the edge length of a cube is 1, find the length of the line segments identified in (a).

   c) How many line segments of each length can be drawn?

16. The top of a cylindrical storage tank, 55.3 m high and 28.4 m in diameter, is reached by means of a helical stairway that circles the tank exactly twice.

   Calculate the length of the stairway to the nearest metre.

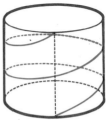

17. A square and a circle have the same area. What is the ratio of the
    a) side of the square to the radius of the circle?

   b) diagonal of the square to the radius of the circle?

1-8 MULTIPLYING RADICALS

Consider the expressions: $\sqrt{4} \times \sqrt{9}$ and $\sqrt{4 \times 9}$.

$$\sqrt{4} \times \sqrt{9} = 2 \times 3 \qquad\qquad \sqrt{4 \times 9} = \sqrt{36}$$
$$= 6 \qquad\qquad\qquad\qquad = 6$$

Therefore, $\sqrt{4} \times \sqrt{9} = \sqrt{4 \times 9}$

The same is true for irrationals. Consider the expressions:
$\sqrt{3} \times \sqrt{5}$ and $\sqrt{3 \times 5}$. Square each expression.

$$(\sqrt{3} \times \sqrt{5})^2 = (\sqrt{3})(\sqrt{3}) \times (\sqrt{5})(\sqrt{5}) \qquad (\sqrt{3 \times 5})^2 = 3 \times 5$$
$$= 3 \times 5 \qquad\qquad\qquad\qquad\qquad = 15$$
$$= 15$$

Therefore, $\sqrt{3} \times \sqrt{5} = \sqrt{3 \times 5}$

The above results suggest the following property:

$$\sqrt{a} \times \sqrt{b} = \sqrt{ab}, \quad (a \geq 0,\, b \geq 0)$$

Example 1.   Simplify:

    a) $3\sqrt{2} \times \sqrt{5}$ b) $5\sqrt{3} \times 4\sqrt{2}$ c) $4\sqrt{3} \times \sqrt{12}$

Solution.   a) $3\sqrt{2} \times \sqrt{5}$ b) $5\sqrt{3} \times 4\sqrt{2}$ c) $4\sqrt{3} \times \sqrt{12}$

            $= 3\sqrt{2 \times 5}$ $= 20\sqrt{6}$ $= 4\sqrt{36}$

            $= 3\sqrt{10}$ $= 4 \times 6$

                                                      $= 24$

Example 2.   Express as a product of radicals:

    a) $\sqrt{21}$ b) $\sqrt{30}$ c) $\sqrt{20}$

Solution.   a) $\sqrt{21} = \sqrt{7 \times 3}$ b) $\sqrt{30} = \sqrt{2 \times 3 \times 5}$ c) $\sqrt{20} = \sqrt{2 \times 2 \times 5}$

              $= \sqrt{7} \times \sqrt{3}$ $= \sqrt{2} \times \sqrt{3} \times \sqrt{5}$ $= \sqrt{2} \times \sqrt{2} \times \sqrt{5}$

In *Example 2c*, since $\sqrt{2} \times \sqrt{2} = 2$, $\sqrt{20}$ may be written, $2\sqrt{5}$. An expression of the form $\sqrt{x}$, $(x > 0)$ is called an *entire radical*, and an expression of the form $a\sqrt{x}$, where a is any real number, is called a *mixed radical*.

$$\sqrt{20} = 2\sqrt{5}$$

         ↗   ↖

    entire radical   mixed radical

These are also entire radicals: $\sqrt{3.5}$, $\sqrt{\dfrac{3}{2}}$. These are also mixed radicals: $\dfrac{3}{2}\sqrt{6}$, $-2\sqrt{7}$.

Any number of the form $\sqrt{x}$, where x has a perfect square as a factor, can be expressed as a mixed radical.

Example 3. Express as a mixed radical where possible:

  a) $\sqrt{18}$ b) $\sqrt{70}$ c) $\sqrt{48}$

Solution. a) 18 has 9 as a perfect-square factor.

$\sqrt{18} = \sqrt{9} \times \sqrt{2}$
$= 3\sqrt{2}$

b) Since 70 does not have a perfect-square factor, $\sqrt{70}$ cannot be expressed as a mixed radical.

c) 48 has 16 as a perfect-square factor.

$\sqrt{48} = \sqrt{16} \times \sqrt{3}$
$= 4\sqrt{3}$

In *Example 3c*, both 4 and 16 are perfect-square factors of 48. We always choose the *greatest* perfect-square factor. This ensures that the result will be in simplest form.

Example 4. Arrange in order from least to greatest:

  $7\sqrt{2}$ $3\sqrt{7}$ $2\sqrt{15}$ $4\sqrt{6}$

Solution. Express each mixed radical as an entire radical.

$7\sqrt{2} = \sqrt{49} \times \sqrt{2}$ $3\sqrt{7} = \sqrt{9} \times \sqrt{7}$
$= \sqrt{98}$ $= \sqrt{63}$

$2\sqrt{15} = \sqrt{4} \times \sqrt{15}$ $4\sqrt{6} = \sqrt{16} \times \sqrt{6}$
$= \sqrt{60}$ $= \sqrt{96}$

Arranged from least to greatest:
$2\sqrt{15}, \quad 3\sqrt{7}, \quad 4\sqrt{6}, \quad 7\sqrt{2}.$

EXERCISES 1-8

Ⓐ

1. Simplify.
  a) $\sqrt{7} \times \sqrt{8}$ b) $\sqrt{11} \times \sqrt{14}$ c) $\sqrt{8} \times (-\sqrt{18})$
  d) $2\sqrt{5} \times 3\sqrt{2}$ e) $-4\sqrt{2} \times 3\sqrt{8}$ f) $(-7\sqrt{3})(-5\sqrt{8})$

2. Express as a product of radicals.
  a) $\sqrt{24}$ b) $\sqrt{18}$ c) $\sqrt{45}$ d) $\sqrt{28}$ e) $\sqrt{72}$ f) $\sqrt{60}$
  g) $\sqrt{39}$ h) $\sqrt{65}$ i) $\sqrt{96}$ j) $\sqrt{120}$ k) $\sqrt{126}$ l) $\sqrt{105}$

3. Express as a mixed radical.
  a) $\sqrt{32}$ b) $\sqrt{50}$ c) $\sqrt{27}$ d) $\sqrt{96}$ e) $\sqrt{8}$ f) $\sqrt{75}$

4. Express as a mixed radical in simplest form.
  a) $\sqrt{147}$ b) $\sqrt{54}$ c) $\sqrt{76}$ d) $\sqrt{180}$ e) $3\sqrt{20}$ f) $5\sqrt{18}$

Ⓑ

5. Simplify.
   a) $2\sqrt{6} \times 3\sqrt{2}$
   b) $3\sqrt{5} \times 7\sqrt{10}$
   c) $-8\sqrt{6} \times 6\sqrt{8}$
   d) $5\sqrt{10} \times 4\sqrt{6}$
   e) $(-7\sqrt{12})(-2\sqrt{6})$
   f) $11\sqrt{3} \times 5\sqrt{6}$

6. Simplify.
   a) $12\sqrt{3} \times (-3\sqrt{18})$
   b) $(-3\sqrt{5})(-5\sqrt{3})$
   c) $-7\sqrt{\dfrac{6}{35}} \times 2\sqrt{\dfrac{5}{9}}$
   d) $-3\sqrt{\dfrac{6}{15}} \times 6\sqrt{\dfrac{10}{9}}$
   e) $-5\sqrt{0.3} \times 2\sqrt{0.7}$
   f) $4\sqrt{9} \times 11\sqrt{0.4}$

7. Simplify.
   a) $\sqrt{24} \times \sqrt{18}$
   b) $2\sqrt{24} \times 5\sqrt{6}$
   c) $3\sqrt{20} \times 2\sqrt{5}$
   d) $2\sqrt{6} \times 7\sqrt{8} \times 5\sqrt{2}$
   e) $3\sqrt{7} \times 2\sqrt{6} \times 5\sqrt{2}$
   f) $4\sqrt{8} \times 3\sqrt{6} \times 7\sqrt{3}$

8. a) Use the diagram to show that $\sqrt{8} = 2\sqrt{2}$.
   b) Draw a similar diagram to show that $\sqrt{18} = 3\sqrt{2}$.

9. Arrange in order from least to greatest.
   a) $4\sqrt{3}, \ 3\sqrt{5}, \ 5\sqrt{2}, \ 2\sqrt{10}, \ 2\sqrt{13}, \ 3\sqrt{6}$
   b) $-6\sqrt{2}, \ -3\sqrt{7}, \ -2\sqrt{17}, \ -4\sqrt{5}, \ -2\sqrt{21}, \ -5\sqrt{3}$
   c) $6\sqrt{0.1}, \ 3\sqrt{0.7}, \ 7\sqrt{0.05}, \ 2\sqrt{0.8}, \ 4\sqrt{0.5}, \ 5\sqrt{0.3}$

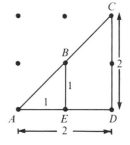

10. Simplify.
   a) $\sqrt{24} \times \sqrt{54} \times \sqrt{18}$
   b) $\sqrt{20} \times \sqrt{32} \times \sqrt{18} \times \sqrt{125}$
   c) $\sqrt{27} \times \sqrt{12} \times \sqrt{45} \times \sqrt{80}$
   d) $5\sqrt{18} \times 3\sqrt{8} \times 6\sqrt{32}$
   e) $3\sqrt{20} \times 5\sqrt{8} \times 4\sqrt{180} \times 6\sqrt{72}$
   f) $0.8\sqrt{80} \times 0.125\sqrt{90} \times 0.5\sqrt{50}$

Ⓒ

11. In the diagram, what is the area of square $WXYZ$?

12. A square and a rectangle have the same width. If the diagonal of the rectangle is 5 times the diagonal of the square, what is the ratio of the length of the rectangle to the length of the square?

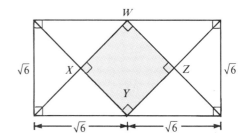

13. Simplify.
   a) $\sqrt{3a} \times \sqrt{5b}$
   b) $\sqrt{7x} \times \sqrt{2x}$
   c) $3\sqrt{2m} \times 4\sqrt{3m}$
   d) $3\sqrt{2x} \times 2\sqrt{3x} \times 4\sqrt{2y}$
   e) $5\sqrt{3m} \times 2\sqrt{2m} \times 3\sqrt{3m}$
   f) $7\sqrt{6x} \times 3\sqrt{2y} \times 2\sqrt{3xy}$

1-9 ADDING AND SUBTRACTING RADICALS

In the same way that $2x$ and $3x$ are called like terms, radicals such as $2\sqrt{3}$ and $3\sqrt{3}$ are called *like* radicals. Like radicals can be combined, that is, added or subtracted, using the distributive law. Radicals such as $2\sqrt{5}$ and $4\sqrt{7}$ are called *unlike* radicals; they cannot be combined.

Example 1. Simplify, if possible:

a) $2\sqrt{3} + 3\sqrt{3}$ b) $6\sqrt{2} - 4\sqrt{2} + \sqrt{2}$ c) $4\sqrt{6} + 2\sqrt{10}$

Solution. a) $2\sqrt{3} + 3\sqrt{3}$ b) $6\sqrt{2}\ \ 4\sqrt{2} + \sqrt{2}$ c) $4\sqrt{6} + 2\sqrt{10}$ cannot be
$\qquad\qquad = (2 + 3)\sqrt{3}\qquad\quad = (6 - 4 + 1)\sqrt{2}\qquad$ combined because they
$\qquad\qquad = 5\sqrt{3}\qquad\qquad\quad = 3\sqrt{2}\qquad\qquad\quad$ are unlike radicals.

Express radicals in simplest form before combining them.

Example 2. Simplify:

a) $\sqrt{18} - \sqrt{2}$ b) $2\sqrt{98} + \sqrt{10} - 5\sqrt{8} - 3\sqrt{40}$

Solution. a) $\sqrt{18} - \sqrt{2}$ b) $2\sqrt{98} + \sqrt{10} - 5\sqrt{8} - 3\sqrt{40}$
$\qquad\qquad = 3\sqrt{2} - \sqrt{2}\qquad\qquad = 2 \times 7\sqrt{2} + \sqrt{10} - 5 \times 2\sqrt{2} - 3 \times 2\sqrt{10}$
$\qquad\qquad = 2\sqrt{2}\qquad\qquad\qquad = 14\sqrt{2} + \sqrt{10} - 10\sqrt{2} - 6\sqrt{10}$
$\qquad\qquad\qquad\qquad\qquad\qquad\quad = 4\sqrt{2} - 5\sqrt{10}$

In *Example 2b*, $4\sqrt{2}$ and $5\sqrt{10}$ cannot be combined because they are unlike radicals. If required, the approximate numerical value can be found by using a calculator.

Although $\sqrt{a} \times \sqrt{b} = \sqrt{ab}$, it is not true that, in general, $\sqrt{a} + \sqrt{b} = \sqrt{a + b}$. Consider the expressions $\sqrt{4} + \sqrt{9}$ and $\sqrt{4 + 9}$.

$$\sqrt{4} + \sqrt{9} = 2 + 3 \qquad\qquad \sqrt{4 + 9} = \sqrt{13}$$
$$= 5 \qquad\qquad\qquad\qquad\quad \doteq 3.6056$$

Therefore, $\sqrt{4} + \sqrt{9} \neq \sqrt{4 + 9}$.   Similarly, in general, $\sqrt{a} - \sqrt{b} \neq \sqrt{a - b}$.

Example 3.   Bay City is 8 km due west of Keyport and is linked to it by a straight stretch of railroad track. To travel from Bay City to Keyport by car one must go through Grenville, which is 1 km east and 1 km north of Bay City. How much farther is it by road than by train from Bay City to Keyport?

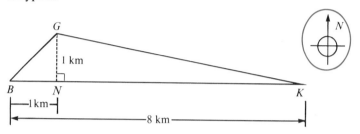

Solution.   Let B, K, and G represent, respectively, the locations of Bay City, Keyport, and Grenville. N is the point on the track between B and K which is directly south of G.

Since $\triangle BNG$ is a right triangle, $BG = \sqrt{2}$.
Since $NK = 7$ and $\triangle GNK$ is a right triangle,
$$GK = \sqrt{1^2 + 7^2}$$
$$= \sqrt{50}$$
Total distance from B to G to K:
$$BG + GK = \sqrt{2} + \sqrt{50}$$
$$= \sqrt{2} + 5\sqrt{2}$$
$$= 6\sqrt{2}$$
That is, the distance from Bay City to Keyport by car is $6\sqrt{2}$ km.
Since it is 8 km by train, it is $(6\sqrt{2} - 8)$ km, or 0.5 km, farther by car.

EXERCISES 1-9

1. Simplify.
   a) $5\sqrt{7} - 3\sqrt{7}$
   b) $11\sqrt{6} + 5\sqrt{6}$
   c) $2\sqrt{13} - 8\sqrt{13}$
   d) $6\sqrt{19} - 31\sqrt{19}$
   e) $4\sqrt{3} + 29\sqrt{3}$
   f) $7\sqrt{15} - 2\sqrt{15}$

2. Simplify.
   a) $4\sqrt{5} - 11\sqrt{5} + 3\sqrt{5}$
   b) $2\sqrt{10} + 7\sqrt{10} - 6\sqrt{10}$
   c) $5\sqrt{2} - 16\sqrt{2} + 29\sqrt{2}$
   d) $2\sqrt{6} - 6\sqrt{2} + 11\sqrt{6}$
   e) $4\sqrt{10} - 10\sqrt{10} + 3\sqrt{5}$
   f) $3\sqrt{5} - 9\sqrt{2} + 5\sqrt{5} - 2\sqrt{2}$

3. Simplify.
   a) $\sqrt{40} + \sqrt{90}$
   b) $\sqrt{32} + \sqrt{8}$
   c) $\sqrt{12} - \sqrt{75}$
   d) $\sqrt{20} - \sqrt{45}$
   e) $\sqrt{50} - \sqrt{18}$
   f) $\sqrt{24} - \sqrt{96}$
   g) $3\sqrt{20} - 2\sqrt{80}$
   h) $\sqrt{54} + \sqrt{150}$

(B)

4. Simplify.

a) $\sqrt{54} + \sqrt{150} - \sqrt{6}$ b) $\sqrt{28} - \sqrt{63} + \sqrt{112}$ c) $\sqrt{80} + \sqrt{45} - \sqrt{125}$

d) $\sqrt{12} + \sqrt{27} + \sqrt{48}$ e) $\sqrt{75} - \sqrt{3} + \sqrt{147}$ f) $\sqrt{98} - \sqrt{72} - \sqrt{50}$

g) $\sqrt{20} - \sqrt{45} - \sqrt{125}$ h) $\sqrt{32} - \sqrt{8} - \sqrt{128}$ i) $\sqrt{75} - \sqrt{108} - \sqrt{147}$

5. Simplify.

a) $2\sqrt{3} + 4\sqrt{12}$ b) $5\sqrt{48} - 7\sqrt{3}$ c) $3\sqrt{8} + 6\sqrt{18}$

d) $4\sqrt{50} - 7\sqrt{32}$ e) $2\sqrt{24} + 3\sqrt{54}$ f) $6\sqrt{20} - 2\sqrt{45}$

g) $3\sqrt{8} + 5\sqrt{18} - 6\sqrt{2}$ h) $5\sqrt{28} - 3\sqrt{63} + 2\sqrt{112}$ i) $8\sqrt{24} - 2\sqrt{54} - \sqrt{28}$

6. A straight stretch of railroad track connects Goshen to Humber, 16 km due west. The highway between the two towns passes through Ironton, 2 km east and 2 km north of Humber. How much farther is it to drive from Humber to Goshen than to take the train?

7. Simplify.

a) $5\sqrt{12} - 2\sqrt{48} - 7\sqrt{75}$ b) $3\sqrt{7} + 2\sqrt{11} - \sqrt{11} + 4\sqrt{7}$

c) $\sqrt{48} - \sqrt{20} - \sqrt{27} - \sqrt{45}$ d) $4\sqrt{18} - 2\sqrt{63} + \sqrt{175} + 5\sqrt{98}$

e) $2\sqrt{12} + 3\sqrt{50} - 2\sqrt{75} - 6\sqrt{32}$ f) $7\sqrt{24} + 3\sqrt{28} + 9\sqrt{54} + 6\sqrt{175}$

g) $3\sqrt{27} - 2\sqrt{50} - 5\sqrt{75} + 2\sqrt{32}$ h) $2\sqrt{112} - 3\sqrt{18} - 2\sqrt{175} - \sqrt{98}$

8. A rectangle has a 2 cm width and a 6 cm diagonal. Find the
   a) length   b) area   c) perimeter

9. Find the area and perimeter of a rectangle with diagonal 8 cm and one side 6 cm.

10. Simplify.

a) $\frac{1}{2}\sqrt{8} + \frac{3}{5}\sqrt{50} - \frac{2}{3}\sqrt{18}$ b) $2\sqrt{20} + \frac{3}{4}\sqrt{80} - \sqrt{125}$

c) $7\sqrt{32} - \frac{1}{5}\sqrt{50} - \frac{2}{3}\sqrt{18} + \frac{3}{4}\sqrt{128}$ d) $\frac{2}{5}\sqrt{125} - \frac{2}{3}\sqrt{243} - \frac{1}{3}\sqrt{45} + \frac{1}{2}\sqrt{48}$

e) $\frac{2}{3}\sqrt{72} - \frac{2}{3}\sqrt{54} - \frac{1}{2}\sqrt{96} - \frac{5}{7}\sqrt{98}$ f) $\frac{1}{4}\sqrt{54} - \frac{1}{4}\sqrt{150}$

11. In $\triangle XYZ$, $\angle Y = 90°$, $XY = \sqrt{12}$, and $YZ = \sqrt{8}$.

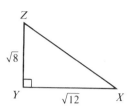

   a) Find the length of XZ.

   b) Is it true that $\sqrt{12} + \sqrt{8} = \sqrt{20}$?

   c) Explain your answer to b).

12. In $\triangle ABC$, $\angle B = 90°$, $AB = \sqrt{x}$, and $BC = \sqrt{y}$.

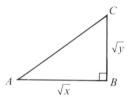

   a) Find an expression for the length of the hypotenuse, AC.

   b) Explain how the diagram shows that $\sqrt{x} + \sqrt{y} \neq \sqrt{x + y}$.

13. Is $\sqrt{x^2} = |x|$ for all real numbers, x? Explain.

14. Simplify.
   a) $5\sqrt{x} + 2\sqrt{x} - 3\sqrt{x}$
   b) $\sqrt{8a} + \sqrt{18a}$
   c) $3\sqrt{12m} - 4\sqrt{3m} + 2\sqrt{48m}$
   d) $\sqrt{20x} - \sqrt{24y} + \sqrt{45x} - \sqrt{54y}$
   e) $5\sqrt{8a} + 2\sqrt{27b} - 3\sqrt{50a} - 4\sqrt{75b}$
   f) $4\sqrt{32x} - 2\sqrt{72x} - 6\sqrt{45y} + 5\sqrt{125y}$

15. Each right triangle in the figure shown has a hypotenuse 4 cm and the shortest side 2 cm. Find the perimeter of the figure.

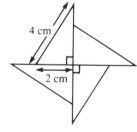

16. a) Prove that $\angle BAC \neq 90°$.
   b) If P is a point on AD such that $\angle BPC = 90°$, find the length of PD.

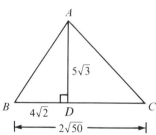

INVESTIGATE

Can you find any numbers a and b such that $\sqrt{a} + \sqrt{b} = \sqrt{a + b}$?

1-10 COMBINED OPERATIONS WITH RADICALS

Products involving radicals can be expanded using the distributive law.

Example 1. Expand and simplify:

a) $\sqrt{5}(4\sqrt{2} - \sqrt{5})$

b) $3\sqrt{2}(5\sqrt{3} - \sqrt{8} + 4\sqrt{10})$

Solution.

a) $\sqrt{5}(4\sqrt{2} - \sqrt{5})$
$= \sqrt{5} \times 4\sqrt{2} - \sqrt{5} \times \sqrt{5}$
$= 4\sqrt{10} - 5$

b) $3\sqrt{2}(5\sqrt{3} - \sqrt{8} + 4\sqrt{10})$
$= 3\sqrt{2} \times 5\sqrt{3} - 3\sqrt{2} \times \sqrt{8}$
$\qquad + 3\sqrt{2} \times 4\sqrt{10}$
$= 15\sqrt{6} - 3\sqrt{16} + 12\sqrt{20}$
$= 15\sqrt{6} - 3 \times 4 + 12 \times 2\sqrt{5}$
$= 15\sqrt{6} - 12 + 24\sqrt{5}$

Example 2. Expand and simplify: $(5\sqrt{3} + 4\sqrt{7})(2\sqrt{3} - \sqrt{7})$

Solution. The pattern below shows how the products are obtained.
$(5\sqrt{3} + 4\sqrt{7})(2\sqrt{3} - \sqrt{7})$
$= 5 \times 2 \times (\sqrt{3})^2 - 5 \times \sqrt{3} \times \sqrt{7} + 4 \times 2 \times \sqrt{7} \times \sqrt{3} - 4 \times (\sqrt{7})^2$
$= 30 - 5\sqrt{21} + 8\sqrt{21} - 28$
$= 2 + 3\sqrt{21}$

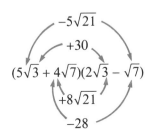

EXERCISES 1-10

1. Expand and simplify.
   a) $\sqrt{2}(\sqrt{5} - \sqrt{7})$
   b) $\sqrt{3}(\sqrt{11} + \sqrt{2})$
   c) $\sqrt{6}(\sqrt{13} - \sqrt{5})$
   d) $2\sqrt{3}(\sqrt{5} + 3\sqrt{7})$
   e) $\sqrt{5}(\sqrt{6} - \sqrt{10})$
   f) $4\sqrt{2}(3\sqrt{11} + 5\sqrt{13})$

2. Expand and simplify.
   a) $\sqrt{13}(\sqrt{3} + \sqrt{13})$
   b) $3\sqrt{3}(\sqrt{3} - 2\sqrt{6})$
   c) $3\sqrt{2}(2\sqrt{2} - 5\sqrt{8})$
   d) $2\sqrt{5}(3\sqrt{2} + 4\sqrt{3})$
   e) $6\sqrt{6}(3\sqrt{2} - 4\sqrt{3})$
   f) $2\sqrt{6}(3\sqrt{6} - 5\sqrt{8})$

Ⓑ

3. Expand and simplify.

    a) $2\sqrt{3}(5\sqrt{7} - 2\sqrt{3} + 3\sqrt{6})$ b) $4\sqrt{7}(2\sqrt{3} + 3\sqrt{6} - \sqrt{7})$

    c) $5\sqrt{2}(3\sqrt{18} + 7\sqrt{2} - 4\sqrt{8})$ d) $12\sqrt{3}(2\sqrt{5} - 6\sqrt{6} - 3\sqrt{12})$

4. Expand and simplify.

    a) $-7\sqrt{5}(-2\sqrt{20} - 4\sqrt{30} + 3\sqrt{5})$ b) $8\sqrt{6}(3\sqrt{2} - 4\sqrt{3} - 2\sqrt{6})$

    c) $2\sqrt{3}(5\sqrt{8} + 2\sqrt{3} - 4\sqrt{5} + 3\sqrt{6})$ d) $4\sqrt{2}(2\sqrt{5} - 6\sqrt{3} - 2\sqrt{8} + 5\sqrt{32})$

5. Simplify.

    a) $(\sqrt{3} + 2)(\sqrt{3} + 1)$ b) $(\sqrt{7} - 6)(\sqrt{7} + 1)$ c) $(\sqrt{8} - 5)(\sqrt{2} - 3)$

    d) $(2 + \sqrt{12})(4 - \sqrt{3})$ e) $(\sqrt{5} + \sqrt{2})(\sqrt{5} - \sqrt{2})$ f) $(\sqrt{6} - \sqrt{3})(\sqrt{12} - \sqrt{6})$

    g) $(3 - \sqrt{2})^2$ h) $(1 + \sqrt{3})^2$ i) $(5 - 2\sqrt{2})^2$

6. Simplify.

    a) $(5 + 3\sqrt{2})(4 - \sqrt{2})$ b) $(6 - 4\sqrt{2})(2 - 5\sqrt{2})$ c) $(2\sqrt{3} + 1)(\sqrt{3} - 4)$

    d) $(\sqrt{7} - 3)(4\sqrt{7} + 1)$ e) $(4 + 2\sqrt{3})(4 - 2\sqrt{3})$ f) $(2\sqrt{5} + \sqrt{2})(2\sqrt{5} - \sqrt{2})$

    g) $(3\sqrt{7} - \sqrt{2})^2$ h) $(\sqrt{6} + 2\sqrt{3})^2$ i) $(2\sqrt{2} - 3\sqrt{10})^2$

7. Simplify.

    a) $(2\sqrt{5} + 3\sqrt{2})^2$ b) $(4\sqrt{2} - 5\sqrt{3})(4\sqrt{2} + 5\sqrt{3})$

    c) $(7 - 3\sqrt{2})^2$ d) $(6\sqrt{3} - 2\sqrt{7})(6\sqrt{3} + 2\sqrt{7})$

    e) $(6\sqrt{5} - 2\sqrt{10})^2$ f) $(3\sqrt{5} - 2\sqrt{3})(3\sqrt{5} + 2\sqrt{3})$

    g) $(7\sqrt{3} - 5\sqrt{2})^2$ h) $(3\sqrt{6} + 2\sqrt{2})(2\sqrt{6} - 3\sqrt{2})$

    i) $(6\sqrt{8} - 3\sqrt{2})^2$ j) $(2\sqrt{7} + 3\sqrt{3})(2\sqrt{7} - 3\sqrt{3})$

8. a) Square each of the following.

         $\sqrt{6} + \sqrt{10}, \quad \sqrt{13} + \sqrt{3}, \quad \sqrt{15} + \sqrt{1}, \quad \sqrt{5} + \sqrt{11}$

    b) Arrange the radical expressions in (a) in order from greatest to least.

9. Arrange in order from greatest to least.

    $\sqrt{18} - \sqrt{8}, \quad \sqrt{14} - \sqrt{12}, \quad \sqrt{20} - \sqrt{6}, \quad \sqrt{15} - \sqrt{11}$

1-11 DIVIDING RADICALS

Division is the inverse of multiplication.
 We know $56 \div 8 = 7$ because $7 \times 8 = 56$.
Similarly, $\sqrt{10} \div \sqrt{2} = \sqrt{5}$ because $\sqrt{5} \times \sqrt{2} = \sqrt{10}$
This suggests the following property for radicals:

$$\frac{\sqrt{a}}{\sqrt{b}} = \sqrt{\frac{a}{b}}, \quad (a \geq 0, b > 0)$$

Example 1. Simplify:

a) $\dfrac{2\sqrt{15}}{\sqrt{3}}$ b) $\dfrac{\sqrt{36}}{\sqrt{2}}$ c) $\dfrac{9\sqrt{24}}{2\sqrt{18}}$

Solution. a) $\dfrac{2\sqrt{15}}{\sqrt{3}}$ $\times$ b) $\dfrac{\sqrt{36}}{\sqrt{2}} = \sqrt{18}$

$= 2\sqrt{\dfrac{15}{3}}$ $= 3\sqrt{2}$

$= 2\sqrt{5}$ or $\dfrac{\sqrt{36}}{\sqrt{2}} = \dfrac{6}{\sqrt{2}}$

c) The radicals should be expressed in simplest form before dividing.

$$\frac{9\sqrt{24}}{2\sqrt{18}} = \frac{9 \times 2\sqrt{6}}{2 \times 3\sqrt{2}}$$

$$= \frac{3\sqrt{6}}{\sqrt{2}}$$

$$= 3\sqrt{3}$$

 The answers to *Example 1b* found by two different methods must
be equal. We can show that they are by multiplying the numerator and
the denominator of $\dfrac{6}{\sqrt{2}}$ by $\sqrt{2}$.

$$\frac{6}{\sqrt{2}} = \frac{6}{\sqrt{2}} \times \boxed{\frac{\sqrt{2}}{\sqrt{2}}}$$

$$= \frac{6\sqrt{2}}{2}$$

$$= 3\sqrt{2}$$

This procedure is called *rationalizing the denominator*.

Example 2.   Obtain equivalent expressions by rationalizing the denominator:

a) $\dfrac{1}{\sqrt{7}}$ b) $\dfrac{5}{\sqrt{20}}$ c) $\dfrac{4\sqrt{27}}{3\sqrt{72}}$

Solution.   a) $\dfrac{1}{\sqrt{7}}$ b) $\dfrac{5}{\sqrt{20}}$ c) $\dfrac{4\sqrt{27}}{3\sqrt{72}}$

$= \dfrac{1}{\sqrt{7}} \times \dfrac{\sqrt{7}}{\sqrt{7}}$ $= \dfrac{5}{2\sqrt{5}} \times \dfrac{\sqrt{5}}{\sqrt{5}}$ $= \dfrac{4 \times 3\sqrt{3}}{3 \times 6\sqrt{2}}$

$= \dfrac{\sqrt{7}}{7}$ $= \dfrac{5\sqrt{5}}{10}$ $= \dfrac{2\sqrt{3}}{3\sqrt{2}} \times \dfrac{\sqrt{2}}{\sqrt{2}}$

$= \dfrac{\sqrt{5}}{2}$ $= \dfrac{2\sqrt{6}}{6}$

$= \dfrac{\sqrt{6}}{3}$

Example 3.   Simplify.

a) $\dfrac{1}{\sqrt{12}} - \dfrac{1}{\sqrt{27}}$ b) $\dfrac{3}{\sqrt{12}} - \dfrac{5}{\sqrt{8}}$

Solution.   a) $\dfrac{1}{\sqrt{12}} - \dfrac{1}{\sqrt{27}}$ b) $\dfrac{3}{\sqrt{12}} - \dfrac{5}{\sqrt{8}}$

$= \dfrac{1}{2\sqrt{3}} - \dfrac{1}{3\sqrt{3}}$ $= \dfrac{3}{2\sqrt{3}} - \dfrac{5}{2\sqrt{2}}$

$= \dfrac{1}{2\sqrt{3}} \times \dfrac{\sqrt{3}}{\sqrt{3}} - \dfrac{1}{3\sqrt{3}} \times \dfrac{\sqrt{3}}{\sqrt{3}}$ $= \dfrac{3}{2\sqrt{3}} \times \dfrac{\sqrt{3}}{\sqrt{3}} - \dfrac{5}{2\sqrt{2}} \times \dfrac{\sqrt{2}}{\sqrt{2}}$

$= \dfrac{\sqrt{3}}{6} - \dfrac{\sqrt{3}}{9}$ $= \dfrac{3\sqrt{3}}{6} - \dfrac{5\sqrt{2}}{4}$

$= \dfrac{3\sqrt{3} - 2\sqrt{3}}{18}$ $= \dfrac{6\sqrt{3} - 15\sqrt{2}}{12}$

$= \dfrac{\sqrt{3}}{18}$ $= \dfrac{2\sqrt{3} - 5\sqrt{2}}{4}$

EXERCISES 1-11

Ⓐ

1. Simplify.

a) $\dfrac{\sqrt{24}}{\sqrt{3}}$

b) $\dfrac{\sqrt{56}}{\sqrt{8}}$

c) $\dfrac{\sqrt{72}}{\sqrt{6}}$

d) $\dfrac{3\sqrt{35}}{\sqrt{7}}$

e) $\dfrac{6\sqrt{18}}{2\sqrt{6}}$

f) $\dfrac{5\sqrt{30}}{2\sqrt{15}}$

g) $\dfrac{4\sqrt{20}}{2\sqrt{5}}$

h) $\dfrac{3\sqrt{12}}{6\sqrt{3}}$

i) $\dfrac{\sqrt{24}}{7\sqrt{12}}$

j) $\dfrac{\sqrt{8}}{6\sqrt{18}}$

2. Simplify.

a) $\dfrac{3\sqrt{48}}{2\sqrt{27}}$

b) $\dfrac{6\sqrt{50}}{5\sqrt{18}}$

c) $\dfrac{4\sqrt{54}}{3\sqrt{12}}$

d) $\dfrac{3\sqrt{20}}{2\sqrt{10}}$

e) $\dfrac{5\sqrt{24}}{2\sqrt{18}}$

f) $\dfrac{7\sqrt{32}}{5\sqrt{63}}$

g) $\dfrac{10\sqrt{27}}{3\sqrt{20}}$

h) $\dfrac{16\sqrt{24}}{4\sqrt{96}}$

i) $\dfrac{4\sqrt{45}}{3\sqrt{54}}$

j) $\dfrac{3\sqrt{60}}{2\sqrt{27}}$

3. Express in simplest form.

a) $\dfrac{1}{\sqrt{6}}$

b) $\dfrac{3}{\sqrt{5}}$

c) $\dfrac{12}{\sqrt{17}}$

d) $\dfrac{10}{\sqrt{5}}$

e) $\dfrac{6}{\sqrt{12}}$

f) $\dfrac{3}{2\sqrt{7}}$

g) $\dfrac{2\sqrt{6}}{5\sqrt{3}}$

h) $\dfrac{6\sqrt{10}}{3\sqrt{5}}$

i) $\dfrac{3\sqrt{20}}{4\sqrt{12}}$

j) $\dfrac{8\sqrt{18}}{3\sqrt{75}}$

Ⓑ

4. Simplify.

a) $\dfrac{1}{\sqrt{5}} + \dfrac{1}{\sqrt{3}}$

b) $\dfrac{1}{\sqrt{2}} - \dfrac{1}{\sqrt{6}}$

c) $\dfrac{1}{\sqrt{3}} + \dfrac{1}{\sqrt{6}}$

d) $\dfrac{2}{\sqrt{7}} - \dfrac{3}{\sqrt{5}}$

e) $\dfrac{4}{\sqrt{3}} + \dfrac{2}{\sqrt{10}}$

f) $\dfrac{3}{\sqrt{7}} - \dfrac{9}{\sqrt{6}}$

g) $\dfrac{5}{\sqrt{5}} - \dfrac{8}{\sqrt{2}}$

h) $\dfrac{6}{\sqrt{7}} - \dfrac{3}{\sqrt{3}}$

5. Simplify.

a) $\dfrac{3}{\sqrt{12}} + \dfrac{2}{\sqrt{18}}$

b) $\dfrac{5}{\sqrt{8}} - \dfrac{2}{\sqrt{6}}$

c) $\dfrac{7}{\sqrt{20}} - \dfrac{4}{\sqrt{12}}$

d) $\dfrac{3\sqrt{2}}{\sqrt{12}} - \dfrac{5\sqrt{3}}{\sqrt{8}}$

e) $\dfrac{4\sqrt{3}}{\sqrt{18}} - \dfrac{2\sqrt{2}}{\sqrt{6}}$

f) $\dfrac{3\sqrt{5}}{\sqrt{20}} + \dfrac{4\sqrt{3}}{\sqrt{27}}$

g) $\dfrac{3\sqrt{48}}{2\sqrt{75}} - \dfrac{2\sqrt{24}}{\sqrt{96}}$

h) $\dfrac{2\sqrt{3}}{\sqrt{9}} - \dfrac{3\sqrt{5}}{\sqrt{125}}$

 INVESTIGATE

Is it possible to find real numbers a and b such that
a) both $\sqrt{a} \times \sqrt{b}$ and $\sqrt{a} \div \sqrt{b}$ are rational? irrational?
b) only one of $\sqrt{a} \times \sqrt{b}$ and $\sqrt{a} \div \sqrt{b}$ is rational?

```
============( MATHEMATICS AROUND US )============
```

Simple Interest

Interest is the money paid for the use of money. If you have a savings account, the bank pays you interest for the use of your savings. If you borrow money from a bank, the bank charges you interest for the use of its money. The charge is expressed as a rate, usually a percent, called the *interest rate*. The amount borrowed or placed on deposit is called the *principal*.

QUESTIONS

1. Copy and complete the table.

Principal of a loan, P	Interest rate, r	Interest for 1 year, I	Amount owing at the end of 1 year, A
$\$\quad 200$	22%	22% of $200 = $44	$244
$\$\quad 1000$	18%		
$\$\quad 3000$	19.5%		
$\$\quad 3200$		$528	
$17\ 500$			$21\ 262.50

2. Using the definitions of P, r, I, and A in the table above, write a formula for

   a) I in terms of P and r

   b) A in terms of P and r

3. A store's finance department charges 2% per month on overdue accounts. An account for $325.47 becomes due. If no payment is made, calculate

   a) the interest charges at the end of the next month

   b) the amount due at the end of the next month.

4. A bank pays 12.75% annual interest on Daily Interest Savings Accounts, interest being credited to the accounts at the end of each month. What interest will be credited at the end of the month to an account which has

   a) a balance of $100 through January?

   b) a balance of $100 on May 1 which is increased on May 9 by a deposit of $200?

   c) a balance of $600 on September 1 which is decreased on September 17 by a withdrawal of $150?

Review Exercises

1. Express as the product of prime factors.
   a) 26   b) 44   c) 210   d) 182   e) 429   f) 172   g) 88

2. Find the g.c.f. of each pair of numbers.
   a) 15, 72   b) 39, 143   c) 20, 75   d) 14, 77   e) 12, 84   f) 18, 148

3. Find the l.c.m. of each pair of numbers.
   a) 20, 48   b) 30, 42   c) 40, 75   d) 36, 56   e) 24, 56   f) 33, 105

4. The lights on one airport tower flash every 35 s. The lights on another tower flash every 42 s. If they started flashing together, what is the time interval between simultaneous flashes?

5. Simplify.
   a) $(-3)(+5) + (-2)(-4)$ b) $(-6)(+1) - (-3)(-2)$ c) $-2[3(-4) - 7 + 8]$
   d) $3 + 5[8 \div 2 - (-4)(-2)]$ e) $5 - 6[3(-4) - (-1)]$ f) $[(14 \div 7) - (15 \div 5)]$

6. If $x = -3$, $y = 2$, and $z = -1$, evaluate.
   a) $xz^2 - x^2z^2 - xyz$ b) $4xy^2 - 4x^2y + 4xyz$ c) $x^2y^2 - xz^3 - 2yz$

7. Simplify.
   a) $3|6 - 4 - 12|$ b) $5|7 - 2| - 3|2 - 8| + 2|3 - 7|$ c) $2|8 - 3|-5|3 - 7|-3|4 - 9|$

8. Simplify.
   a) $\dfrac{5}{-8} - \dfrac{-3}{4}$ b) $\dfrac{11}{3} - \left(\dfrac{-7}{4}\right)$ c) $-\dfrac{13}{6} + \dfrac{17}{8}$ d) $\dfrac{13}{5} - \left(\dfrac{5}{-6}\right)$ e) $-\dfrac{8}{9} - \left(\dfrac{-5}{8}\right)$

9. Simplify.
   a) $\sqrt[3]{-8}$ b) $\sqrt[3]{125}$ c) $\sqrt[4]{81}$ d) $\sqrt[3]{64}$ e) $\sqrt[5]{-32}$ f) $\sqrt[3]{0.001}$

10. If $x = \dfrac{-1}{4}$ and $y = \dfrac{2}{-3}$, evaluate.

    a) $3x + 2y - 5xy$ b) $3x^2 - \dfrac{1}{3}xy$ c) $5y^2 - \dfrac{1}{2}x^2 + xy$ d) $x^2 - y^2$

11. Express in decimal form.
    a) $\dfrac{2}{9}$ b) $\dfrac{-6}{11}$ c) $3\dfrac{3}{5}$ d) $-5\dfrac{1}{6}$ e) $-10\dfrac{1}{4}$ f) $\dfrac{9}{13}$ g) $\dfrac{8}{11}$

12. Express in the form $\dfrac{m}{n}$.

    a) 3.23 b) $0.\overline{43}$ c) $1.\overline{27}$ d) $3.1\overline{13}$ e) $2.2\overline{873}$ f) $3.46\overline{89}$

13. Which of the following numbers are irrational?
    a) $\sqrt{48}$ b) $\sqrt{49}$ c) $\sqrt{1\dfrac{7}{9}}$ d) $\sqrt{3.6}$ e) $\sqrt{289}$ f) $\sqrt{0.25}$

14. Evaluate the following for $x = \sqrt{3}$. Say whether the result is rational or irrational.
    a) $x^2 + 3x - 9$ b) $2x^3 - x^2 - 6x - 1$ c) $x^2 - 9$ d) $x^4 - x$

15. Find x, rounded to one decimal place.
    a)   b)   c)

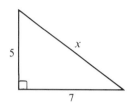
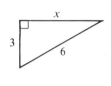
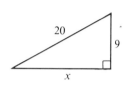

16. An Air Muskoka pilot radios his position as 12 km south and 5 km east of the airport tower. The altimeter reads 9000 m. How far is the aircraft from the tower?

17. Express as a mixed radical in simplest form.
    a) $\sqrt{98}$ b) $\sqrt{27}$ c) $2\sqrt{45}$ d) $-3\sqrt{360}$ e) $2\sqrt{60}$ f) $\sqrt{300}$

18. Simplify.
    a) $4\sqrt{6} \times 2\sqrt{3}$ b) $(-4\sqrt{12})(-3\sqrt{3})$ c) $-5\sqrt{20} \times 2\sqrt{5}$ d) $-5\sqrt{6} \times 5\sqrt{12}$
    e) $(-3\sqrt{5})(-2\sqrt{15})$ f) $-2\sqrt{8} \times 3\sqrt{6} \times \sqrt{12}$ g) $(-3\sqrt{5})(2\sqrt{6})$ h) $(-2\sqrt{13})(-\sqrt{52})$

19. Simplify.
    a) $3\sqrt{5} - 6\sqrt{5} + 8\sqrt{5}$ b) $4\sqrt{2} + 3\sqrt{2} - 2\sqrt{8}$ c) $2\sqrt{8} + 3\sqrt{18} - \sqrt{50}$
    d) $\frac{1}{2}\sqrt{27} + \frac{1}{3}\sqrt{108} - \frac{1}{4}\sqrt{12}$ e) $\frac{1}{3}\sqrt{32} - \frac{1}{4}\sqrt{98} + \frac{1}{5}\sqrt{50}$ f) $\frac{1}{5}\sqrt{180} - \sqrt{245} - \sqrt{405}$

20. Expand and simplify.
    a) $\sqrt{2}(\sqrt{8} - \sqrt{3})$ b) $\sqrt{3}(\sqrt{2} - 3\sqrt{27})$ c) $\sqrt{5}(\sqrt{8} - \sqrt{3})$ d) $\sqrt{5}(\sqrt{6} - 2\sqrt{7})$

21. Simplify.
    a) $(\sqrt{3} - \sqrt{2})(2\sqrt{3} + 3\sqrt{2})$ b) $(2\sqrt{2} - 3\sqrt{3})(2\sqrt{2} + 3\sqrt{3})$ c) $(2\sqrt{5} - 3\sqrt{2})(2\sqrt{5} + 3\sqrt{2})$

22. Simplify.
    a) $\dfrac{\sqrt{24}}{\sqrt{2}}$ b) $\dfrac{3\sqrt{32}}{\sqrt{2}}$ c) $\dfrac{\sqrt{2}}{\frac{1}{2}}$ d) $\dfrac{3\sqrt{12}}{4\sqrt{27}}$ e) $\dfrac{2\sqrt{45}}{7\sqrt{80}}$

23. Express in simplest form.
    a) $\dfrac{2\sqrt{3}}{\sqrt{2}}$ b) $\dfrac{3}{\sqrt{27}}$ c) $\dfrac{5}{\sqrt{50}}$ d) $\dfrac{3\sqrt{24}}{\sqrt{54}}$ e) $\dfrac{\sqrt{28}}{5\sqrt{63}}$

Matter is made up of tiny particles called atoms. If the mass of a sample of gold is known, how can the number of atoms in the sample be determined? (See *Example 3* in Section 2-4.)

2-1 TERMS, VARIABLES, EXPONENTS AND COEFFICIENTS

In the forestry industry, it is important to estimate the volume of wood in a tree. One formula for the volume, V, in cubic metres is:

$$V = 0.05hc^2$$

where h is the height in metres, and c is the circumference of the trunk, in metres. To find the volume of wood in a 30 m tree with a trunk circumference of 2.40 m, substitute 30 for h and 2.40 for c in the formula:

$$V = 0.05(30)(2.40)^2$$
$$= 1.5(5.76)$$
$$= 8.64$$

The tree has about 8.6 m³ of wood in it.

The expression on the right side of the formula is called a *term*. The parts of the term are named below.

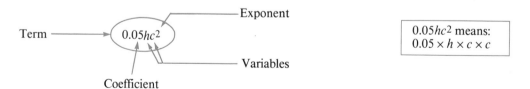

0.05hc^2 means:
$0.05 \times h \times c \times c$

It is not necessary for a term to be part of a formula in algebra. It is important to remember the meaning of exponents when terms are being evaluated or operated on.

Example 1. Evaluate when $x = -3$ and $y = 2$:

a) $-x^2y^3$ b) $\dfrac{x}{y^4}$ c) $(-x)^3(-y^2)$

Solution. When $x = -3$ and $y = 2$:

a) $-x^2y^3 = -(-3)^2(2)^3$ b) $\dfrac{x}{y^4} = \dfrac{-3}{24}$ c) $(-x)^3(-y^2) = (3)^3(-2^2)$
$= -9 \times 8$ $= 27(-4)$
$= -72$ $= -\dfrac{3}{16}$ $= -108$

Example 2. The volume, V, of a cone is given by the formula $V = \dfrac{1}{3}\pi r^2 h$, where r is the radius of the base and h is the height. What is the volume of a conical pile of sand of height 4.6 m and radius 8.2 m?

Solution. When $r = 8.2$ and $h = 4.6$,

$$V = \frac{1}{3}\pi(8.2)^2 \, (4.6)$$

$$\doteq \frac{1}{3}(3.14)(8.2)^2(4.6)$$

$$\doteq 323.74$$

The pile contains about 320 m³ of sand.

EXERCISES 2-1

Ⓐ

1. Name the variables, coefficients and exponents.

   $-ab^3$, $4x^2y$, $-5m^3n^2$, $7x^4y^2z$, $\dfrac{1}{3}p^6q^2$, $6x$,   8

2. If $x = -2$ and $y = 3$, evaluate.
  a) xy b) x^2y c) xy^2 d) $2x^2y^2$ e) $-(3x^2y^2)$

  f) $\dfrac{x^3}{y^2}$ g) $\dfrac{-3x^2}{y^3}$ h) $\dfrac{x^3y^2}{4}$ i) $\left(\dfrac{-xy}{2}\right)^2$ j) $\left(\dfrac{-x^2y}{2}\right)^2$

3. If $p = 2$ and $q = -4$, evaluate.
  a) p^4 b) p^2q^2 c) $\dfrac{p^5}{q^2}$ d) $\left(\dfrac{p^2}{q}\right)^2$ e) $\dfrac{12q^2}{p^3}$ f) $\left(\dfrac{-2q}{p}\right)^3$

Ⓑ

4. A rectangle has length, l, and width, w.
  a) Write a formula for the area, A, and the perimeter, P.
  b) Find the area of a rectangle 15 m by 12 m.

5. The circumference of a circle is π times its diameter.
  a) Write a formula for the circumference, C, in terms of π and the radius, r.
  b) Find the circumference of a circle with radius 25 cm.

6. The area, A, of a circle is π times the square of its radius, r.
   a) Write a formula for the area in terms of π and r.
   b) Find the area of a circle with radius 15 cm.

7. The volume, V, of a cylinder of radius r and height h is given by the formula:
   $V = \pi r^2 h$. What is the volume of a cylindrical tank of radius 50 cm and height 3 m?

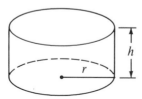

8. Write a formula for the area of the curved surface of a cylinder of length l and radius r.

9. In house construction, the safe load, m, in kilograms, that can be supported by a horizontal joist of length l metres is given by the formula:

   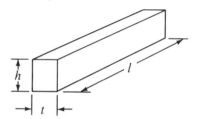

   $$m = \frac{4th^2}{l}$$

   where t is the thickness and h the height in centimetres. Find the safe load for a beam 4 m long when
   a) $t = 5$ cm and $h = 10$ cm   b) $t = 10$ cm and $h = 5$ cm

10. The stopping distance of a vehicle on an icy road depends on its speed and its mass. A typical formula for estimating stopping distance, d, in metres is:
    $d = 0.75 \, sm^2$, where s is its speed in kilometres per hour and m its mass in tonnes. Estimate the stopping distance for a
    a) 2000 kg car travelling at 100 km/h   b) 5000 kg truck travelling at 40 km/h

11. The pressure, P, in kilopascals, exerted on the floor by the heel of a shoe is given by the formula:

    $$P = \frac{100m}{x^2}$$

    where m is the wearer's mass, in kilograms, and x is the width of the heel, in centimetres. Find the pressure exerted by a
    a) 90 kg man wearing shoes with heels   b) 60 kg woman wearing shoes with
       7 cm wide   heels 2 cm wide

12. A term contains the variables x and y. When $x = 3$ and $y = 2$, the value of the term is $\frac{9}{2}$. When $x = 4$ and $y = 5$, the value of the term is $\frac{16}{5}$. Find the term.

THE MATHEMATICAL MIND

The Four Squares Problem

1

More than 2000 years ago, the Greeks discovered that they could express any given natural number as the sum of four or fewer perfect squares.

$$34 = 25 + 4 + 4 + 1$$
$$47 = 36 + 9 + 1 + 1$$
$$62 = 49 + 9 + 4$$
$$85 = 49 + 36$$

2

Although they could not find a single exception to this rule, they were unable to prove that *all* natural numbers can be expressed in this way.

$$129 = 121 + 4 + 4$$
$$254 = 144 + 100 + 9 + 1$$
$$306 = 225 + 81$$
$$321 = 121 + 100 + 100$$

3

For a long time this was an unsolved problem in mathematics. One of the greatest mathematicians of the 18th century, Leonhard Euler, tried unsuccessfully over a period of 40 years to solve this problem.

Leonhard Euler
1707–1783

4

Finally, in 1770, Euler's successor, Joseph Lagrange, succeeded in proving that every natural number, no matter how great, can be expressed as the sum of four or fewer perfect squares.

$$n = a^2 + b^2 + c^2 + d^2$$

1. Express as the sum of four or fewer perfect squares.
   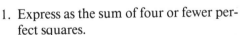
   a) 29   b) 56   c) 87   d) 115
   e) 130   f) 168   g) 204   h) 435

2. How many natural numbers less than 100 can be expressed as the sum of
   a) three or fewer perfect squares?
   b) two perfect squares?

3. How many natural numbers less than 100 can be expressed as the sum of two perfect squares in two different ways?

Joseph Lagrange **1736–1813**

 COMPUTER POWER

Compound Interest

	Savings Accounts
Regular	$5\frac{1}{4}$%
Daily Interest	$4\frac{3}{4}$%

	Guaranteed Investment Certificates
Annual	$8\frac{1}{2}$%
Semi-annual	$8\frac{1}{4}$%
Quarterly	8 %
Monthly	8 %

When you deposit money in a savings account you may earn interest on interest, or *compound interest*. For example, if you deposit $100 in an account paying 8.5% compounded annually, you will receive 0.085 × $100, or $8.50 interest after one year. The balance becomes $108.50, and if you leave the money in the account, you will receive 0.085 × $108.50, or $9.22 after the second year. This kind of calculation is best set out in a table:

Year	Amount at Start of Year	Year's Interest	Amount at End of Year
1	$100	0.085 × $100 = $8.50	$100 + $8.50 = $108.50
2	$108.50	0.085 × $108.50 = $9.22	$108.50 + $9.22 = $117.72
3	$117.72		

1. Copy the table shown and complete the calculations to the end of the 5th year.

2. This program can be used to print a table showing the amount after any number of years for any initial deposit and any interest rate (expressed as a decimal). Run the program and verify the results in 1.

```
100 REM *** COMPOUND INTEREST ***
110 INPUT "WHAT IS THE INITIAL
        DEPOSIT? ";P
120 INPUT "WHAT IS THE INTEREST
        RATE (DECIMAL)? ";I
130 INPUT "HOW MANY YEARS? ";N
140 FOR K=1 TO N
150     IN=INT(P*I*100+0.5)/100
160     PRINT K;"  ";P,IN,P+IN
170     P=P+IN
180 NEXT K
190 END
```

3. Gary deposited $250 in an account which pays 9.5% interest compounded annually. If no deposits or withdrawals are made, use the program to determine
   a) the amount in the account after 10 years
   b) how many years it would take for his investment to amount to $500, $1000, $2000.

There is a pattern in compound interest calculations which can be used to develop a formula for the amount at any time. For example, assume you deposit $100 in an account which pays 8% interest compounded annually.

Interest after the first year is:
$$\$100 \times 0.08 = \$8.00$$
Balance at the end of the year is:
$$\$100 + \$8 = \$108$$
(This is also $\$100 \times 1.08 = \$108$)

Interest after the second year is:
$$\$108 \times 0.08 = \$8.64$$
Balance at the end of the year is:
$$\$108 + \$8.64 = \$116.64$$
(This is also $\$108 \times 1.08 = \$116.64$)

Interest after the third year is:
$$\$116.64 \times 0.08 = \$9.33$$
Balance at the end of the year is:
$$\$116.64 + \$9.33 = \$125.97$$
(This is also $\$116.64 \times 1.08 = \$125.97$)

We see that:

Amount at the end of any year	=	Amount at the beginning of the year	× 1.08

Balance, in dollars, at the end of
Year 1 is:
$$100 \times 1.08 \qquad = 100(1.08)^1$$
Year 2 is:
$$100 \times 1.08 \times 1.08 \qquad = 100(1.08)^2$$
Year 3 is:
$$100 \times 1.08 \times 1.08 \times 1.08 = 100(1.08)^3$$
Year 4 is: $\longrightarrow 100(1.08)^4$

.   .   .
.   .   .

Year n is: $\longrightarrow 100(1.08)^n$

This result suggests the following general formula:

> When an amount of money, P (the principal), is invested at an interest rate, i, compounded annually, the amount, A, after n years is given by the formula:
> $$A = P(1 + i)^n$$

4. A savings account has interest compounded annually. Determine the amount in the account
   a) after 3 years at 7% with a deposit of $200.
   b) after 5 years at 9.5% with a deposit of $450.
   c) after 4 years at 6.75% with a deposit of $850.

To use the compound interest formula in the program given in 2, change the program as follows. Type LIST, and then enter the following lines.

```
140 A=P*(1+I)^N
150 A=INT(A*100+0.5)/100
160 PRINT "AFTER ";N;" YEARS THE
    AMOUNT IS ";A
170 END
```

With this modified program, the final amount is calculated directly without calculating the amount for each year. The program also allows the calculation to be repeated for a different number of years.

5. Use the modified program to verify the results of 4.

6. Use the program to determine how many years it will take for an investment to double in value if the annual interest rate is
   a) 6% b) 8% c) 10% d) 12%

2-2 INTEGRAL EXPONENTS

An expression of the form a^n is called a *power*.

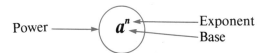

Power ⟶ a^n ⟵ Exponent
— Base

The definition of a power depends on whether the exponent is a positive integer, a negative integer, or zero.

Positive Integral Exponent

$$a^n = a \cdot a \cdot a \cdot \ldots a$$

n factors

Negative Integral Exponent

a^{-n} is defined to be the reciprocal of a^n.

$$a^{-n} = \frac{1}{a^n}, \quad (a \neq 0)$$

Zero Exponent

a^0 is defined to be equal to 1.
$$a^0 = 1, \quad (a \neq 0)$$

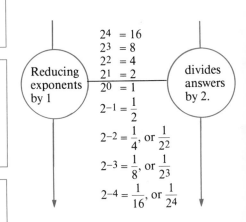

Reducing exponents by 1

$2^4 = 16$
$2^3 = 8$
$2^2 = 4$
$2^1 = 2$
$2^0 = 1$
$2^{-1} = \frac{1}{2}$
$2^{-2} = \frac{1}{4}$, or $\frac{1}{2^2}$
$2^{-3} = \frac{1}{8}$, or $\frac{1}{2^3}$
$2^{-4} = \frac{1}{16}$, or $\frac{1}{2^4}$

divides answers by 2.

These definitions can be used to evaluate a power with any integral exponent.

Example 1. Simplify:

a) 4^3 b) 3^{-2} c) $(-2)^{-3}$ d) $\left(\frac{1}{2}\right)^0$

Solution.

a) $4^3 = (4)(4)(4)$
$= 64$

b) $3^{-2} = \frac{1}{3^2}$
$= \frac{1}{9}$

c) $(-2)^{-3} = \frac{1}{(-2)^3}$
$= -\frac{1}{8}$

d) $\left(\frac{1}{2}\right)^0$
$= 1$

Evaluate powers first before doing any operations unless brackets indicate otherwise.

Example 2. If $m = -5$ and $n = 2$, evaluate:

a) $m^2 - n^{-1}$

b) $(-mn^2)^{-2}$

c) $\left(\dfrac{m}{n}\right)^{-3}$

d) $(m^{-1} + n^0)^{-1}$

Solution.

a) $m^2 - n^{-1} = (-5)^2 - 2^{-1}$

$= 25 - \dfrac{1}{2}$

$= 24\dfrac{1}{2}$

b) $(-mn^2)^{-2} = (5 \times 4)^{-2}$

$= \dfrac{1}{20^2}$

$= \dfrac{1}{400}$

c) $\left(\dfrac{m}{n}\right)^{-3} = \left(-\dfrac{5}{2}\right)^{-3}$

$= \dfrac{1}{\left(-\dfrac{5}{2}\right)^3}$

$= \dfrac{1}{-\dfrac{125}{8}}$

$= -\dfrac{8}{125}$

d) $(m^{-1} + n^0)^{-1} = [(-5)^{-1} + 2^0]^{-1}$

$= \left(-\dfrac{1}{5} + 1\right)^{-1}$

$= \left(\dfrac{4}{5}\right)^{-1}$

$= \dfrac{5}{4}$

Expressions involving repeated factors can be written as powers with positive or negative integral exponents.

Example 3. Write as a power:

a) $(-r)(-r)(-r)(-r)(-r)$

b) $\left(\dfrac{1}{r}\right)\left(\dfrac{1}{r}\right)\left(\dfrac{1}{r}\right)$

Solution.

a) $(-r)(-r)(-r)(-r)(-r) = (-r)^5$

b) $\left(\dfrac{1}{r}\right)\left(\dfrac{1}{r}\right)\left(\dfrac{1}{r}\right) = \dfrac{1}{r \cdot r \cdot r}$

$= \dfrac{1}{r^3}$

$= r^{-3}$

Example 4. Write as a product of powers:

a) $\dfrac{x}{y} \cdot \dfrac{x}{y} \cdot \dfrac{x}{y} \cdot \dfrac{x}{y}$

b) $\dfrac{1}{x} \cdot \dfrac{1}{y} \cdot \dfrac{1}{x} \cdot \dfrac{1}{x} \cdot \dfrac{1}{y}$

Solution.

a) $\dfrac{x}{y} \cdot \dfrac{x}{y} \cdot \dfrac{x}{y} \cdot \dfrac{x}{y} = \dfrac{x \cdot x \cdot x \cdot x}{y \cdot y \cdot y \cdot y}$

$= \dfrac{x^4}{y^4}$

$= x^4 y^{-4}$

b) $\dfrac{1}{x} \cdot \dfrac{1}{y} \cdot \dfrac{1}{x} \cdot \dfrac{1}{x} \cdot \dfrac{1}{y} = \dfrac{1}{x \cdot y \cdot x \cdot x \cdot y}$

$= \dfrac{1}{x^3 y^2}$

$= x^{-3} y^{-2}$

EXERCISES 2-2

Ⓐ

1. Simplify.

   a) 2^4

   b) 5^{-2}

   c) 3^{-1}

   d) $\left(\dfrac{1}{4}\right)^{-1}$

   e) $\left(\dfrac{2}{3}\right)^{-1}$

   f) $\left(\dfrac{3}{4}\right)^{-2}$

   g) $(0.5)^{-1}$

   h) $(1.5)^0$

2. Simplify.

   a) 10^0

   b) $(-3)^{-2}$

   c) $\left(-\dfrac{1}{2}\right)^3$

   d) $\left(-\dfrac{2}{3}\right)^{-1}$

   e) $\left(-\dfrac{3}{5}\right)^{-2}$

   f) $(-1)^{-4}$

   g) $(0.1)^{-4}$

   h) $\dfrac{1}{2^{-3}}$

3. Write as a power.

   a) $(-7)(-7)(-7)$

   b) $\dfrac{1}{b \times b \times b \times b \times b}$

   c) $\left(\dfrac{1}{x}\right)\left(\dfrac{1}{x}\right)\left(\dfrac{1}{x}\right)\left(\dfrac{1}{x}\right)$

   d) $\dfrac{1}{3 \times 3}$

   e) $\dfrac{1}{1.5 \times 1.5}$

   f) $\dfrac{1}{(-3.5)(-3.5)}$

4. Write as a product of powers.

   a) $x \cdot x \cdot y \cdot y \cdot y$

   b) $x \cdot y \cdot x \cdot y \cdot x$

   c) $\dfrac{x \cdot x \cdot x}{z \cdot z}$

   d) $\dfrac{x \cdot x}{y \cdot y \cdot y}$

   e) $\left(\dfrac{a}{b}\right)\left(\dfrac{a}{b}\right)\left(\dfrac{a}{b}\right)\left(\dfrac{a}{b}\right)$

   f) $\left(\dfrac{a}{b}\right)\left(\dfrac{a}{b}\right)\left(\dfrac{a}{1}\right)$

Ⓑ

5. Simplify.

   a) $2^3 + 2^{-3}$

   b) $2^{-1} + 2^{-2}$

   c) $10^{-1} - 10^{-2}$

   d) $(3^2 - 2^2)^{-2}$

   e) $\dfrac{1}{(4^2 - 2^3)^{-1}}$

   f) $(10^{-2})(-3)^3$

   g) $(-1)^{-2} + (-2)^{-1}$

   h) $2^{-3} \div 3^{-2}$

6. Evaluate for $a = 2$ and $a = -2$.

   a) a^3

   b) $(-a)^3$

   c) $-a^3$

   d) a^{-3}

   e) $-(-a)^3$

   f) $-a^{-3}$

7. Evaluate $x - x^{-1}$ for these values of x.

   a) 2

   b) -1

   c) -2

   d) 10

   e) $\dfrac{1}{2}$

   f) 0.1

   g) $\dfrac{1}{4}$

8. Evaluate for $x = 2$, $y = -5$.

   a) $x^{-1} + y^0$

   b) $x^2 - y^{-2}$

   c) $x^{-1}y^2$

   d) $(-x^2y)^2$

   e) $(4x^{-2}y)^{-1}$

   f) $(2x^{-1} - y^2)^2$

   g) $(2x^{-1} - y)^2$

   h) $x^{-1} - y^{-1}$

9. Evaluate for $x = 2$, $y = -1$.

   a) $x^{-4}y$

   b) $(xy)^{-2}$

   c) $\left(\dfrac{1}{xy}\right)^{-1}$

   d) $(2x^2y^3)^{-1}$

   e) $y^{-2} - x^{-2}$

   f) $4x^{-2}y^{-7}$

   g) $y^3 - x^{-3}$

   h) $y^{-9} + x^{-2}$

10. Evaluate for $x = 2$, $y = -3$.
   a) $x^{-4}y$
   b) $(xy)^{-2}$
   c) $(-x^2y)^3$
   d) $2x^{-1} + 3y^{-1}$
   e) $3x^2y^{-3}$
   f) $x^{-2}y^{-2}$
   g) $\left(\dfrac{x}{y}\right)^{-1}$
   h) $\left(\dfrac{x}{y}\right)^{-2}$

11. Express the first number as a power of the second.
   a) $64, 4$
   b) $\dfrac{1}{9}, 3$
   c) $-\dfrac{1}{32}, -2$
   d) $0.001, 10$
   e) $\dfrac{1}{25}, -5$
   f) $1, 5$
   g) $2, \dfrac{1}{2}$
   h) $\dfrac{3}{4}, \dfrac{4}{3}$

12. Express as powers with positive exponents.
   a) 100
   b) -1000
   c) $\dfrac{27}{64}$
   d) -32
   e) -0.001
   f) 7^{-3}
   g) $\dfrac{1}{2^{-6}}$
   h) $\left(\dfrac{3}{4}\right)^{-3}$

13. Express as powers with negative exponents other than -1.
   a) $\dfrac{1}{9}$
   b) $\dfrac{1}{36}$
   c) 0.0001
   d) $\dfrac{8}{27}$
   e) 0.04
   f) $\dfrac{1}{8}$
   g) $\dfrac{1}{5^2}$
   h) $\left(\dfrac{2}{3}\right)^3$

14. Which is greater?
   a) $(1.5)^{-1}$ or $(5.1)^{-1}$
   b) $\left(\dfrac{1}{4}\right)^3$ or $\left(\dfrac{1}{2}\right)^2$
   c) 2^{-3} or 3^{-2}
   d) $\left(\dfrac{1}{2}\right)^{-5}$ or 5^2
   e) $(-5)^{-3}$ or $(-2)^{-5}$
   f) $\left(\dfrac{7}{2}\right)^{-3}$ or $\left(\dfrac{2}{7}\right)^{-3}$

15. Solve by inspection.
   a) $7^x = 1$
   b) $5^x = \dfrac{1}{5}$
   c) $3^x = \dfrac{1}{27}$
   d) $10^x = 0.0001$
   e) $(-2)^x = \dfrac{1}{16}$
   f) $x^{-1} = \dfrac{3}{2}$
   g) $x^{-3} = 8$
   h) $x^{-2} = 0.04$

INVESTIGATE

There are three 1-digit numbers greater than 1 that are powers with exponents greater than 1 : $4 = 2^2$, $8 = 2^3$, $9 = 3^2$

How many 2-digit numbers are powers with exponents greater than 1?

How many 3-digit numbers are powers with exponents greater than 1?

2-3 THE EXPONENT LAWS

Astronomers estimate that there are about 10^{11} stars in the universe, and that each galaxy has about 10^{11} stars. This means that the total number of stars in the universe is estimated to be:

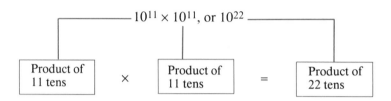

$$10^{11} \times 10^{11}, \text{ or } 10^{22}$$

| Product of 11 tens | × | Product of 11 tens | = | Product of 22 tens |

The above result follows from the meaning of an exponent.

The definitions of integral exponents lead to some basic laws for working with exponents. Study the following examples and the laws they illustrate.

Examples

$$x^3 \cdot x^2 = x \cdot x \cdot x \ \cdot \ x \cdot x$$
$$= x^{3+2}, \text{ or } x^5$$

$$x^5 \div x^3 = \frac{x \cdot x \cdot x \cdot x \cdot x}{x \cdot x \cdot x}$$
$$= x^{5-3}, \text{ or } x^2$$

$$(x^3)^2 = (x \cdot x \cdot x)(x \cdot x \cdot x)$$
$$= x^{3 \times 2}, \text{ or } x^6$$

$$(xy)^3 = xy \cdot xy \cdot xy$$
$$= x \cdot x \cdot x \ \cdot \ y \cdot y \cdot y$$
$$= x^3 y^3$$

$$\left(\frac{x}{y}\right)^2 = \frac{x}{y} \cdot \frac{x}{y}$$
$$= \frac{x^2}{y^2}$$

Exponent Law

$$x^m \cdot x^n = x^{m+n}$$

$$x^m \div x^n = x^{m-n}, \ (x \neq 0)$$

$$(x^m)^n = x^{mn}$$

$$(xy)^n = x^n y^n$$

$$\left(\frac{x}{y}\right)^n = \frac{x^n}{y^n}, \ (y \neq 0)$$

The exponent laws may be used to simplify products and quotients involving powers.

Example 1. Simplify:

a) $(x^3y^2)(x^2y^4)$ b) $\dfrac{a^5b^3}{a^2b^2}$ c) $\left(\dfrac{x^2}{z^3}\right)^2$

Solution.   a) $(x^3y^2)(x^2y^4)$
$= x^3 \cdot y^2 \cdot x^2 \cdot y^4$
$= x^3 \cdot x^2 \cdot y^2 \cdot y^4$
$= x^5y^6$

b) $\dfrac{a^5b^3}{a^2b^2} = \dfrac{a^5}{a^2} \cdot \dfrac{b^3}{b^2}$
$= a^3b$

c) $\left(\dfrac{x^2}{z^3}\right)^2 = \dfrac{x^2}{z^3} \cdot \dfrac{x^2}{z^3}$
$= \dfrac{x^4}{z^6}$

The expressions in *Example 1* can be simplified using either the laws of exponents or the definition of a positive integral exponent. This is also true for expressions containing negative integral exponents.

Example 2. Simplify:

a) $x^{-3} \cdot x^5$ b) $m^2 \div m^{-3}$

Solution.   a) $x^{-3} \cdot x^5 = x^{-3+5}$
$= x^2$

b) $m^2 \div m^{-3} = m^{2-(-3)}$
$= m^5$

or $x^{-3} \cdot x^5 = \dfrac{1}{x^3} \cdot x^5$
$= \dfrac{x^5}{x^3}$
$= x^2$

or $m^2 \div m^{-3} = \dfrac{m^2}{\frac{1}{m^3}}$
$= m^2 \cdot m^3$
$= m^5$

Example 2 illustrates why a power with a negative integral exponent is defined as a reciprocal. With this definition, the laws of exponents apply to all powers with integral exponents.

Example 3. Simplify:

a) $\dfrac{x^{-2}y}{x^{-4}y^{-3}}$ b) $(a^{-3}b^2)^3(a^2b^{-3})^2$

Solution.   a) $\dfrac{x^{-2}y}{x^{-4}y^{-3}} = \dfrac{x^{-2}}{x^{-4}} \cdot \dfrac{y}{y^{-3}}$
$= x^{-2-(-4)} \cdot y^{1-(-3)}$
$= x^2y^4$

b) $(a^{-3}b^2)^3(a^2b^{-3})^2 = a^{-9}b^6a^4b^{-6}$
$= a^{-9+4} \cdot b^{6-6}$
$= a^{-5}b^0$
$= a^{-5}$

EXERCISES 2-3

Ⓐ

1. Simplify.
   a) $x^3 \cdot x^4$ b) $a^2 \cdot a^5$ c) $b^3 \cdot b^5 \cdot b$ d) $m^2 \cdot m^3 \cdot m^4$

2. Simplify.
   a) $x^4 \div x^2$ b) $y^7 \div y^3$ c) $n^6 \div n^5$ d) $a^8 \div a^5$

3. Simplify.
   a) $(x^3)^3$ b) $(y^2)^3$ c) $(a^2b^2)^3$ d) $(xy^3)^2$

4. Simplify.
   a) $x^2 \div x^5$ b) $c^3 \div c^4$ c) $y^2 \div y^7$ d) $a^2 \div a^6$

Ⓑ

5. Simplify.
   a) $x^{-2} \cdot x^3$ b) $m^{-3} \cdot m^{-1}$ c) $a^6 \cdot a^{-2}$ d) $y^4 \cdot y^{-4}$
   e) $x^5 \cdot x^{-1} \cdot x^{-3}$ f) $b^4 \cdot b^{-3} \cdot b^2$ g) $d^6 \cdot d^{-2} \cdot d^{-5}$ h) $p^{-1} \cdot p^7 \cdot p^{-6}$

6. Simplify.
   a) $x^{-4} \div x^2$ b) $y^3 \div y^{-2}$ c) $m^5 \div m^{-5}$ d) $a^{-3} \div a^{-3}$
   e) $c^{-1} \div c^{-2}$ f) $x^{-2} \div x^{-4}$ g) $b^{-8} \div b^{-3}$ h) $t^4 \div t^{-7}$

7. Simplify.
   a) $(x^{-2})^3$ b) $(y^{-1})^{-2}$ c) $(m^{-3})^2$ d) $(c^3)^{-3}$
   e) $(a^4)^{-1}$ f) $(x^{-1}y^2)^{-1}$ g) $(x^2y^{-3})^2$ h) $(a^{-2}b^2)^{-2}$

8. Simplify.
   a) $(a^{-2}b^4)(a^2b^{-5})$ b) $(x^{-2})^3 \div (x^3)^{-2}$ c) $x^2y^{-2} \div y^{-1}$
   d) $(x^{-1}y^2)^{-3}(x^2)^{-1}$ e) $(c^{-3}d)^{-1} \div (c^2d)^{-2}$ f) $(m^3n^{-2})(m^{-1}n^2)^{-1}$

9. Evaluate for $x = -1$ and $y = 2$.

   a) $(x^3y^2)(x^2y^3)$ b) $\dfrac{x^4y^5}{xy^3}$ c) $(x^3y^2)^3$

   d) $(x^{-1}y^{-2})(x^{-2}y^{-3})$ e) $\dfrac{x^{-3}y^{-2}}{x^2y^{-6}}$ f) $(x^{-4}y^{-3})^{-2}$

10. Make a table of powers of 5 from 5^{-8} to 5^{10} and use it to simplify the following without actually doing the arithmetic.
    a) 125×625 b) 625^2 c) $0.0016 \times 78\ 125$
    d) $125 \div 0.000\ 32$ e) $78\ 125^{-1}$ f) $390\ 625 \div 15\ 625$

Ⓒ

11. Simplify.
    a) $45x^{-3} \div 5x^5 \times 3x^{-7}$ b) $4a^{-7} \times 12a^{-5} \div (-8a^{-4})$ c) $(2x^2y^2)^{-1} \div (2x^2y)^{-2}$

    d) $\left(\dfrac{p^2}{q}\right)^{-3} \div \left(\dfrac{q}{p^6}\right)$ e) $\left(\dfrac{-2x^2}{3y}\right)^{-3} \div \dfrac{1}{x}$ f) $\left(\dfrac{a^{-2}b}{c^3}\right)^{-3} \div \left(\dfrac{a^5b^{-2}}{c^3}\right)^{-1}$

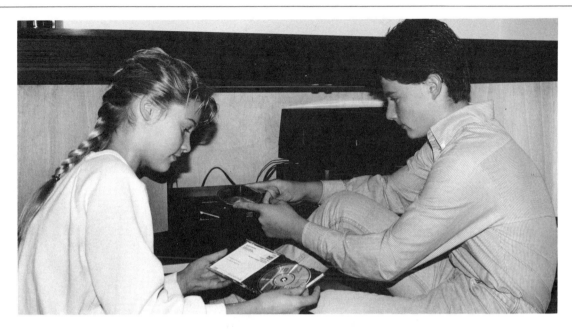

2-4 SCIENTIFIC NOTATION

Digital sound discs reproduce music more faithfully than the best records. The information is permanently encoded on the disc in the form of tiny pits made by a laser beam. On one side of a disc there are as many as 8 200 000 000 pits, each measuring approximately 0.000 000 5 m across.

We use scientific notation to express very large and very small numbers in a more compact way. To write a number in scientific notation, follow this method.

Place the decimal point after the first non-zero digit. Write using a power of 10.

8 200 000 000	0.000 000 5
$= 8.2 \times 1\ 000\ 000\ 000$	$= 5.0 \times 0.000\ 000\ 1$
$= 8.2 \times 10^9$	$= 5.0 \times 10^{-7}$

The position of the decimal point is 9 places to the right.	The position of the decimal point is 7 places to the left.

Scientific notation can be used to simplify calculations involving very large and very small numbers.

Example 1. Use a scientific calculator to simplify:
a) 45 800 000 000 000 000 × 0.000 068 8
b) 2390 ÷ 863 000 000 000 000

Solution. a) This is the same as finding $4.58 \times 10^{16} \times 6.88 \times 10^{-5}$.

Key in: $\boxed{4}\boxed{\cdot}\boxed{5}\boxed{8}\boxed{\text{EXP}}\boxed{1}\boxed{6}\boxed{\times}\boxed{6}\boxed{\cdot}\boxed{8}\boxed{8}\boxed{\text{EXP}}\boxed{+/-}\boxed{5}\boxed{=}$

The result is displayed as: $\boxed{3.15104 \quad 12}$
That is, $45\,800\,000\,000\,000\,000 \times 0.000\,068\,8 \doteq 3.15 \times 10^{12}$.

b) Key in: $\boxed{2}\boxed{\cdot}\boxed{3}\boxed{9}\boxed{\text{EXP}}\boxed{3}\boxed{\div}\boxed{8}\boxed{\cdot}\boxed{6}\boxed{3}\boxed{\text{EXP}}\boxed{1}\boxed{4}\boxed{=}$

The result is displayed as: $\boxed{2.76941 - 12}$
That is, $2390 \div 863\,000\,000\,000\,000 \doteq 2.77 \times 10^{-12}$.

Example 2. Simplify:
$$\frac{8\,520\,000\,000\,000 \times 0.000\,075}{365\,000}$$

Solution.
$$\frac{8\,520\,000\,000\,000 \times 0.000\,075}{365\,000} = \frac{8.52 \times 10^{12} \times 7.5 \times 10^{-5}}{3.65 \times 10^{5}}$$
$$= \frac{8.52 \times 7.5}{3.65} \times \frac{10^{12} \times 10^{-5}}{10^{5}}$$
$$\doteq 17.5 \times 10^{2}$$
$$\doteq 1.75 \times 10^{3}$$

Example 3. In chemistry, each element is assigned a number, called its atomic mass. That number of grams of the element contains 6.02×10^{23} atoms. The atomic mass of gold is 197.0.
a) How many gold atoms are in 197.0 g of gold?
b) How many gold atoms are in a 31.1 g gold coin?

Solution. a) 197.0 g of gold contain 6.02×10^{23} atoms.

b) In 1 g of gold, there are $\dfrac{1}{197} \times 6.02 \times 10^{23}$ atoms.

In 31.1 g of gold, the number of atoms is
$$\frac{31.1}{197} \times 6.02 \times 10^{23}$$
$$\doteq 0.950 \times 10^{23}$$
$$\doteq 9.50 \times 10^{22}$$
A 31.1 g gold coin contains 9.50×10^{22} atoms of gold.

EXERCISES 2-4

(A)

1. Express in scientific notation.
    a) 5 940 000 000
    b) 75 300 000
    c) 0.000 092
    d) 0.000 000 000 007
    e) 0.000 000 014 7
    f) 295 600 000 000 000

2. Express in scientific notation.
    a) Volume of fresh water on Earth   23 700 000 km^3
    b) Distance to the sun   150 000 000 000 m
    c) Number of red blood cells in an adult 30 000 000 000 000
    d) Size of bacteria   0.0001 cm

3. Express the number in its usual form.
    a) Mass of a jumbo jet 3.5×10^5 kg
    b) Number of nerve cells in the human brain 5×10^{10}
    c) Number of ways to jumble Rubik's cube 4.325×10^{19}
    d) Least movement detectable by fingers 2×10^{-5} mm

(B)

4. Use a scientific calculator to simplify.
    a) 590 000 × 472 000 000
    b) 3 500 000 000 ÷ 0.000 087
    c) 0.000 003 88 × 44 700 000
    d) 0.000 000 023 ÷ 56 900

5. Use scientific notation to simplify.
    a) $\dfrac{275\ 000 \times 410\ 000}{31\ 800}$
    b) $\dfrac{0.000\ 015 \times 7\ 140\ 000\ 000}{22\ 400\ 000}$
    c) $\dfrac{3\ 290\ 000\ 000 \times 0.000\ 057}{0.000\ 061\ 4}$
    d) $\dfrac{0.000\ 002\ 17 \times 0.000\ 35}{39\ 500}$

6. The smallest hole ever made in solid material is so small that 4 000 000 of them side by side are needed to make a line 1 cm long. Find the number of these holes that could be made in a square with a side of 1 cm; 1 m; 1 mm.

7. Determine the number of atoms in 1.0×10^2 g of carbon if there are 6.0×10^{23} atoms in 12.0 g of carbon.

(C)

8. New optical disks being developed for computers can record up to 2.6 billion bytes of information. One page of a daily newspaper contains roughly 5000 bytes of information (A byte stores one character—a letter or a digit). Assume that a newspaper averages 100 pages each day.
    a) How many newspapers could be recorded on one disk?
    b) If you recorded your daily newspaper on the disk each day, how long could you do this before the disk becomes full?

9. The sun consumes about 400 million tonnes of hydrogen every second. Hydrogen constitutes about 50% of the total mass of the sun, which is about 1.0×10^{27} t. Estimate the number of years required for the sun to consume all of its hydrogen content.

Check for Hidden Assumptions

Steve cycled 60 km to a cottage, at 30 km/h, and returned at 20 km/h. What was his average speed?

Understand the problem

• What is meant by average speed?

$$\text{average speed} = \frac{\text{total distance travelled}}{\text{total time taken}}$$

Think of a strategy

• Find the total distance travelled, and the total time taken, and then use the above formula.

Carry out the strategy

• On the trip to the cottage, the distance travelled is 60 km, and the time taken is $\frac{60}{30}$, or 2 h.

Total distance is 60 km + 60 km, or 120 km. Total time is 2 h + 3 h, or 5 h.

• On the return trip, the distance travelled is 60 km, and the time taken is $\frac{60}{20}$, or 3 h.

Average speed is $\frac{120 \text{ km}}{5 \text{ h}}$, or 24 km/h

Look back

• How does the result compare with the average of the two speeds?
• What would happen to the average speed if Steve had cycled at
  a) 40 km/h on the way to the cottage? b) 10 km/h on the return trip?

   When you first read this problem, you may have made an assumption that the average speed is the average of the two given speeds. This is not correct because more time was spent travelling at the lower speed.

Solve each problem

1. Mrs. Matthews drove 40 km at 80 km/h, and returned at 60 km/h. What was her average speed?

2. On a trip to his cottage, Mr. Yu drove for 2 h at 100 km/h and then for 2 h at 80 km/h. What was his average speed?

3. Tickets for the school play were numbered in sequence. Mr. Young's class sold tickets with numbers from 145 to 275 inclusive. How many tickets did Mr. Young's class sell?

4. Dianne began a fitness program on May 3, and finished on May 23. How many days did she participate in the program?

5. Lisa had her final marks for English, History, and French. She calculated the average mark for these three subjects to be 80%. If she receives a mark of 90 in Science, what is her average for the four subjects?

6. The manager of a record store bought 100 records at \$3 each, and 200 records at \$4 each. What was the average cost of the records?

7. Tony cycles up a hill at 20 km/h. How fast does he have to go down the other side to average 30 km/h? Assume that both sides of the hill are the same length.

8. Here is a pattern of squares made with matchsticks.

   a) How many squares are there?

   b) Remove six matchsticks so that only three squares remain.

9. Using no other symbols or signs, what is the greatest number that can be represented by writing three 2s? four 2s?

10. Which of these lists contain both the square of an integer and the cube of a different integer?

    List A: 1, 2, 3, 4, 5   List B: 5, 6, 7, 8, 9   List C: 4, 5, 6, 7, 8

11. If x has a value between 1 and 5, and y has a value between 5 and 10, then what are the possible values for each of the following?

    a) $x + y$ b) $x - y$ c) xy d) $\dfrac{x}{y}$

MATHEMATICS AROUND US

Tiny Plants With Shells

Diatoms are one-celled plants that live in shells and are a primary source of food in the sea. They produce oxygen by means of photosynthesis, and because of their great numbers they produce enormous amounts of it.

A diatom has a mass of about 10^{-12} g, and measures about 5×10^{-7} m across. It is estimated that 1 L of seawater contains as many as 10^7 diatoms, but they do not live at depths greater than 1 m.

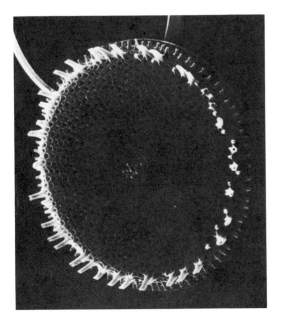

QUESTIONS

1. If diatoms were placed side by side, about how many would be needed to make a line 1 cm long?

2. Estimate the mass in kilograms of the diatoms in 1 L of seawater.

3. If the surface area of the world's oceans is about 4×10^{14} m^2, estimate the total number of diatoms in the oceans.

4. Diatoms reproduce by binary fission, which means that a plant splits into two halves, each half becoming a new diatom.
   a) If a diatom divides every 6 h, about how many would result from one diatom after one day? two days? three days?
   b) About how long would it take for there to be 1000 diatoms? 1 000 000 diatoms? 1 000 000 000 diatoms?

2-5 FRACTIONAL EXPONENTS

Before the sixteenth century, people believed that the heavenly bodies moved around the Earth. In 1543, Nicolas Copernicus suggested instead that the Earth and the other planets revolved around the sun. The discovery that the Earth was not the centre of the solar system had a profound effect on civilization.

Later, the astronomer Johann Kepler found a formula which can be used to determine the number of earth-days it takes each planet to travel once around the sun. His formula is:

$$N \doteq 0.2 \, R^{\frac{3}{2}}$$

where R is the mean distance from the planet to the sun in millions of kilometres. Kepler's formula is unusual because it contains an exponent which is not an integer.

A calculator with a $\boxed{y^x}$ key can be used to evaluate powers with fractional exponents, such as $3^{\frac{1}{2}}$ and $4^{\frac{1}{3}}$. The fractional exponent is expressed as a decimal in the keying sequence.

Press: $\boxed{3}$ $\boxed{y^x}$ $\boxed{\cdot}$ $\boxed{5}$ $\boxed{=}$ Display: $\boxed{1.7320508}$

Press: $\boxed{4}$ $\boxed{y^x}$ $\boxed{\cdot}$ $\boxed{3}$ $\boxed{3}$ $\boxed{3}$ $\boxed{3}$ $\boxed{3}$ $\boxed{3}$ $\boxed{3}$ $\boxed{=}$ Display: $\boxed{1.5874010}$

To give meaning to expressions such as $3^{\frac{1}{2}}$ and $4^{\frac{1}{3}}$, we *extend* the exponent law $x^m \cdot x^n = x^{m+n}$ to the cases where m and n are fractions. By extending the law:

$$3^{\frac{1}{2}} \times 3^{\frac{1}{2}} = 3^{\frac{1}{2}+\frac{1}{2}} \qquad\qquad 4^{\frac{1}{3}} \times 4^{\frac{1}{3}} \times 4^{\frac{1}{3}} = 4^{\frac{1}{3}+\frac{1}{3}+\frac{1}{3}}$$
$$= 3 \qquad\qquad\qquad\qquad\qquad = 4$$

But: $\sqrt{3} \times \sqrt{3} = 3$ But: $\sqrt[3]{4} \times \sqrt[3]{4} \times \sqrt[3]{4} = 4$

Therefore, $\boxed{3^{\frac{1}{2}} = \sqrt{3}}$ Therefore, $\boxed{4^{\frac{1}{3}} = \sqrt[3]{4}}$

We can now check the calculator results found above:

$(1.732\ 050\ 8)^2 \doteq 2.999\ 999\ 9$ $(1.5874010)^3 \doteq 3.999\ 999\ 6$
         $\doteq 3$ $\doteq 4$

These examples demonstrate that:

> $x^{\frac{1}{2}}$ means the principal square root of x.
> Therefore, $x^{\frac{1}{2}} = \sqrt{x}, (x \geq 0)$
> $x^{\frac{1}{3}}$ means the cube root of x. Therefore, $x^{\frac{1}{3}} = \sqrt[3]{x}$

Example 1. Find: a) $81^{\frac{1}{2}}$ b) $(-27)^{\frac{1}{3}}$

Solution.   a) $81^{\frac{1}{2}} = \sqrt{81}$ b) $(-27)^{\frac{1}{3}} = \sqrt[3]{-27}$
                     $= 9$ $= -3$

Example 2. Express as a power:
         a) $\sqrt{10}$ b) $\sqrt[3]{18}$

Solution.   a) $\sqrt{10} = 10^{\frac{1}{2}}$ b) $\sqrt[3]{18} = 18^{\frac{1}{3}}$

Example 3. Find: a) $(8^{\frac{1}{3}})^2$ b) $(25^{\frac{1}{2}})^3$

Solution.   Perform the operations in the brackets first:

         a) $(8^{\frac{1}{3}})^2 = (\sqrt[3]{8})^2$ b) $(25^{\frac{1}{2}})^3 = (\sqrt{25})^3$
                     $= 2^2$ $= 5^3$
                     $= 4$ $= 125$

     The expressions in *Example 3* can also be written using the exponent laws:

$$(8^{\frac{1}{3}})^2 = 8^{\frac{1}{3} \times 2} \qquad\qquad (25^{\frac{1}{2}})^3 = 25^{\frac{1}{2} \times 3}$$
$$= 8^{\frac{2}{3}} \qquad\qquad\qquad\qquad = 25^{\frac{3}{2}}$$

This example demonstrates that:

$x^{\frac{2}{3}}$ means the square of the cube root of x. $x^{\frac{2}{3}} = (\sqrt[3]{x})^2$	$x^{\frac{3}{2}}$ means the cube of the square root of x. $x^{\frac{3}{2}} = (\sqrt{x})^3, (x \geq 0)$

                         and

Example 4. Simplify:
         a) $1000^{\frac{2}{3}}$ b) $36^{\frac{3}{2}}$

Solution.   a) $1000^{\frac{2}{3}} = (\sqrt[3]{1000})^2$ b) $36^{\frac{3}{2}} = (\sqrt{36})^3$
                       $= 10^2$ $= 6^3$
                       $= 100$ $= 216$

EXERCISES 2-5

(A)

1. Simplify.
    a) $16^{\frac{1}{2}}$ b) $36^{\frac{1}{2}}$ c) $100^{\frac{1}{2}}$ d) $8^{\frac{1}{3}}$ e) $144^{\frac{1}{2}}$ f) $64^{\frac{1}{3}}$
    g) $27^{\frac{1}{3}}$ h) $(-64)^{\frac{1}{3}}$ i) $125^{\frac{1}{3}}$ j) $49^{\frac{1}{2}}$ k) $(-27)^{\frac{1}{3}}$ l) $(-1000)^{\frac{1}{3}}$

2. Express as a power.
    a) $\sqrt{5}$ b) $\sqrt{21}$ c) $\sqrt[3]{17}$ d) $\sqrt[3]{100}$ e) $\sqrt{27}$ f) $\sqrt[3]{156}$
    g) $\sqrt[3]{-55}$ h) $\sqrt{85}$ i) $\sqrt[3]{111}$ j) $\sqrt{2}$ k) $\sqrt[3]{-9}$ l) $\sqrt[3]{25}$

Ⓑ

3. Simplify.

a) $(4^3)^{\frac{1}{2}}$ b) $(4^{\frac{1}{2}})^3$ c) $(9^{\frac{1}{2}})^3$ d) $(9^3)^{\frac{1}{2}}$ e) $(100^{\frac{1}{2}})^3$ f) $(100^3)^{\frac{1}{2}}$

4. Simplify.

a) $8^{\frac{2}{3}}$ b) $9^{\frac{3}{2}}$ c) $27^{\frac{2}{3}}$ d) $4^{\frac{3}{2}}$ e) $25^{\frac{3}{2}}$ f) $16^{\frac{3}{2}}$

5. Simplify.

a) $(-27)^{\frac{2}{3}}$ b) $36^{\frac{3}{2}}$ c) $(-64)^{\frac{2}{3}}$ d) $125^{\frac{2}{3}}$ e) $100^{\frac{3}{2}}$ f) $(-8000)^{\frac{2}{3}}$

6. Use Kepler's formula, $N \doteq 0.2\,R^{\frac{3}{2}}$, to determine the number of Earth-days in the year of each of these planets.

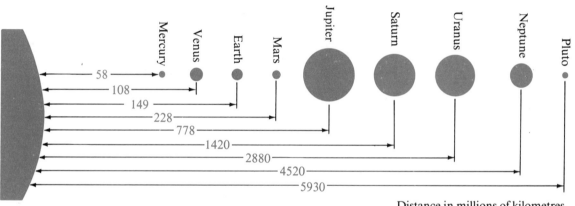

Distance in millions of kilometres

7. Simplify.

a) $x \cdot x^{\frac{1}{2}}$ b) $m^{\frac{1}{3}} \cdot m$ c) $y^{\frac{3}{2}} \cdot y^{\frac{1}{2}}$ d) $b^{\frac{5}{2}} \cdot b^{\frac{3}{2}}$

e) $x \div x^{\frac{1}{2}}$ f) $m \div m^{\frac{1}{3}}$ g) $d^{\frac{3}{2}} \div d^{\frac{1}{2}}$ h) $p^{\frac{5}{3}} \div p^{\frac{1}{3}}$

8. Simplify.

a) $4^{\frac{5}{2}}$ b) $8^{\frac{4}{3}}$ c) $27^{\frac{4}{3}}$ d) $9^{\frac{5}{2}}$ e) $(-64)^{\frac{4}{3}}$ f) $16^{\frac{5}{2}}$

Ⓒ

9. Simplify.

a) $4^{-\frac{1}{2}}$ b) $8^{-\frac{1}{3}}$ c) $9^{-\frac{1}{2}}$ d) $27^{-\frac{1}{3}}$ e) $25^{-\frac{1}{2}}$ f) $(-64)^{-\frac{1}{3}}$

10. Simplify.

a) $\left(\dfrac{1}{16}\right)^{-\frac{1}{2}}$ b) $8^{-\frac{4}{3}}$ c) $\left(-\dfrac{1}{27}\right)^{-\frac{2}{3}}$ d) $9^{-\frac{3}{2}}$ e) $\left(-\dfrac{8}{125}\right)^{\frac{2}{3}}$ f) $\left(\dfrac{9}{16}\right)^{-\frac{3}{2}}$

1. If $a = -5$ and $b = 2$, evaluate.
   a) $a^2 + b^2$ b) $(a + b)^2$ c) $a^2 - b^2$ d) $(a - b)^2$
   e) a^2b^2 f) $-a^2b$ g) $-ab^2$ h) $(-ab)^2$

2. The volume of a sphere of radius r is given by the formula $V = \frac{4}{3}\pi r^3$.
   Find the volume of a sphere with a
   a) radius of 2 cm   b) diameter of 7 cm

3. Simplify.
   a) 2^0 b) $(-2)^{-3}$ c) $\left(-\frac{1}{3}\right)^2$ d) $3^2 + 3^{-2}$

   e) $(2^3 - 3^2)^{-2}$ f) $(3^{-2})(2^{-3})$ g) $(2^{-3})(4^3)$ h) $\left(\frac{1}{2}\right)^{-2}(2^{-2})$

4. Evaluate for $x = 2$, $y = -1$.
   a) $x^{-3}y$ b) $(xy)^{-3}$ c) $\left(\frac{1}{x^2y}\right)^{-1}$ d) $(3x^3y^2)^{-1}$

   e) $y^{-3} - x^{-2}$ f) $4x^{-2}y^{-5}$ g) $x^{-3} - y^{-2}$ h) $\left(\frac{1}{x^3y^3}\right)^2$

5. Use scientific notation to simplify.
   a) $\dfrac{38\ 400\ 000\ 000 \times 604\ 000}{0.002\ 41}$ b) $\dfrac{0.000\ 088 \times 0.005\ 7}{34\ 000}$

6. The volume of the Earth is about 1.08×10^{21} m^3.
   a) The volume of the Earth is about 49.5 times the volume of the moon. What is the volume of the moon?
   b) The volume of the sun is about 1.3×10^6 times the volume of the Earth. What is the volume of the sun?

7. Simplify.
   a) $x^2 \cdot x^5$ b) $c^3 \cdot c^4 \cdot c$ c) $y^6 \div y^3$
   d) $a^8 \div a^3$ e) $(x^2)^4$ f) $(a^3b^2)^2$
   g) $x^{-3} \cdot x^2$ h) $x^3 \cdot x^{-2} \cdot x^4$ i) $x^{-4} \div x^2$
   j) $x^{-1} \div x^{-2}$ k) $(x^{-3})^2$ l) $(x^{-3}y^2)^{-1}(x^2)^{-2}$

8. Evaluate for $x = -1$, $y = 2$.
   a) $(x^2y^3)(x^3y^2)$ b) $\dfrac{x^3y^5}{xy^3}$ c) $(x^{-3}y^{-2})^{-2}$ d) $\left(\frac{1}{xy}\right)^{-3}$

Cumulative Review (Chapters 1-2)

1. Find the g.c.f. and l.c.m. for each pair of numbers.
   a) $20, 45$ b) $18, 60$ c) $24, 156$ d) $42, 390$ e) $210, 308$

2. Simplify.
   a) $[8 - (12 \div 4 \times 2)][10 - 24 \div 3]$ b) $3[3 \times (-2) + 8(-6)]$

3. If $x = -2$, $y = 3$, and $z = -1$, evaluate.
   a) $x^2z - x^2y^2 - yz$ b) $2x^2z - 2x^2y + 2xz^2 + 2yz^2$

4. If $x = -\dfrac{1}{3}$ and $y = -\dfrac{3}{4}$, evaluate.

   a) $6x + 4y - 24xy$ b) $12x + y - \dfrac{1}{2}xy$ c) $4x^2 - \dfrac{1}{3}xy + 4y^2$

5. Simplify.
   a) $\sqrt{32}$ b) $\sqrt{72}$ c) $-3\sqrt{75}$
   d) $3\sqrt{5} \times 4\sqrt{10}$ e) $(-2\sqrt{12})(3\sqrt{6})$ f) $3\sqrt{8} \times 2\sqrt{6} \times 4\sqrt{12}$

6. Find x, rounded to one decimal place.
   a)   b)   c)

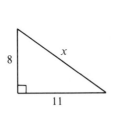
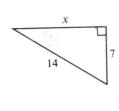
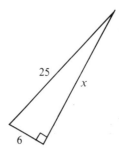

7. Expand and simplify.
   a) $\sqrt{3}(\sqrt{8} - \sqrt{2})$ b) $\sqrt{2}(\sqrt{3} - 2\sqrt{27})$ c) $\sqrt{5}(\sqrt{45} - 3\sqrt{125})$
   d) $\sqrt{3}(\sqrt{5} - \sqrt{8})$ e) $\sqrt{3}(\sqrt{108} - \sqrt{12})$ f) $\sqrt{7}(\sqrt{175} - \sqrt{63})$

8. Simplify.
   a) $\dfrac{1}{3}\sqrt{27} + \dfrac{1}{2}\sqrt{48} - 3\sqrt{3}$ b) $2\sqrt{32} - 4\sqrt{50} + \sqrt{98}$

9. Express in simplest form.

a) $\dfrac{4\sqrt{32}}{\sqrt{2}}$ b) $\dfrac{10}{\sqrt{50}}$ c) $\dfrac{4\sqrt{54}}{3\sqrt{24}}$ d) $\dfrac{\sqrt{3}}{\sqrt{\dfrac{1}{3}}}$ e) $\dfrac{\sqrt{48}}{3\sqrt{300}}$

10. Simplify.

a) $\left(\dfrac{1}{4}\right)^{-3}$ b) $36^{\frac{1}{2}}$ c) $8^{\frac{2}{3}}$ d) $25^{\frac{3}{2}}$

e) $\dfrac{1}{(3^2 + 2^2)^{-1}}$ f) $3^{-1} + 3^{-2}$ g) $(-3)^0$ h) $\left(\dfrac{1}{4}\right)^{-\frac{3}{2}}$

11. Simplify:

a) $c^2 \cdot c^3 \cdot c$ b) $y^3 \cdot y^2 \cdot y^4$ c) $d^5 \cdot d^8 \cdot d^3$ d) $e \cdot e^6 \cdot e^7$
e) $x^4 \div x$ f) $y^9 \div y^7$ g) $b^{15} \div b^3$ h) $e^4 \div e^3$
i) $(c^5)^2$ j) $(a^3b^2)^3$ k) $(x^3y^2)^2$ l) $(x^4y^2)^2$
m) $b^5 \div b^8$ n) $x^3 \div x^9$ o) $e^2 \div e^9$ p) $d^2 \div d^3$

12. Express the first number as a power of the second.

a) $125, 5$ b) $-64, -4$ c) $\dfrac{1}{8}, 2$ d) $-32, -2$ e) $\dfrac{1}{27}, 3$

13. Explain why the following are incorrect.

a) $2^2 \times 2^3 = 2^6$ b) $3^4 \times 3^2 = 9^6$ c) $x^{12} \div x^6 = x^2$
d) $(2x^2)^3 = 8x^5$ e) $(2y^3)^2 = 2y^6$ f) $6^8 \div 3^4 = 2^4$

14. Use scientific notation to simplify.

a) $\dfrac{35\,200\,000 \times 0.000\,075}{0.000\,44}$ b) $\dfrac{0.000\,038\,2 \times 45\,900\,000}{39\,200\,000 \times 0.007\,88}$

c) $\dfrac{1\,460\,000\,000 \times 0.000\,049}{0.001\,25 \times 37\,600\,000}$ d) $\dfrac{26\,500\,000 \times 0.000\,17}{490\,000\,000 \times 0.000\,381}$

15. Simplify.

a) $4^{\frac{1}{2}}$ b) $(-8)^{\frac{1}{3}}$ c) $16^{\frac{1}{2}}$ d) $27^{\frac{1}{3}}$ e) $9^{\frac{3}{2}}$ f) $8^{\frac{2}{3}}$

16. Express as a power.

a) $\sqrt{25}$ b) $\sqrt[3]{27}$ c) $\sqrt[5]{32}$ d) $(\sqrt{36})^2$ e) $(\sqrt{49})^3$

3 Polynomials

In an intramural baseball tournament, each team plays all the other teams once. If you know how many teams there are, how can you tell how many games must be played? (See *Example 3* in Section 3-4.)

3-1 ADDING AND SUBTRACTING MONOMIALS

Algebraic terms such as $5x^2$ and $-9x^3y$ are called monomials. A *monomial* is the product of a coefficient and one or more variables.

$$5x^2$$
coefficient   variable

$$-9x^3y$$
coefficient   variables

Monomials that have the same variables raised to the same exponent are called *like terms*, and they can be added or subtracted.

Example 1.   Simplify:
  a) $6a - 4b - 2c - 5a + 5b + 3c$
  b) $5x - 3x^2 + 4 - 7x^2 - 6x - 1$
  c) $6x^2y - 3xy^2 + 2xy^2 - 5x^2y + 2x^2y^2$

Solution.   a) $6a - 4b - 2c - 5a + 5b + 3c$ b) $5x - 3x^2 + 4 - 7x^2 - 6x - 1$
  $= 6a - 5a - 4b + 5b - 2c + 3c$ $= -3x^2 - 7x^2 + 5x - 6x + 4 - 1$
  $= a + b + c$ $= -10x^2 - x + 3$

  c) $6x^2y - 3xy^2 + 2xy^2 - 5x^2y + 2x^2y^2$
  $= 6x^2y - 5x^2y - 3xy^2 + 2xy^2 + 2x^2y^2$
  $= x^2y - xy^2 + 2x^2y^2$

Example 2. In the 200 m sprint, competitors must stay in their own lanes, which are 1.22 m wide. Since the track is curved, staggered start positions are needed to equalize the distances run. How far apart are the start positions?

Solution. Let the curved part of the track be a semicircle with radius r. Then, from A to B, the runner in the inside lane runs a distance of πr. The runner in the next lane runs a distance of $\pi(r + 1.22)$. The difference in the distances run is:

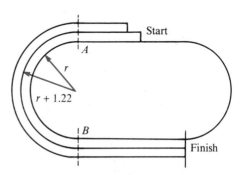

$$\begin{aligned} \pi(r + 1.22) - \pi r &= \pi r + 1.22\pi - \pi r \\ &= \pi r - \pi r + 1.22\pi \\ &= 1.22\pi \\ &\doteq 1.22(3.14) \\ &\doteq 3.83 \end{aligned}$$

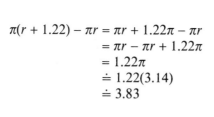

The start positions must be approximately 3.83 m apart.

The result in *Example 2* is the same for all tracks, provided that the entire semicircle is covered.

EXERCISES 3-1

1. Simplify.

   a) $3x - 5y - x + 2y$

   b) $7a + 6b - 11a + 9b$

   c) $8c + 11d - 13c - 4d$

   d) $2x - 4y - 9x - 3y$

   e) $19m - 4n + 11m - 17n + 9n$

   f) $5a + 2b - 8a - 7b + 3a$

2. Simplify.

   a) $5r - 9t + 16s - 11t - 14r + 16t$

   b) $13m - 5n + 6p + 11m + 17n - 15p$

   c) $8x - 5y + 3z - 13x - 22y + 11z$

   d) $2h - 9k - 14l - 14k + 2k + 8l$

   e) $4a + 7b + 3c - 10a - 4b + 8c$

   f) $4x - 9y + 7z - 17x - 13z + 7y - 5x$

   g) $a^2 + 4a - 5 + 3a^2 - 6a + 1$

   h) $5x^2 - 2x + 8 - 7x - 3 + x^2$

   i) $-8m^2 + 6m - 9 - 13m + 3m^2 + 2$

   j) $12p^2 + 9p - 4 - 7p^2 - 13p + 17$

(B)

3. Simplify.
   a) $5xy + 7xz - 19xy - 4xz + 15xy$
   b) $mn + 8mp - 3np + 5mn - 3mp - 8np$
   c) $4ab + 7ac - 5bc + 6ab - 3ac - bc$
   d) $4de + 7df - 3ef - 9de - 4df - 12ef$
   e) $7pq - 3pr + 8qr - 12pq + 11pr - 5qr$
   f) $12xy - 2xz - 7xy - 18xz - 9xz + 20xy$
   g) $3ab - 5ac + 9ab + 7ac$
   h) $41xy + 71xy - 37xy + 5xy - 22xy$
   i) $6x^2 - 3xy + xy - 4x^2 - 11xy$
   j) $5m^2 - 9mn - 12m^2 + 4mn$
   k) $8y^2 + 7xy - 3xy - 12y^2 - 5xy$
   l) $-14c^2 + 3cd + 5c^2 - 17cd - 9c^2$

4. Simplify.
   a) $5x^2y - 3xy^2 + 2x^2y + 3xy^2 - 4x^2y^2$
   b) $3p^3q^2 - 7p^2q^2 + 3p^2q^3 - 3p^3q^2$
   c) $2y^2z^3 - 3y^2z^3 + y^3z^3 - 3yz^3$
   d) $a^3b^2 - a^2b^3 - a^3b - ab^3 + a^2b^3$
   e) $m^2n^2 - 7m + 2n - 2mn - 3m^2n^2$
   f) $a^2 + b^2 - c^2 - 2ab - 2c^2 - b^2 + 2$

5. In the 400 m sprint, competitors run once around both ends of the track, but must stay in their own lanes, which are 1.22 m wide. How far apart are the staggered start positions? (Assume that the entire semicircle at each end is covered.)

(C)

6. In Olympic speed-skating two skaters at a time race counterclockwise around a track with a 400 m circumference. The lanes are 5 m wide, and to equalize the distances skated, the skaters must change lanes each time they come to the crossing area. The starting and finishing positions of the different races are shown on the diagram.

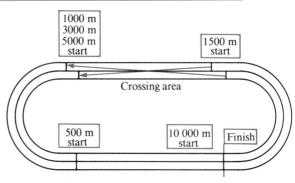

a) Explain why there are no staggered start positions for the 500 m and 10 000 m races.
b) Explain why there must be staggered start positions for the other races.
c) Calculate the distance between the start positions for the other races.

INVESTIGATE

Assume that the Earth is a perfect sphere, with radius R metres. Imagine that a rope encircles the Earth, just touching it, at the equator. The rope is to be cut and raised a distance of x m above the Earth. Find an expression to represent the length of rope that would have to be added so that it would encircle the Earth again.

Investigate this problem for other spheres, such as the sun, the moon, or a basketball.

MATHEMATICS AROUND US

Gwennap Pit

Gwennap Pit is an historical amphitheatre in Cornwall, England. It was converted from a tin-mining pit in the 16th century. The famous clergyman, John Wesley, delivered sermons on 17 different occasions to crowds that overflowed the amphitheatre.

The lowest ring, or stage, of the amphitheatre has a radius of about 3 m. Each successive ring of seats is 1 m wide.

Ring Number	Radius of		Area of	
	Inner Circle	Outer Circle	Inner Circle	Outer Circle
1				
2				
3				
4				
⋮				

QUESTIONS

1. Each ring of the amphitheatre has two circles, an inner circle, and an outer circle. Complete the chart below showing the information for the first four or five rings.

2. Let n represent the number of any ring in the amphitheatre.
   a) Find expressions for the radius, in metres, of its inner circle; the radius of its outer circle.
   b) Find an expression for its area, in square metres.

3. If each person requires a seating area of 0.25 m², write an expression for the number of people that can be seated in the nth ring.

3-2 MULTIPLYING AND DIVIDING MONOMIALS

Products and quotients of monomials can be found using the exponent laws.

Using the law for multiplying powers	Using the law for dividing powers
Add the exponents	Subtract the exponents
$(2x^6y^2)(-5x^2y) = -10x^8y^3$	$\dfrac{20x^6y^2}{-5x^2y} = -4x^4y$
Multiply the coefficients	Divide the coefficients

Example 1. Simplify:

      a) $(5x^3y^4)(2xy^2)$ b) $(5ab^2)(-2a^2b)^3$

      c) $\dfrac{9x^5y^4}{6x^3y}$ d) $\dfrac{(6m^2n^2)(8m^4n^3)}{(-4mn^2)^2}$

Solution.   a) $(5x^3y^4)(2xy^2) = 10x^4y^6$ b) $(5ab^2)(-2a^2b)^3 = (5ab^2)(-8a^6b^3)$
$$= -40a^7b^5$$

            c) $\dfrac{9x^5y^4}{6x^3y} = \dfrac{3}{2}x^2y^3$ d) $\dfrac{(6m^2n^2)(8m^4n^3)}{(-4mn^2)^2} = \dfrac{48m^6n^5}{16m^2n^4}$
$$= 3m^4n$$

Many formulas for volume involve monomials:

Sphere

$V = \dfrac{4}{3}\pi r^3$

Cone

$V = \dfrac{1}{3}\pi r^2h$

Cylinder

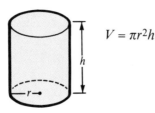

$V = \pi r^2h$

Rectangular Prism

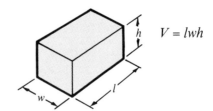

$V = lwh$

Example 2. Three golf balls fit snugly into a rectangular box.
What fraction of the space in the box do they take up?

Solution.   Each golf ball is a sphere. Let the radius be r.

Dimensions of the box: $6r \times 2r \times 2r$

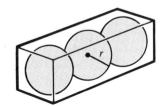

Volume of the box: $24r^3$

Volume of each golf ball: $\frac{4}{3}\pi r^3$

Volume of three golf balls: $3 \times \frac{4}{3}\pi r^3 = 4\pi r^3$

Fraction of the space
occupied by the balls: $\dfrac{4\pi r^3}{24r^3} = \dfrac{\pi}{6}$

$\doteq 0.52$

The golf balls occupy slightly over half the space in the box.

EXERCISES 3-2

1. Simplify.
   a) $(7x^2)(5x^4)$ b) $(3a)(4a)$ c) $(-6m^3)(9m^2)$ d) $(5n^2)(2n)$
   e) $(-8y^5)(-7y^4)$ f) $(-7b^3)(4b)$ g) $-(t^3)(-6t^5)$ h) $(12p^5)(-3p^3)(-2p)$

2. Simplify.
   a) $(6x)(3y)$ b) $(8p^2)(4q)$ c) $(-5m^3)(-7n)$ d) $(2ab)(7a)$
   e) $(-9r)(5rs^3)$ f) $(4cd)(-11c)$ g) $(-2st^2)(-3st)$ h) $(2b^2c^3)(bc^2)$

3. Simplify.
   a) $(-4ab)(2b^2)$ b) $(6m^2n^3)(-2m^3n^4)$ c) $(7a^2b^2)(3ab^3)$
   d) $(-8p^2q^5)(-3pq^2)$ e) $(2xy)(3x^2y)(4x^3y)$ f) $(-3ab)(2ab^2)(a^2b)$

4. Simplify.
   a) $\dfrac{12x^5}{3x^2}$ b) $\dfrac{36m^6}{4m^2}$ c) $\dfrac{54a^8}{-6a^2}$ d) $\dfrac{-52b^3}{-13b^2}$

   e) $\dfrac{-24cd^3}{-6cd}$ f) $\dfrac{28m^2n^5}{-7m^2n^3}$ g) $\dfrac{-32a^3b^6}{-4a^3b^2}$ h) $\dfrac{30p^4q^5}{3p^2q^2}$

5. Simplify.
   a) $\dfrac{36r^6s^4}{8r^2s^2}$ b) $\dfrac{-45x^8y^5}{15x^4y^2}$ c) $\dfrac{-35p^9q^6}{-14p^3q^2}$

   d) $\dfrac{(3a^4b^2)(6ab^3)}{9a^3b^4}$ e) $\dfrac{(4m^4n^2)(6m^8n^4)}{-3m^6n^6}$ f) $\dfrac{(-9x^3y^6)(8x^7y^4)}{(2x^2y^3)(-6x^3y)}$

6. Simplify.
   a) $(2x^5)(3x^2)^3$
   b) $(-3a^2b)(2a^4)^2$
   c) $(5s^2t^5)(3s^4)^2$
   d) $(-4pq^3)(-5p^3)^2$
   e) $(3m^2n^3)(-2mn^2)^3$
   f) $(5x^2y)^2(3x^2y^4)^3$

7. Simplify.
   a) $\dfrac{(2xy^2)^3(3x^5y^4)}{4x^2y^5}$
   b) $\dfrac{(-3p^2q^5)(-4pq^3)^2}{8p^4q^4}$
   c) $\dfrac{(-7a^2b^4)(4a^3b^5)}{(-2ab^2)^3}$
   d) $\dfrac{(-5x^4y^5)^2(2xy^2)^3}{(10x^3y^8)^2}$
   e) $\dfrac{(-4m^2n^4)^3(-3m^3n)^2}{(-6m^2n^3)^2}$
   f) $\dfrac{(3a^6b^2)^2(-2a^2b^4)^3}{(6ab)^2(-2a^4b)}$

8. Express these formulas in terms of the diameter, d.
   a) The area, A, of a circle is $A = \pi r^2$.
   b) The surface area, A, of a sphere is $A = 4\pi r^2$.
   c) The volume, V, of a sphere is $V = \dfrac{4}{3}\pi r^3$.

9. A circle is inscribed in a square. Find the ratio of their areas.

10. A square is inscribed in a circle. Find the ratio of their areas.

11. A cone has the same height as a cylinder but the radius of its base is twice as great. Find the ratio of their volumes.

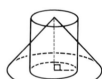

12. The base of a hemisphere is also the base of an inscribed cone. Find the ratio of the volumes of the hemisphere and cone.

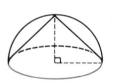

13. What is the height of a cylindrical silo with a capacity of $3x^2y$ units^3 and a base area of $2xy$ units^2? Calculate the height when $x = 7$ units and $y = 12$ units.

14. If $x = 5k$ and $y = -2k$, write the expression $x^2 + 2xy + y^2$ in terms of k, and simplify.

15. If $x = 2a^2b$ and $y = -ab^2$, write in terms of a and b.
    a) $3xy$
    b) $8xy^3$
    c) $-10x^3y^2$
    d) $(5xy)^2$
    e) $5xy^{-1}$
    f) $\sqrt{4x^2y^4}$

16. Tennis balls are packed in cans of 3. What fraction of the can do they occupy?

3-3 ADDING AND SUBTRACTING POLYNOMIALS

Monomials and expressions formed by adding or subtracting monomials are called *polynomials*. Examples are:

$$y^2 \qquad 3x^3 \qquad 5x - 6y^2$$

$$3a^2b^3 - 5ab - 6b^3 + 7ab^2$$

Polynomials are added and subtracted in the same way as monomials. Like terms are combined. The term with the greatest exponent, or exponent sum, determines the degree of the polynomial.

Example 1. Simplify, and state the degree of the polynomial:
a) $(2x - 5z + y) - (7x + 4y - 2z)$
b) $(2x^3 - 4xy^2 + 5x^2y^2) + (3x^3 + 2x^2y - 6x^2y^2)$

Solution. a) $(2x - 5z + y) - (7x + 4y - 2z)$
$= 2x - 5z + y - 7x - 4y + 2z$
$= -5x - 3y - 3z$
This is a first-degree polynomial.

b) $(2x^3 - 4xy^2 + 5x^2y^2) + (3x^3 + 2x^2y - 6x^2y^2)$
$= 2x^3 - 4xy^2 + 5x^2y^2 + 3x^3 + 2x^2y - 6x^2y^2$
$= 5x^3 - x^2y^2 + 2x^2y - 4xy^2$

The second term, x^2y^2, has the greatest exponent sum, 4. This is a fourth-degree polynomial.

To identify and collect like terms it is helpful to write all terms so that the variables in each appear in the same order, usually alphabetical.

Example 2. Simplify and state the degree of the polynomial:
$(6x^3y^2 - 2y^3x^2 - 3x^2y^2) - (5y^2x^2 - 2x^2y^3 + 4y)$

Solution. $(6x^3y^2 - 2y^3x^2 - 3x^2y^2) - (5y^2x^2 - 2x^2y^3 + 4y)$
$= (6x^3y^2 - 2x^2y^3 - 3x^2y^2) - (5x^2y^2 - 2x^2y^3 + 4y)$
$= 6x^3y^2 - 2x^2y^3 - 3x^2y^2 - 5x^2y^2 + 2x^2y^3 - 4y$
$= 6x^3y^2 - 8x^2y^2 - 4y$

The greatest exponent sum is 5. This is a fifth-degree polynomial.

Example 3. The cost, in dollars, of producing n video cassettes is $2.5n + 8500$. The income, in dollars, from sales is $6n$.

a) Write a formula for the profit from producing and selling n cassettes.

b) Calculate the profit from the production and sale of 10 000 cassettes.

Solution. a) Profit, P, is income less cost:
$$P = 6n - (2.5n + 8500)$$
$$= 6n - 2.5n - 8500$$
$$= 3.5n - 8500$$

A formula for the profit from making and selling n cassettes is $P = 3.5n - 8500$.

b) When $n = 10\ 000$:
$$P = 3.5(10\ 000) - 8500$$
$$= 26\ 500$$

The profit from the production and sale of 10 000 cassettes is \$26 500.

EXERCISES 3-3

Ⓐ

1. Simplify.
   a) $(6a + 9) + (4a - 5)$ b) $(2x - 7y) + (8x - 3y)$

   c) $(3m^2 + 4) - (7 + 9m^2)$ d) $(5\hat{p} + 11) - (2p + 4)$

   e) $(17x^2 - 9x) - (6x^2 - 5x)$ f) $(7k + 3l) - (12k - 8l)$

Ⓑ

2. Simplify.
   a) $(3m^2 - 5m + 9) + (8m^2 + 2m - 7)$

   b) $(7a^3 - 2a^2 + 5a) + (-3a^3 + 6a^2 - 2a)$

   c) $(x^2 - 5x + 6y) - (4x^2 + 15x - 11y)$

   d) $(5t^2 - 13t + 17) + (9t^3 - 7t^2 + 3t - 26) - (16t^2 + 5t - 8)$

   e) $(2 + 8a^2 - a^3) + (2a^3 - 3a^2 - 8) - (12 - 7a^3 + 5a^2)$

   f) $(4x^2 - 7x + 3) - (x^2 - 5x + 9) - (8x^2 + 6x - 11)$

3. The cost, in dollars, of producing n board games is $4.5n + 30\ 000$. The income, in dollars, from sales is $20n$.
   a) Write a formula for the profit from producing and selling n board games.
   b) What is the profit from the production and sale of 5000 games? 10 000 games? 20 000 games?

4. Simplify, and state the degree of the polynomial.
   a) $(5x^2 - 3x^2y + 2y^2x - y) - (2xy^2 - y - 5x^2 + 3yx^2)$

   b) $(p^3q^2 + 7q^2p^2 - 3p) + (2q - 6p^2q^2 - q^2p^3)$

   c) $(3m^2 - 3m + 7) - (2n^2 - 2n + 7)$

   d) $(2ab - 2ac - 2bc) + (2ca + 2cb - 2ba + 3)$

   e) $(xy + 3yx + 2x^2y - 3xy^2) - (2xy + 2yx^2)$

5. Add.
   a) $3x^2 - 6x + 7$
      $\underline{7x^2 - 2x + 9}$

   b) $7z^3 - 6z^2 + z - 3$
      $\underline{2z^3 + 4z^2 - z + 4}$

6. Subtract.
   a) $5x^2y - 3xy + 2xy^2$
      $\underline{3x^2y + 4xy - 3xy^2}$

   b) $6m^2n^2 - 4mn + 3mn^3$
      $\underline{2m^2n^2 + 2mn - 4mn^3}$

7. Simplify, and state the degree of the polynomial.
   a) $(3x^2 - 2y^2) + (y^2 - 2x^2) - (4x^2 + 2)$

   b) $(m^2 - n^2) - (n^2 - m^2) + (2n^2 + m^2)$

   c) $(4x^2y - 2yx) + (3yx^2 - 6xy^2) - (3x^2y^2 + 2y^2x^2 - xy)$

   d) $(a^2b^2 - b^2) - (3b^2a + 2a^2b) - (b^2 - b^2a^2 - b^2a)$

8. Give an example of a polynomial of degree
   a) 4 with 3 terms
   b) 3 with 4 terms
   c) 2 with 1 term
   d) 5 with 2 terms

 INVESTIGATE

Choose any two numbers. Find their sum and their difference, and add the results. How is the answer related to the numbers you started with?
Will this always happen?

Solve a Simpler Problem

How many squares are there on a checkerboard?

Understand the problem

- Are there squares of different sizes?

Think of a strategy

- Try solving a simpler problem or problems.

Carry out the strategy

- *Simpler problem 1.*

  How many 1×1 squares are there?

  There are 64 squares, 8 across and 8 down.

- *Simpler problem 2.*

  How many 2×2 squares are there?

  There are 49 squares, 7 across and 7 down.

Simpler problem 3.

How many 3×3 squares are there?

There are 36 squares, 6 across and 6 down.

- Look for a pattern in the above results that could be extended to squares of other sizes. It appears that the number of squares on the checkerboard is $8^2 + 7^2 + 6^2 + 5^2 + 4^2 + 3^2 + 2^2 + 1^2 = 204$.

Look back

- How could you find the number of squares on an $n \times n$ grid?
- How could you find the number of rectangles on a checkerboard?

Solve each problem

1. At 08:00, when he was on his way to school, John noticed a man carrying a sign on which was written: "Beware—the world will end 23 997 hours from now." What time of day was the world supposed to end?

2. How many different 9-digit numbers can be written using all the digits 1, 2, 3, 4, 5, 6, 7, 8, 9?

3. How many of the numbers in *Problem 2* are even? How many are odd?

4. What number less than 2000 leaves a remainder of 1 when divided by 7, 11, and 13?

5. A hostess considered seating her guests in pairs but there was one guest left over. She considered groups of 3, 4, 5, and 6 but each time there was one guest left over. Finally, she seated them around small tables with 7 at each table, and there were no guests left over. How many guests were at her party?

6. a) What is the sum of the first 50 odd numbers, $1 + 3 + 5 + \ldots + 99$?
   b) What is the sum of the first 100 natural numbers, $1 + 2 + 3 + \ldots + 100$?

7. Mr. Jackson asked the students in his class to write down as many second-degree polynomials in x and y as they could find in which the coefficient of each term is 1. How many such polynomials can you find?

8. A typist numbered the pages of a book from 1 to 1250.
   a) How many digits did he type?
   b) How many 1s did he type?
   c) How many 0s did he type?

9. A rectangle whose length is double its width is called a *domino*. How many dominoes are there on a checkerboard?

10. Chinese checkers is played on a board like this one. How many hexagons are there on a Chinese checkerboard?

11. How many equilateral triangles are there on a Chinese checkerboard?

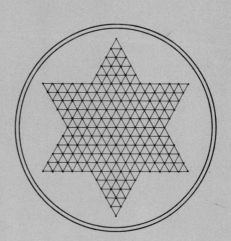

3-4 MULTIPLYING MONOMIALS AND POLYNOMIALS

To multiply a polynomial by a monomial, use the distributive law. The result is another polynomial.

Example 1. Expand:

     a) $4x^2(2x - 5)$ b) $-5a^3b(3ab - 2a^2 + b)$

Solution.   a) $4x^2(2x - 5)$ b) $-5a^3b(3ab - 2a^2 + b)$

                   $= 8x^3 - 20x^2$ $= -15a^4b^2 + 10a^5b - 5a^3b^2$

Example 2. Simplify:

     a) $4(2a - 3b + c) - 3(a + 5b - 2c)$ b) $2x(3x^2 - 5xy + y^2) - 5y^2(x - 2y)$

Solution.   a) $4(2a - 3b + c) - 3(a + 5b - 2c)$

                 $= 8a - 12b + 4c - 3a - 15b + 6c$

                 $= 5a - 27b + 10c$

        b) $2x(3x^2 - 5xy + y^2) - 5y^2(x - 2y)$

                 $= 6x^3 - 10x^2y + 2xy^2 - 5xy^2 + 10y^3$

                 $= 6x^3 - 10x^2y - 3xy^2 + 10y^3$

Example 3. In an intramural baseball tournament, each team plays all the other teams once. If you know how many teams there are, how can you tell how many games must be played?

Solution. We use the strategy of solving a simpler problem. For example, if there were 4 teams, then each team would play the other 3 teams once. There seems to be 4×3, or 12 games.

A plays B	B plays A	C plays A	D plays A
A plays C	B plays C	C plays B	D plays B
A plays D	B plays D	C plays D	D plays C

Since A vs. B and B vs. A is the same game, we have counted this game twice. Similarly, all the other games have been counted twice. Therefore, the number of games played is $\dfrac{12}{2}$, or 6.

Similarly, if there are n teams, each team would play the other $(n - 1)$ teams once. This gives $n(n - 1)$ games. But, again each game is counted twice. Therefore, the number of games to be played is $\dfrac{n(n - 1)}{2}$.

Example 3 can be solved in a different way. If a schedule is drawn up, four squares are shaded because a team cannot play itself. The empty spaces correspond to games. For 4 teams, the number of spaces is $4^2 - 4$, or 12. But this counts each game twice. Therefore, the number of games to be played is 6. Similarly, for n teams, the number of spaces would be $n^2 - n$, and the number of games to be played is $\dfrac{n^2 - n}{2}$.

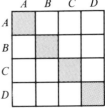

This result is the same as in *Example 3*, since $\dfrac{n(n - 1)}{2} = \dfrac{n^2 - n}{2}$.

EXERCISES 3-4

1. Simplify.
   a) $4(5x^2 + 10)$
   b) $7(2a - 5)$
   c) $-8(3k^2 - 2k)$

   d) $12(2b^2 - 3b + 9)$
   e) $-9(-5m^2 + 7m - 3)$
   f) $3(8p^2 - 5p + 7)$

2. Simplify.
   a) $3(x + 4) + 7$
   b) $-8(2a - 3) + 11a$
   c) $5(y + 2) - 7y$

   d) $4(7m - 5) - 13$
   e) $-6(3p^2 + 2p) + 5p^2$
   f) $7(5x - 3y) - 43x$

3. Simplify.
   a) $12x(5x - 4)$
   b) $3a(-7a + 2)$
   c) $6p(2p - q)$

   d) $-15n^2(6 - 9n)$
   e) $7m^3(3mn + 6)$
   f) $-8x^2(5x + 7y)$

Ⓑ

4. Simplify.
   a) $3(x + 2) + 2(x - 6)$
   b) $2(x + 9) - 3(x + 7)$
   c) $3(2a + 10b - 2c) - 6(a - 2b + 5c)$
   d) $3(2m - 4n + 3) - 5(-2m + 5n - 1)$

5. Simplify.
   a) $3x^2(x + y) + 2x^2(3x + 5y)$
   b) $3a^3(2a - 5b) - 4a^3(2a + 3b)$

   c) $5p^2(4p - q) - 8p^2(2p - 7q)$
   d) $6a^3(-3a + 7b - 4) - 8a^3(2a - 3b + 7)$

6. In a hockey league, each team plays all other teams 4 times. If there are n teams, write a formula for the total number of games to be played.

7. Simplify.
   a) $-2ab^2(ab - a^2 + b)$
   b) $3x^2y(xy^2 + xy - y)$

   c) $-5m^2n(3mn + mn^2 - n^2)$
   d) $5x(x - y) - 2y(x + y - 1) + y^2$

   e) $2b(b^2 - bc) - 2c(b - c) + (7bc - 4c^2)$ f) $7x(x^2 - y^2) - 2xy - 2y(x^2 + y^2)$

8. The design shown was made by marking 12 equally-spaced points on a circle, and joining them in all possible ways with line segments.
   a) How many of these line segments are there on the diagram?
   b) How many such line segments would there be on a similar diagram with n points?

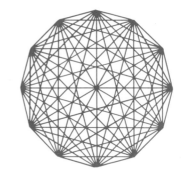

9. Simplify, and state the degree of the polynomial.

   a) $3a^2b - 7a(a - 4) + (5ba^2 - 13a)$

   b) $6m(2mn - n^2) - 3(m^2n - 19mn^2) + 6n(-5mn - 7m^2)$

   c) $4xy(x + 2y) - 5x(2xy - 3y^2) - 3y(3x^2 + 7xy)$

   d) $5s(3s^2 - 7s + 2) + 2s(5s^2 + s - 6) + 9s(2s^2 + 6s - 4)$

   e) $4x(5x^2 - 2xy + y^2) - 9x(2x^2 + 6y^2 - xy) + 3x(x^2 - 5xy - y^2)$

   f) $5xy - 3y(2x - y) + 7x(8y - x) + 9(x^2 - 2y^2)$

10. Simplify.
    a) $(11a + 3)(9a)$
    b) $(3x - 5)(-2x)$
    c) $2.5x(16x + 12)$
    d) $(5a^2 + 2a - 3)(-4a)$
    e) $1.2n(3n - 7)$
    f) $5x(2x^2 - 6x + 3)$

11. Simplify.
    a) $5[(3p + 7) - 4q] + 2[(7p - 3) + q]$

    b) $8[2k - (3l + 5)] - 5[9k - (4l - 7)]$

    c) $3x[(x - 3) + y] - 2y[(y + 7) - x]$

    d) $2a[3a + 2(5a - 4)] + 3a[a - 4(2a + 7)]$

    e) $3x[x - 4x(y - 4)] - 2x^2(x - 2y + 3)$

    f) $5m[m - 2n(m + 3)] - 2m[3m - 4n(5m - 8)]$

12. If $x = a + b$ and $y = a - b$, write in terms of a and b, and simplify.
    a) $3x - 2y$ b) $7x + 3y$

    c) $ax - by$ d) $a^2y - b^2x$

13. Write a formula for the surface area of a closed cylinder in terms of its radius and height.

14. Find the surface area of a closed cylinder when the
    a) radius is 5 cm and the height is 24 cm
    b) height is three times the radius
    c) height is 5 units less than three times the radius
    d) height is 7 units more than half the radius

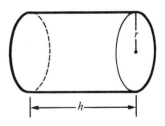

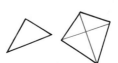

INVESTIGATE

1. Count the number of diagonals in each polygon shown, and complete the table.

Number of sides	3	4	5	6	7
Number of diagonals	▪	▪	▪	▪	▪

2. A formula for the number of diagonals in a polygon with n sides can be found in two ways. Assume that the polygon has n sides.
    a) How many diagonals pass through each vertex of the polygon? How many diagonals are there in all?
    b) How many different line segments (including the sides) can be drawn joining the vertices of the polygon? How many of these are not diagonals of the polygon?

3-5 MULTIPLYING POLYNOMIALS

Polynomials with two terms are called *binomials*, and polynomials with three terms are called *trinomials*. Examples are:

Binomials: $2x - 5$ $3a + 2b$ $-4x^2y + 5xy$

Trinomials: $3x^2 - 4x + 2$ $2m^2 - 3mn + n^2$

To find the product of two binomials, multiply each term of one binomial by each term of the other binomial.

Example 1. Find the product:
  a) $(3x - 2)(x + 7)$ b) $(x + 5y)^2$

Solution.   a) $(3x - 2)(x + 7)$

$= (3x - 2)(x + 7)$

$= 3x^2 + 21x - 2x - 14$

$= 3x^2 + 19x - 14$

b) $(x + 5y)^2$

$= (x + 5y)(x + 5y)$

$= x^2 + 5xy + 5xy + 25y^2$

$= x^2 + 10xy + 25y^2$

When squaring binomials, recognize and use these patterns:

$$(a + b)^2 = a^2 + 2ab + b^2$$
$$(a - b)^2 = a^2 - 2ab + b^2$$

Example 2. Simplify:

$(2x - 1)(3x + 4) - (2x - 3)^2$

Solution. $(2x - 1)(3x + 4) - (2x - 3)^2$

$= (6x^2 + 5x - 4) - (4x^2 - 12x + 9)$

$= 6x^2 + 5x - 4 - 4x^2 + 12x - 9$

$= 2x^2 + 17x - 13$

Example 3. What is the area of the shaded part of the rectangle?

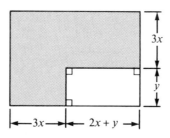

Solution.

Rectangle	Length	Width	Area	
Large	$5x + y$	$3x + y$	$(5x + y)(3x + y)$	...①
Small	$2x + y$	y	$(2x + y)y$	...②

Shaded area: ① – ②

$$(5x + y)(3x + y) - (2x + y)y$$
$$= 15x^2 + 8xy + y^2 - 2xy - y^2$$
$$= 15x^2 + 6xy$$

The method of finding the product of two binomials can be extended to find the product of a binomial and a trinomial.

Example 4. Simplify:

$$(a - 2)(a^2 + 2a + 4) + 8(a + 1)(a - 1)^2$$

Solution. $(a - 2)(a^2 + 2a + 4) + 8(a + 1)(a - 1)^2$

$$= (a^3 + 2a^2 + 4a - 2a^2 - 4a - 8) + 8(a + 1)(a^2 - 2a + 1)$$
$$= (a^3 - 8) + 8(a^3 - 2a^2 + a + a^2 - 2a + 1)$$
$$= a^3 - 8 + 8(a^3 - a^2 - a + 1)$$
$$= a^3 - 8 + 8a^3 - 8a^2 - 8a + 8$$
$$= 9a^3 - 8a^2 - 8a$$

EXERCISES 3-5

Ⓐ

1. Find the product.
   a) $(4x + 1)(2x + 3)$
   b) $(5m - 2)(6m + 1)$
   c) $(2c - 3)(4c - 5)$
   d) $(3x - 7)(3x + 7)$
   e) $(4t + 5)(4t - 8)$
   f) $(8x - 2)(3x - 7)$

2. Square the binomial.
   a) $(g + h)$
   b) $(x + y)$
   c) $(m + n)$
   d) $(b + c)$
   e) $(p - q)$
   f) $(k - l)$
   g) $(s - t)$
   h) $(u - v)$

3. Find the product.
   a) $(3x + y)^2$
   b) $(x + 5y)^2$
   c) $(3a + 2)^2$
   d) $(5x - 9)^2$
   e) $(4m - 7)^2$
   f) $(-4y - 11)^2$
   g) $(-5t + 10)^2$
   h) $(-5 - 6b)^2$

4. Find the product.
   a) $(2x + y)(3x + y)$
   b) $(3a + b)(5a - b)$
   c) $(2x - y)(3x + 4y)$
   d) $(x + 3y)(x + 4y)$
   e) $(5m - 2n)(7m - n)$
   f) $(6x - 2y)(3x - 7y)$

5. Find the product.
   a) $(3a + 5b)^2$
   b) $(2m - 7n)^2$
   c) $(6s - 2t)^2$
   d) $(4p - 3q)^2$
   e) $(8x - 3y)^2$
   f) $(-3s - 5t)^2$
   g) $(-5f + 4g)^2$
   h) $(5y^2 + 7z^2)^2$

6. Find the product.
   a) $(x - y)(x + y)$
   b) $(2m + 5n)(2m - 5n)$
   c) $(9a - 4b)(9a + 4b)$
   d) $(6x - 2y)(6x + 2y)$
   e) $(7p + 2q)(7p - 2q)$
   f) $(-12m + 9)(-12m - 9)$

Ⓑ

7. Simplify.
   a) $(x - 3)(x + 2) + (2x - 5)(x - 1)$
   b) $(2x + 4)(3x - 2) + (5x - 2)(3x - 4)$
   c) $(2m + 3)(3m + 5) + (m - 7)(6m - 3)$
   d) $(c + 2d)(c + d) - (c - 2d)(c - d)$
   e) $(2a - 5b)(3a + b) - (6a - b)(4a + 7b)$
   f) $(3x - 2y)(5x - y) - (2x + 5y)(3x - y)$

8. Simplify.
   a) $(2x - 3)^2 + (x + 2)(3x - 5)$
   b) $(s - 2t)^2 - (s - 3t)(4s - 5t)$
   c) $(2x - y)(2x + y) - (x - 2y)^2$
   d) $(7m - 2n)(3m + 5n) - (4m - 11n)^2$
   e) $(5x - 2y)^2 - (5x + 2y)^2$
   f) $(2x^2 + 3)(x^2 - 5) - (3x^2 + 2)^2$

9. Find the product.
   a) $(3x - 1)(2x^2 + 3x - 4)$
   b) $(m - 3)(4m^2 - 7m + 12)$
   c) $(2a - 5)(3a^2 + 8a - 9)$
   d) $(3p + 2)(5p^2 - 6p + 2)$

10. Find the product.
    a) $(3x + 4)(x - 5)(2x + 8)$
    b) $(4p - 3)(2p - 7)(5p - 6)$
    c) $(3x + 2)(2x - 5)(4x - 3)$
    d) $(2x - 5)(3x + 4)^2$
    e) $(5a - 3)^2(2a - 7)$
    f) $(5m - 2)^3$

11. Find the perimeter and area of each shaded region.
   a)   b)   c)

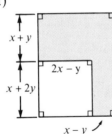
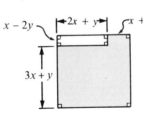
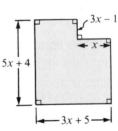

12. Simplify.
   a) $3(m - 5)(m + 2)$
   b) $2(x + y)(3x - 5y)$
   c) $5(2p - 7)(3p - 4)$
   d) $4x(x - 7y)(2x - 3y)$
   e) $3a(2a - 5b)(3a + b)$
   f) $3x(2x + 4y)^2$

13. Simplify.
   a) $2(3x + 1)(x + 5) + 4(2x + 3)(3x + 5)$
   b) $5(2m - 4)(3m + 2) - 2(4m - 1)(3m - 4)$
   c) $3(2x + 5y)(7x - 8y) + 5(x + 3y)(2x + 4y)$
   d) $2(xy - 1)(xy + 1) - 5(xy - 2)(xy + 3)$
   e) $3(2a - 3b)(a + 2b) - 2(3a - b)^2$
   f) $4(xy - 2)^2 + 3(xy + 5)^2$

14. Simplify.
   a) $(2x - 5)(3x + 6) + (3x - 2)(4x + 9) - (5x - 3)(2x - 7)$
   b) $2(3s + 5)(2s - 2) - 5(3s^2 + 7s - 9) - (s + 6)^2$
   c) $(2x + 3)(3x^2 - 5x + 4) + (x - 4)(2x^2 + 3x - 7)$
   d) $(3m + 4)(m - 4n - 1) - (5m - 2)(3m - 6n - 8)$
   e) $(4y - 5)(3y + 2)^2 - (3y + 2)(4y - 5)^2$
   f) $4(3x - 2)(5x^2 + x + 6) - (2x + 6)(3x - 1)^2$

© ───

15. If $x = m + 3$, write these expressions in terms of m, and simplify.
   a) $x^2 + 5x + 2$ b) $3x^2 - 2x + 7$ c) $x^3 - 4x^2 + 3x - 5$

16. If $x = a + b$ and $y = a - b$, write these expressions in terms of a and b, and simplify.
   a) $3x^2 + y^2$ b) $x^2 - xy - 5y^2$ c) $4x^2 + 3xy + y^2$

17. An artist has 120 cm of frame for a picture. If w, l, and A represent its width, length, and area, respectively, write an expression in terms of w for the
   a) length   b) area
   c) change in length when the width is increased by 1 cm

 **INVESTIGATE**

1. Choose any two natural numbers that differ by 2.
   a) Multiply the numbers.
   b) Find the average of the numbers you started with. Square it, and compare with the product in (a).

2. Try this with other natural numbers. Based on these results, state a probable conclusion.

3. Investigate whether the conclusion is still true if the two chosen numbers which differ by 2 are:
   a) decimals   b) rational numbers
   c) negative numbers   d) irrational numbers

4. For what numbers is the conclusion true? Can you prove this?

5. The product of two numbers differing by 2 can be represented by the area of a rectangle (below, left). The square of the average of the two numbers can be represented by the area of a square (below, right).

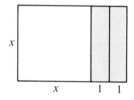   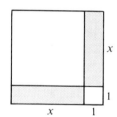

   a) How do these diagrams illustrate your conclusion above?

   b) For what numbers is this geometrical illustration of the conclusion valid?

6. Repeat the investigation for two numbers that differ by other even numbers, such as 4, 6, 8 and 10.

7. Find out what happens if the two numbers differ by odd numbers, such as 1, 3, 5, 7 and 9.

8. Write a report of your findings.

3-6 COMMON FACTORS

The greatest common factor of two or more monomials is formed from the greatest common factor of their coefficients and the greatest common factor of their variables.

Example 1. Find the greatest common factor:
$$3x^2y^3, \qquad -9x^3y^4, \qquad 12x^3y^2$$

Solution. The greatest common factor of the coefficients is 3.
The greatest common factor of the variables is x^2y^2.
Therefore, the greatest common factor is $3x^2y^2$.

To factor a polynomial means to express it as a product. This can be done, using the distributive law, when all the terms share a common factor.

Example 2. Express as a product: $3x^2y^3 - 9x^3y^4 + 12x^3y^2$

Solution. The greatest common factor of the three terms is $3x^2y^2$.
$$3x^2y^3 - 9x^3y^4 + 12x^3y^2 = 3x^2y^2(y - 3xy^2 + 4x)$$

Example 3. Factor:
  a) $12a^2b - 8ab^2$ b) $5x^2y^2 + 15x^3y^2 - 10x^4y$

Solution. a) $12a^2b - 8ab^2$ b) $5x^2y^2 + 15x^3y^2 - 10x^4y$
  $= 4ab(3a - 2b)$ $= 5x^2y(y + 3xy - 2x^2)$

Some expressions have binomials or trinomials as common factors.

Example 4. Factor:
  a) $3a(4a + 5b) - 2b(4a + 5b)$ b) $(2 - 3x - x^2)x + 5(x^2 + 3x - 2)$

Solution. a) $3a \boxed{(4a + 5b)} - 2b \boxed{(4a + 5b)}$

  $= \boxed{(4a + 5b)} (3a - 2b)$

  b) $(2 - 3x - x^2)x + 5(x^2 + 3x - 2)$

  $= (2 - 3x - x^2)x - 5(2 - 3x - x^2)$

  $= (2 - 3x - x^2)(x - 5)$

Example 5.   The curved surface of a bar of circular cross section is to be
nickel plated, the ends being left untreated. What fraction
of the total surface area, S, of the bar will be plated?

Solution.   Let the radius of the bar be r and its length be l.
Total surface area:

$$S = \text{Area of ends} + \text{Area of curved surface}$$
$$= 2 \times \pi r^2 + 2\pi r l$$

$$\frac{\text{Area of curved surface}}{\text{Total surface area}} = \frac{2\pi r l}{2\pi r^2 + 2\pi r l}$$

$$= \frac{2\pi r l}{2\pi r(r + l)}$$

$$= \frac{l}{r + l}$$

The fraction of the surface to be plated is $\dfrac{l}{r + l}$.

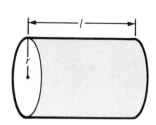

EXERCISES 3-6

Ⓐ

1. Find the greatest common factor.
   a) $21x^2,\ 28x^4,\ -14x$
   b) $-3y^4,\ 8y^6,\ -6y^9$
   c) $12a^3b,\ -16a^2b^2,\ -24a^2b^3$
   d) $16m^2n^5,\ 24m^3n^4,\ 32m^5n^2$
   e) $9x^2y^3,\ -12x^3y^2,\ 15x^2y^4$
   f) $-54s^3t^2,\ 36s^5t,\ -72s^2t^2$

2. Express as products.
   a) $3x^2 + 6x$
   b) $8y^3 - 4y^2$
   c) $5p^3 - 15p^2$
   d) $24m^2n + 16mn^2$
   e) $12a^2b^2 + 18a^3b^2$
   f) $-28x^2y^3 - 35x^3y^2$

3. Express as products.
   a) $3w^2 - 7w^3 + 4w$
   b) $-2x^5 + 4x^2 - 6x + 2x^3$
   c) $8x^2 - 12x^4 + 16$
   d) $5ab^2 + 10ab - 15a^2b$
   e) $51x^2y + 39xy^2 - 72xy$
   f) $9m^4n^2 - 6m^3n^3 + 12m^2n^4$

4. Factor.
   a) $5y - 10$
   b) $8m + 24$
   c) $6 + 12x^2$
   d) $35a + 10a^2$
   e) $49b^2 - 7b^3$
   f) $35z^2 - 14z^6$
   g) $45d^5 - 36d$
   h) $52s^3 - 13s^2$

Ⓑ

5. Factor.

 a) $3x^2 + 12x - 6$

 b) $3x^2 + 5x^3 + x$

 c) $a^3 + 9a^2 - 3a$

 d) $3x^2 + 6x^3 - 12x$

 e) $16y^2 - 32y + 24y^3$

 f) $8x^2y - 32xy^2 + 16x^2y^2$

6. Factor.

 a) $6b^7 - 3b + 12$

 b) $5y^3 + 6y^2 + 3y$

 c) $16x + 32x^2 + 48x^4$

 d) $12y^4 - 12y^2 + 24y^3$

 e) $9a^3 + 7a^2 + 18a$

 f) $10z^3 - 15z^2 + 30z$

7. Factor.

 a) $25xy + 15x^2$

 b) $14m^2n - 21mn^2$

 c) $9a^2b^3 - 12a^2b^2$

 d) $4x^2y - 16xy^2$

 e) $12p^2q + 18pq^2$

 f) $27m^3n^2 - 15m^2n^3$

8. Factor.

 a) $10a^3b^2 + 15a^2b^4 - 5a^2b^2$

 b) $12mn^2 - 8mn - 20m^2n$

 c) $20x^2y - 15x^2y^2 + 25x^3y^2$

 d) $7a^3b^3 + 14a^2b^2 - 21ab^2$

 e) $8x^4y^4 - 16x^3y^3 + 32x^2y^2$

 f) $18a^2bc - 6abc + 30abc^2 - 24ab^2c^2$

9. Express as a product.

 a) $3x(a + b) + 7(a + b)$

 b) $m(2x - y) - 5(2x - y)$

 c) $(x + 4)x^2 + (x + 4)y^2$

 d) $5x(a + 3b) - 9y(a + 3b)$

 e) $10y(x - 3) + 7(x - 3)$

 f) $7w(x + w) - 10(w + x)$

10. Express as a product.

 a) $3x^2(x - 7) + 2x(x - 7) + 5(x - 7)$

 b) $2m(a - b) - 3n(b - a) - 7(a - b)$

 c) $5a^2(x^2 + y) - 7a(x^2 + y) + 8(x^2 + y)$

 d) $6a(b - a) + 4b(a - b) - 3(b - a)$

 e) $4m^2(2x + y) - 3m(2x + y) - 7(2x + y)$

 f) $2x^2(3a - 2b) + 5x(3a - 2b) - 9(2b - 3a)$

11. Find the area of the shaded region.
    a)   b)

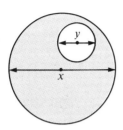

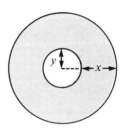

12. Four congruent circular arcs are drawn with
    centres at the vertices of a square of side x.
    Find an expression for the shaded area in
    terms of x.

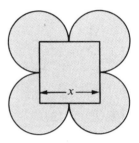

13. A cylindrical silo has a hemispherical top.
    Find expressions in terms of r and h to represent the
    a) volume of the silo
    b) total surface area.

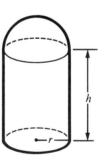

Ⓒ ───

14. Factor.
    a) $x^2 + 3x + xy + 3y$ b) $x^3 + x^2 + x + 1$
    c) $5am + a + 10bm + 2b$ d) $3x^2 - 6xy + 5x - 10y$
    e) $5m^2 + 10mn - 3m - 6n$ f) $2a^2 - 6ab - 3a + 9b$

15. Write three different binomials which have
    a) $5x$ as a common factor   b) $2a^2$ as a common factor

16. Write a polynomial of degree 4 which has $3mn^2$ as a common factor.

MATHEMATICS AROUND US

The World's Tallest Building

The world's tallest building is the Sears Tower in Chicago. It is 440 m high and 69 m square at the base.

QUESTIONS

Use the information in the diagram to calculate the following.

1. The total floor area, in square metres.

2. The total volume of the building in cubic metres.

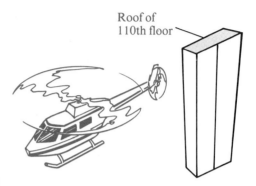

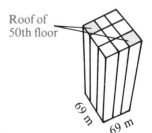

Roof of 110th floor

Roof of 89th floor

Roof of 66th floor

Roof of 50th floor

69 m

69 m

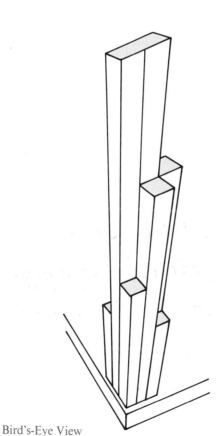

Bird's-Eye View

Cut-Away View

3-7 FACTORING TRINOMIALS OF THE FORM $x^2 + bx + c$

The result of multiplying one binomial by another binomial is often a trinomial:

$$(x + 6)(x + 2) = x^2 + 8x + 12$$

Product of +6 and +2

Sum of +6 and +2

To express a trinomial of the form $x^2 + bx + c$ as a product, two integers must be found that have a product of c and a sum of b.

Example 1. Factor:

   a) $x^2 + 11x + 24$ b) $a^2 + a - 12$ c) $m^2 - 6m + 9$

Solution.   a) $x^2 + 11x + 24 = (x + 3)(x + 8)$

Product is +24

Sum is +11

            b) $a^2 + a - 12 = (a + 4)(a - 3)$

Product is −12

Sum is +1

            c) $m^2 - 6m + 9 = (m - 3)(m - 3)$

Product is +9

Sum is −6

In *Example 1c* the two binomial factors are the same. We say that $m^2 - 6m + 9$ is a *perfect square*, and write:

$$m^2 - 6m + 9 = (m - 3)^2$$

In some trinomials of the form $x^2 + bx + c$, b and c may be monomials in another variable. To factor, b must be the sum of two monomials and c the product.

Example 2. Factor:

    a) $x^2 + 12xy + 35y^2$ b) $p^2 - 3pq - 28q^2$ c) $m^2 - 10mn + 25n^2$

Solution.   a) $x^2 + 12xy + 35y^2 = (x + 7y)(x + 5y)$

Product is $35y^2$

Sum is $12y$

            b) $p^2 - 3pq - 28q^2 = (p - 7q)(p + 4q)$

Product is $-28q^2$

Sum is $-3q$

            c) $m^2 - 10mn + 25n^2 = (m - 5n)(m - 5n)$

Product is $25n^2$

Sum is $-10n$

$$= (m - 5n)^2$$

If the terms of the trinomial have a common factor, it should be removed before the other factors are found.

Example 3. Factor:

a) $5x^2 - 45x + 90$ b) $3x^4 + 9x^3 - 12x^2$ c) $-2a^4 + 2a^3b + 12a^2b^2$

Solution.
a) $5x^2 - 45x + 90$ b) $3x^4 + 9x^3 - 12x^2$ c) $-2a^4 + 2a^3b + 12a^2b^2$
$= 5(x^2 - 9x + 18)$ $= 3x^2(x^2 + 3x - 4)$ $= -2a^2(a^2 - ab - 6b^2)$
$= 5(x - 6)(x - 3)$ $= 3x^2(x + 4)(x - 1)$ $= -2a^2(a - 3b)(a + 2b)$

Example 4. Factor:

a) $x^4 + 7x^2 + 12$ b) $2a^4 + 18a^2b^2 + 36b^4$

Solution.
a) $x^4 + 7x^2 + 12$ b) $2a^4 + 18a^2b^2 + 36b^4$
$= (x^2 + 3)(x^2 + 4)$ $= 2(a^4 + 9a^2b^2 + 18b^4)$
$= 2(a^2 + 3b^2)(a^2 + 6b^2)$

EXERCISES 3-7

Ⓐ

1. Factor.
   a) $x^2 + 10x + 24$ b) $m^2 + 5m + 6$ c) $a^2 + 10a + 16$
   d) $p^2 + 8p + 16$ e) $y^2 + 13y + 42$ f) $d^2 + 4d + 4$
   g) $x^2 - 7x + 12$ h) $c^2 - 17c + 72$ i) $a^2 - 7a + 6$
   j) $b^2 - 12b + 32$ k) $s^2 - 12s + 20$ l) $x^2 - 14x + 49$

2. Factor.
   a) $y^2 + 4y - 5$ b) $b^2 + 19b - 20$ c) $p^2 + 15p - 54$
   d) $x^2 + 12x - 28$ e) $a^2 + 2ab - 24b^2$ f) $k^2 + 3kl - 18l^2$
   g) $x^2 - 2x - 8$ h) $n^2 - 5n - 24$ i) $a^2 - a - 20$
   j) $d^2 - 4d - 45$ k) $m^2 - 9mn - 90n^2$ l) $y^2 - 2yz - 48z^2$

Ⓑ

3. Factor.
   a) $x^2 + 14x + 24$ b) $m^2 - 15m + 50$ c) $a^2 - 11a + 30$
   d) $x^2 + 6x + 9$ e) $x^2 + 17xy + 72y^2$ f) $a^2 - 12ab + 36b^2$
   g) $x^2 + 8x - 20$ h) $d^2 - 6d - 16$ i) $b^2 + 7b - 18$
   j) $m^2 - 7m - 60$ k) $a^2 - 12ab - 45b^2$ l) $y^2 + yz - 20z^2$

4. Factor.
   a) $p^2 + 15p + 26$ b) $x^2 + 40x - 41$ c) $m^2 - m - 72$
   d) $t^2 - 13t + 12$ e) $y^2 + 13yz + 36z^2$ f) $m^2 + 4mn - 96n^2$
   g) $s^2 + 21s - 100$ h) $c^2 - 8c + 16$ i) $p^2 - p - 90$
   j) $k^2 + 11k + 30$ k) $r^2 - 10rs + 9s^2$ l) $c^2 - 16cd - 80d^2$

5. Factor.
   a) $a^2b^2 + 2ab + 1$ b) $m^2n^2 - 5mn - 36$ c) $x^2y^2 - 15xy + 54$
   d) $p^2q^2 - 20pq + 51$ e) $c^2d^2 - 9cd - 36$ f) $x^2y^2 - 21xy - 72$
   g) $a^2b^2 + 19ab + 48$ h) $m^2n^2 - 28mn - 60$ i) $s^2t^2 - 18st + 72$

6. Find integers to replace ▮ so that each trinomial can be factored.
   a) $x^2 + \blacksquare x + 18$
   b) $a^2 - \blacksquare a - 12$
   c) $m^2 + \blacksquare m + 36$
   d) $y^2 - \blacksquare y - 60$
   e) $n^2 - \blacksquare n + 39$
   f) $b^2 + \blacksquare b - 51$

7. Find integers to replace ▮ so that each trinomial can be factored.
   a) $x^2 + 5x + \blacksquare$
   b) $m^2 - 4m + \blacksquare$
   c) $y^2 - 2y - \blacksquare$
   d) $a^2 + 12a - \blacksquare$
   e) $n^2 - 3n - \blacksquare$
   f) $b^2 - 7b + \blacksquare$

8. Factor.
   a) $2x^2 + 8x + 6$
   b) $5a^2 + 15a - 20$
   c) $3y^2 - 12y - 36$
   d) $5y^2 - 40y + 80$
   e) $2m^2 + 2mn - 112n^2$
   f) $9x^2y + 54xy + 45y$

9. Factor.
   a) $4x^2 + 28x + 48$
   b) $5a^2 - 20a - 60$
   c) $3n^2 - 27n + 60$
   d) $3p^2 + 15p - 108$
   e) $7x^2 - 84xy - 196y^2$
   f) $3a^2 - 18ab + 15b^2$

10. Factor.
    a) $4y^2 - 20y - 56$
    b) $3m^2 + 18m + 24$
    c) $4x^2 + 4x - 48$
    d) $10x^2 + 80x + 120$
    e) $5am^2 - 40am + 35a$
    f) $7c^2d - 35cd^2 + 42d^3$

11. Factor.
    a) $15a^3 + 90a^2b + 135ab^2$
    b) $6p^3 + 6p^2q - 180pq^2$
    c) $7x^3y^3 - 63x^2y^2 + 140xy$
    d) $3m^2n^2 + 36mn^2 + 96n^2$
    e) $4a^3 - 4a^2b - 48ab^2$
    f) $5x^3y^2 + 10x^2y^3 - 120xy^4$

12. Factor.
    a) $x^4 + 7x^2 + 10$
    b) $a^4 + 9a^2b^2 + 14b^4$
    c) $m^4 + 13m^2 + 36$
    ⓒ d) $2b^4 + 16b^2 + 30$
    e) $3c^4 + 24c^2 + 21$
    f) $5x^4 + 25x^2y^2 + 30y^4$

13. Factor.
    a) $(x + y)^2 + 9(x + y) - 10$
    b) $(p - 2q)^2 - 11(p - 2q) + 24$
    c) $(3y - 4)^2 - 2(3y - 4) - 63$
    d) $(x^2 + 4x)^2 + 8(x^2 + 4x) + 15$
    e) $(2m - n)^2 - (2m - n)p - 20p^2$
    f) $3(2x + 4)^2 + 12(2x + 4)y - 36y^2$

14. If $x = a + b$ and $y = a - b$, write in terms of a and b, and simplify.
    a) $x^2 + 2xy + y^2$
    b) $x^2 - 5xy + 6y^2$
    c) $x^2 + 4xy - 12y^2$
    d) $x^2y^2 - xy - 2$

15. a) Write three different trinomials which have $(x + 2)$ as a factor.
    b) Write a polynomial of degree 3 which has $(x + 2)$ as a factor.

16. Write a polynomial of degree 4 which has only two terms, and also has $(x + 2)$ as a factor.

INVESTIGATE

If $x^2 + bx + c$ is a perfect square, how are b and c related?
If $ax^2 + bx + c$ is a perfect square, how are a, b and c related?

3-8 FACTORING TRINOMIALS OF THE FORM $ax^2 + bx + c$

A method for factoring a trinomial of the form $ax^2 + bx + c$ is suggested by a study of how one is formed from the product of two binomials:

$$(3x + 2)(x + 5) = 3x(x + 5) + 2(x + 5)$$
$$= 3x^2 + 15x + 2x + 10$$
$$= 3x^2 + 17x + 10$$

> The integers 15 and 2 have a sum of 17 and a product of 30—the same as the product of 3 and 10.

A trinomial of the form $ax^2 + bx + c$ can be factored if two integers can be found with a sum of b and a product of ac.

Example 1. Factor: $3x^2 - 10x + 8$

Solution.

$$3x^2 - 10x + 8$$

> What two integers have a sum of -10 and a product of 24?

The integers needed are -6 and -4, and the trinomial can be factored by first writing the second term as $-6x - 4x$:

$$3x^2 - 10x + 8 = 3x^2 - 6x - 4x + 8$$
$$= 3x(x - 2) - 4(x - 2)$$
$$= (x - 2)(3x - 4)$$

The order in which the decomposition of the second term is written is unimportant. The solution for *Example 1* could have proceeded as follows:

$$3x^2 - 10x + 8 = 3x^2 - 4x - 6x + 8$$
$$= x(3x - 4) - 2(3x - 4)$$
$$= (3x - 4)(x - 2)$$

Example 2. Factor: $8a^2 + 18ab - 5b^2$

Solution.

$$8a^2 + 18ab - 5b^2$$

> What two integers have a sum of 18 and a product of -40?

The integers needed are 20 and -2:

$$8a^2 + 18ab - 5b^2 = 8a^2 + 20ab - 2ab - 5b^2$$
$$= 4a(2a + 5b) - b(2a + 5b)$$
$$= (2a + 5b)(4a - b)$$

As always, look for a common monomial factor before factoring any trinomial.

Example 3. Factor:

a) $6a^2 + 7ab - 10b^2$ b) $10y^2 - 28y + 16$

Solution.   a) $6a^2 + 7ab - 10b^2 = 6a^2 + 12ab - 5ab - 10b^2$
$$= 6a(a + 2b) - 5b(a + 2b)$$
$$= (a + 2b)(6a - 5b)$$

b) $10y^2 - 28y + 16 = 2(5y^2 - 14y + 8)$
$$= 2(5y^2 - 10y - 4y + 8)$$
$$= 2[5y(y - 2) - 4(y - 2)]$$
$$= 2(y - 2)(5y - 4)$$

EXERCISES 3-8

Ⓐ

1. Find two integers with the given properties.

	Product	Sum
a)	6	5
b)	18	9
c)	15	-8

	Product	Sum
d)	-15	-2
e)	-30	7
f)	-24	-2

2. Factor.
   a) $2x^2 + 7x + 6$ b) $2a^2 + 11a + 12$ c) $6y^2 + 11y + 3$
   d) $2k^2 + 3k + 1$ e) $3s^2 + 4s + 1$ f) $8x^2 + 10x + 3$

3. Factor.
   a) $5x^2 - 7x + 2$ b) $3n^2 - 11n + 6$ c) $14c^2 - 13c + 3$
   d) $2x^2 - 11x + 15$ e) $3x^2 - 22xy + 7y^2$ f) $4a^2 - 4ab + b^2$

4. Factor.
   a) $3t^2 + 7t - 6$ b) $6k^2 + 5k - 4$ c) $8r^2 + 2r - 3$
   d) $4m^2 + 3m - 10$ e) $5y^2 + 19y - 4$ f) $4d^2 + 4d - 15$

Ⓑ

5. Factor.
   a) $5a^2 - 7a - 6$ b) $3x^2 - 13x - 10$ c) $2m^2 - m - 21$
   d) $4k^2 - 9k - 9$ e) $6x^2 - xy - 12y^2$ f) $15a^2 - ab - 2b^2$

6. Factor.
   a) $3x^2 + 13x + 4$ b) $2m^2 - 11m + 12$ c) $4s^2 - 20s + 25$
   d) $9x^2 + 12x + 4$ e) $6y^2 + 17yz + 12z^2$ f) $8a^2 - 14ab + 3b^2$

7. Factor.
   a) $10x^2 - x - 3$
   b) $6k^2 + k - 5$
   c) $15g^2 - 7g - 2$
   d) $9p^2 + 7p - 2$
   e) $8c^2 + 18cd - 5d^2$
   f) $15x^2 - 4xy - 4y^2$

8. Factor.
   a) $4x^2 - 4x + 1$
   b) $2h^2 + 5h + 2$
   c) $4q^2 - 23q + 15$
   d) $10u^2 - 29u + 10$
   e) $10m^2 - 17mn - 6n^2$
   f) $8c^2 + 14cd - 15d^2$

9. Factor.
   a) $6h^2 - 17h + 12$
   b) $10r^2 + 13r - 3$
   c) $2w^2 + 13w + 15$
   d) $14t^2 - 19t - 3$
   e) $10x^2 - 33xy - 7y^2$
   f) $9a^2 - 24ab + 16b^2$

10. Factor.
    a) $3xy^2 - 11xy + 6x$
    b) $3m^2n - 13mn + 12n$
    c) $4x^2y - 17xy - 15y$
    d) $2x^3y + 7x^2y - 15xy$
    e) $2m^3n - m^2n - 21mn$
    f) $6x^3y - 7x^2y^2 - 3xy^3$

11. Factor.
    a) $20x^2 + 70x + 60$
    b) $15a^2 - 65a + 20$
    c) $18a^2 + 15a - 18$
    d) $16r^2 - 12r - 10$
    e) $24x^2 - 72xy + 54y^2$
    f) $12a^2 - 52ab - 40b^2$

12. Factor.
    a) $6x^3 + 33x^2 + 45x$
    b) $6a^3 + 26a^2 - 20a$
    c) $18x^2y - 3xy - 45y$
    d) $10m^3 - 25m^2 - 60m$
    e) $9a^3 - 39a^2 + 42a$
    f) $42ab^2 + 49ab - 21a$

©

13. Find two integers with the given properties.

	Product	Sum
a)	300	37
b)	72	17
c)	−120	2

	Product	Sum
d)	−220	−12
e)	264	−34
f)	−462	−1

14. Factor.
    a) $32x^2 - 20x + 3$
    b) $24s^2 - 13s - 2$
    c) $4a^2 + 19a + 21$
    d) $4x^2 + 21xy - 18y^2$
    e) $10a^2 - 19ab - 15b^2$
    f) $21x^2 + 25xy - 4y^2$

15. Factor.
    a) $21x^2 + 17x - 30$
    b) $72x^2 + 11x - 6$
    c) $15x^2 - 28x - 32$
    d) $48x^2 - 22xy - 15y^2$
    e) $24c^2 + 26cd - 15d^2$
    f) $40y^2 + yz - 6z^2$

3-9 FACTORING A DIFFERENCE OF SQUARES

A polynomial that can be expressed in the form $x^2 - y^2$ is called a *difference of squares*.

$$x^2 - y^2 = (x - y)(x + y)$$

Using the above pattern, it is always possible to express a difference of squares as a product.

Example 1.   Factor:

a) $36x^2 - 49$
b) $16m^2 - 121n^2$

Solution.   a) $36x^2 - 49$
$= (6x - 7)(6x + 7)$

b) $16m^2 - 121n^2$
$= (4m - 11n)(4m + 11n)$

A difference of squares may occur after a common factor is removed.

Example 2.   Factor:

a) $8m^2 - 2n^2$
b) $3a^3 - 12ab^2$

Solution.   a) $8m^2 - 2n^2$
$= 2(4m^2 - n^2)$
$= 2(2m - n)(2m + n)$

b) $3a^3 - 12ab^2$
$= 3a(a^2 - 4b^2)$
$= 3a(a - 2b)(a + 2b)$

An additional step is required if one of the factors is itself a difference of squares.

Example 3.   Factor:
$81a^4 - 16$

Solution. $81a^4 - 16 = (9a^2 - 4)(9a^2 + 4)$
$= (3a - 2)(3a + 2)(9a^2 + 4)$

A difference of squares may have terms that are not monomials.

Example 4.   Factor:

a) $(x + 3)^2 - y^2$
b) $x^4 - (2x - 1)^2$

Solution.   a) $(x + 3)^2 - y^2$
$= [(x + 3) - y][(x + 3) + y]$
$= (x - y + 3)(x + y + 3)$

b) $x^4 - (2x - 1)^2$
$= [x^2 - (2x - 1)][x^2 + (2x - 1)]$
$= (x^2 - 2x + 1)(x^2 + 2x - 1)$
$= (x - 1)^2(x^2 + 2x - 1)$

Differences of squares often occur in applications of the Pythagorean Theorem.

Example 5. A ship leaves port A and travels due south to port B. From port B it travels to port C which is due east of A. It has then travelled a distance of 121 km. If B is 9 km closer to A than to C, how far east of port A is port C?

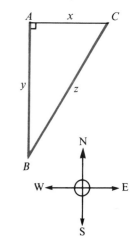

Solution. Let x, y and z, represent respectively the distances AC, AB, and BC. Then from right triangle ABC:

$$x^2 = z^2 - y^2$$
$$= (z - y)(z + y)$$

Since $z + y = 121$ and $z - y = 9$:

$$x^2 = (121)(9)$$
$$= (11^2)(3^2)$$
$$x = (11)(3)$$
$$= 33$$

Port C is 33 km due east of port A.

EXERCISES 3-9

Ⓐ

1. Factor.
   a) $x^2 - 49$ b) $4b^2 - 121$ c) $9m^2 - 64$ d) $81f^2 - 16$
   e) $25y^2 - 144$ f) $49x^2 - 36$ g) $16 - 81y^2$ h) $169 - 16t^2$
   i) $100m^2 - 49$ j) $64b^2 - 1$ k) $121a^2 - 400$ l) $36b^2 - 25$
   m) $25p^2 - 81$ n) $144m^2 - 49$ o) $36 - 121x^2$ p) $1 - 25q^2$

Ⓑ

2. Factor.
   a) $4s^2 - 9t^2$ b) $16x^2 - 49y^2$ c) $81a^2 - 64b^2$ d) $121c^2 - 100d^2$
   e) $p^2 - 36q^2$ f) $144y^2 - 81z^2$ g) $25m^2 - 169n^2$ h) $4e^2 - 225f^2$
   i) $16m^2 - 81n^2$ j) $64x^2 - 225y^2$ k) $49a^2 - 121b^2$ l) $36b^2 - 100c^2$

3. Factor.
   a) $8m^2 - 72$ b) $6x^2 - 150$ c) $20x^2 - 5y^2$ d) $18b^2 - 128$
   e) $12a^2 - 75$ f) $18p^2 - 98$ g) $80s^2 - 405$ h) $12p^2 - 363$
   i) $12x^3 - 27x$ j) $32m^3 - 98m$ k) $63a^2b - 28b$ l) $75s^2t^2 - 27t^2$
   m) $(x - y)^2 - z^2$ n) $(2a + b)^2 - 81$ o) $81a^2 - (3a + b)^2$ p) $4(2x - y)^2 - 25z^2$

4. Factor.
   a) $(x + 2)^2 - (x + 7)^2$ b) $(5m - 2)^2 - (3m - 4)^2$ c) $(2a + 3)^2 - (2a - 3)^2$
   d) $(3y + 8z)^2 - (3y - 8z)^2$ e) $(3p - 7)^2 - (8p + 2)^2$ f) $(2x - 1)^2 - (7x + 4)^2$
   g) $x^4 - 13x^2 + 36$ h) $a^4 - 17a^2 + 16$ i) $y^4 - 5y^2 - 36$

5. A circular fountain, 150 cm in diameter, is surrounded by a circular flowerbed 325 cm wide. Find the area of the flowerbed.

6. The formula for the volume, V, of a square-based pyramid is: $V = \frac{1}{3}l^2h$, where l is the length of a side of the base and h is its height.

   a) Express V in terms of s and h, where s is the slant height, that is, the height measured from the apex to the midpoint of a side of the base.

   b) Find the volume of the Great Pyramid of Khufu (Cheops), for which $h = 146$ m and $s = 186$ m.

7. Explain how the two pieces of the diagram below (left) can be rearranged to show that $x^2 - y^2 = (x - y)(x + y)$.

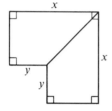
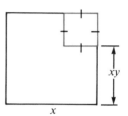

8. A small square is cut from the corner of a large square (above, right). From the dimensions shown, find an expression for the area

   a) of the small square   b) remaining when the small square is removed.

---

9. Factor, if possible.

   a) $8d^2 - 32e^2$ b) $25m^2 - \frac{1}{4}n^2$ c) $18x^2y^2 - 50y^4$ d) $10a^2 - 7b^2$

   e) $25s^2 + 49t^2$ f) $p^2 - \frac{1}{9}q^2$ g) $5x^4 - 80$ h) $\frac{x^2}{16} - \frac{y^2}{49}$

10. Find all primes, p, such that $5p + 1$ is a perfect square.

11. A metal strip of length l is secured at both ends to fixed points. When the strip is heated its length increases by a factor x, causing the strip to buckle.

   a) Find an approximate expression for the distance, h, through which the middle point of the strip moves.

   b) Estimate h to two decimal places for each strip in the table.

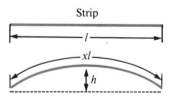

Metal	Length l	Expansion factor x
Steel	250 cm	1.0012
Brass	250 cm	1.0020
Aluminum	250 cm	1.0024

1. Simplify.
   a) $-12s^2 - 4s + 11 + 7s^2 - 10s - 6$
   b) $14g^2 - 5g + 10 - 8g^2 - 6g - 19$
   c) $4x^2 - xy + 3xy - 3x^2 + 7xy$
   d) $6a^2b - 2a^2b^2 - 11a^2b + 5a^2b^2 - 3ab$

2. Simplify.
   a) $(8xy)(-5y)$
   b) $(-3a^2b)(2ab^2)$
   c) $(3xy)(-2x^2y)(-4xy^2)$

3. Simplify.
   a) $\dfrac{35m^4n^3}{-5mn^2}$
   b) $\dfrac{(8x^4y^5)(3x^2y)}{6x^2y^2}$
   c) $\dfrac{(4a^2b^2)^2(-3a^4b^2)}{(2ab)^3(6a^2b)}$

4. Simplify.
   a) $(3x^2 + 17xy) - (12x^2 - 3xy)$
   b) $(3m^2 - 5mn) - (3mn - 7n^2)$
   c) $2x(x + y) - 3x(2x - 3y)$
   d) $2a(3a - 5b) - a(2b + 3a)$
   e) $3xy(x - 2y) - 3x(2xy + 3y^2) - y(2x^2 + 5xy)$
   f) $5m(3mn - 2n^2) - 2(m^2n - 15mn^2) + 5n(-3mn - 5m^2)$

5. Simplify.
   a) $6(2x^2 - 5x) - 14(3x - x^2) + 3(x - x^2)$
   b) $-7(c - 3d + 5e) + 4(2c - 11d - 3e) - 5(3c - 7d + 2e)$
   c) $7m(2m - 5n + 3) + 2m(-3m + 9n - 4)$
   d) $4x^2(5x - 2y - 8) - 3x^2(4x - 8y - 2)$

6. Simplify.
   a) $(2x^2 - 7x - 4)(2x - 5)$
   b) $(8y^2 + 3y - 7)(3y + 4)$

7. Find the perimeter and area of the shaded region of the rectangle shown.
   a)
   b)

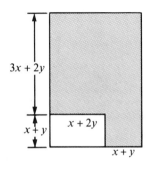

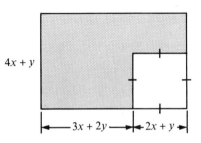

8. Factor.
   a) $8m^3 - 4m^2$
   b) $8y^2 - 12y^4 + 24$
   c) $28a^2 - 7a^3$
   d) $6a^2b^3c - 15a^2b^2c^2$
   e) $30x^2y - 20x^2y^2 + 10x^3y^2$
   f) $8mn^2 - 12mn - 16m^2n$

9. Factor.
   a) $m^2 + 8m + 16$
   b) $a^2 - 7a + 12$
   c) $y^2 - 2y - 8$
   d) $n^2 - 4n - 45$
   e) $s^4 - 15s^2 + 54$
   f) $k^4 - 9k^2 - 90$

10. Factor.
    a) $a^2 + 14ab + 24b^2$
    b) $m^2 + 9mn + 18n^2$
    c) $s^2 + 20st + 36t^2$
    d) $x^2 - xy - 20y^2$
    e) $c^2 + 21cd - 100d^2$
    f) $p^2 - 19pq - 120q^2$

11. Factor.
    a) $4x^2 - 7x + 3$
    b) $6a^2 - 13a - 5$
    c) $21n^2 + 8n - 4$
    d) $6r^2 - 31r + 5$
    e) $12t^2 - 15t - 18$
    f) $56x^2 + 18x - 8$

12. Factor.
    a) $b^2 - 36$
    b) $81k^4 - 1$
    c) $36x^2 - 49y^2$
    d) $4a^2 - 9b^2$
    e) $25m^2 - 81n^2$
    f) $1 - 16s^4$
    g) $196x^2 - 25z^2$
    h) $256p^2 - 625q^2$
    i) $289s^2 - 324t^2$

13. Factor.
    a) $8a^2 - 72$
    b) $150 - 6n^2$
    c) $7x^4 - 7y^4$
    d) $27m^3 - 12m$
    e) $\dfrac{a^2}{36} - \dfrac{b^2}{49}$
    f) $125p^2q^2 - 180q^2$

14. Factor.
    a) $(2c - 5)^2 - 121$
    b) $x^2 - (y + z)^2$
    c) $a^2 - (b - c)^2$

15. Factor.
    a) $-98m^3 + 32m$
    b) $125x^2y^2 - 180y^2$
    c) $128x^2y - 50y^3$

16. Factor.
    a) $x^4 - 29x^2y^2 + 100y^4$
    b) $m^4 - 38m^2n^2 + 72n^4$

4 Rational Expressions

In a training session, Carole directs her boat crew to row with constant power both with and against the current. How can the average speed over the training course be determined? (See *Example 2* in Section 4-5.)

4-1 SIMPLIFYING RATIONAL EXPRESSIONS

In arithmetic,

we saw that the sum, difference, or product of any pair of integers is an integer, but that the quotient of two integers is not necessarily an integer. In order to include quotients of integers in arithmetic, the number system was extended to include rational numbers.

In algebra,

we saw that the sum, difference, or product of any two polynomials is a polynomial, but that the quotient of two polynomials is not necessarily a polynomial. In order to include quotients of polynomials in algebra, the set of algebraic expressions is extended to include rational expressions.

> Any algebraic expression that can be written as the quotient of two polynomials is called a *rational expression*.

These are rational expressions:

$$\frac{x+1}{x-3} \qquad \frac{3m^2-n}{2m+5} \qquad \frac{5a^3-2b^2+3}{2ab} \qquad 2x^2+4$$

These are not rational expressions:

$$\frac{2m^2+n}{3\sqrt{n}} \qquad \frac{1+5\sqrt{a}}{b^2+3} \qquad 7\sqrt{x}+5$$

To evaluate a rational expression, substitute a number for each variable in the expression.

Example 1. Evaluate, if possible, for $x = -3$ and $y = 2$:

a) $\dfrac{5x+2y}{x}$

b) $\dfrac{x+4}{y-2}$

Solution.   a) $\dfrac{5x+2y}{x} = \dfrac{5(-3)+2(2)}{-3}$

$$= \frac{-15+4}{-3}$$

$$= \frac{-11}{-3}$$

$$= \frac{11}{3}$$

b) $\dfrac{x+4}{y-2}$

$$= \frac{-3+4}{2-2}$$

This reduces to $\dfrac{1}{0}$, which is not defined.

In Example *1b*, we say that the expression $\dfrac{x+4}{y-2}$ is *not defined* when $y = 2$, since 2 is a value of y for which the *denominator* of the expression equals 0. Similarly, the expression in *Example 1a*, $\dfrac{5x+2y}{x}$, is not defined when $x = 0$.

A rational expression is not defined when its denominator is equal to 0.

Example 2. For what value of the variable is the given rational expression not defined?

  a) $\dfrac{3mn}{2m}$ b) $\dfrac{a^2-5a}{a-3}$ c) $\dfrac{x}{x^2+1}$

Solution.   In each case, let the denominator equal zero.

  a) If $2m = 0$, then $m = 0$.

  The expression $\dfrac{3mn}{2m}$ is not defined when $m = 0$.

  b) If $a - 3 = 0$, then $a = 3$.

  The expression $\dfrac{a^2-5a}{a-3}$ is not defined when $a = 3$.

  c) Since x is a real number, $x^2 \geq 0$. Therefore, $x^2 + 1$ cannot equal zero.

  The expression $\dfrac{x}{x^2+1}$ is defined for all real values of x.

Viewed as an algebraic fraction, a rational expression can be reduced to lower terms by dividing numerator and denominator by a common factor. The result is true only for values of the variable for which the expression is defined.

Example 3. Given: a) $\dfrac{-21y}{35x}$ b) $\dfrac{24m^3n}{56mn^2}$

Reduce each expression to lowest terms and state the value(s) of the variables for which the result is true.

Solution.   a) $\dfrac{-21y}{35x} = \dfrac{(7)(-3y)}{(7)(5x)}$

$$= \frac{-3y}{5x}$$

The original expression is not defined when $x = 0$. Therefore, the result is true for all real values of x and y except $x = 0$.

     b) $\dfrac{24m^3n}{56mn^2} = \dfrac{(8mn)(3m^2)}{(8mn)(7n)}$

$$= \frac{3m^2}{7n}$$

The original expression is not defined when $m = 0$ or $n = 0$. Therefore, the result is true for all real values of m and n except $m = 0$ and $n = 0$.

Example 4.   Given: a) $\dfrac{3x^2 + 4x}{7x}$ b) $\dfrac{2m - 6}{3 - m}$

Simplify each expression and state the value(s) of the variables for which the result is true.

Solution.   a) $\dfrac{3x^2 + 4x}{7x} = \dfrac{x(3x + 4)}{7x}$

$$= \frac{3x + 4}{7}$$

The original expression is not defined when $x = 0$. Therefore $\dfrac{3x^2 + 4x}{7x} = \dfrac{3x + 4}{7}$ for all real values of x except $x = 0$.

     b) $\dfrac{2m - 6}{3 - m} = \dfrac{2(m - 3)}{-1(m - 3)}$

$$= -2$$

The original expression is not defined when $3 - m = 0$, or $m = 3$. Therefore $\dfrac{2m - 6}{3 - m} = -2$ for all real values of m except $m = 3$.

When working with rational expressions, it is usually inconvenient to write the restrictions on the variable for every expression. Therefore, when no restriction is stated, we assume that the expression is defined for all values of the variable for which the denominator is not equal to zero.

Example 5. Simplify:

a) $\dfrac{x^2 - 3x - 18}{x^2 + x - 6}$

b) $\dfrac{81a^2 - b^2}{b^2 - 6ab - 27a^2}$

Solution. a) $\dfrac{x^2 - 3x - 18}{x^2 + x - 6}$

b) $\dfrac{81a^2 - b^2}{b^2 - 6ab - 27a^2}$

$= \dfrac{(x - 6)(x + 3)}{(x - 2)(x + 3)}$

$= \dfrac{(9a - b)(9a + b)}{(b - 9a)(b + 3a)}$

$= \dfrac{x - 6}{x - 2}$

$= \dfrac{(9a - b)(9a + b)}{-(9a - b)(b + 3a)}$

$= -\dfrac{9a + b}{b + 3a}$

EXERCISES 4-1

Ⓐ

1. Evaluate for $x = -1$ and $y = 4$.

a) $\dfrac{x + y}{3}$

b) $\dfrac{4x - y}{2}$

c) $\dfrac{x - y}{x}$

d) $\dfrac{y + x}{x - 1}$

e) $\dfrac{2x + y}{xy}$

f) $\dfrac{x + 3}{y - 2}$

g) $\dfrac{xy + y}{xy + x}$

h) $\dfrac{xy^2 + 1}{xy^2 - 1}$

2. For what value of the variable is the given rational expression not defined?

a) $\dfrac{3a}{2b}$

b) $\dfrac{5cd}{3d}$

c) $\dfrac{x^2 - 3x}{x - 1}$

d) $\dfrac{r}{r + 3}$

e) $\dfrac{m^2 - 4}{m - 5}$

f) $\dfrac{x}{x^2 + 2}$

g) $\dfrac{x^2 - 8}{x + 1}$

h) $\dfrac{x^3 - 1}{x^2 + 1}$

3. Reduce to lowest terms.

a) $\dfrac{24x}{3}$

b) $\dfrac{36x}{-4y}$

c) $\dfrac{132a^4}{12a^2}$

d) $\dfrac{-28m^3}{7m}$

e) $\dfrac{5x^2}{15x}$

f) $\dfrac{-20s^3}{-35s^3}$

g) $\dfrac{102a^3}{17ab}$

h) $\dfrac{216m^2}{-18mn}$

4. Reduce to lowest terms.

a) $\dfrac{6m + 4}{2}$

b) $\dfrac{3a^2 + 3b}{3}$

c) $\dfrac{12x^2 - 8x}{4x}$

d) $\dfrac{12mn - 24m}{-6m}$

e) $\dfrac{12x^2y + 16xy}{4xy^2}$

f) $\dfrac{21ab - 28a}{7a}$

g) $\dfrac{10cd + 25d^2}{5cd}$

h) $\dfrac{15x^2y - 40xy^2}{10xy}$

i) $\dfrac{24mn^2 + 42m^2n}{12mn}$

(B)

5. Reduce to lowest terms.

a) $\dfrac{3m}{3m - 6}$

b) $\dfrac{12x}{8x^2 - 20x}$

c) $\dfrac{5ab}{5a^2 + 10ab}$

d) $\dfrac{9xy}{6x^2 - 15xy}$

e) $\dfrac{6s^2t}{12s^2t + 9st^2}$

f) $\dfrac{10m^2n^2}{15m^2n - 25mn}$

g) $\dfrac{14x^2y}{21x^2y - 35xy^2}$

h) $\dfrac{18xy}{27xy + 36xy^2}$

i) $\dfrac{4b^2c^3}{24bc^4 - 36b^3c^3}$

6. Reduce to lowest terms.

a) $\dfrac{4x + 8}{2x + 4}$

b) $\dfrac{a - 9b}{3a - 27b}$

c) $\dfrac{2x - 10}{3x - 15}$

d) $\dfrac{x - 5}{10 - 2x}$

e) $\dfrac{3m - 12n}{20n - 5m}$

f) $\dfrac{16 - 4a}{32 - 8a}$

g) $\dfrac{3a + 12}{6a + 24}$

h) $\dfrac{7x + 14}{5x + 10}$

7. Simplify, and state the values of x for which the result is true.

a) $\dfrac{2x^2 + 6x}{5x}$

b) $\dfrac{2x^2 - 10x}{4x - 20}$

c) $\dfrac{5x^2 + 7x}{3x}$

d) $\dfrac{4x^2 - 12x}{x - 3}$

e) $\dfrac{3x^2 - 6x}{14 - 7x}$

f) $\dfrac{9 - 3x}{x - 3x}$

g) $\dfrac{x^2 + 7x + 12}{x + 4}$

h) $\dfrac{x^2 + x - 6}{2 - x}$

i) $\dfrac{x^2 - 10x + 25}{5 - x}$

8. Reduce to lowest terms.

a) $\dfrac{4ab}{8ac}$

b) $\dfrac{6a^2c}{8ab}$

c) $\dfrac{-18x^2y}{3xy^2}$

d) $\dfrac{45a^2bc^3}{60ab^2c}$

e) $\dfrac{-8x^2yz}{-24xyz^2}$

f) $\dfrac{-15a^2bc^4}{-27a^2b^3c^2}$

g) $\dfrac{-9m^2n}{-m^5}$

h) $\dfrac{-25a^3b^2c}{40ab^7}$

9. Simplify.

a) $\dfrac{5m - 5n}{3m - 3n}$

b) $\dfrac{c - d}{d - c}$

c) $\dfrac{2a - 2b}{3b - 3a}$

d) $\dfrac{3xy - 18y^2}{12y^2 - 2xy}$

e) $\dfrac{10xy - 15x^2y}{6x^2 - 4x}$

f) $\dfrac{60a^2b^2 - 24ab}{16ab - 40a^2b^2}$

10. Reduce to lowest terms.

a) $\dfrac{a^2 + 7a + 10}{a^2 + 5a + 6}$

b) $\dfrac{x^2 - 10x + 25}{x^2 - 4x - 5}$

c) $\dfrac{x^2 - 16}{x^2 + 4x - 32}$

d) $\dfrac{x^2 - 9}{x^2 + 6x + 9}$

e) $\dfrac{r^2 + 7r + 12}{r^2 + 3r - 4}$

f) $\dfrac{x^2 - 3x - 28}{x^2 - 9x + 14}$

g) $\dfrac{x^2 + 8xy + 12y^2}{x^2 + 2xy - 24y^2}$

h) $\dfrac{m^2 + 4mn - 12n^2}{m^2 + 9mn + 18n^2}$

i) $\dfrac{a^2 - 4ab - 5b^2}{a^2 + 6ab + 5b^2}$

11. Simplify.

a) $\dfrac{x^2 + 9xy + 18y^2}{2x^2 + 12xy}$

b) $\dfrac{m^2 - 9mn + 20n^2}{3m^2 - 15mn}$

c) $\dfrac{9a^2 - 16b^2}{6a^2 - 8ab}$

d) $\dfrac{a^2 - ab - 6b^2}{a^2 + 2ab}$

e) $\dfrac{9x^2 - 4y^2}{3x^2 - 2xy}$

f) $\dfrac{m^2 + 2mn - 3n^2}{3m^2 + 9mn}$

g) $\dfrac{x^2 - 25}{x^2 - 5x}$

h) $\dfrac{3m^2 - 15m}{3m^2 - 16m + 5}$

i) $\dfrac{8t^2 - 32}{2t^2 + 12t + 16}$

12. Simplify.

a) $\dfrac{c^2 - 5cd - 24d^2}{c^2 + 7cd + 12d^2}$

b) $\dfrac{x^2 + xy - 30y^2}{x^2 + 11xy + 30y^2}$

c) $\dfrac{a^2 + 10ab + 24b^2}{a^2 - 36b^2}$

d) $\dfrac{4u^2 - 25v^2}{4u^2 + 20uv + 25v^2}$

e) $\dfrac{m^2 - 2mn - 48n^2}{m^2 - 64n^2}$

f) $\dfrac{x^2 - 36y^2}{x^2 - 3xy - 54y^2}$

g) $\dfrac{(x^2 - 1)(x^2 - 4)}{x^2 - 3x - 4}$

h) $\dfrac{(x^2 - 36)(x^2 - 25)}{x^2 + x - 30}$

i) $\dfrac{(e^2 - 81)(e^2 - 64)}{e^2 - e - 72}$

13. Simplify.

a) $\dfrac{7x^2 - 21x}{7x^2 - 28x + 21}$

b) $\dfrac{5x^2 - 20}{x^2 + 14x + 24}$

c) $\dfrac{x^3 - 9x^2 + 20x}{x^3 - 25x}$

d) $\dfrac{32 - 2a^2}{4a^2 - 44a + 112}$

e) $\dfrac{3x^2 - 75}{6x^2 + 30x}$

f) $\dfrac{2x^3 - 28x^2 - 102x}{18x - 2x^3}$

g) $\dfrac{2m^2 + 4m - 16}{3m^2 - 48}$

h) $\dfrac{3a^2 + 33a + 90}{6a^2 + 6a - 120}$

i) $\dfrac{3b^2 + 3b - 60}{2b^2 + 4b - 48}$

14. Simplify, if possible.

a) $\dfrac{4x + 2}{2}$

b) $\dfrac{2x + 6}{x + 3}$

c) $\dfrac{2x + 6x}{2}$

d) $\dfrac{4x^2 - 12x}{x - 3}$

e) $\dfrac{2x - 1}{2x - 1}$

f) $\dfrac{x - 7}{7 - x}$

g) $\dfrac{x + 5}{x - 5}$

h) $\dfrac{x^2 - 1}{x^2 + 1}$

ⓒ

15. Simplify.

a) $\dfrac{x - 4}{2x^2 - 11x + 12}$

b) $\dfrac{2x - 7}{2x^2 - x - 21}$

c) $\dfrac{2x - 9}{2x^2 - 3x - 27}$

d) $\dfrac{3y - 4}{3y^2 - 16y + 16}$

e) $\dfrac{2x^2 + 3xy + y^2}{3x^2 + 2xy - y^2}$

f) $\dfrac{4x^2 - 6xy + 2y^2}{3x^2 - 4xy + y^2}$

16. If $x = a + b$ and $y = a - b$, write the following expressions in terms of a and b and simplify.

a) $\dfrac{2x + 6y}{10x + 2y}$

b) $\dfrac{x^2 + 2xy + y^2}{x^2 - y^2}$

c) $\dfrac{6x^2 - 5xy + y^2}{6x^2 - xy - y^2}$

d) $\dfrac{3x^2 - 8x + 5}{4x^2 + x - 5}$

4-2 MULTIPLYING AND DIVIDING RATIONAL EXPRESSIONS

The same procedures are used to multiply and divide rational expressions as are used to multiply and divide rational numbers.

Example 1. Simplify:

a) $\dfrac{x^2}{6} \times \dfrac{2y}{3x}$

b) $\dfrac{10t^2(r+3)}{5(r-3)} \times \dfrac{2(r-3)}{rt}$

Solution.   a) $\dfrac{x^2}{6} \times \dfrac{2y}{3x}$

$= \dfrac{2x^2y}{18x}$

$= \dfrac{xy}{9}$

b) $\dfrac{10t^2(r+3)}{5(r-3)} \times \dfrac{2(r-3)}{rt}$

$= \dfrac{20t^2(r+3)(r-3)}{5rt(r-3)}$

$= \dfrac{4t(r+3)}{r}$

Example 2. Simplify:

a) $\dfrac{3a^3}{-5} \div \dfrac{(3a)^2}{10}$

b) $\dfrac{4(x-2y)}{x^2y} \div \dfrac{8(x-2y)}{xy^2(x+y)}$

Solution.   a) $\dfrac{3a^3}{-5} \div \dfrac{(3a)^2}{10}$

$= \dfrac{3a^3}{-5} \times \dfrac{10}{9a^2}$ $\boxed{\text{Multiply by the reciprocal.}}$

$= \dfrac{30a^3}{-45a^2}$

$= -\dfrac{2a}{3}$

b) $\dfrac{4(x-2y)}{x^2y} \div \dfrac{8(x-2y)}{xy^2(x+y)}$

$= \dfrac{4(x-2y)}{x^2y} \times \dfrac{xy^2(x+y)}{8(x-2y)}$

$= \dfrac{y(x+y)}{2x}$

Sometimes expressions in the numerator or denominator must be factored before the whole expression can be simplified.

Example 3.   Simplify:

a) $\dfrac{x^2+7x+10}{x^2+x-6} \times \dfrac{x+3}{x+5}$

b) $\dfrac{3m-2n}{m^2-2mn+n^2} \div \dfrac{9m^2-4n^2}{3m^2n-3mn^2}$

Solution.   a) $\dfrac{x^2+7x+10}{x^2+x-6} \times \dfrac{x+3}{x+5}$

$= \dfrac{(x+2)(x+5)}{(x+3)(x-2)} \times \dfrac{(x+3)}{(x+5)}$

$= \dfrac{x+2}{x-2}$

b) $\dfrac{3m-2n}{m^2-2mn+n^2} \div \dfrac{9m^2-4n^2}{3m^2n-3mn^2}$

$= \dfrac{(3m-2n)}{(m-n)(m-n)} \times \dfrac{3mn(m-n)}{(3m-2n)(3m+2n)}$

$= \dfrac{3mn}{(m-n)(3m+2n)}$

EXERCISES 4-2

Ⓐ

1. Simplify.

a) $\dfrac{5}{8} \times \dfrac{2a}{3}$

b) $\dfrac{m^2}{4} \times \dfrac{2}{m}$

c) $\dfrac{-3x}{10} \times \dfrac{5x}{9}$

d) $\dfrac{2c^2}{15} \times \dfrac{5}{3c}$

e) $\dfrac{-6t}{35} \times \dfrac{14t}{3}$

f) $\dfrac{9r^2}{4} \times \dfrac{8}{3r}$

g) $\dfrac{8t^3}{4} \times \dfrac{16}{2t}$

h) $\dfrac{25b^2}{7} \times \dfrac{14}{5b}$

2. Simplify.

a) $\dfrac{5}{8} \div \dfrac{3b}{4a}$

b) $\dfrac{x^2}{14} \div \dfrac{x}{2}$

c) $\dfrac{-6xy}{15} \div \dfrac{2x^2}{5}$

d) $\dfrac{9a}{4} \div \dfrac{3b}{2}$

e) $\dfrac{7m}{-3} \div \dfrac{5m}{-6}$

f) $\dfrac{15a}{2} \div \dfrac{25c^2}{3a^2}$

g) $\dfrac{3ab}{13c} \div \dfrac{9b^2}{52}$

h) $\dfrac{4st^2}{35} \div \dfrac{16s}{7t^2}$

3. Simplify.

a) $\dfrac{8t}{21s^2} \times \dfrac{3s}{4}$

b) $\dfrac{15x^2}{4x} \times \dfrac{6x^3}{5x^2}$

c) $\dfrac{14e}{8} \times \dfrac{12f^2}{49e^3}$

d) $\dfrac{-10x^3}{18x} \div \dfrac{-15x}{-27}$

e) $\dfrac{8n}{-21} \div \dfrac{-4n}{7n}$

f) $\dfrac{3x^2}{8y} \div \dfrac{9x}{28}$

g) $\dfrac{5a^2}{12b} \div \dfrac{25a}{6}$

h) $\dfrac{14st^3}{5s^2} \div \dfrac{4t}{15st^2}$

4. Simplify.

a) $\dfrac{3x^2}{2y} \times \dfrac{4y}{9x}$

b) $\dfrac{4a}{3b} \times \dfrac{9b^2}{6a}$

c) $\dfrac{2m}{9n} \div \dfrac{-4m}{3n^2}$

d) $\dfrac{3x^3y^2}{6xy} \times \dfrac{4xy}{5x^2y^2}$

e) $\dfrac{-8m^2n^5}{15mn^2} \div \dfrac{2m^4}{-25n^2}$

f) $\dfrac{4c^2d}{8cd} \div \dfrac{3c^2d^3}{6cd^3}$

Ⓑ

5. Simplify.

a) $\dfrac{3a^2b}{12ab} \times \dfrac{8a^5b^4}{6ab^2}$

b) $\dfrac{-5x^2y}{(2xy)^3} \times \dfrac{-12x^2y^2}{-6x^2y}$

c) $\dfrac{2x^2y}{3xy} \times \dfrac{(6xy)^2}{4xy}$

d) $\dfrac{12mn^2}{9mn} \div \dfrac{(3mn)^2}{6mn^2}$

e) $\dfrac{2x}{3y} \times \dfrac{3y}{4z} \times \dfrac{4z}{5x}$

f) $\dfrac{(2m)^2}{5n} \times \dfrac{10m}{8n} \div \dfrac{15m}{(4n)^2}$

6. Simplify.

a) $\dfrac{2a}{a-3} \times \dfrac{7(a-3)}{4a}$

b) $\dfrac{5(x-2)}{8x} \times \dfrac{2x}{15(x-2)}$

c) $\dfrac{4(x-3)}{x+1} \div \dfrac{4}{x+1}$

d) $\dfrac{12m^2}{5(m+4)} \times \dfrac{10(m+4)}{3m}$

e) $\dfrac{3(s-2)}{4(s+5)} \div \dfrac{9(s-2)}{s+5}$

f) $\dfrac{3(5-a)}{2a} \div \dfrac{3(a-5)}{4(a+1)}$

7. Simplify.

   a) $\dfrac{a+b}{3b} \times \dfrac{6b^2}{5(a+b)}$

   b) $\dfrac{3x^2y}{12x} \times \dfrac{4xy^3}{2xy}$

   c) $\dfrac{3y^3}{x^2-9} \times \dfrac{2x-6}{2y^2}$

   d) $\dfrac{3xy}{9x^2-12x} \times \dfrac{9x^2-16}{12y}$

   e) $\dfrac{10m^2n}{6m-9} \div \dfrac{25mn^2}{2m-3}$

   f) $\dfrac{4a^2-10}{a-3b} \div \dfrac{6a^2-15}{2a^2-18b^2}$

8. Simplify.

   a) $\dfrac{15x}{2x+6} \div \dfrac{10x}{3x+9}$

   b) $\dfrac{x^2-121}{x^2-4} \times \dfrac{x+2}{x-11}$

   c) $\dfrac{5x-10}{6x+6} \times \dfrac{2x-4}{x+1}$

   d) $\dfrac{y+2}{ay-by} \div \dfrac{y^2+2y}{ay^2-by^2}$

   e) $\dfrac{3xy}{x^2-4} \times \dfrac{(x-2)^2}{4y^2}$

   f) $\dfrac{(x+1)^2}{x^2-1} \times \dfrac{x^2-4}{(x+2)(x+1)}$

9. Simplify.

   a) $\dfrac{a^2-3a-10}{25-a^2} \div \dfrac{a+2}{a+5}$

   b) $\dfrac{x^2-2x-15}{x^2-9} \times \dfrac{x-3}{x-5}$

   c) $\dfrac{x^2+x-2}{x^2-x} \times \dfrac{x^2+x}{x^2-1}$

   d) $\dfrac{x^2-2x-15}{x^2-9} \times \dfrac{3-x}{x-5}$

   e) $\dfrac{a^2+2a-15}{a^2-8a+7} \times \dfrac{a^2-5a-14}{a^2+7a+10}$

   f) $\dfrac{x^2+5x+6}{x^2-5x+6} \div \dfrac{x^2-x-6}{x^2+x-6}$

©

10. Simplify.

   a) $\dfrac{x^2-16y^2}{6x^2y} \div \dfrac{x^2+xy-20y^2}{4x^3y^2}$

   b) $\dfrac{a^2+11ab+30b^2}{a^2-25b^2} \times \dfrac{3a^2-15ab}{6a^2+36ab}$

   c) $\dfrac{x^2+5xy+6y^2}{x^2+4xy-5y^2} \times \dfrac{x^2+3xy-10y^2}{x^2+xy-6y^2}$

   d) $\dfrac{m^2-9mn+14n^2}{m^2+7mn+12n^2} \div \dfrac{3m^2-21mn}{4m^3+16m^2n}$

11. Simplify.

   a) $\dfrac{3x^2+3x-6}{x^2y-7xy} \times \dfrac{x^2y-13xy+42y}{6x^2+12x}$

   b) $\dfrac{x^2+5xy+6y^2}{x^2+7xy+10y^2} \times \dfrac{x^2+6xy+5y^2}{x^2+2xy-3y^2}$

   c) $\dfrac{x+2y}{x-3y} \times \dfrac{x^2-9y^2}{x^2-4y^2} \div \dfrac{x+3y}{x-2y}$

   d) $\dfrac{(3a+7b)^2}{2a-5b} \times \dfrac{4a^2-25b^2}{9a^2-49b^2} \div \dfrac{2a+5b}{3a-7b}$

12. If $x = a + b$ and $y = a - b$, write the following expressions in terms of a and b and simplify.

   a) $\dfrac{x^2-xy-12y^2}{x^2-2xy-3y^2} \times \dfrac{x^2+5xy+4y^2}{x^2-16y^2}$

   b) $\left(\dfrac{3x-21y}{6x+12y}\right)^2 \div \dfrac{x^2-49y^2}{2x^2+8xy+8y^2}$

MATHEMATICS AROUND US

Meeting the World's Water Needs

The demand for fresh water for human consumption increases not only as the world's population increases but also as the standard of living improves. With our lawns, swimming pools, and cleaning methods, we are using water at a far greater rate than did our great-grandparents of only 100 years ago. Where is all the water to come from?

One of the ideas that has been put forward is to tow large icebergs from the polar regions to suitable points adjacent to large coastal cities. It would then be relatively simple technically to melt the ice and pump the water into the city's supply. As large industrial cities in Canada require an estimated 800 L of fresh water per person per day, no possible source can be overlooked.

QUESTIONS

1. The population of Vancouver is about 1 500 000. How many cubic metres of fresh water does the city need each day?

2. The visible portion of an iceberg (11% of the whole iceberg) is 1 km long, 500 m wide, and 20 m high.

   a) What is the total volume of the iceberg?

   b) How many days' supply of water could be available to Vancouver from this iceberg assuming that 75% is recoverable?

4-3 ADDING AND SUBTRACTING RATIONAL EXPRESSIONS WITH MONOMIAL DENOMINATORS

In Section 4-1, rational expressions were reduced to lowest terms. To add and subtract rational expressions it is sometimes necessary to raise them to higher terms in order to obtain the lowest common denominator.

Example 1.   Write an expression equivalent to $\dfrac{x+5}{x}$ with a denominator of:

   a) $3x$ b) x^2

   c) x^2y d) $x(x-2)$

Solution.   a) $\dfrac{x+5}{x} = \dfrac{x+5}{x} \times \dfrac{3}{3}$

   $\qquad = \dfrac{3x+15}{3x}$

b) $\dfrac{x+5}{x} = \dfrac{x+5}{x} \times \dfrac{x}{x}$

   $\qquad = \dfrac{x^2+5x}{x^2}$

   c) $\dfrac{x+5}{x} = \dfrac{x+5}{x} \times \dfrac{xy}{xy}$

   $\qquad = \dfrac{xy(x+5)}{x^2y}$

   $\qquad = \dfrac{x^2y+5xy}{x^2y}$

d) $\dfrac{x+5}{x} = \dfrac{x+5}{x} \times \dfrac{x-2}{x-2}$

   $\qquad = \dfrac{(x+5)(x-2)}{x(x-2)}$

   $\qquad = \dfrac{x^2+3x-10}{x(x-2)}$

   Rational expressions are added and subtracted in the same way that rational numbers are added and subtracted.

Example 2.   Simplify:

   a) $\dfrac{4}{3x} - \dfrac{7x}{6}$ b) $\dfrac{3}{8a} + \dfrac{5}{12a^2}$ c) $\dfrac{3y}{x} + \dfrac{7x}{y^2} - \dfrac{2x+1}{4y}$

Solution.   a)   The lowest common denominator is $6x$:

   $\dfrac{4}{3x} - \dfrac{7x}{6} = \dfrac{4}{3x} \times \dfrac{2}{2} - \dfrac{7x}{6} \times \dfrac{x}{x}$

   $\qquad = \dfrac{8}{6x} - \dfrac{7x^2}{6x}$

   $\qquad = \dfrac{8-7x^2}{6x}$

b) The lowest common denominator is $24a^2$:

$$\frac{3}{8a} + \frac{5}{12a^2} = \frac{3}{8a} \times \frac{3a}{3a} + \frac{5}{12a^2} \times \frac{2}{2}$$

$$= \frac{9a}{24a^2} + \frac{10}{24a^2}$$

$$= \frac{9a + 10}{24a^2}$$

c) The lowest common denominator is $4xy^2$:

$$\frac{3y}{x} + \frac{7x}{y^2} - \frac{2x+1}{4y} = \frac{3y}{x} \times \frac{4y^2}{4y^2} + \frac{7x}{y^2} \times \frac{4x}{4x} - \frac{2x+1}{4y} \times \frac{xy}{xy}$$

$$= \frac{12y^3}{4xy^2} + \frac{28x^2}{4xy^2} - \frac{xy(2x+1)}{4xy^2}$$

$$= \frac{12y^3 + 28x^2 - 2x^2y - xy}{4xy^2}$$

EXERCISES 4-3

Ⓐ

1. Write each expression with a denominator of $24mn$.

a) $\dfrac{-2}{3mn}$ b) $\dfrac{5m}{8mn}$ c) $\dfrac{-5}{6m}$ d) $-\dfrac{13}{24}$ e) $\dfrac{-1}{4}$

f) $\dfrac{3}{-8}$ g) $\dfrac{7m}{12}$ h) $\dfrac{-7m}{8n}$ i) $\dfrac{11n}{-12m}$ j) $\dfrac{5mn}{-6n}$

2. Write an expression equivalent to

a) $\dfrac{2x}{3}$ with a denominator of   i) 6   ii) $12x$ iii) $3x^2$

b) $\dfrac{3m+1}{4}$ with a denominator of   i) -12 ii) $8x$ iii) $16x^2$

c) $\dfrac{a-7}{a}$ with a denominator of   i) $3a$ ii) a^2 iii) $5a^4$

d) $\dfrac{5y-3}{2y}$ with a denominator of   i) $6y$ ii) $4y^3$ iii) $-2y^2$

e) $\dfrac{4x+10}{2x^2}$ with a denominator of   i) $-4x^2$ ii) $20x^3$ iii) x^2

3. For each pair of expressions write an equivalent pair with a common denominator.

a) $\dfrac{x}{2}, \dfrac{x}{3}$ b) $\dfrac{2}{x}, \dfrac{x}{5}$ c) $\dfrac{3}{2a}, \dfrac{2}{a}$ d) $\dfrac{5}{2a}, \dfrac{4}{3a}$

e) $\dfrac{5}{n}, \dfrac{2}{n^2}$ f) $\dfrac{1}{6x}, \dfrac{5}{8x}$ g) $\dfrac{x+1}{5x^2}, \dfrac{x-1}{4x}$ h) $\dfrac{x+2}{3x^2}, \dfrac{x-3}{2x}$

4. Simplify.

a) $\dfrac{2}{x} - \dfrac{5}{x}$

b) $\dfrac{4}{3x} + \dfrac{2}{3x}$

c) $\dfrac{7}{4x} - \dfrac{5x}{4x}$

d) $\dfrac{2}{3m^2} - \dfrac{9m}{3m^2}$

e) $\dfrac{5a}{2a} + \dfrac{7a}{2a}$

f) $\dfrac{16x}{5y^2} - \dfrac{11x}{5y^2}$

g) $\dfrac{9a}{7b^2} + \dfrac{5a}{7b^2}$

h) $\dfrac{33s^2}{9t^3} - \dfrac{6s^2}{9t^3}$

Ⓑ

5. Simplify.

a) $\dfrac{2a}{3} - \dfrac{4a}{5}$

b) $\dfrac{2}{3a} - \dfrac{4}{5a}$

c) $\dfrac{2a}{3} - \dfrac{4}{5a}$

d) $\dfrac{2}{3a} - \dfrac{4a}{5}$

e) $\dfrac{2}{3a} - \dfrac{4a}{5a^2}$

f) $\dfrac{2a}{3a^2} - \dfrac{4}{5}$

g) $\dfrac{3a}{2} - \dfrac{7}{6a^2}$

h) $\dfrac{3a}{2a} - \dfrac{7}{6a}$

6. Simplify.

a) $\dfrac{2}{x} + \dfrac{5}{2x}$

b) $\dfrac{4}{x} + \dfrac{27}{5x}$

c) $\dfrac{7}{10x} + \dfrac{4}{15x}$

d) $\dfrac{5}{2a} + \dfrac{3}{4a}$

e) $\dfrac{7}{8m} + \dfrac{5}{6m}$

f) $\dfrac{2}{9k} - \dfrac{5}{6k}$

g) $\dfrac{5}{9t} + \dfrac{2}{5t}$

h) $\dfrac{6}{7b} - \dfrac{5}{8b}$

7. Simplify.

a) $\dfrac{7a}{10} - \dfrac{2a}{5} + \dfrac{3a}{10}$

b) $\dfrac{5m}{6} - \dfrac{3m}{4} + \dfrac{m}{8}$

c) $\dfrac{4x}{9} - \dfrac{2x}{3} + \dfrac{5x}{6}$

d) $\dfrac{7c}{12} - \dfrac{5c}{9} - \dfrac{5c}{6}$

e) $\dfrac{2e}{3} - \dfrac{5e}{6} + \dfrac{3e}{4}$

f) $\dfrac{3m}{8} - \dfrac{2m}{3} + \dfrac{5m}{6}$

8. Simplify.

a) $\dfrac{1}{2a} + \dfrac{1}{3a} + \dfrac{1}{4a}$

b) $\dfrac{2}{3x} - \dfrac{3}{4x} - \dfrac{1}{2x}$

c) $\dfrac{3}{8m} - \dfrac{2}{3m} + \dfrac{5}{6m}$

d) $\dfrac{7}{6x} - \dfrac{5}{2x} - \dfrac{1}{3x}$

e) $\dfrac{3}{4y} + \dfrac{2}{3y} - \dfrac{5}{6y}$

f) $\dfrac{3}{8y} - \dfrac{5}{6y} + \dfrac{1}{4y}$

9. Simplify.

a) $\dfrac{x+3}{x} + \dfrac{x-5}{x}$

b) $\dfrac{5m-2}{m} - \dfrac{4m+7}{m}$

c) $\dfrac{4a-2}{3a} + \dfrac{7a+11}{3a}$

d) $\dfrac{6x+7}{5x^2} - \dfrac{2x-19}{5x^2}$

e) $\dfrac{7m+4}{2m} - \dfrac{12m+11}{2m}$

f) $\dfrac{2x-8}{4x} - \dfrac{10x-7}{4x}$

10. Simplify.

a) $\dfrac{k-7}{4} - \dfrac{k+2}{5}$

b) $\dfrac{c+5}{3} + \dfrac{c-8}{2}$

c) $\dfrac{x+4}{3} - \dfrac{x+2}{4}$

d) $\dfrac{m-5}{4} + \dfrac{m+3}{6}$

e) $\dfrac{2a+3}{8} - \dfrac{5a-4}{6}$

f) $\dfrac{4x-7}{6} + \dfrac{2x-7}{9}$

11. Simplify.

a) $\dfrac{x+2}{3x} + \dfrac{2x-5}{2x}$

b) $\dfrac{2n-7}{8n} - \dfrac{3n-4}{6n}$

c) $\dfrac{5a-9}{6a} - \dfrac{3a+1}{9a}$

12. Simplify.

a) $\dfrac{5a}{a} - \dfrac{5}{2a}$

b) $\dfrac{2}{3m} - \dfrac{1}{2n}$

c) $\dfrac{4}{x} + \dfrac{3}{xy}$

d) $1 + \dfrac{a}{2b}$

13. Simplify.

a) $\dfrac{3}{x} - \dfrac{2}{y} + 1$

b) $\dfrac{2}{a} - \dfrac{3}{b} + \dfrac{4}{c}$

c) $\dfrac{1}{2x} + \dfrac{3}{4y} - \dfrac{5}{6z}$

14. Simplify.

a) $\dfrac{7x}{6y} + \dfrac{5x}{3x}$

b) $\dfrac{5m}{3n} - \dfrac{4n}{3m}$

c) $\dfrac{3a}{5b} - \dfrac{4b}{3a}$

d) $\dfrac{3x}{2a} - \dfrac{4a}{5x}$

Ⓒ

15. Simplify.

a) $\left(a - \dfrac{1}{a}\right)\left(a - \dfrac{2}{a}\right)$

b) $\left(k + \dfrac{3}{k}\right)\left(k - \dfrac{5}{k}\right)$

c) $\left(2a - \dfrac{3}{a}\right)^2$

16. a) Simplify $\left(x + \dfrac{1}{x}\right)^2 - \left(x^2 + \dfrac{1}{x^2}\right)$ b) If $x + \dfrac{1}{x} = 3$, find the value of $x^2 + \dfrac{1}{x^2}$

17. Write as a sum or a difference.

a) $\dfrac{12-a}{3}$

b) $\dfrac{2x-5}{10x}$

c) $\dfrac{x^2+xy}{xy}$

d) $\dfrac{7x^2+x+1}{x}$

18. If $\dfrac{x}{y} = \dfrac{3}{2}$, find the value of

a) $\dfrac{y}{x}$

b) $\dfrac{x+y}{y}$

c) $\dfrac{x+y}{x}$

d) $\dfrac{x+y}{x-y}$

 INVESTIGATE

Consider the product: $\left(x + \dfrac{1}{x}\right)\left(x + \dfrac{2}{x}\right)$

First multiply the factors and then simplify the result. Then simplify each factor and multiply. Are the answers given by both methods the same? Why?

4-4 ADDING AND SUBTRACTING RATIONAL EXPRESSIONS

The procedures of Section 4-3 are also used to add and subtract rational expressions with denominators that are not monomials.

Example 1. Simplify: a) $\dfrac{m-4}{m-2} - \dfrac{m-10}{m-2}$ b) $\dfrac{5}{x} + \dfrac{6x}{x+4}$

c) $a - \dfrac{3}{a+b}$ d) $\dfrac{x+3}{x-5} - \dfrac{x-7}{x-2}$

Solution. a) Since the terms have a common denominator, the numerators can be combined:

$$\frac{m-4}{m-2} - \frac{m-10}{m-2} = \frac{(m-4)-(m-10)}{m-2}$$

$$= \frac{m-4-m+10}{m-2}$$

$$= \frac{6}{m-2}$$

b) The lowest common denominator is $x(x+4)$:

$$\frac{5}{x} + \frac{6x}{x+4} = \frac{5}{x} \times \frac{x+4}{x+4} + \frac{6x}{x+4} \times \frac{x}{x}$$

$$= \frac{5(x+4) + 6x(x)}{x(x+4)}$$

$$= \frac{5x + 20 + 6x^2}{x(x+4)}$$

$$= \frac{6x^2 + 5x + 20}{x(x+4)}$$

c) Since $a = \dfrac{a}{1}$, the lowest common denominator is $a+b$:

$$a - \frac{3}{a+b} = a \times \frac{a+b}{a+b} - \frac{3}{a+b} \times \frac{1}{1}$$

$$= \frac{a(a+b) - 3}{a+b}$$

$$= \frac{a^2 + ab - 3}{a+b}$$

d) The lowest common denominator is $(x - 5)(x - 2)$:

$$\frac{x + 3}{x - 5} - \frac{x - 7}{x - 2} = \frac{x + 3}{x - 5} \times \frac{x - 2}{x - 2} - \frac{x - 7}{x - 2} \times \frac{x - 5}{x - 5}$$

$$= \frac{(x + 3)(x - 2) - (x - 7)(x - 5)}{(x - 5)(x - 2)}$$

$$= \frac{(x^2 + x - 6) - (x^2 - 12x + 35)}{(x - 5)(x - 2)}$$

$$= \frac{x^2 + x - 6 - x^2 + 12x - 35}{(x - 5)(x - 2)}$$

$$= \frac{13x - 41}{(x - 5)(x - 2)}$$

Frequently, the denominators of rational expressions must be factored so that the lowest common denominator can be more readily determined.

Example 2. Simplify:

a) $\dfrac{7}{2x + 4} - \dfrac{5}{3x + 6}$ b) $\dfrac{b}{a - 3} - \dfrac{b}{a + 3} + \dfrac{1}{a^2 - 9}$

Solution. a) $\dfrac{7}{2x + 4} - \dfrac{5}{3x + 6}$

$$= \frac{7}{2(x + 2)} - \frac{5}{3(x + 2)}$$

$$= \frac{7}{2(x + 2)} \times \frac{3}{3} - \frac{5}{3(x + 2)} \times \frac{2}{2}$$

$$= \frac{7 \times 3 - 5 \times 2}{6(x + 2)}$$

$$= \frac{21 - 10}{6(x + 2)}$$

$$= \frac{11}{6(x + 2)}$$

b) $\dfrac{b}{a-3} - \dfrac{b}{a+3} + \dfrac{1}{a^2-9}$

$= \dfrac{b}{a-3} - \dfrac{b}{a+3} + \dfrac{1}{(a-3)(a+3)}$

$= \dfrac{b}{a-3} \times \dfrac{a+3}{a+3} - \dfrac{b}{a+3} \times \dfrac{a-3}{a-3} + \dfrac{1}{(a-3)(a+3)}$

$= \dfrac{b(a+3) - b(a-3) + 1}{(a-3)(a+3)}$

$= \dfrac{ba + 3b - ba + 3b + 1}{(a-3)(a+3)}$

$= \dfrac{6b+1}{(a-3)(a+3)}$

When possible, the sum or difference of rational expressions should be reduced to lowest terms.

Example 3. Simplify:

$$\dfrac{x}{x^2 - 9x + 18} - \dfrac{x-2}{x^2 - 10x + 24}$$

Solution. $\dfrac{x}{x^2 - 9x + 18} - \dfrac{x-2}{x^2 - 10x + 24}$

$= \dfrac{x}{(x-6)(x-3)} - \dfrac{x-2}{(x-6)(x-4)}$

$= \dfrac{x(x-4) - (x-2)(x-3)}{(x-6)(x-3)(x-4)}$ ⟶ lowest common denominator

$= \dfrac{x^2 - 4x - (x^2 - 5x + 6)}{(x-6)(x-3)(x-4)}$

$= \dfrac{x^2 - 4x - x^2 + 5x - 6}{(x-6)(x-3)(x-4)}$

$= \dfrac{x-6}{(x-6)(x-3)(x-4)}$

$= \dfrac{1}{(x-3)(x-4)}$

EXERCISES 4-4

Ⓐ

1. Simplify.

a) $\dfrac{3m - 5}{m + 3} + \dfrac{m + 4}{m + 3}$

b) $\dfrac{2s + 7}{s - 5} - \dfrac{6s - 4}{s - 5}$

c) $\dfrac{5k - 9}{k - 4} - \dfrac{2k + 3}{k - 4}$

d) $\dfrac{2x + 7}{x + 6} + \dfrac{2x + 11}{x + 6}$

e) $\dfrac{4m - 9}{2m + 1} - \dfrac{m - 4}{2m + 1}$

f) $\dfrac{3a - 8}{a^2 + 4} - \dfrac{7a + 3}{a^2 + 4}$

2. Simplify.

a) $\dfrac{4}{a - 3} - \dfrac{1}{a}$

b) $\dfrac{2}{y - 5} - \dfrac{6}{y}$

c) $\dfrac{7}{m} - \dfrac{3}{m - 4}$

d) $\dfrac{2c}{c - 1} - \dfrac{5}{c}$

e) $\dfrac{3x}{x + 2} - \dfrac{6}{x}$

f) $\dfrac{3}{x} + \dfrac{5}{x + 2}$

3. Simplify.

a) $\dfrac{3}{2a} - 4$

b) $\dfrac{7}{y + 1} - 2$

c) $4 - \dfrac{9}{n - 5}$

d) $x - \dfrac{2}{x + 4}$

e) $\dfrac{3}{s - 8} - 2s$

f) $\dfrac{2w}{w + 3} - 4w$

g) $\dfrac{4}{x - 1} - (x - 2)$

h) $\dfrac{4}{x - 1} - x - 2$

i) $x - 5 + \dfrac{2}{x - 3}$

j) $x + 3 + \dfrac{5}{x - 2}$

k) $\dfrac{2}{x - 4} - x - 8$

l) $4 - \dfrac{3}{x + 2} - x$

Ⓑ

4. Simplify.

a) $\dfrac{2}{x + 5} + \dfrac{3}{x + 2}$

b) $\dfrac{4}{x - 3} - \dfrac{2}{x + 1}$

c) $\dfrac{x}{x + 1} - \dfrac{2}{x - 1}$

d) $\dfrac{3x}{x + 4} + \dfrac{2}{x + 4}$

e) $\dfrac{5x}{x - 1} - \dfrac{2x}{x + 3}$

f) $\dfrac{2x}{x + 5} + \dfrac{3x}{x - 3}$

5. Simplify.

a) $\dfrac{1}{x + 1} - \dfrac{1}{x - 1}$

b) $\dfrac{x - 3}{x - 2} + \dfrac{1}{x - 3}$

c) $\dfrac{3x - 1}{x + 7} - \dfrac{2x + 1}{x - 3}$

d) $\dfrac{x - 2}{x + 2} + \dfrac{x + 1}{x - 4}$

e) $\dfrac{x + 6}{x - 3} + \dfrac{x - 4}{x - 5}$

f) $\dfrac{x + 1}{x - 2} - \dfrac{x - 1}{x + 2}$

6. Simplify.

a) $\dfrac{2}{x} - \dfrac{3x}{x - 2}$

b) $\dfrac{7}{2(x + 3)} - \dfrac{4}{5(x + 3)}$

c) $\dfrac{3y}{2(y + 9)} + \dfrac{5y}{3(y + 9)}$

d) $\dfrac{5}{3(a - 7)} - \dfrac{2}{3(a + 1)}$

e) $\dfrac{3}{a + 1} + \dfrac{1}{a - 1}$

f) $\dfrac{3x}{x - 2} - \dfrac{4x}{x - 3}$

7. Simplify.

a) $\dfrac{6}{2x + 4} + \dfrac{9}{3x + 6}$ b) $\dfrac{3}{5x - 10} + \dfrac{7}{2x - 4}$ c) $\dfrac{5x}{3x + 9} - \dfrac{9x}{2x + 6}$

d) $\dfrac{5x}{10x - 15} - \dfrac{4x}{16x - 24}$ e) $\dfrac{2x + 5}{3x - 12} + \dfrac{2x}{x - 4}$ f) $\dfrac{3x}{2x + 8} - \dfrac{2x - 3}{3x + 12}$

8. Simplify.

a) $\dfrac{4x}{x^2 - 9x + 18} + \dfrac{2x - 1}{x - 6}$ b) $\dfrac{x - 7}{x^2 - 2x - 15} - \dfrac{3x}{x - 5}$ c) $\dfrac{2x}{x - 2} - \dfrac{3}{x^2 - 4}$

d) $\dfrac{4x + 1}{x + 3} + \dfrac{x - 6}{x^2 - 9}$ e) $\dfrac{3x}{x - 1} - \dfrac{2x}{x^2 + x - 2}$ f) $\dfrac{8x - 3}{x^2 - 7x + 12} - \dfrac{2x + 1}{x - 4}$

9. Simplify.

a) $\dfrac{3m}{2(m - 1)} - \dfrac{5m}{2(m + 1)}$ b) $\dfrac{x - 1}{x(x + 5)} + \dfrac{2x - 3}{x(x - 1)}$ c) $\dfrac{8a}{5(a - 2)} + \dfrac{5a - 1}{3(a + 3)}$

d) $\dfrac{5k}{4(k - 3)} - \dfrac{4k}{k - 4}$ e) $\dfrac{3x - 1}{2(x - 2)} + \dfrac{5x + 1}{x + 7}$ f) $\dfrac{4m + 3}{3(2m - 1)} - \dfrac{m - 5}{2(3m + 7)}$

10. Simplify.

a) $\dfrac{x + 3}{x^2 + 11x + 24} - \dfrac{2x + 10}{x^2 + 11x + 30}$ b) $\dfrac{m - 4}{m^2 - 8m + 16} + \dfrac{3m + 21}{m^2 + 12m + 35}$

c) $\dfrac{3x + 9}{x^2 + 5x + 6} - \dfrac{2x - 2}{x^2 + x - 2}$ d) $\dfrac{5m + 25}{m^2 + 7m + 10} - \dfrac{10m - 20}{m^2 - 4}$

e) $\dfrac{4x^2 - 20x}{x^2 + 2x - 35} + \dfrac{3x - 6}{x^2 - 12x + 20}$ f) $\dfrac{2x - 6}{x^2 - 5x + 6} - \dfrac{3x - 12}{x^2 - x - 12}$

©

11. Simplify.

a) $\dfrac{3x^2 + 6xy}{3x} - \dfrac{4y^2 - 2xy}{2y}$ b) $\dfrac{x^2 - 5xy + 6y^2}{x - 3y} - \dfrac{x^2 - xy - 12y^2}{x - 4y}$

c) $\dfrac{x^2 - 4xy - 21y^2}{3x - 21y} + \dfrac{x^2 + 2xy - 24y^2}{2x + 2y}$ d) $\dfrac{a - b}{a^2 + 2ab - 3b^2} + \dfrac{a + b}{a^2 - 2ab - 3b^2}$

12. If $a = \dfrac{1}{x}$ and $b = \dfrac{1}{y}$, write the following expressions in terms of x and y and simplify.

a) $a + b$ b) $\dfrac{a + b}{a - b}$ c) $\dfrac{1}{a + b} + \dfrac{1}{a - b}$ d) $\dfrac{a}{a - b} - \dfrac{b}{a + b}$

13. If $x = \dfrac{a + 1}{a + 2}$, write the following in terms of a and simplify.

a) $x + 1$ b) $x^2 - 1$ c) $\dfrac{x + 1}{x}$ d) $\dfrac{x + 1}{x + 2}$

THE MATHEMATICAL MIND

A Genius From India

Srinivasa Ramanujan
1887-1920

"On the contrary," Ramanujan replied. "1729 is a very interesting number. It is the smallest number that can be expressed as the sum of two cubes in two different ways."

The brilliant Indian mathematician, Srinivasa Ramanujan, developed many new and complicated results about numbers. He had an amazing memory and an unusual ability to see patterns in numbers quickly.

When he was 25 years of age, he sent a collection of 120 of his theorems to the British mathematician, G.H. Hardy. One of these theorems is shown below.

Hardy wrote, "I had never seen anything in the least like them before. A single look at them is enough to show that they could only be written down by a mathematician of the highest class. They must be true because, if they were not true, no one would have had the imagination to invent them."

Once, when Hardy was visiting Ramanujan in a hospital where he was being treated for tuberculosis, he mentioned that he had come in a taxi with the number 1729. He remarked that the number seemed to be a dull one, and hoped that this was not an unfavorable omen.

1. Find natural numbers a, b, c, d such that $a^3 + b^3 = 1729$ and $c^3 + d^3 = 1729$.

2. What is the smallest number that can be expressed as the sum of two perfect squares in two different ways?

3. Find numbers which can be expressed as the sum of three perfect squares in two different ways.

$$\text{If } u = \cfrac{x}{1 + \cfrac{x^5}{1 + \frac{x^{10}}{1 + \ldots}}} \quad \text{and} \quad v = \cfrac{x^{\frac{1}{5}}}{1 + \cfrac{x}{1 + \frac{x^2}{1 + \ldots}}}$$

$$\text{then} \quad v^5 = u\left(\frac{1 - 2u + 4u^2 - 3u^3 + u^4}{1 + 3u + 4u^2 + 2u^2 + u^4}\right).$$

PROBLEM SOLVING

Introduce a Variable

From train windows, passengers often see passing hydro poles. If you know that the poles are 75 m apart, and you count the number of poles that pass by in one minute, how could you calculate the speed of the train, in kilometres per hour?

Understand the problem

- Why does timing the poles that pass by give information about the speed of the train?
- Is it reasonable to assume that the speed of the train is constant?

Think of a strategy

- Introduce a variable, n, to represent the number of poles that pass by in one minute.

Carry out the strategy

- Since the poles are 75 m apart, in 1 min the train travels $75n$ metres. In 1 h (60 min) the train travels $60(75n)$ or $4500n$ metres.

  This distance is $\dfrac{4500n}{1000}$ or $4.5n$ kilometres.

- This expression indicates how to calculate the speed of the train. Simply count the number of poles passing by in one minute, and multiply by 4.5. The result is the distance travelled in 1 h or the approximate speed of the train in kilometres per hour.

Look back

- What would be the speed of the train, in kilometres per hour, if 32 poles were counted in 1 min?

- For how long should the poles be counted so that their number gives the speed of the train, without multiplying?

- How many poles should pass by in one minute if the speed of the train is 120 km/h?

Solve each problem

1. The clicking sound of a train passing over the joints in the rails can be heard by passengers. Assume that the joints are 40 m apart. If you count the number of clicks in one minute, how could you calculate the speed of the train?

2. The Japanese *Shinkansen* is one of the world's fastest trains. On one of its runs it passes through the world's longest railway tunnel, 22.2 km long.
   a) If you were on the train, and measured the time in seconds it took to pass through the tunnel, how could you calculate the speed of the train?
   b) The *Shinkansen* normally takes about 6 min 12 s to pass through the tunnel. What is the speed of the train in the tunnel?

3. In ice hockey, the face-off circles have a circumference of 28.27 m. What is the area of a face-off circle?

4. In ice hockey, the referee's crease is a semicircle. If the perimeter of this semicircle is 10.71 m, find its area.

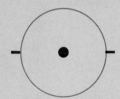

5. How many examples can you find of prime numbers that are one less than a perfect square? Can you prove that you have found them all?

6. Two sides of a triangle have lengths 8 cm and 5 cm. Find out as much as you can about the
   a) perimeter of the triangle
   b) area of the triangle

7. Figure *EFGH* is a square with sides of length 6 cm, and *M* is the midpoint of *EF*. *MR* and *MS* divide the square into three regions with equal areas. Find the lengths of *HR, RS,* and *SG*.

8. In right △*ABC*, the median from *A* to *BC* has length 8 cm, while the median from *C* to *AB* has length 6 cm. How long is the hypotenuse *AC*?

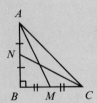

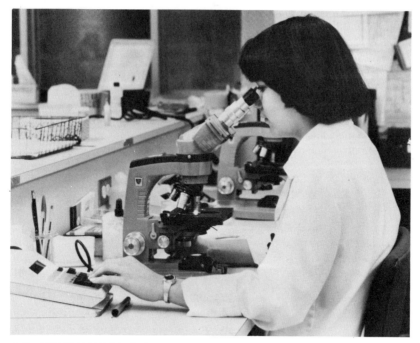

4-5 APPLICATIONS OF RATIONAL EXPRESSIONS

Many formulas in mathematics and science involve rational expressions. The expressions are almost always simpler than those worked with earlier in the chapter.

Example 1. The focal length, f, of a lens is related to the object and image distances, p and q respectively, by the formula $\dfrac{1}{f} = \dfrac{1}{p} + \dfrac{1}{q}$. Express f in terms of p and q.

Solution.

$$\frac{1}{f} = \frac{1}{p} + \frac{1}{q}$$

$$= \frac{1}{p} \times \frac{q}{q} + \frac{1}{q} \times \frac{p}{p}$$

$$= \frac{q + p}{pq}$$

Therefore, $f = \dfrac{pq}{q + p}$

When developing a formula for a specific purpose, it is sometimes helpful to use numerical data before generalizing.

Example 2. In a training session, Carole directs her boat crew to row with constant power both with and against the current.

a) If the boat's speed upstream is 14 km/h and downstream is 18 km/h, and the distance each way is 3 km, calculate the average speed over the training course, to the nearest tenth of a kilometre per hour.

b) Find an expression for the average speed if the distance each way is r km, and u km/h and v km/h are the upstream and downstream speeds respectively.

Solution.   a) Since average speed is found by dividing the total distance travelled by the total time, we must calculate the total time for the upstream and downstream runs.

On the upstream run:

The boat requires $\dfrac{3}{14}$ h $\doteq 0.214$ h to travel 3 km.

On the downstream run:

The boat requires $\dfrac{3}{18}$ h $\doteq 0.167$ h to travel 3 km.

The total time, in hours, is $0.214 + 0.167 \doteq 0.381$ h.

The average speed, in kilometres per hour, is:

$$\frac{\text{Total distance}}{\text{Total time}} \doteq \frac{6}{0.381}$$
$$\doteq 15.7$$

The boat's average speed over the training course is 15.7 km/h.

b) The time, in hours, for the upstream run is $\dfrac{r}{u}$.

The time, in hours, for the downstream run is $\dfrac{r}{v}$.

The total time, in hours, is:

$$\frac{r}{u} + \frac{r}{v} = \frac{r}{u} \times \frac{v}{v} + \frac{r}{v} \times \frac{u}{u}$$
$$= \frac{rv + ru}{uv}$$
$$= \frac{r(v + u)}{uv}$$

The average speed, in kilometres per hour, is:

$$2r \div \frac{r(v + u)}{uv} = 2r \times \frac{uv}{r(v + u)}$$
$$= \frac{2uv}{v + u}$$

An expression for the average speed, in kilometres per hour, is $\dfrac{2uv}{v + u}$.

Example 3.   An aircraft maintains an airspeed of V km/h between two airports d km apart on both the outbound and return trips. On the outbound trip there is a headwind of w km/h and on the return trip a tailwind of the same speed. Write an expression for the time taken for the round trip.

Solution. $\text{Time} = \dfrac{\text{distance}}{\text{groundspeed}}$, where groundspeed = airspeed $\pm$ windspeed

Outbound time (hours): $\dfrac{d}{V - w}$

Return time (hours): $\dfrac{d}{V + w}$

Total time (hours):

$$\dfrac{d}{V - w} + \dfrac{d}{V + w}$$

$$= \dfrac{d(V + w) + d(V - w)}{(V - w)(V + w)}$$

$$= \dfrac{dV + dw + dV - dw}{V^2 - w^2}$$

$$= \dfrac{2dV}{V^2 - w^2}$$

The time taken for the round trip is $\dfrac{2dV}{V^2 - w^2}$ hours.

EXERCISES 4-5

Ⓐ

1. The lens formula is $\dfrac{1}{f} = \dfrac{1}{p} + \dfrac{1}{q}$. Calculate f when $p = 8$ and $q = 12$.

2. Tek Yew cycles from his home to the store and back again.
   a) If the store is 12 km away and he averages 9 km/h going and 18 km/h returning because of the wind, calculate his average speed for the trip.

   b) If the store is d km away and he averages x km/h going and y km/h returning, find an expression for his average speed for the trip.

3. In *Example 3*, find an expression for the average speed of the aircraft for the round trip.

4. An aircraft maintains an airspeed of 325 km/h between two airports on both the outbound and return trips. On the outbound trip there is a tailwind of 75 km/h and on the return trip a headwind of the same speed. If the airports are 1000 km apart, how long does the aircraft take to fly the round trip?

5. The trip to a cottage is 150 km on a highway then 60 km on a gravel road. How long does the trip take if the average speed of
   a) 90 km/h on the highway is reduced by 40 km/h on the gravel road?
   b) v km/h on the highway is reduced by x km/h on the gravel road?

6. The speed of a boat in still water is x km/h. It travels 200 km upriver and returns to its starting point. If the river current is y km/h, find the time for the round trip.

Ⓑ

7. When two resistances, r and s, are connected in parallel, the total resistance, R, is given by the formula:

$$\frac{1}{R} = \frac{1}{r} + \frac{1}{s}$$

   a) Express R in terms of r and s.
   b) Express r in terms of R and s.
   c) Express s in terms of R and r.

8. What time is saved on a trip of 150 km if the average speed is increased from
   a) 80 km/h to 90 km/h?   b) v km/h to $(v + x)$ km/h?

9. A rectangular poster has an area of 4000 cm². Write an expression for

   a) its width when its length is l cm

   b) the increase in its width when its length is decreased by x cm

---

Ⓒ

10. The density, d, in kilograms per cubic metre at $t°$C, of a space-age alloy is given by the formula:

$$d = \frac{3000}{1 + 0.000\ 125\ t}$$

   a) Calculate the alloy's density when the temperature is 40°C and −20°C.

   b) At about what temperature will its density be 2992.5 kg/m³?

PROBLEM SOLVING

Choose the Strategy

1. A house and a lot are worth $100 000. The house is worth four times as much as the lot. How much are each worth?

2. The cost for 33 students to go on a camping trip is $1250. At the last minute, a certain number of students decide not to go. If you know how many students cancelled, how could you find the increase in the cost for the other students?

3. You walked for 20 km at 5 km/h. Later you returned running at 10 km/h. What was your average speed?

4. It was reported that a person once typed every number from one to one million. The task took five years.
   a) How many digits did the person type?
   b) Estimate the number of hours of typing time that would be needed to do this. About how much time each day was needed?

5. Find a number which has this property. If you add 3 to it, and if you add 4 to it, the sum of the two numbers obtained is the same as adding 12 to it.

6. When a transversal intersects two parallel lines, two pairs of alternate angles are formed.
   a) How many pairs of alternate angles are formed by a transversal and 3 parallel lines? 4 parallel lines? 10 parallel lines?
   b) Suppose you know the number of parallel lines. Find a rule that gives the number of pairs of alternate angles.

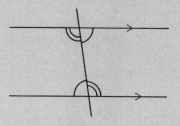

7. On freezing, water expands 5%. If water is poured into a tin can 10 cm high, how high should the water level be such that, on freezing, it just reaches the top of the can?

8. Find two whole numbers with the least possible difference which have a product of 123 456.

9. Two numbers have a sum of 10 and a product of 20. Find the sum of the reciprocals of the two numbers.

Review Exercises

1. Reduce to lowest terms.

   a) $\dfrac{78a^3b}{6a^2}$

   b) $\dfrac{9m+6}{3}$

   c) $\dfrac{20y^2-8y}{4y}$

   d) $\dfrac{36s^2-48s}{24s}$

   e) $\dfrac{9ab-18a}{-3a}$

   f) $\dfrac{6xy}{3x^2+15xy}$

   g) $\dfrac{6m^2-15mn}{4m-10n}$

   h) $\dfrac{7s^2-35st}{5s-25t}$

2. Simplify.

   a) $\dfrac{36-12x}{4x-12}$

   b) $\dfrac{a^2-25}{3a^2-15a}$

   c) $\dfrac{n^2-10n+24}{n^2-6n+8}$

   d) $\dfrac{a^2-9}{a^2+6a+9}$

   e) $\dfrac{b^2-3b-28}{b^2-9b+14}$

   f) $\dfrac{m^2-8m+15}{m^2-3m-10}$

3. Simplify.

   a) $\dfrac{9a^3}{4}\times\dfrac{8}{3a}$

   b) $\dfrac{-6mn}{15}\div\dfrac{2m^2}{5}$

   c) $\dfrac{4x^2y}{8xy}\div\dfrac{3x^2y^3}{6xy^3}$

   d) $\dfrac{15x^4y^2}{24xy^2}\times\dfrac{8x^2y}{5xy^2}$

   e) $\dfrac{2m^2n}{3mn}\times\dfrac{(6mn)^2}{4mn}$

   f) $\dfrac{2x}{3y}\times\dfrac{3z}{4y}\div\dfrac{4z}{5x}$

4. Simplify.

   a) $\dfrac{12a^2}{5(a+4)}\times\dfrac{10(a+4)}{3a}$

   b) $\dfrac{3(5-a)}{2a}\div\dfrac{3(a-5)}{8(a+1)}$

   c) $\dfrac{6mn^2}{2(2m-5)}\times\dfrac{3(2m-5)}{9m^2n}$

   d) $\dfrac{3x^2y(2x-y)}{15xy}\div\dfrac{2xy^2(2x-y)}{5x^2y^3}$

5. Simplify.

   a) $\dfrac{3b^3}{a^2-9}\times\dfrac{2a-b}{2b^2}$

   b) $\dfrac{m^2-2m+1}{m^2-1}\div\dfrac{m^2-4}{m^2+3m+2}$

   c) $\dfrac{x^2-3x-10}{25-x^2}\div\dfrac{x+2}{x+5}$

   d) $\dfrac{y^2+2y-15}{y^2-8y+7}\times\dfrac{y^2-5y-14}{y^2+7y+10}$

6. Simplify.

   a) $\dfrac{4}{3a}+\dfrac{5}{3a}$

   b) $\dfrac{3}{2x}-\dfrac{5}{3x}$

   c) $\dfrac{5}{m}+\dfrac{3}{4m}$

   d) $\dfrac{5x}{6}-\dfrac{3x}{4}+\dfrac{x}{8}$

   e) $\dfrac{2}{3a}-\dfrac{3}{4a}+\dfrac{1}{2a}$

   f) $\dfrac{7}{6n}-\dfrac{5}{2n}+\dfrac{1}{5n}$

7. Simplify.

a) $\dfrac{a+3}{a} + \dfrac{a-5}{a}$

b) $\dfrac{3x-2}{x} - \dfrac{2x+7}{x}$

c) $\dfrac{y-5}{4} - \dfrac{y+2}{5}$

d) $\dfrac{a+2}{3a} + \dfrac{2a-5}{2a}$

e) $\dfrac{3x-7}{8x} - \dfrac{2x-4}{6x}$

f) $\dfrac{3}{4x} - \dfrac{2}{3x} + 1$

g) $\dfrac{7x+3}{4x} - \dfrac{5x+2}{6x}$

h) $\dfrac{2m-9}{4m} + \dfrac{7m+5}{8m}$

i) $\dfrac{2a+3}{10a^2} - \dfrac{7a-4}{15a^2}$

8. Simplify.

a) $\dfrac{2}{3a} + \dfrac{5}{b}$

b) $\dfrac{3}{4m} - \dfrac{5}{6n}$

c) $1 + \dfrac{s}{t}$

d) $2 + \dfrac{b}{2c}$

e) $\dfrac{9p}{7q} + \dfrac{7q}{6p}$

f) $\dfrac{3x}{5y} - \dfrac{2y}{3x}$

g) $\dfrac{3c}{7d} + \dfrac{5d}{3c}$

h) $\dfrac{8x}{9y} - \dfrac{3x}{5x}$

9. Simplify.

a) $\dfrac{5x-9}{x-4} - \dfrac{2x+3}{x-4}$

b) $\dfrac{2a}{a-1} - \dfrac{5}{a}$

c) $\dfrac{7}{x+1} - 2$

d) $\dfrac{m}{m+1} - \dfrac{2}{m-1}$

e) $\dfrac{y-3}{y-2} + \dfrac{1}{y-3}$

f) $\dfrac{3a-1}{a+7} - \dfrac{2a+1}{a-3}$

10. Simplify.

a) $\dfrac{5a}{10a-15} - \dfrac{4a}{16a-24}$

b) $\dfrac{2m+5}{3m-12} + \dfrac{2m}{m-4}$

c) $\dfrac{2k}{k-2} - \dfrac{3}{k^2-4}$

d) $\dfrac{8b-3}{b^2-7b+12} - \dfrac{2b+1}{b-4}$

e) $\dfrac{8x}{5(x-2)} + \dfrac{5x-1}{3(x+3)}$

f) $\dfrac{4x+3}{3(2x-1)} - \dfrac{x-5}{2(3x+7)}$

11. Simplify.

a) $\dfrac{x}{x+2} - \dfrac{3}{x-2}$

b) $\dfrac{3a}{8a-12} + \dfrac{2a}{6a-9}$

c) $\dfrac{5a}{6a-10} + \dfrac{4a}{15a-25}$

d) $\dfrac{2x+3}{2x-8} - \dfrac{3x}{x-4}$

e) $\dfrac{3m}{2(m-2)} + \dfrac{2m-1}{3(m+2)}$

f) $\dfrac{3t}{3(t-1)} + \dfrac{2t}{5(t+1)}$

12. Barbara flew her airplane 500 km against the wind in the same time that it took her to fly it 600 km with the wind. If the speed of the wind was 20 km/h, what was the average speed of her airplane?

5 Equations and Inequalities

In football, to kick the ball as far as possible it must be kicked high. How can we estimate how high it is at any time? (See *Example 3* in Section 5-10.)

5-1 SOLVING EQUATIONS IN ONE VARIABLE

Many problems in business, science, engineering and industry are solved using equations. To solve an equation means to find all the values of the variable which satisfy the equation. These values are called the *solutions*, or *roots*, of the equation.

> To solve an equation, isolate the variable. This will require performing one or more operations on both sides of the equation.

Example 1. Solve: $3(x - 4) - 10 = 9 - 5(x + 3)$

Solution. $3(x - 4) - 10 = 9 - 5(x + 3)$

Apply the distributive law:
$$3x - 12 - 10 = 9 - 5x - 15$$
$$3x - 22 = -5x - 6$$

Add $5x$ and 22 to both sides:
$$3x + 5x = -6 + 22$$
$$8x = 16$$

Divide both sides by 8:
$$x = 2$$

Check. Substitute 2 for x in both sides of the equation:

L.S. $= 3(x - 4) - 10$	R.S. $= 9 - 5(x + 3)$
$= 3(2 - 4) - 10$	$= 9 - 5(2 + 3)$
$= 3(-2) - 10$	$= 9 - 25$
$= -16$	$= -16$

Both sides simplify to the same number.
Therefore, $x = 2$ is the correct solution.

When using a formula, it is often necessary to isolate the variable.

Example 2. The cost, C, in dollars, of producing n tennis rackets is given by the formula: $C = 5000 + 20n$. How many tennis rackets can be produced for $30 000?

Solution. Substitute 30 000 for C in the formula:
$$C = 5000 + 20n$$
$$30\ 000 = 5000 + 20n$$
$$25\ 000 = 20n$$

Divide both sides by 20:
$$n = 1250$$

For $30 000 the number of tennis rackets that can be produced is 1250.

When an equation contains fractions, multiply both sides by a common denominator to obtain an equivalent equation without fractions.

Example 3.   Solve: $\dfrac{5(y + 6)}{4} + 3 = \dfrac{-(1 - 10y)}{3}$

Solution. $\dfrac{5(y + 6)}{4} + 3 = \dfrac{-(1 - 10y)}{3}$

Multiply both sides by 12:

$$12\left[\frac{5(y + 6)}{4} + 3\right] = 12\left[\frac{-1(1 - 10y)}{3}\right]$$
$$15(y + 6) + 36 = -4(1 - 10y)$$
$$15y + 90 + 36 = -4 + 40y$$
$$15y + 126 = 40y - 4$$
$$15y - 40y = -4 - 126$$
$$-25y = -130$$
$$y = \frac{-130}{-25}$$
$$= 5.2$$

In some equations the coefficients are represented by letters, not numbers. These are called *literal coefficients*.

Example 4.   Solve for x:

a) $ax + b = c$

b) $a(x - 2) = 2a - bx$

Solution.   a) $ax + b = c$

Subtract b from both sides:

$$ax = c - b$$

Divide both sides by a,

$(a \neq 0)$:

$$x = \frac{c - b}{a}$$

b) $a(x - 2) = 2a - bx$

$$ax - 2a = 2a - bx$$

Add $2a$ and bx to both sides:

$$ax + bx = 4a$$
$$x(a + b) = 4a$$

Divide both sides by $(a + b)$, $(a + b \neq 0)$:

$$x = \frac{4a}{a + b}$$

EXERCISES 5-1

(A)

1. Solve and check.
   a) $3x - 4 = 23$
   b) $2m + 5 = -21$
   c) $-5a - 7 = -62$
   d) $8y + 3 = -37$
   e) $2(3x - 5) = 32$
   f) $5(3x + 4) = -10$
   g) $9x - (4x + 7) = 28$
   h) $4x - (7x - 8) = -25$
   i) $4(x - 3) + 9x = -38$

2. Solve.
   a) $7m + 2 = 5m + 18$
   b) $11x - 18 = 3 + 8x$
   c) $9x - 30 = -3(5x - 6)$
   d) $13b - 12 = 49b + 24$
   e) $4(5 + x) = x + 5$
   f) $6x + 10 = 15x + 64$
   g) $3(x - 5) = 2(5x - 11)$
   h) $3(2r + 4) = 4(5r - 4)$
   i) $19m + 42 = 25m + 6$

3. Find the root of each equation.
   a) $x - 5 = 8 - 2(x + 2)$
   b) $4(x + 1) = 10 - (2x + 6)$
   c) $3 - (2 + 4x) = 4 + 2(3x + 1)$
   d) $12(a - 3) - 35 = 5(13 - a)$
   e) $3(y - 2) - 8 = 68 - 2(2y - 1)$
   f) $3x + 7(2 - x) = 14 - 9x - 3$
   g) $17x - 9(1 + x) = 4(3x - 1) + 7$
   h) $4(x - 9) + 52 = 2(3x + 17) + 2x$
   i) $2(5x - 11) - 6 = 3(x - 7) - 15$
   j) $13x - (3x + 12) - 5x = 7x - (5x - 3)$

4. The cost, C, in dollars, of producing n videos is given by the formula:
   $C = 12\,000 + 3n$. How many videos can be produced for $30\,000$?

(B)

5. The cost, C, in dollars, of renting a car for one day is given by the formula:
   $C = 25 + 0.15d$, where d is the number of kilometres driven. How far could you drive for 60?

6. In a province where the rate of sales tax is 8%, the total cost, C, of a taxable item is given by the formula: $C = 1.08s$, where s is the sticker price. If you have 20, what is the highest sticker price on an item you could buy?

7. Certain bank accounts give daily interest according to the formula: $I = \dfrac{Prt}{365}$, where P is the principal, r is the annual interest rate expressed as a decimal, and t is the time in days. Teri deposits 50 in an account which pays 7% annual interest.

   a) What interest would she receive after 23 days?
   b) How many days would she need to keep the money in the account to earn $1 in interest?

8. Solve.
   a) $\dfrac{7x}{6} = \dfrac{7}{2}$
   b) $\dfrac{x}{5} + \dfrac{1}{2} = \dfrac{3}{10}$
   c) $\dfrac{3m}{5} - \dfrac{1}{2} = \dfrac{7}{10}$
   d) $\dfrac{2x}{9} + \dfrac{1}{3} = -\dfrac{1}{6}$
   e) $\dfrac{1}{2}x - \dfrac{1}{3}x = \dfrac{7}{3}$
   f) $\dfrac{2x}{5} + \dfrac{3}{4} = \dfrac{4x}{5} - \dfrac{1}{2}$

9. Solve and check.
   a) $2(5x - 11) + 7 = 3(x - 7) - 15$
   b) $13x - (3x + 12) = 12x - (5x - 3)$
   c) $2(x - 6) + 3x = 2(x + 2) - x$
   d) $9(3 + y) - 16 = 8(y + 4) + 5$
   e) $15 - 2(3 + 2x) = 4 + 3(2x - 5)$
   f) $3x(x - 5) - 3x(x + 7) = 72$
   g) $4(3x + 1) - 6(x - 3) = 4(2x - 7) + 34$
   h) $2x(3x + 4) - 19 = x(6x - 2) + 31$

10. Solve.
    a) $3(a - 2) - 5(a - 3) = 17$
    b) $2(3k - 5) + 3(k - 5) = 7(k - 1)$
    c) $5(2n - 3) - 2(n - 1) = 5(n - 1) - 2$
    d) $8(y + 8) + 11 = 2(2y - 7) - 3(4y - 3)$
    e) $3(3x - 2) - 4(x - 1) = 14 + x$
    f) $2(2c - 5) + 20 = 3c(c + 5) - 3c(c + 7)$
    g) $15r^2 - 7 - 5r(3r + 4) = 3(7 - 4r)$
    h) $6 + 2(g + 4) = -11g + 4(g - 9) + 5$
    i) $5z(z - 2) - 3(2z - 1) = 5z(z - 3) + 7$
    j) $3(4p - 5) - 2(p + 1) = 4 - (p - 5)$

11. Solve.
    a) $\dfrac{5m}{6} + \dfrac{2m}{3} = \dfrac{9}{2}$
    b) $\dfrac{y + 3}{3} = \dfrac{3y - 5}{2}$
    c) $\dfrac{a - 2}{6} - 5 = \dfrac{a + 3}{3}$

    d) $\dfrac{x + 4}{3} - \dfrac{x - 5}{6} = 4$
    e) $\dfrac{2s + 7}{3} = \dfrac{s + 3}{5} + \dfrac{s - 1}{-1}$
    f) $\dfrac{5x + 2}{3} + 2 = \dfrac{2x - 3}{4} + \dfrac{1}{2}$

12. Solve for x.
    a) $ax - b = 7$
    b) $bx + 3x - d = e$
    c) $2bx = 3a + cx$
    d) $ax + b = cx + d$
    e) $3ax - b = 2x + c$
    f) $2a - 3x = 5(b - x)$
    g) $b(x + b) = b^2 - bc$
    h) $c(x - c) - b(x - b) = 0$
    i) $2(ax - b) - 5c = 5x + 2b$

13. For which of these equations is $x = -3$ a root? the only root?
    a) $3(2 - x) + x = 2(3 - x)$
    b) $2 + 5(x - 1) = 3(9 + 5x)$
    c) $2(3x - 1) + x = 10 - 3(5 - 2x)$
    d) $5x + 4 - 3(x + 1) = (3 - 2x) + 2(2x - 1)$

14. If 5 is the root of each equation, find the value of each k.
    a) $2x - k = 3 - x$
    b) $2 + 3x = 8 - (x - k)$
    c) $kx - 6 = 2x + k$
    d) $2(x - 3) + k(1 + 2x) = k - x - 1$

INVESTIGATE

If $a^2 - bc = 0$, and $b^2 - ac = 0$, what does $c^2 - ab$ equal?

5-2 SOLVING EQUATIONS INVOLVING RATIONAL EXPRESSIONS

When an equation contains a rational expression, first identify the values of the variable for which the expression is not defined. Then multiply both sides of the equation by a common denominator.

Example 1.   Given the equation: $\dfrac{x}{5} = \dfrac{2}{x} + \dfrac{x+3}{5}$

        a) For what value of x is the equation not defined?
        b) Solve the equation.

Solution.   a) The equation is not defined when $x = 0$.

        b) $\dfrac{x}{5} = \dfrac{2}{x} + \dfrac{x+3}{5}$

Multiply both sides by $5x$, $(x \neq 0)$:

$$5x\left(\frac{x}{5}\right) = 5x\left(\frac{2}{x}\right) + 5x\left(\frac{x+3}{5}\right)$$

$$x^2 = 10 + x^2 + 3x$$

$$-3x = 10$$

$$x = -\frac{10}{3}$$

Example 2. The average cost, A, in dollars, of producing n videos is given by the formula: $A = \dfrac{12\,000 + 3n}{n}$. How many videos would have to be produced for the average cost to be $3.25?

Solution. Substitute 3.25 for A in the formula:

$$A = \frac{12\,000 + 3n}{n}$$

$$3.25 = \frac{12\,000 + 3n}{n}$$

Multiply both sides by n, $(n \neq 0)$:

$$3.25n = 12\,000 + 3n$$
$$0.25n = 12\,000$$
$$n = \frac{12\,000}{0.25}$$
$$= 48\,000$$

For the average cost to be $3.25, 48 000 videos must be produced.

If an equation has a single rational expression on each side, it can be solved by cross-multiplying.

Example 3. Solve: $\dfrac{5}{x - 2} = \dfrac{4}{3x - 6}$

Solution. The equation is not defined when
$$x - 2 = 0 \quad \text{or} \quad 3x - 6 = 0$$
$$x = 2 \qquad\qquad x = 2$$

Assume that $x \neq 2$, and cross-multiply:

$$5(3x - 6) = 4(x - 2)$$
$$15x - 30 = 4x - 8$$
$$11x = 22$$
$$x = 2$$

Since this is the value of x for which the equation is not defined, we conclude that the equation $\dfrac{5}{x - 2} = \dfrac{4}{3x - 6}$ has no solution.

Example 3 underlines the importance of identifying the value(s) of the variable for which an equation is not defined.

EXERCISES 5-2

Ⓐ

1. State the value of x for which each of the following are undefined and solve.

   a) $\dfrac{4}{3} = \dfrac{12}{x}$

   b) $\dfrac{3}{5} = \dfrac{18}{x}$

   c) $\dfrac{15}{x} = \dfrac{3}{4}$

   d) $\dfrac{9}{x} = \dfrac{9}{8}$

   e) $\dfrac{x}{3} = \dfrac{12}{x}$

   f) $\dfrac{x}{8} = \dfrac{18}{x}$

   g) $\dfrac{30}{x} = \dfrac{3x}{10}$

   h) $\dfrac{90}{x} = \dfrac{2x}{5}$

2. State the value of x for which each of the following are undefined and solve.

   a) $\dfrac{x}{3} = \dfrac{2}{x} + \dfrac{x+1}{3}$

   b) $\dfrac{x}{5} = \dfrac{x-2}{5} - \dfrac{3}{x}$

   c) $\dfrac{x}{4} - \dfrac{x-3}{4} = \dfrac{2}{x}$

   d) $\dfrac{x}{3} - \dfrac{3}{x} = \dfrac{x-1}{3}$

   e) $\dfrac{2x}{7} - \dfrac{2x-5}{7} = \dfrac{3}{x}$

   f) $\dfrac{3x}{5} = \dfrac{2}{x} + \dfrac{3x+2}{5}$

3. Solve.

   a) $\dfrac{x}{5} + 3 = \dfrac{2}{x} + \dfrac{x+1}{5}$

   b) $\dfrac{x}{3} + \dfrac{4}{x} = \dfrac{x+1}{3}$

   c) $\dfrac{x}{3} + 5 = \dfrac{4}{x} - \dfrac{1-x}{3}$

   d) $\dfrac{2x+1}{3} + \dfrac{2}{x} = \dfrac{2(x+5)}{3}$

   e) $\dfrac{3x-2}{2} + 4 = \dfrac{13}{x} - \dfrac{1-6x}{4}$

   f) $\dfrac{2(1-x)}{3} - 8 = \dfrac{1}{6x} - \dfrac{2x-3}{3}$

4. The average cost, A, in dollars, of producing n tape decks is given by the formula:
   $A = \dfrac{40\,000 + 75n}{n}$. How many tape decks would have to be produced for the average cost to be $100?

Ⓑ

5. In a regular polygon with n sides, the measure of each angle, a, in degrees, is given by the formula: $a = 180 - \dfrac{360}{n}$.

   a) What is the measure of each angle in a regular decagon (10 sides)?

   b) If each angle in a regular polygon measures $156°$, how many sides does it have?

6. When a 1 kg mass is suspended from n similar elastic bands, the length, L, to which they stretch is given by the formula:
   $$L = 15.5 + \dfrac{45.5}{n}$$

   a) What is the length when there are 3 elastic bands?

   b) How many elastic bands are used if the length is 21.2 cm?

7. Find the values of x for which the following are undefined and solve.

a) $\dfrac{3}{x-2} = \dfrac{5}{2x+1}$

b) $\dfrac{5}{x+2} = \dfrac{4}{x-1}$

c) $\dfrac{7}{3x+5} = \dfrac{4}{2x+3}$

d) $\dfrac{3}{2x-4} = \dfrac{3}{x-2}$

e) $\dfrac{3}{5x-2} = \dfrac{2}{4x-5}$

f) $\dfrac{5}{2x+7} = \dfrac{-9}{4x+14}$

8. Solve.

a) $\dfrac{2x}{x-3} = 5$

b) $\dfrac{11x}{2x+3} = 7$

c) $\dfrac{3x+3}{x+1} = 2$

d) $\dfrac{-2+x}{2x+1} = \dfrac{2}{3}$

e) $\dfrac{3x-1}{5x+4} = 4$

f) $\dfrac{2x+1}{3-2x} = \dfrac{3}{5}$

9. Solve.

a) $\dfrac{2x}{x+3} = \dfrac{6x+5}{3x-1}$

b) $\dfrac{x-2}{x+3} = \dfrac{x+4}{x-1}$

c) $\dfrac{2x+1}{3x-2} = \dfrac{4x+3}{6x-5}$

d) $\dfrac{3x-5}{5x-3} = \dfrac{3x-1}{5x-1}$

e) $\dfrac{x-5}{1-x} = \dfrac{3-x}{x-1}$

f) $\dfrac{4x-3}{2x+1} = \dfrac{2x+1}{x-4}$

10. Solve.

a) $\dfrac{2x-3}{3x-4} = \dfrac{2x+7}{3x+4}$

b) $\dfrac{2x^2-2x+8}{2x-1} = x+1$

c) $\dfrac{3-x}{x-2} = 1 - \dfrac{2x-5}{x+2}$

d) $2 - \dfrac{x-1}{x+3} = \dfrac{x+2}{x+3}$

e) $\dfrac{2(x-1)}{x-3} = \dfrac{x-4}{x-5} + 1$

f) $1 - \dfrac{x-5}{5x-1} = \dfrac{4(x-3)}{5x-2}$

11. Solve for x.

a) $\dfrac{a}{x} - \dfrac{b}{x} = c$

b) $\dfrac{1}{x} = \dfrac{1}{p} + \dfrac{1}{q}$

c) $m = \dfrac{na}{nx+b}$

d) $s = \dfrac{t}{x+y}$

e) $u = \dfrac{y}{5-xy}$

f) $\dfrac{a+3}{x} = \dfrac{b-2}{c}$

12. To solve $\dfrac{x-3}{x} = \dfrac{x-3}{x+1}$, Rod reasoned as follows:

"Since the numerators are equal, the denominators must be equal. But this is impossible since x cannot equal $x + 1$. Therefore, there is no solution."

Is Rod correct? Can you find a solution for this equation?

5-3 SOLVING INEQUALITIES

In an *inequality* the greater than sign (>) or the less than sign (<) relate two expressions. We now check to see whether the rules for solving equations apply to inequalities as well.

Consider the inequality: $3 < 7$

Operations on $3 < 7$	Result	True or False
Add 5 to both sides	$8 < 12$	True
Subtract 5 from both sides	$-2 < 2$	True
Multiply both sides by 2	$6 < 14$	True
Multiply both sides by -2	$-6 < -14$	False
Divide both sides by 10	$0.3 < 0.7$	True
Divide both sides by -10	$-0.3 < -0.7$	False

These results suggest that the rules for solving inequalities are the same as those for solving equations with this exception:

> If both sides of an inequality are multiplied or divided by a *negative number*, the inequality sign must be reversed.

Example 1. Solve: $x + 8 \geq 2 - 5x$

Solution.
$$x + 8 \geq 2 - 5x$$
$$x + 5x \geq 2 - 8$$
$$6x \geq -6$$
Divide both sides by 6:
$$x \geq -1$$

In *Example 1*, any number greater than or equal to -1 satisfies the inequality. This can be indicated on a number line as shown below. The solid dot at -1 indicates that -1 is part of the solution. This number line is called the *graph* of the inequality.

Example 2. Solve and graph: $2(x + 3) - 5x < x - 9$

Solution.
$$2(x + 3) - 5x < x - 9$$
$$2x + 6 - 5x < x - 9$$
$$-3x + 6 < x - 9$$
$$-4x < -15$$

Divide both sides by -4, and reverse the inequality sign:
$$\frac{-4x}{-4} > \frac{-15}{-4}$$
$$x > \frac{15}{4}$$
$$x > 3\frac{3}{4}$$

In *Example 2*, any number greater than $3\frac{3}{4}$ satisfies the inequality.

The open dot at $3\frac{3}{4}$ indicates that $3\frac{3}{4}$ is not part of the solution.

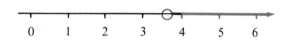

EXERCISES 5-3

1. Solve.
   a) $3x + 7 \le 19$ b) $12 - 3x > 0$ c) $5x - 3 < 15$
   d) $8 + 7x \le 13$ e) $2 - 11x \ge -42$ f) $19 - 6x > 4$

2. Solve and graph.
   a) $3x + 2x - 7 > 8$ b) $7x - 4x + 6 \le 18$ c) $x - 5x + 1 \ge 9$
   d) $3x - x + 5 < 1$ e) $2x - 6x - 3 > 17$ f) $6x - 12x + 5 \le 3$

Ⓑ

3. Solve and graph.
   a) $5x - 2 < 3x - 10$ b) $2x + 7 \ge 8x - 11$ c) $4x - 9 > 7x + 24$
   d) $8 - 3x \le 17 - x$ e) $3x + 19 \ge 8x - 12$ f) $10 - 7x < -4x - 9$

4. Solve and graph.
   a) $2(x + 8) > 4(3 + x)$ b) $9x - 3 \le 3(x - 4)$

   c) $3(1 - x) \le -2(2 - x)$ d) $\frac{1}{2}(2 + 5x) \ge \frac{2}{3}(15 - 3x)$

   e) $11 - 2(3 - x) > 13 - 3(1 - x)$ f) $-9(x + 3) - 9x < -3x - (3 - x) + 8$

Ⓒ

5. Solve and graph.
   a) $2 - \frac{1}{x} < 3$ b) $1 + \frac{1}{x} \ge 2$ c) $\frac{2}{x} + 3 < 4$

5-4 REARRANGING FORMULAS

Every so often countries compete for the America's Cup, which is awarded to the winner of a series of yachting races. The yachts are known as *12-metre* yachts, but this does not mean that they are 12 m long. It means that certain dimensions of the yacht satisfy this formula:

$$\frac{L + 2D - F + \sqrt{A}}{2.37} = 12$$

L is the length of the yacht, in metres.
D is the girth difference, which is related to the shape of the hull.
F is the height from the deck of the yacht to the water.
A is the sail area, in square metres.

A change in any one of these dimensions requires an adjustment in one or more of the others, because the four quantities must always satisfy the formula. The actual dimensions of the yachts are closely guarded secrets.

Example 1.   A typical yacht may have these dimensions:

$$L = 16.6 \qquad D = 0.2 \qquad F = 1.26$$

Find the sail area required for a yacht with these dimensions.

Solution.   Substitute the given values into the formula:

$$\frac{L + 2D - F + \sqrt{A}}{2.37} = 12$$

$$\frac{16.6 + 0.4 - 1.26 + \sqrt{A}}{2.37} = 12$$

$$\frac{15.74 + \sqrt{A}}{2.37} = 12$$

Multiply both sides by 2.37:

$$15.74 + \sqrt{A} = 28.44$$

$$\sqrt{A} = 12.7$$

Square both sides:

$$A = (12.7)^2$$

$$\doteq 161.29$$

Approximately 161.3 m² of sail is required.

To calculate the required sail area for several different values of L, D and F, it would be more efficient to solve the formula once to obtain a formula for A than to repeat the solution each time. A rearranged formula is particularly useful when several equations of the same type are being solved using a calculator or computer.

Example 2.   Solve the above formula for A.

Solution.

$$\frac{L + 2D - F + \sqrt{A}}{2.37} = 12$$

Multiply both sides by 2.37:

$$L + 2D - F + \sqrt{A} = 2.37 \times 12$$

$$= 28.44$$

$$\sqrt{A} = 28.44 - L - 2D + F$$

Square both sides: $A = (28.44 - L - 2D + F)^2$

The formula found in *Example 2* could be used if the designers of a yacht changed its length and decided to adjust the sail area to compensate. They would substitute the values of L, D and F in the right side of this formula, and the result would be the required sail area.

EXERCISES 5-4

(A)

1. Solve each formula for the variable indicated.

   a) $A = lw$, w

   b) $A = \frac{1}{2}bh$, h

   c) $g = a + w$, a

   d) $P = s - e$, s

   e) $v = u + at$, u

   f) $W = R + Ht$, t

2. Solve each formula for the variable indicated.

   a) $V = lwh$, h

   b) $I = prt$, r

   c) $C = 2\pi r$, r

   d) $V = \frac{1}{3}\pi r^2 h$, h

   e) $C = F + Rn$, R

   f) $V = A - Dn$, D

3. The formula: $s = \frac{d}{t}$ is used to find the average speed of an object which has moved a distance d in time t. Solve the formula for d and then for t.

4. The great Swiss mathematician, Leonhard Euler, established a formula relating the number of faces (F), edges (E), and vertices (V) of any polyhedron.

   Solve the formula, $F + V = E + 2$ for each variable.

5. The formula: $\dfrac{L + 2D - F + \sqrt{A}}{2.37} = 12$ is used to classify yachts.

   Solve the formula for each variable.

(B)

6. The formula for the circumference of a circle is $C = \pi d$, where $\pi \doteq 3.14$.
   a) Solve the formula for d.
   b) Canada's largest tree is a Douglas fir on Vancouver Island. Its circumference is 12.54 m. Use the formula to find the diameter of Canada's largest tree.
   c) What are the diameters of trees having a circumference of 8.54 m ? 6.33 m? 1.92 m?

7. A formula for the perimeter of a rectangle is $P = 2(l + w)$.
   a) Solve the formula for w.
   b) What is the width of a rectangle which has a perimeter of 48 cm and a length of 18 cm? 20 cm? 23 cm?

8. The formula: $d = \frac{m}{v}$ defines the density of an object in terms of its mass and its volume. Solve the formula for m and then for v.

9. Use the formula in *Exercise 8* to find the mass of

   a) 55.2 cm³ of aluminum

   b) 82.3 cm³ of mercury

10. Use the formula in *Exercise 8* to find the volume of

   a) 144.0 g of gold

   b) 23.8 g of lead

Element	Density (g/cm³)
Aluminum	2.70
Gold	19.3
Lead	11.3
Mercury	13.6

11. Solve for the variable indicated.

a) $v = u + at$, t

b) $s = ut + \dfrac{1}{2}at^2$, a

c) $\dfrac{1}{f} = \dfrac{1}{p} - \dfrac{1}{q}$, f

d) $C = \dfrac{nE}{nr + R}$, E

e) $L_2 = L_1(1 + at)$, a

f) $A = \dfrac{h}{2}(a + b)$, b

12. Solve for the variable indicated.

a) $s = ut + \dfrac{1}{2}at^2$, u

b) $C = 2\pi(R + x)$, x

c) $\dfrac{1}{R} = \dfrac{1}{r} + \dfrac{1}{s}$, s

d) $F = \dfrac{mn}{d^2}$, n

e) $L = \dfrac{6000}{W + 1}$, W

f) $d = \dfrac{D}{1 + at}$, t

13. The cost, C, in dollars, of producing a school yearbook is given by the formula: $C = 925 + 4n$, where n is the number of yearbooks printed.

a) Solve the formula for n.
b) How many yearbooks can be printed for $2000? $3000? $5000?

14. The total cost, C, in dollars, of renting a car is given by the formula: $C = 28d + 0.15k$, where d is the number of days and k is the number of kilometres driven.

a) Solve the formula for k.
b) How many kilometres can be driven for $200 if the car is rented for 2 days? 3 days? 4 days?

15. The average cost, A, of producing n stereo sets is given by the formula:
$$A = \dfrac{15\,000 + 60n}{n}.$$

a) Solve the formula for n.
b) How many stereo sets would have to be produced for the average cost to be $100? $80? $65? $62.50?

16. Sales personnel are paid a monthly salary, A, given by the formula: $A = 0.03s + 400$, where s represents the total sales in dollars for the month. What must the monthly sales be to earn these salaries?

a) $1000

b) $2000

c) $5000

17. The temperature below the Earth's surface, T, in degrees Celsius, is given by the formula: $T = 10d + 20$, where d is the depth in kilometres.

a) The deepest hole in the Earth is a test drilling hole in the U.S.S.R. At the bottom of the hole the temperature is expected to reach 170°C. Estimate the depth of the drilling.
b) Estimate the depth of a mine in which the temperature is 30°C, 42°C, 54°C.

18. In an electrical circuit, when two conductors are connected in parallel their combined resistance, R, may be found from the formula: $\frac{1}{R} = \frac{1}{r} + \frac{1}{s}$, where r and s are their separate resistances. Express R in terms of r and s.

19. Use the formula given in *Exercise 18* to find R for the values of r indicated if s is 25 Ω (ohms).
    a) 5 Ω   b) 10 Ω   c) 15 Ω   d) 25 Ω

20. A shallow circular mirror has radius, r. If the distance to an object is d, and the distance to its image is i, then $\frac{d}{r} = \frac{r}{i}$. Solve the formula for i.

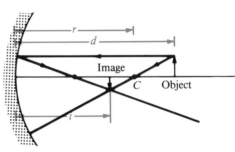

21. A mirror has radius 24 cm. Use the formula given in *Exercise 20* to find i for the values of d indicated.
    a) 4 cm   b) 8 cm   c) 12 cm   d) 16 cm
    e) 20 cm   f) 24 cm   g) 28 cm   h) 32 cm

© ───

22. When three conductors are connected in parallel, their combined resistance, R, is found from the formula: $\frac{1}{R} = \frac{1}{r} + \frac{1}{s} + \frac{1}{t}$, where r, s, and t are their separate resistances. If the combined resistance is 10 Ω and s is 20 Ω, express r in terms of t.

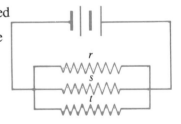

23. Use the formula given in *Exercise 22* to find r when t is
    a) 25 Ω   b) 35 Ω   c) 40 Ω   d) 50 Ω

24. In a right triangle with sides of length a, b, c, the radius of the inscribed circle, r, is given by the formula:
$$r = \frac{ab}{a + b + c}$$

Solve this formula for each of the other three variables.

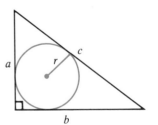

MATHEMATICS AROUND US

Typing Speeds

A person's typing speed, s, in words per minute, is calculated by the formula:

$$s = \frac{w - 10e}{5}$$

where w is the number of words typed in 5 min and e is the number of errors made.

If any two of s, w and e are given, we can use the formula to calculate the third. If this is to be done repeatedly, we can use the chart below instead of doing the arithmetic. A chart like this is called a *nomogram*.

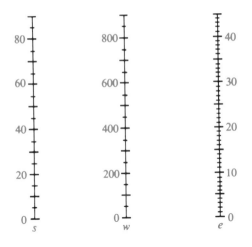

The nomogram is used with a straight-edge. For example, assume you have typed 400 words in 5 min and made 10 errors. Place a straight-edge so that it passes through 400 on the w scale and 10 on the e scale. You will find that it passes through 60 on the s scale, indicating that the typing speed is 60 words/min.

For any position of the straight-edge, values of s, w, and e which satisfy the equation can be read from the scales. Therefore, if any two of s, w and e are given, we can use the nomogram to find the third.

QUESTIONS

1. Use the nomogram to estimate the typing speed for these results in 5 min.
   a) 400 words, 15 errors
   b) 200 words, 5 errors

2. If you make 5 errors, how many words must you type in 5 min to have a typing speed of 50 words/min? 60 words/min?

3. Tony typed 400 words in 5 min and made 10 errors. If Yoko makes no errors, how many words would she have to type in 5 min to have the same typing speed as Tony?

4. What is the penalty for an error? Explain, using both the nomogram and the above formula.

5-5 TRANSLATING WORDS INTO SYMBOLS

Equations are used to solve problems. Before any equation can be written, the facts of the problem must be translated into algebraic symbols. Examine these verbal expressions and their algebraic equivalents.

Verbal	Algebraic
A certain number	x
6 more than the number	$x + 6$
3 times the number	$3x$
5 less than 4 times the number	$4x - 5$
Keith's present age	a
His age 3 years ago	$a - 3$
His age 2 years from now	$a + 2$

When two numbers are involved in a problem, we can use a variable to represent one of them. Then we can use the relation between the numbers to write an expression for the other number.

Verbal	Algebraic
Two consecutive integers	x and $x + 1$
Two consecutive even integers	x and $x + 2$
The sum of two numbers is 50.	n and $50 - n$
A certain number of quarters and their value in cents	x and $25x$

EXERCISES 5-5

Ⓐ

1. Let one number be represented by x. Translate the following into algebra.
   a) Six times the number
   b) Ten less than the number
   c) Four more than double the number
   d) One less than triple the number

2. Let Colleen's present age be x. Translate the following into algebra.
   a) Her age two years from now
   b) Her age five years ago
   c) Double her age three years ago
   d) One-half her age ten years from now

Ⓑ

Translate each verbal expression into algebra.

3. a) A certain number   b) Five more than the number

    c) Four less than the number   d) Double the number

4. a) A certain number   b) Two less than triple the number

    c) One more than double the number   d) The number increased by eight

5. a) A certain number of nickels   b) The value of the nickels, in cents

6. a) A certain number of $10 bills   b) The value of the bills, in dollars

7. a) A certain number of 34¢ stamps

    b) The value of the stamps, in cents

    c) The value of the stamps in dollars

8. The sum of two consecutive numbers

9. The sum of three consecutive even numbers

10. The sum of the squares of two consecutive numbers

11. In each of the following, choose a variable to represent one quantity, and express the other in terms of the first.

    a) The sum of two numbers is 47.

    b) The difference of two numbers is 12.

    c) One number exceeds another number by 3.

    d) Frank weighs 5 kg more than Abdul.

    e) Mary weighs 2 kg less than Renée.

    f) A mother is four times as old as her daughter.

    g) Last year Tom was twice as old as Aziza.

    h) The perimeter of a rectangle which has a length five times the width.

    i) The perimeter of a rectangle which has a length 10 cm greater than the width.

    j) Six times the width of a rectangle exceeds four times the length by 10 cm.

5-6 SOLVING PROBLEMS USING EQUATIONS

Many problems can be solved using an equation. To do this, the information in the problem must be translated into algebra so that an equation can be written. When the equation has been solved, the problem can be answered.

Example 1. Find two consecutive numbers such that the sum of two times the smaller and three times the larger is 113.

Solution. Let the numbers be x and $x + 1$.
Two times the smaller number is $2x$.
Three times the larger number is $3(x + 1)$.

Since the sum is 113:
$$2x + 3(x + 1) = 113$$
$$2x + 3x + 3 = 113$$
$$5x = 110$$
$$x = 22$$

The numbers are 22 and 23.

Check. $2(22) + 3(23) = 44 + 69$, or 113
The solution is correct.

Example 2. Sue is six years older than Josie. Four years ago she was twice as old as Josie. How old is Josie now?

Solution. Let x represent Josie's age now. Organize the information in a table:

Age	Josie	Sue
Now	x	$x + 6$
Four years ago	$x - 4$	$x + 2$

Since Sue's age four years ago was twice Josie's age:
$$x + 2 = 2(x - 4)$$
$$x + 2 = 2x - 8$$
$$x - 2x = -8 - 2$$
$$-x = -10$$
$$x = 10$$

Josie is now 10 years old.

Check. Sue is now 16. Four years ago Sue was 12 and Josie was 6.
The solution is correct.

Example 3. How much antifreeze must be added to 5 L of water to make a solution that is 40% antifreeze?

Solution. Let the volume of antifreeze added be x L:

$$\frac{\text{Volume of antifreeze}}{\text{Total volume}} = \frac{40}{100}$$

$$\frac{x}{x+5} = \frac{40}{100}$$

$$100x = 40x + 200$$

$$60x = 200$$

$$x = \frac{10}{3}$$

About 3.3 L of antifreeze must be added.

Check. Volume of solution: $(5 + 3.3) \text{ L} = 8.3 \text{ L}$

Percent of antifreeze: $\frac{3.3}{8.3} \times 100\% \doteq 40\%$

The solution is correct.

Note that the solution should be checked in the original problem. Substituting in the equation does not prove that the equation is correct.

EXERCISES 5-6

(A)

1. Find two consecutive integers such that the sum of three times the smaller and five times the larger is 93.

2. Find two consecutive integers such that the sum of twice the first and three times the second is 38.

3. Find two consecutive integers such that five times the first is 6 more than four times the second.

4. Find two consecutive even integers such that the sum of double the first and triple the second is 116.

5. Alice is 6 years older than Soula. In two years she will be twice as old as Soula. How old is Soula?

6. Lorenzo is 12 years older than Steve. Last year he was twice as old as Steve. How old are they now?

Ⓑ

7. A mother is three times as old as her son. Six years ago she was five times as old as her son. How old are mother and son now?

8. Alfred is four times as old as his brother. Four years from now he will be twice as old as his brother. How old are they now?

9. Two numbers have a sum of 17. Four times the larger number is 2 less than 6 times the smaller. Find the numbers.

10. Two numbers have a difference of 5. Five times the smaller number is 3 more than three times the larger. Find the numbers.

11. Divide 12 into two parts such that when one part is tripled and the other part is multiplied by 5, the sum is 44.

12. Divide 20 into two parts such that when one part is divided by 3 and the other by 4, the sum of the quotients is 6.

13. Tom weighs 15 kg more than Gunesh. Together they weigh 95 kg. How much does each weigh?

14. Wendy and Mei Lan have a total mass of 90 kg. Five times Wendy's mass is the same as four times Mei Lan's mass. How heavy is each of the girls?

15. Arlene and Shaun have a total mass of 105 kg. Four times Arlene's mass is the same as three times Shaun's mass. How heavy is each person?

16. Trinika weighs 7 kg less than Amanda. Together they weigh 101 kg. How much does each weigh?

17. Find two consecutive even integers such that the sum of one-third of the smaller and one-quarter of the larger is 11.

18. Find three consecutive odd integers such that triple the first is 9 more than double the third.

19. Three sisters have a total age of 68 years. The oldest is seven years older than the youngest and three years older than the second sister. Find their ages.

20. A man is five times as old as his daughter. The man's son is 2 years older than his sister. In 10 years the sum of their three ages will be 81. How old are they now?

21. Find the length and width of a rectangle that has a perimeter of
    a) 48 cm and a length that is twice the width
    b) 32 cm and a length that is 2 cm less than twice the width

22. A rectangular photograph measuring 25 cm by 20 cm is centred in a frame with a length-to-width ratio of 6 : 5. What is the width of the border?

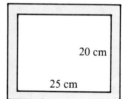

20 cm

25 cm

23. Two strips of equal width are cut from a rectangular piece of card measuring 15 cm by 12 cm, as shown. If the length-to-width ratio of the remaining rectangle is 4 : 3, find the width of the strips.

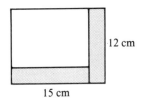

12 cm

15 cm

24. Brenda has 95¢ in nickels and dimes. There are 13 coins altogether. How many of each does she have?

25. Mike has $2.75 in dimes and quarters. There are 14 coins altogether. How many of each does he have?

26. Rouel has a pocketful of nickels, dimes and quarters. He has 3 fewer nickels than dimes and 3 more quarters than dimes. If the coins are worth a total of $4.20, how many of each kind does he have?

27. How much antifreeze should be added to 4 L of water to make a solution that is 60% antifreeze?

28. How much antifreeze should be added to 3 L of water to make a solution that is 80% antifreeze?

29. How much water should be added to 5 L of antifreeze to make a solution that is 80% antifreeze?

30. How much water should be added to 6 L of antifreeze to make a solution that is 70% antifreeze?

31. How much alcohol should be added to 1 L of a 20% solution of alcohol to increase its strength to 50%?

©

32. Find four consecutive even numbers such that if the first is increased by 2, the second decreased by 2, the third multiplied by 2, and the fourth divided by 2, the sum of the four resulting numbers is 58.

33. Find four consecutive odd numbers such that if the first is increased by 2, the second decreased by 3, the third multiplied by 4, and the fourth divided by 5, the sum of the four resulting numbers is 136.

34. In a collection of nickels, dimes and quarters, there are 10 more dimes than nickels, and 5 more quarters than nickels. If there are 45 coins, what is their total value?

35. When three times a number is decreased by 8, the result is equivalent to reducing four times the number by 2. What is the number?

36. The denominator of a fraction exceeds the numerator by 3. If 5 is added to both numerator and denominator, the result is equivalent to $\frac{3}{4}$. Find the fraction.

MATHEMATICS AROUND US

The Line of Best Fit—Speed Records

World Land-Speed Records			
Driver	**Vehicle**	**Year**	**Speed (km/h)**
H. Seagrave	Sunbeam	1927	327.96
M. Campbell	Campbell Special	1935	484.61
A. Arfons	Green Monster	1965	863.73
S. Barrett	Budweiser Rocket	1979	1190.38

Some people have always wanted to drive cars and boats as fast as possible. In 1979 Stan Barrett broke the sound barrier with his rocket-engined car. The table and graph show a selection of the world land-speed records since 1927. Each entry in the table corresponds to a point plotted on the graph.

The plotted points appear to lie very close to a straight line. We draw a line which is as close as possible to the points. This is called the *line of best fit*. We can use it to estimate the speed record at times not shown in the table.

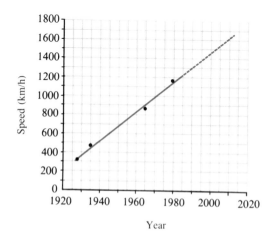

QUESTIONS

1. In 1947, J. Cobb set a new land-speed record in *Railton*. Use the graph to estimate the record at that time.

2. The first person to break the 1000 km/h barrier was G. Gabelich in *The Blue Flame*. Estimate the year he did this.

3. Predict what the world land-speed record might be in 1995.

4. Draw a graph showing the world water-speed records given below.

5. In 1964, D. Campbell set a new water-speed record in *Bluebird*. Use the graph to estimate the record at that time.

6. Predict what the world water-speed record might be in 1995.

In Questions 1 and 2 you estimated the value of a variable *between* values that are known. This is called *interpolating*.	In Question 3 you estimated the value of a variable *beyond* values that are known. This is called *extrapolating*.

7. Did you interpolate or extrapolate in Question 5?

8. Did you interpolate or extrapolate in Question 6?

World Water-Speed Records			
Driver	**Boat**	**Year**	**Speed (km/h)**
G. Wood	Miss America IX	1928	149.44
M. Campbell	Bluebird	1937	208.50
S. Sayres	Slo-Mo-Shun IV	1952	287.26
K. Warby	Spirit of Australia	1978	514.39

5-7 GRAPHING LINEAR EQUATIONS IN TWO VARIABLES

The cost, C, in dollars, of renting a room for a party is given by the formula: $C = 100 + 5n$, where n is the number of people in attendance. To find the cost for 20 people, substitute 20 for n in the formula:

$$C = 100 + 5n$$
$$= 100 + 5(20)$$
$$= 100 + 100$$
$$= 200$$

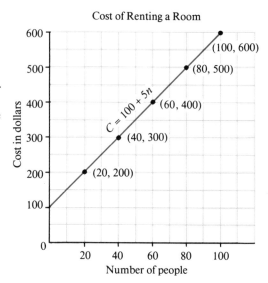

Cost of Renting a Room

For 20 people, it would cost $200 to rent the room. In the same way we can find the cost for other numbers of people. Some of these are shown in the table below.

Number of people, (n)	Cost ($) ($C$)
20	200
40	300
60	400
80	500
100	600

Using these values, we can plot points on a grid and join them with a line. The result is a graph showing the cost for different numbers of people.

The table and the graph represent ordered pairs which relate the cost to the number of people. The set of ordered pairs is called a *relation*. A relation can be represented in different ways:

A table of values		A graph		An equation

To draw the graph of a relation, follow these steps:
Step 1.   Make a table of values, using any suitable values for the variables.
Step 2.   Plot the points on a grid. If they appear to lie on a line, draw a line through them.

Example 1.   Draw the graph of the relation $y = 8 - 2x$.

Solution.   Make a table of values and plot the ordered pairs, (x, y) on a grid.

x	y
-2	12
0	8
2	4
4	0
6	-4
8	-8

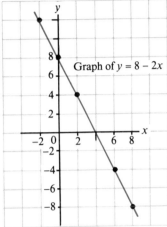

Graph of $y = 8 - 2x$

In *Example 1*, the equation was solved for y. To graph an equation such as $3x - 2y = 6$, it is useful to solve the equation for y before making the table of values.

Example 2.   Draw the graph of $3x - 2y - 6 = 0$.

Solution.   Solve the equation for y:
$$-2y = 6 - 3x$$
$$y = -3 + \frac{3x}{2}$$

Make a table of values by choosing suitable values of x to calculate y. Then plot the ordered pairs on a grid.

x	y
0	-3
2	0
4	3
6	6

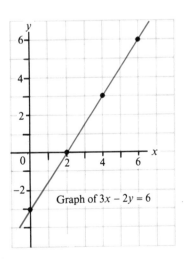

Graph of $3x - 2y = 6$

In *Examples 1, and 2*, the equations are called *linear equations in x and y*, since their graphs are straight lines. In general, any equation which can be written in the form $Ax + By + C = 0$ is a linear equation.

EXERCISES 5-7

Ⓐ

1. Complete the tables of values for the given equations.

a) $y = 2x + 3$

x	y
0	▨
▨	0
▨	▨
▨	▨

b) $y = 5 - 3x$

x	y
0	▨
▨	0
▨	▨
▨	▨

c) $4x + y = 12$

x	y
0	▨
▨	0
▨	▨
▨	▨

d) $2x - 3y = 12$

x	y
0	▨
▨	0
▨	▨
▨	▨

e) $5x + 2y = 20$

x	y
0	▨
▨	0
▨	▨
▨	▨

f) $3x - 2y = 15$

x	y
0	▨
▨	0
▨	▨
▨	▨

2. For each equation make a table of values and draw a graph.
   a) $y = 2x - 4$ b) $y = 3 - 2x$ c) $x + y = 6$

   d) $3x + y = 9$ e) $x - 2y = -10$ f) $4x - 3y = 24$

3. The cost, C, in cents, of making n photocopies is given by the formula: $C = 70 + 6n$.
   a) Make a table of values showing the cost of up to 100 copies.

   b) Draw the graph of the relation.

   c) Use the graph to estimate the cost of 75 copies.

   d) Use the graph to estimate how many copies can be made for $3.50.

Ⓑ

4. The cost, C, in dollars, for a school hockey team to play in a tournament is given by the formula: $C = 300 + 20n$, where n is the number of players.

   a) Make a table of values for values of n up to 20.

   b) Draw the graph of the relation.

   c) Use the graph to estimate how many players could be sent for $550.

5. The time, t, in seconds, it takes to pump v litres of gasoline is given by the formula: $t = 1.5v$.

   a) Make a table of values showing the time it takes to pump up to 100 L of gasoline.

   b) Draw the graph of the relation.

   c) Use the graph to estimate the time it takes to fill a 57 L tank.

   d) Use the graph to estimate the volume filled in 53 s.

6. Draw the graph of each equation.

   a) $2x - y = 10$ b) $4x - y = -8$ c) $-3x + y = 15$

   d) $6x + y = 18$ e) $x + 3y = 0$ f) $2x = 5y$

7. Graph.

   a) $x + 2y = 7$ b) $3x - y = 10$ c) $3x + 2y = -15$

   d) $5x - 3y = 18$ e) $2x + 4y = 9$ f) $5x + 7y = 1$

8. Two students discussed their methods for graphing linear equations. Their discussion went as follows:

   Sean: "When I graph these equations, I always find the two points which have 0 as one coordinate, because they are always the easiest points to find."

   Naomi: "That method only works for certain equations. I can show you some equations that would be hard to graph using your method."

   Give some examples of the equations Naomi is thinking about.

9. Find all the two-digit numbers that are multiples of the sum of their digits. Illustrate your results graphically.

INVESTIGATE

In the equations $x + 3y = 5$ and $2x - y = -4$, the coefficients form patterns:

 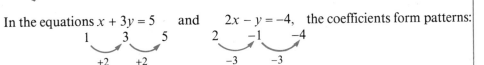

   a) Write several other equations like these.

   b) Graph the equations on the same grid. What do you notice?

   c) Explain why this happens.

THE MATHEMATICAL MIND

Diophantine Equations

People have always been interested in riddles and puzzles. The following example is typical of the arithmetic puzzles that are part of the folklore of times gone by.

Twenty measures of grain are distributed among some people so that each adult receives 3 measures and each child receives 2 measures. How many adults and children are there?

If there are x adults and y children, this puzzle leads to the equation:

$$3x + 2y = 20$$
$$2y = 20 - 3x$$
$$y = \frac{20 - 3x}{2}$$

Since y must be a whole number, $20 - 3x$ is divisible by 2. Therefore, the only possible values for x are 0, 2, 4, and 6. The puzzle has *four* answers.

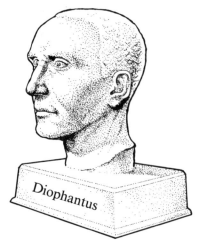

Diophantus

Adults	Children
0	10
2	7
4	4
6	1

When the only valid solutions of an equation are integers, the equation is called a *diophantine equation*, after the Greek mathematician Diophantus of Alexandria (c. A.D. 250). His book, *Arithmetica*, is a collection of problems, many of which have more than one answer.

1. Solve and graph the whole numbers solutions to each diophantine equation.
   a) $4x + y = 17$
   b) $3x + 2y = 12$
   c) $2x + 5y = 9$

2. Fay has $1.70 in quarters and dimes. How many of each could she have?

3. Ivor has $1.70 in quarters and nickels. How many of each could he have?

4. Certain facts about Diophantus' life are found in a collection of problems dated about A.D. 500.

   "His boyhood lasted $\frac{1}{6}$ of his life; his beard grew after $\frac{1}{12}$ more; he married after $\frac{1}{7}$ more; his son was born 5 years later. The son lived to half his father's (final) age, and the father died 4 years after the son."

   How old was Diophantus when he died?

 COMPUTER POWER

Diophantine Equations

The problem of finding the solutions of a diophantine equation in two variables is ideally suited to a computer. The program below can be used to find integral solutions of equations of the form:
$$Ax + By = C$$
To solve this equation, we solve for y: $By = C - Ax$
$$y = \frac{C - Ax}{B}, (B \neq 0)$$

The computer first checks if the greatest common factor of A and B is a factor of C. If not, the message NO SOLUTION IN INTEGERS is printed. Otherwise, the computer proceeds by systematic trial using values of x from -10 to $+10$. If the expression on the right side of the equation is a whole number, the computer prints a solution.

```
100 REM *** DIOPHANTINE EQUATIONS ***
110 PRINT "ENTER COEFFICIENTS (SEPARATED BY
    COMMAS):"
120 INPUT A,B,C
130 P=A:Q=B
140 R=P-INT(P/Q)*Q
150 IF R<>0 THEN P=Q: Q=R: GOTO 140
160 FOR X=-10 TO 10
170 Y=(C-A*X)/B
180   IF Y=INT(Y) THEN PRINT X,Y
190 NEXT X
200 IF C/Q<>INT(C/Q) THEN PRINT "NO SOLUTION IN
    INTEGERS"
210 END
```

1. Use the program to find solutions to the following diophantine equations.

   a) $3x + 2y = 20$ b) $x - 3y = 2$ c) $4x - 7y = 21$

2. A store sells VCRs for $495 and stereos for $330. If a day's receipts were $3960, how many of each could have been sold?

3. Give an example to illustrate why there is no solution in integers if the greatest common factor of A and B is not a factor of C.

5-8 GRAPHING LINEAR INEQUALITIES

The graph shows the line defined by the equation $y = x$. The y-coordinate of every point on this line is equal to the x-coordinate.

x	y
−3	−3
0	0
4	4

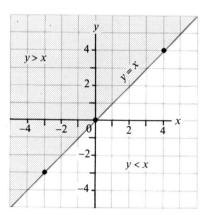

In the region *above* the line, the y-coordinate of every point is *greater* than the x-coordinate. This region is the graph of the inequality $y > x$.

In the region *below* the line, the y-coordinate of every point is *less* than the x-coordinate. This region is the graph of the inequality $y < x$.

In general, the graph of any linear equation is a straight line which divides the plane into two *half-planes*. The half-planes are the graphs of the corresponding inequalities.

To draw the graph of an inequality, follow these steps:
Step 1. Draw the graph of the corresponding equation.
Step 2. Find the coordinates of any point which satisfies the inequality.
Step 3. Plot the point on the graph. The half-plane in which the point is located is the graph of the inequality.

Example 1. Graph the inequality: $4x - 5y < 20$

Solution.   *Step 1.*
The corresponding equation is
$4x - 5y = 20$.
Make a table of values and plot the
ordered pairs (x, y) on a grid.

x	y
0	−4
5	0

Step 2.
A point which satisfies the inequality is
(0, 0), since 4(0) − 5(0) = 0, which is
less than 20.

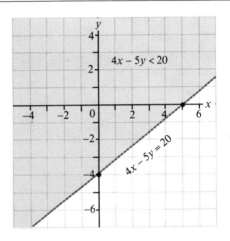

Step 3.
The point (0, 0) is the origin. Since it
lies in the region above the line, this
region is the graph of the inequality
$4x - 5y < 20$.

In *Example 1*, the line defined by $4x - 5y = 20$ is shown as a broken line because it is not part of the region defined by the inequality
$4x - 5y < 20$.

Example 2.   A farmer is willing to use up to 80 ha of land to plant two crops, corn and
wheat. Draw a graph showing the number of hectares of each crop that
could be planted.

Solution.   Let c and w represent respectively the number of hectares of corn and
wheat that the farmer could plant. Since *up to* 80 ha of land can be
planted, $c + w \le 80$.

Step 1.
The corresponding equation is
$c + w = 80$. The graph of this
equation is shown.

c	w
0	80
80	0

Steps 2 and 3.
A point which satisfies the
inequality is (10, 10). Since
(10, 10) lies in the region below
the line, this region is the graph
of the inequality $c + w \le 80$.

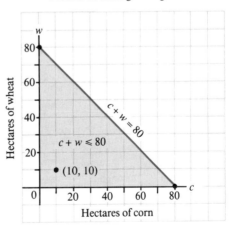

Farmer's Planting Arrangement

In *Example 2*, the line defined by $c + w = 80$ is shown as a solid
line because it is part of the region defined by the inequality $c + w \le 80$.
Only points in the first quadrant are shown, because the number of hectares of corn and wheat cannot be negative.

EXERCISES 5-8

Ⓐ

1. State the coordinates of any point which satisfies each inequality.
   a) $2x + y < 7$ b) $3x - 2y > 12$ c) $x - 4y \leq 8$
   d) $5x + 3y > 9$ e) $2x + 3y \geq 15$ f) $3x + 4y \leq 18$

2. State the coordinates of any point on the graph which satisfies the inequality and whether it lies in the region above or below the line.
   a) $x - 2y > -4$

   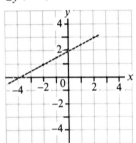

   b) $x + 2y < 4$

   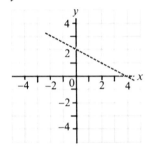

   c) $x - y < -3$

   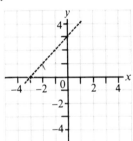

   d) $x + 3y + 3 > 0$

   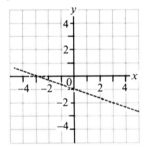

3. Write the inequality that represents the shaded region.

   a)

   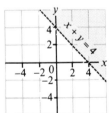

   b)

   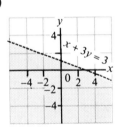

   c)

   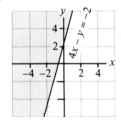

   d)

   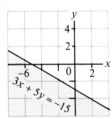

   e)

   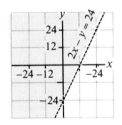

   f)

   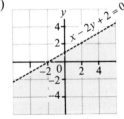

Ⓑ

4. Graph the inequality.
   a) $x + y < 5$ b) $x + y \geq 2$ c) $x - y \leq -3$

   d) $x + 2y < 4$ e) $3x - 2y \geq -6$ f) $y \geq x + 8$

   g) $y \leq -2x + 8$ h) $5x + 2y > -10$ i) $2x - 7y \geq 14$

5. A company makes motorcycles and bicycles. In any given week, a total of up to 400 vehicles can be made. Draw a graph showing the number of motorcycles and bicycles that could be made in one week.

6. Teri plans to spend up to 12 h reviewing Science and French in preparation for examinations. Draw a graph showing how much time she could spend studying each subject.

7. Graph the inequality.
   a) $x - 2y \geq 4$ b) $3x - 2y \leq 6$ c) $4x - y < -4$
   d) $2x + y > -4$ e) $y \geq 3x + 6$ f) $3x - 4y < 12$
   g) $5x + 2y > 10$ h) $4x - 5y > 20$ i) $4x - 6y \geq 12$

Ⓒ

8. Fiona plans to start a physical fitness program which requires that she jog and do calisthenics up to a maximum of 10 h each week. She must spend twice as much time jogging as she does doing calisthenics. Draw a graph showing the amount of time she can give to each activity.

9. Use the information in the news item to draw a graph showing the ages at which Chinese men and women may marry.

> In China, Women Must Be 20 To Marry
>
> Peking. A Chinese law sets minimum legal ages for marrying. The minimum legal age is 22 for men and 20 for women. In addition, couples are urged not to marry until the ages of the bride and groom total more than 52.

5-9 GRAPHING NON-LINEAR RELATIONS

As a general rule, light does not penetrate much below 100 m into the ocean. The table below shows the percent of surface light present at various depths.

Using these values, we can plot points on a grid. Since the points appear to lie on a curve, we draw a smooth curve through them.

Depth (m)	% of Surface Light Present
0	100
20	63
40	40
60	25
80	16
100	10

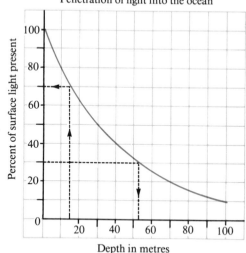

We can use the graph to interpolate between the values given in the table.

Example 1. Use the graph to estimate the
  a) percent of surface light present at a depth of 15 m
  b) depth at which 30% of the surface light is present

Solution.   a) The graph shows that at a depth of 15 m, approximately 70% of the surface light is present.

  b) The graph shows that 30% of the surface light is present at a depth of approximately 53 m.

In *Example 1*, the relation between percent of light present and depth was represented by a table of values and a graph. Since the graph is not a straight line, the relation is called *non-linear*. A non-linear relation can also be represented by an equation. The equation cannot be expressed in the form $Ax + By + C = 0$.

Example 2. Draw the graph of the relation $y = \dfrac{5}{x^2 + 1}$, using values of x between -3 and $+3$.

Solution. Use several values of x between -3 and $+3$ to construct a table:

x	y
0	5.0
±0.5	4.0
±1.0	2.5
±1.5	1.5
±2.0	1.0
±2.5	0.7
±3.0	0.5

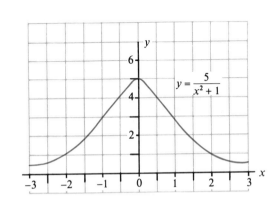

EXERCISES 5-9

Ⓐ

1. When calculating drug dosages, doctors sometimes need to estimate the total area of a patient's skin. The graph shows how this area is related to a person's mass.

   a) Estimate the skin area of a 50 kg person; a 90 kg person.

   b) Estimate the mass of a person who has a skin area of 1 m²; 2 m².

   c) Is the skin area of an 80 kg person double that of a 40 kg person?

   d) Estimate the mass of a person who has double the skin area of a 40 kg person.

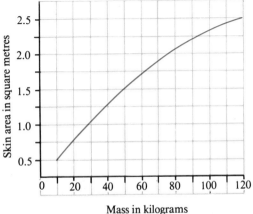

Graph of skin area against mass

2. Lynn and Lisa take a ride on a Ferris wheel. The graph shows how their height above the ground varies during the first 40 s of the ride.

Graph of height against time on a Ferris wheel

a) What is their height after 5 s? after 30 s?
b) When is their height 25 m?
c) How long does it take the Ferris wheel to make one rotation?

3. Data relating to people's forgetfulness are given in the table.

a) Show this information on a graph.
b) Use the graph to estimate after how many days a person might forget 25% of information previously known.
c) Use the graph to estimate how much a person might forget after 90 days.

Number of days	Percent forgotten
1	14
5	29
15	39
30	44
60	46

Ⓑ

4. Complete the tables of values and draw graphs for each of the given relations.

a) $y = \sqrt{x}$

x	y
0	▨
1	▨
4	▨
9	▨
16	▨
25	▨

b) $y = 2^x$

x	y
0	▨
1	▨
2	▨
3	▨
4	▨
5	▨

c) $y = \dfrac{24}{x}$

x	y
1	▨
2	▨
3	▨
4	▨
6	▨
8	▨

5. Draw a graph of each of the following relations using a table of values. Use values of x between -3 and $+3$.

a) $y = x^2$

b) $y = x^3$

c) $y = \dfrac{10}{x^2 + 5}$

6. In t seconds, an object falls from rest, a distance of h metres. The relation between h and t is: $t = 0.45\sqrt{h}$.

   a) Make a table of values using values of h between 0 and 400 and graph the relation.

   b) Estimate how long a pebble takes to fall 70 m.

   c) Estimate how far the pebble fell if it took 2.7 s to reach the ground.

7. If $1250 is invested at 12% per annum compound interest, the amount, A, to which it grows after n years is given by: $A = 1250(1.12)^n$.
   a) Make a table of values using values of n from 0 to 10.

   b) Graph the relation.

   c) Find the amount after four years.

   d) Estimate how long it takes for the investment to double in value.

8. The average cost, A, of producing n records is given by the formula: $A = \dfrac{10\ 000 + 2n}{n}$.

   a) Make a table of values using reasonable values of n and graph the relation.

   b) Estimate how many records would have to be produced for the average cost to be $3.50; $2.75.

9. A square box, x cm deep, is to be made from a piece of cardboard, 50 cm square, by cutting equal squares from the corners and turning up the sides.
   a) Find an expression for the volume, V, of the box.
   b) Draw a graph of this relation for reasonable values of x.
   c) For what value of x will the volume be greatest?

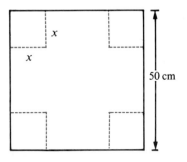

10. The cost per hour, C, in dollars, of operating a river steamer is given by the formula: $C = \dfrac{100v^2}{v - 4}$, where v is the steamer's speed, in knots, relative to the water.

    a) Graph this relation for values of v from 4.5 to 10 knots.

    b) Find the speed of the steamer which results in the lowest value of C.

11. For each equation, make a table of values and draw the graph.
    a) $y = |x|$
    b) $y = |x| + 5$
    c) $|x| + |y| = 5$
    d) $x^2 + y^2 = 25$
    e) $x^2 - y^2 = 0$
    f) $(x + 5)(y - 5) = 0$

Work Backwards

The game of Nim is one of the oldest mathematical games. In one version of Nim, 12 pennies are arranged in three horizontal rows as shown. Players take turns removing one or more pennies according to the following rule. On any turn, the pennies removed must come from the same horizontal row. The person who takes the last penny wins.

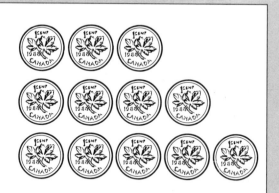

Can you find a winning strategy for this game? Does it matter who goes first?

Understand the problem

* How many pennies can you take on any move?
* How is the winner determined?

Think of a strategy

* Try working backwards to determine positions that would guarantee a win.

Carry out the strategy

* Could you win if you leave the pennies like this after one of your turns?

a) ●
   ●

b) ● ●
   ● ●

c) ● ● ●
   ● ● ●

d) ● ● ● ●
   ● ● ● ●

e) ●
   ●
   ● ●

f) ●
   ● ●
   ● ● ●

g) ●
   ● ● ●
   ● ● ● ●

h) ●
   ● ● ● ●
   ● ● ● ● ●

* Which player can arrange to leave one of the above positions, the first player, or the second?
* What is the winning strategy for that player?

Look back

* Suppose the rules are changed so that the player who takes the last penny loses. Can you find a winning strategy for one of the players?
* Investigate similar games with a different number of pennies, or a different number of rows.

Solve each problem

1. Sara keyed a number into her calculator. Then she pressed these keys.

$$\boxed{+}\ \boxed{2}\ \boxed{5}\ \boxed{=}\ \boxed{\times}\ \boxed{2}\ \boxed{=}\ \boxed{\sqrt{}}\ \boxed{+}\ \boxed{2}\ \boxed{=}$$

   The final display showed 18. What number did Sara key into her calculator?

2. When asked for his height, Tony replied, "If I double my height in centimetres and add 50, then divide the result by 2, take the positive square root, then subtract 10 and take the positive square root again, the result is 2." What is Tony's height?

3. Find the number which is 5 less than one-half of one-third of one-quarter of 960.

4. Guiseppe has a 4 L pail and a 9 L pail. How can he use them to obtain exactly 6 L of water? There are no markings on either pail.

5. Donna deposited $10 in her bank account, and then withdrew half the balance. The next day she deposited $10 and then withdrew half the balance. On the third day she deposited $10 again, and withdrew half the balance. The balance was then $100.
   a) What was the balance at the beginning?
   b) How much money did Donna withdraw in all?

6. Solve by working backwards.
   a) $5(3x + 2) = 100$
   b) $\dfrac{3(x - 1) + 1}{2} = 5$
   c) $\sqrt{x + 3} = 4$

   d) $\sqrt{2x - 1} = 3$
   e) $(x - 2)^2 = 9$
   f) $\left(\dfrac{x + 1}{4}\right)^2 = 1$

7. Yin entered an orchard through three gates, and took a certain number of apples. When he left the orchard he gave the first guard half the apples that he had, and one apple more. To the second guard he gave half his remaining apples, and one apple more. He did the same to the third guard, and left the orchard with one apple. How many apples did Yin gather in the orchard?

8. Play this game with a friend. The game is played on a 3 × 3 grid. One player marks X's on the grid, the other marks O's, according to the following rule. On each turn, a player can place as many marks as desired in any adjacent unoccupied squares in the same row, column, or diagonal. The player who fills in the last square wins.
   a) Can you find a winning strategy for the player who goes first?
   b) If the player who fills in the last square loses, can you find a winning strategy?

5-10 SOLVING QUADRATIC EQUATIONS

In the equations you have studied up until now, the variable has never been squared. Examples of equations in which the variable is squared are:

$$x^2 + 3x - 28 = 0 \qquad 3x^2 + 10x - 8 = 0 \qquad 4x^2 = 25$$

These are called *quadratic equations*.

Quadratic equations such as $4x^2 = 25$, in which there is no first-degree term, can be solved by isolating the variable and taking the square root of both sides.

Example 1. Solve: a) $4x^2 = 25$ b) $9a^2 - 2 = 8$

Solution.   a) $4x^2 = 25$ b) $9a^2 - 2 = 8$

$$x^2 = \frac{25}{4}$$

$$9a^2 = 10$$

$$a^2 = \frac{10}{9}$$

$$x = \pm\frac{5}{2}$$

$$a = \pm\frac{\sqrt{10}}{3}$$

Many quadratic equations have first-degree terms, and some of these can be solved by factoring. The solution of a quadratic equation by factoring depends on the following important property:

If $(A)(B) = 0$, then either $A = 0$, or $B = 0$, or both.

Example 2. Solve and check.

a) $x^2 - x - 6 = 0$ b) $x^2 + 10x + 25 = 0$

Solution.   a) $x^2 - x - 6 = 0$ b) $x^2 + 10x + 25 = 0$

Factor: $(x - 3)(x + 2) = 0$ Factor: $(x + 5)(x + 5) = 0$

Either $x - 3 = 0$ or $x + 2 = 0$ That is, $x + 5 = 0$

$x = 3$ or $x = -2$ $x = -5$

Check.   a) If $x = 3$,   If $x = -2$, b)   If $x = -5$,
$$\begin{array}{ll} x^2 - x - 6 & x^2 - x - 6 \\ = (3)^2 - (3) - 6 & = (-2)^2 - (-2) - 6 \\ = 9 - 3 - 6 & = 4 + 2 - 6 \\ = 0 & = 0 \end{array}$$

$$\begin{array}{l} x^2 + 10x + 25 \\ (-5)^2 + 10(-5) + 25 \\ = 25 - 50 + 25 \\ = 0 \end{array}$$

Both solutions are correct. The solution is correct.

When an object is projected into the air, its speed changes. The speed decreases as the object goes up, then increases as the object falls back to the ground. Problems involving this situation often involve quadratic equations. The actual equation depends on the initial speed.

Example 3. If a football is kicked with a vertical speed of 20 m/s, its height, h, in metres after t seconds is given by the formula:
$$h = 20t - 5t^2$$
How long after the kick is the football at a height of 15 m?

Solution. Substitute 15 for h in the formula:
$$15 = 20t - 5t^2$$
$$5t^2 - 20t + 15 = 0$$
$$t^2 - 4t + 3 = 0$$
$$(t - 1)(t - 3) = 0$$
$$\text{Either } t - 1 = 0 \text{ or } t - 3 = 0$$
$$t = 1 \qquad\qquad t = 3$$
The football is at a height of 15 m on the way up, 1 s after the kick, and on the way down 3 s after the kick.

Equations involving rational expressions can lead to quadratic equations. Be sure to determine the value(s) of the variable for which each expression is not defined.

Example 4. Solve: a) $x + \dfrac{18}{x + 7} = 4$ b) $\dfrac{5}{x - 1} - \dfrac{12}{x^2 - 1} = 1$

Solution. a) $x + \dfrac{18}{x + 7} = 4$

The equation is not defined when $x + 7 = 0$, or $x = -7$.
Assume that $x \ne -7$.

Multiply both sides by $(x + 7)$:
$$x(x + 7) + 18 = 4(x + 7)$$
$$x^2 + 7x + 18 = 4x + 28$$
$$x^2 + 3x - 10 = 0$$
$$(x + 5)(x - 2) = 0$$

Therefore, $x + 5 = 0$ or $x - 2 = 0$
$$x = -5 \qquad\qquad x = 2$$

b) $\dfrac{5}{x-1} - \dfrac{12}{x^2-1} = 1$

$\dfrac{5}{x-1} - \dfrac{12}{(x-1)(x+1)} = 1$

The equation is not defined when

$$x - 1 = 0 \quad \text{or} \quad (x-1)(x+1) = 0$$
$$x = 1 \qquad\qquad x = 1 \text{ or } x = -1$$

Assume that $x \neq 1$ and $x \neq -1$.

Multiply both sides of the equation by $(x-1)(x+1)$:

$$\dfrac{5(x-1)(x+1)}{(x-1)} - \dfrac{12(x-1)(x+1)}{(x-1)(x+1)} = 1(x-1)(x+1)$$

$$5(x+1) - 12 = (x-1)(x+1)$$

$$5x + 5 - 12 = x^2 - 1$$

$$-x^2 + 5x - 6 = 0$$

Multiply both sides by -1:

$$x^2 - 5x + 6 = 0$$

$$(x-3)(x-2) = 0$$

Therefore, $x = 3 \quad \text{or} \quad x = 2$

EXERCISES 5-10

Ⓐ

1. Solve.
   a) $x^2 - 2 = 7$ b) $3x^2 = 75$ c) $2x^2 - 3 = 5$ d) $4p^2 - 5 = 11$

   e) $3t^2 + 7 = 10$ f) $2a^2 = 12$ g) $2n^2 - 49 = n^2$ h) $8b^2 = 49 + b^2$

2. Solve and check.
   a) $x^2 + 8x + 15 = 0$ b) $x^2 - 7x + 12 = 0$ c) $x^2 - x - 20 = 0$

   d) $x^2 + 5x - 24 = 0$ e) $x^2 + 8x + 12 = 0$ f) $x^2 - 5x - 36 = 0$

   g) $x^2 - 10x + 24 = 0$ h) $x^2 + 15x + 56 = 0$ i) $x^2 - x - 42 = 0$

3. Solve.
   a) $x^2 - 9x + 25 = 5$ b) $x^2 - 16x + 50 = -13$ c) $x^2 - 6x - 20 = -4$

   d) $x^2 + 10x + 25 = 4$ e) $x^2 - 5x - 20 = -6$ f) $x^2 + 6x - 15 = 4x$

   g) $x^2 - 5x + 16 = 3x$ h) $x^2 - 10x + 16 = 4 - 2x$ i) $x^2 - 8x - 40 = 4 - x$

Ⓑ

4. The height, h, in metres, of an infield fly ball t seconds after being hit is given by the formula: $h = 30t - 5t^2$. How long after being hit is the ball at a height of 25 m?

5. Solve.
   a) $3x^2 + 15x + 18 = 0$
   b) $2x^2 - 24x + 54 = 0$
   c) $4x^2 - 12x - 40 = 0$
   d) $2x^2 - 26x + 60 = 0$
   e) $3x^2 + 6x - 72 = 0$
   f) $5x^2 - 20x + 20 = 0$

6. The area, A, of a picture is given by the formula: $A = 28x - x^2$. Calculate the dimensions of a picture that has an area of
   a) 192 cm²
   b) 196 cm²
   c) 160 cm²

7. The sum, S, of the first n terms of the number pattern $2 + 4 + 6 + 8 + \ldots$ is given by the formula: $S = n(n + 1)$.
   a) Find the sum of the first 20 terms.
   b) If the sum of the first n terms is 110, find n.

8. The sum, S, of the first n terms of the number pattern: $10 + 8 + 6 + 4 + \ldots$ is given by the formula: $S = n(11 - n)$.
   a) Find the sum of the first 20 terms.
   b) If the sum of the first n terms is 28, find n.
   c) Why are two values of n possible in (b)?

9. If the sides of a right triangle are x cm, $(x + 7)$ cm, and $(x + 9)$ cm, what is the actual length of the hypotenuse?

10. Solve for the variable indicated. Assume all variables represent positive real numbers.
    a) $A = \pi r^2$, r
    b) $E = \frac{1}{2}mv^2$, v
    c) $V = \frac{1}{3}\pi r^2 h$, h
    d) $F = \frac{mn}{d^2}$, d

11. An object falls d metres in t seconds when dropped from rest. The relation between d and t is given by the formula: $d = 4.9t^2$.
    a) Solve the formula for t.
    b) How long would it take an object to hit the ground when dropped from a height of 10 m? 20 m? 40 m?

12. From a height of 2500 m, a parachutist lands on a circular target with an area of 20 m². What is the radius of the target?

13. The area of an equilateral triangle is given approximately by the formula: $A = 0.433x^2$, where x is the length of its sides.
    a) Solve the formula for x.
    b) What is the side length of an equilateral triangle with area 10 cm²? 20 cm²? 40 cm²?

14. For which values of x is each expression not defined?

a) $\dfrac{x+2}{x^2+7x+12}$

b) $\dfrac{x-4}{x^2-9x+20}$

c) $\dfrac{2x-1}{x^2+3x-18}$

d) $\dfrac{3x-5}{x^2-2x-35}$

e) $\dfrac{x-5}{x^2-10x+25}$

f) $\dfrac{x+7}{2x^2-11x+12}$

g) $\dfrac{2x+1}{2x^2+7x+3}$

h) $\dfrac{3x+4}{3x^2-13x-10}$

i) $\dfrac{7x-3}{6x^2-x-2}$

15. Solve.

a) $3x-\dfrac{2}{x}=1$

b) $x+\dfrac{6}{x+5}=2$

c) $4+\dfrac{1}{x-4}=x$

d) $\dfrac{8}{x-2}-\dfrac{20}{x^2-4}=1$

e) $\dfrac{x}{x-3}+\dfrac{2}{x+3}=0$

f) $\dfrac{2x-1}{x+1}=\dfrac{x-2}{x-3}$

g) $\dfrac{1}{x+2}+\dfrac{4}{2x-1}=1$

h) $\dfrac{x+3}{3x-5}+1=\dfrac{3(x-2)}{x-1}$

i) $\dfrac{3x-8}{5x-2}=\dfrac{x-2}{x+5}$

16. Solve.

a) $5x^2+19x-4=0$

b) $2x^2+15=11x$

c) $6x^2-11x-17=18$

d) $3x^2+5x=2$

e) $(x-2)^2=x+10$

f) $(2x-3)^2=5-x^2$

g) $(3x-1)^2=(2x+3)^2$

h) $(7x+2)^2=(2x-5)^2$

i) $(4x-2)^2=(2x-8)^2$

17. Solve.

a) $(x+1)(3x-2)=(x-1)(4x+2)$

b) $(x+1)(2x+1)=(x-1)^2$

c) $(x-3)(2x+5)=(x-3)(x+1)$

d) $(x+2)(x-7)=(3x+4)(x+2)$

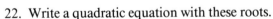

18. Two numbers differ by 6. The sum of their squares is 90. Find the numbers.

19. Two numbers have a sum of 12. The square of one number is double the other number. Find the numbers.

20. The ones digit of a two-digit number is 1 less than the tens digit. The sum of the squares of the digits is 85. Find the number.

21. A rectangular lawn measures 40 m by 30 m. If it is being cut from the outside in, how wide a strip has been cut when the job is half finished?

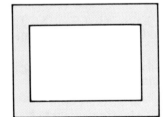

40 m

30 m

22. Write a quadratic equation with these roots.

a) $9, -2$ b) $4, 10$ c) $-5, -\dfrac{1}{3}$ d) $\dfrac{7}{8}, -\dfrac{1}{4}$

 INVESTIGATE

Is it possible for a quadratic equation to have no solution in the set of real numbers?

Review Exercises

1. Solve.

   a) $3(m - 5) = 2(5m - 11)$

   b) $\frac{4}{3}m + \frac{5}{6} = \frac{1}{2}m - \frac{5}{3}$

   c) $\frac{3x - 2}{6} = \frac{5}{3}$

   d) $\frac{5(x - 2)}{4} = \frac{6(x - 2)}{5}$

   e) $3(x - 2) - 8 = 68 - 2(2x - 1)$

   f) $4(3y + 1) - 6(y - 3) = 4(2y - 7) + 34$

2. Solve for x.

   a) $ax + b = c$

   b) $a(x + b) = c$

   c) $a(x + b) = c(x + d)$

   d) $\frac{x}{a} + \frac{b}{2} = c$

   e) $\frac{x}{a} + \frac{x}{b} = c$

   f) $\frac{a}{x} + \frac{b}{x} = c$

3. Solve.

   a) $\frac{x}{5} + 3 = \frac{2}{x} + \frac{x + 1}{5}$

   b) $\frac{y}{3} + \frac{4}{y} = \frac{y + 1}{3}$

   c) $\frac{3x - 2}{2} + 4 = \frac{13}{x} - \frac{1 - 6x}{4}$

   d) $\frac{2(1 - x)}{3} - 8 = \frac{1}{6x} - \frac{2x - 3}{3}$

   e) $2 - \frac{x - 1}{x + 3} = \frac{x - 3}{x - 4}$

   f) $\frac{3 - x}{x - 2} = 1 - \frac{2x - 5}{x + 2}$

4. Solve for the variable indicated.

   a) $v = u + at$, t

   b) $A = bh$, b

   c) $y = m(x - a)$, x

   d) $A = P(1 + rt)$, P

   e) $A = 2\pi r + 2\pi rh$, h

   f) $C = \frac{nE}{nr + R}$, R

5. The length, l, in centimetres, of a rubber band suspending a mass of m grams is given by the formula: $l = 15.5 + 0.07m$.
   a) Calculate l when the suspended mass is 250 g.

   b) What mass stretches the band to a length of 45.6 cm?

6. The sum of the interior angles, S, in degrees, in any polygon with n sides is given by the formula: $S = 180(n - 2)$.
   a) Solve the formula for n.

   b) How many sides does a polygon have if the sum of its interior angles is 720°? 1260°? 2340°?

7. Find two consecutive numbers such that the sum of four times the first and triple the second is 157.

8. Find three consecutive odd integers with a sum of 171.

9. Arlene is fifteen years older than Sharon. In three years she will be twice as old as Sharon. How old are the girls now?

10. Divide 40 into two parts such that when one part is divided by 2 and the other part multiplied by 2 the results will be equal.

11. Two numbers have a sum of 19. Four times the smaller is one less than three times the larger. What are the numbers?

12. Find the length and width of a rectangle that has a perimeter of 140 cm and a length 1 cm more than twice the width.

13. Make a table of values and draw the graph of each equation.
    a) $3x - y = 9$ b) $x + 2y = 10$ c) $4x - 3y = -12$

14. Mr. Singh estimates that the annual cost, C, in dollars, of operating his car is given by the formula: $C = 500 + 0.2n$, where n is the number of kilometres he drives in one year.
    a) Make a table of values for values of n up to 10 000.
    b) Draw the graph of the relation.
    c) Use the graph to estimate how far he drove if his annual expenses were \$1850.
    d) Use the graph to estimate how far he drove if his annual expenses were \$2350.

15. The time, T, in seconds, it takes for a pendulum to make one complete swing is given by the formula: $T \doteq 2\sqrt{l}$, where l is the length of the pendulum in metres.
    a) Make a table of values using values of l from 0 to 9.
    b) Draw the graph of the relation.
    c) Use the graph to estimate the length of a pendulum if the time for one complete swing is 3 s.
    d) Estimate the length of a pendulum if the time for one complete swing is 5 s.

16. Write the inequality that represents
    a) the shaded region   b) the unshaded region

    i)   ii)   iii)

    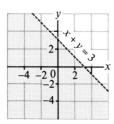   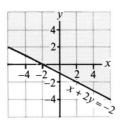   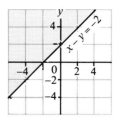

17. Graph the inequality.
    a) $x + 2y \geq 4$ b) $3x - 2y \leq -6$ c) $5x - 2y > -10$

18. Solve.
    a) $x^2 - 4x - 21 = 0$ b) $x^2 + x - 56 = 0$ c) $4x^2 - 12x + 9 = 0$
    d) $x - \dfrac{6}{x-2} = 7$ e) $\dfrac{x-5}{3x-1} = \dfrac{x+5}{x-4}$ f) $\dfrac{6}{x-2} = \dfrac{21}{x^2-4} + 1$

1. Simplify.
   a) $(5x^2 - 12xy + 7y^2) + (10x^2 - 3y^2 - 4xy) + (-3xy + 2x^2 - y^2)$
   b) $3x(x + y) - 2x(5x - 2y) - 4x(3x + 5y)$

2. Simplify.
   a) $(-7x^2y)(6xy^2)$

   b) $(-4ab^3)(-3a^2b)$

   c) $(-x^2y)(3xy)^2(-4x^2y^2)$

   d) $\dfrac{(3a^2b^3)(-6a^3b^2)}{(2ab)^2(9ab^2)}$

3. Factor.
   a) $9x^3 - 18x^2$
   d) $a^2 + 8a + 16$
   g) $m^2 - 17m + 72$

   b) $14y^4 - 7y^3$
   e) $x^2 - x - 20$
   h) $c^2 - 2cd - 24d^2$

   c) $m^2 + 2m + mn + 2n$
   f) $y^2 - 4y - 21$
   i) $x^2 + 5xy - 24y^2$

4. Factor.
   a) $2x^2y^2 + 12x^2y + 16x^2$
   c) $5m^3n + 20m^2n - 105mn$

   b) $8x^2 - 72$
   d) $180 - 5m^2$

5. If $x = 90$ and $y = 10$, evaluate.
   a) $x^2 - xy - 12y^2$
   d) $x^2 + 2xy - 35y^2$

   b) $x^2 - 2xy - 15y^2$
   e) $x^2 - 8xy - 65y^2$

   c) $x^2 - 3xy - 18y^2$
   f) $x^2 + 9xy - 52y^2$

6. Simplify.
   a) $\dfrac{84x^3y^2}{6xy}$

   b) $\dfrac{x^2 - 36}{3x^2 - 18x}$

   c) $\dfrac{m^2 - m - 12}{m^2 - 2m - 15}$

   d) $\dfrac{a^2 - 16}{a^2 + 8a + 16}$

   e) $\dfrac{x^2 - 2x - 24}{x^2 - x - 20}$

   f) $\dfrac{y^2 + 12y + 36}{y^2 + y - 30}$

7. Simplify.
   a) $\dfrac{3x^3}{2y} \times \dfrac{16x^2y^2}{4x^4}$

   b) $\dfrac{2(5 - x)}{3x} \div \dfrac{2(x - 5)}{9(x + 1)}$

   c) $\dfrac{4c^3}{c^2 - 4} \times \dfrac{2c - 4}{3c}$

   d) $\dfrac{a^2 - 2a - 8}{16 - a^2} \div \dfrac{a^2 + a - 2}{a^2 + 3a - 4}$

8. Simplify.
   a) $\dfrac{5}{2x} - \dfrac{3}{5x}$

   b) $\dfrac{2}{3m} + \dfrac{5}{4m}$

   c) $\dfrac{1}{5b} - \dfrac{5}{6b}$

   d) $\dfrac{3}{4a} - \dfrac{2}{3a} + \dfrac{5}{6a}$

   e) $\dfrac{x + 3}{5} - \dfrac{x - 4}{3}$

   f) $\dfrac{x + 5}{3} - \dfrac{x - 2}{5}$

9. Simplify.
   a) $\dfrac{x}{x + 2} - \dfrac{3}{x - 2}$

   b) $\dfrac{3a}{8a - 12} + \dfrac{2a}{6a - 9}$

   c) $\dfrac{2t}{4t - 10} + \dfrac{3t}{6t - 15}$

   d) $\dfrac{2x + 3}{2x - 8} - \dfrac{3x}{x - 4}$

   e) $\dfrac{3m}{2(m - 2)} + \dfrac{2m - 1}{3(m + 2)}$

   f) $\dfrac{b}{2(b - 3)} - \dfrac{2b + 1}{(b + 3)}$

10. Solve, and state the value of x for which the equation is not defined.

a) $\dfrac{x}{2} = \dfrac{3}{x} + \dfrac{x-1}{2}$

b) $\dfrac{3x}{7} - \dfrac{3(x-2)}{7} = \dfrac{2}{x}$

c) $\dfrac{2x+1}{3} + 2 = \dfrac{5}{x} - \dfrac{1-4x}{6}$

d) $2 - \dfrac{x+2}{3} = \dfrac{1}{4x} - \dfrac{2-x}{4}$

11. Solve for x.

a) $\dfrac{3x}{x+1} = \dfrac{3x-2}{x+2}$

b) $2 - \dfrac{x+1}{x-1} = \dfrac{x+2}{x-3}$

c) $a = \dfrac{3b}{bx-c}$

12. Solve for the variable indicated.

a) $m = 3a - \dfrac{1}{2}b$, b

b) $A = 2\pi r^2 + 2\pi rh$, h

c) $P = 2(l + w) - 5$, w

d) $C = \dfrac{24a}{na - b}$, b

13. If $x = \dfrac{3z^2}{2}$ and $y = 3z + 2$, find an expression for x in terms of y.

14. Two numbers have a difference of 7. Three times the larger exceeds five times the smaller by 3. Find the numbers.

15. Find the dimensions of a rectangle with a perimeter of 62 cm and a length 7 cm more than twice the width.

16. Mike has three more dimes than nickels, and 5 quarters fewer than twice the number of nickels. In total, he has $3.60. How many quarters does he have?

17. How much water should be added to 4 L of antifreeze to make a solution that is 60% antifreeze?

18. A woman is 5 years older than her husband and 10 times as old as their daughter. In 14 years, the sum of their ages will be 100. How old is each one now?

19. Graph the equation.

a) $3x - y = 5$

b) $4x + 3y = 24$

c) $5x + 2y = 20$

20. Graph the inequality.

a) $3x + 2y \le 12$

b) $2x + 7y \ge -14$

c) $2x - y < 6$

21. If a coin were dropped from the observation deck of the CN tower, its height above ground, in metres, after t seconds is given by the formula: $h = 350 - 4.9t^2$. Graph the relation between h and t.

Certain ocean waves tend to fall over, or break. Is there a way of predicting when a wave should break? (See *Example 1* in Section 6-3.)

6-1 LENGTH OF A LINE SEGMENT

Coordinate systems are used to identify the locations of stars in the sky, the locations of cities on the Earth's surface, and the locations of streets and buildings within cities. The Cartesian coordinate system is useful for describing the positions of points in the plane. In this system, the distance between any two points is easily found.

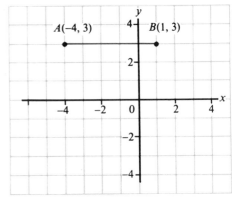

   In the diagram, line segment AB is parallel to the x-axis. Its length is the difference between the x-coordinates of A and B. That is, either

$$1 - (-4) = 5 \qquad \text{or} \qquad (-4) - 1 = -5$$

depending on the order of subtraction. If the length is defined to be the absolute value of the difference, then the order of subtraction does not matter.

$$
\begin{aligned}
AB &= |1 - (-4)| & \text{or} & & AB &= |(-4) - 1| \\
&= |5| & & & &= |-5| \\
&= 5 & & & &= 5
\end{aligned}
$$

This method is used for segments parallel to either axis.

Example 1.   Find the lengths of line segments CD and EF.

Solution.
$$
\begin{aligned}
CD &= |4 - (-3)| & EF &= |-5 - 4| \\
&= |7| & &= |-9| \\
&= 7 & &= 9
\end{aligned}
$$
CD is 7 units long and EF is 9 units long.

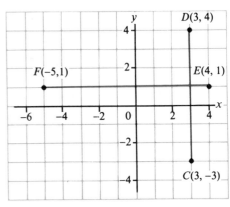

   The Pythagorean Theorem is used to determine the lengths of line segments that are not parallel to an axis.

Example 2.   Find the length of line segment PQ.

Solution.   Draw a right $\triangle PQR$ for which PQ is the hypotenuse. By the Pythagorean Theorem:

$$
\begin{aligned}
PQ^2 &= PR^2 + RQ^2 \\
&= |(-2) - 3|^2 + |4 - (-3)|^2 \\
&= 25 + 49 \\
PQ &= \sqrt{74} \\
&\doteq 8.6
\end{aligned}
$$

PQ is approximately 8.6 units long.

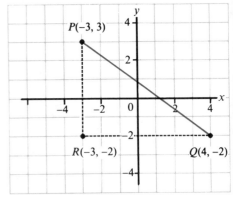

The method of *Example 2* can be used to develop a formula for the distance between any two points $P_1(x_1, y_1)$ and $P_2(x_2, y_2)$ as follows:

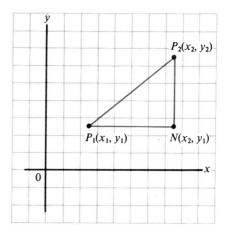

In the diagram, $\triangle P_1NP_2$ is a right triangle. The coordinates of N are (x_2, y_1).

$$P_1N = |x_2 - x_1| \quad \text{and} \quad NP_2 = |y_2 - y_1|$$

By the Pythagorean Theorem:

$$(P_1P_2)^2 = (P_1N)^2 + (NP_2)^2$$
$$= (x_2 - x_1)^2 + (y_2 - y_1)^2$$
$$P_1P_2 = \sqrt{(x_2 - x_1)^2 + (y_2 - y_1)^2}$$

The distance between any two points $P_1(x_1, y_1)$ and $P_2(x_2, y_2)$ is given by the formula:

$$P_1P_2 = \sqrt{(x_2 - x_1)^2 + (y_2 - y_1)^2}$$

Example 3. The points $L(1, 5)$, $M(-3, 1)$, and $N(6, -4)$ are the vertices of $\triangle LMN$.
  a) Draw $\triangle LMN$ on a grid and find the lengths of its sides correct to one decimal place.
  b) What type of triangle is $\triangle LMN$?

Solution. a) $LM = \sqrt{(-3 - 1)^2 + (1 - 5)^2}$
                        $= \sqrt{(-4)^2 + (-4)^2}$
                        $= \sqrt{16 + 16}$
                        $= \sqrt{32}$
                        $\doteq 5.7$

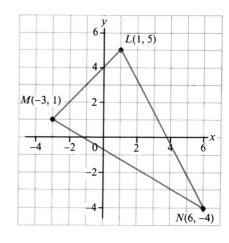

$MN = \sqrt{(6 + 3)^2 + (-4 - 1)^2}$
      $= \sqrt{81 + 25}$
      $= \sqrt{106}$
      $\doteq 10.3$

$LN = \sqrt{(6 - 1)^2 + (-4 - 5)^2}$
      $= \sqrt{25 + 81}$
      $= \sqrt{106}$
      $\doteq 10.3$

  b) Since two sides of $\triangle LMN$ have the same length, it is an isosceles triangle.

EXERCISES 6-1

Ⓐ

1. Plot each pair of points and find the distance between them.
   a) (7, 3), (7, −2)
   b) (−3, −5), (−3, 2)
   c) (−4, 3), (7, 3)
   d) (6, −4), (−6, −4)
   e) (0, 0), (0, −8)
   f) (12.5, 5), (−1.5, 5)

2. Find the length of each line segment on the grid.

3. Plot each pair of points and find the distance between them.
   a) (5, 4), (1, 2)
   b) (−2, 3), (4, −1)
   c) (−8, 9), (−3, 4)
   d) (−3, 0), (8, −4)
   e) (0, 0), (−5, 2)
   f) (3.5, 5), (7.5, 8.5)

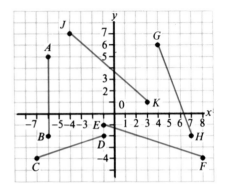

4. For each triangle shown on the grid, find the
   a) lengths of the sides
   b) area

5. Find the lengths of the line segments with these endpoints.
   a) (5, 9), (−2, 2)
   b) (1, −6), (5, 2)
   c) (−3, 7), (5, 2)
   d) (−9, −3), (−3, 4)

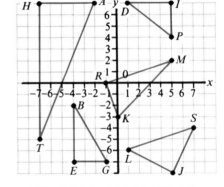

Ⓑ

6. On a grid, draw the triangles with these vertices and classify them as scalene, isosceles, or equilateral.
   a) *A*(−4, 3), *B*(−2, −4), *C*(3, 5)
   b) *P*(−1, 2), *Q*(1, −5), *R*(5, −2)
   c) *J*(−2, 5), *K*(4, −1), *L*(6, 7)

7. On a grid, draw the rectangles with these vertices, and find the lengths of the sides and the perimeters of each.
   a) *A*(−6, −3), *B*(3, −3), *C*(3, 5), *D*(−6, 5)
   b) *J*(−3, 3), *K*(0, −6), *L*(3, −5), *M*(0, 4)
   c) *P*(−8, −1), *Q*(−4, −7), *R*(8, 1), *S*(4, 7)

8. Find the lengths of the diagonals and the areas of the rectangles in *Exercise 7*.

9. Find the lengths of the line segments AB, BC, and AC and compare the lengths $AB + BC$ and AC. What do you conclude about the points A, B, and C?
   a) $A(9, 7)$, $B(5, 4)$, $C(1, 1)$
   b) $A(-4, 8)$, $B(2, 0)$, $C(5, -4)$
   c) $A(-5, -2)$, $B(3, 2)$, $C(7, 4)$

10. A circle has centre $(2, 1)$ and radius 5. Which of the following points are on the circle?
    a) $(6, 4)$ b) $(3, 6)$ c) $(-3, 1)$ d) $(6, -1)$

11. An ocean freighter sends a distress signal from a location given by $(240, 160)$. A second freighter at $(50, 420)$ and a coastguard cutter at $(520, 100)$ hear the distress call. Which ship is closer to the ship in distress?

12. A surveyor establishes the corner points of a field to be $(-75, 375)$, $(-75, -100)$, $(150, -100)$, and $(250, 150)$, where the numbers represent the distances, in metres, from a pair of reference axes. Find the length of each diagonal, the perimeter, and the area of the field.

ⓒ

13. Which points are equidistant from $(4, 0)$ and $(0, 2)$?
    a) $P(0, -3)$ b) $Q(3, 7)$ c) $R(5, 7)$ d) $S(2, 1)$

14. Find the coordinates of the points on the x-axis which are 5 units from $(5, 4)$.

15. Find the coordinates of the point on the y-axis which is equidistant from the points
    a) $(3, 0)$ and $(3, 6)$ b) $(4, 0)$ and $(2, 6)$ c) $(5, 0)$ and $(1, 6)$

16. In the Bell telephone system, long distance charges are based on the straight line distance between the caller and the receiver. Each telephone exchange in North America is given a set of coordinates, and distances are calculated using the formula for the distance between two points.
    a) Find the phone distance from Ottawa to Toronto, Quebec City, Washington.
    b) Would it be cheaper to call Chicago or Washington from Toronto?

City	Coordinates
Chicago	$(3364, 6119)$
Ottawa	$(2241, 4388)$
Quebec City	$(1930, 3638)$
Toronto	$(2488, 4981)$
Washington	$(1489, 5605)$

COMPUTER POWER

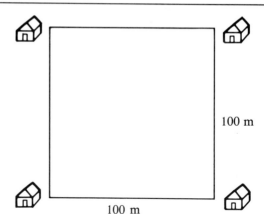

100 m

100 m

Shortest Networks

In a new housing development, four houses at the vertices of a 100 m square are to be connected with cable television lines. Where should the wires be located so that the total length of wire is as small as possible?

Two possibilities are shown below, but each of these uses more wire than is necessary to connect the four houses.

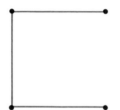

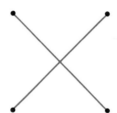

Diagrams like these, which show points connected are called *networks*. A model can be used to find a network which has a shorter length than either of the above.

The diagram below shows two parallel sheets of Plexiglas joined by four rods at the vertices of a square. When the model is dipped in a soap solution, a soap film connects the four rods.

When viewed from above, the pattern formed by the film indicates the shortest network joining the four points. The least amount of wire is used when it follows a pattern like this.

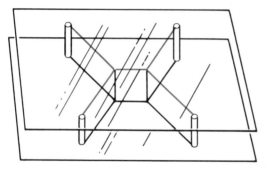

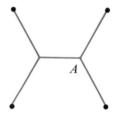

The computer program below can be used to find the length of the shortest network. The computer first asks for the side length of the square. Then it calculates the total length of the network shown for different positions of point A, starting at the centre of the square, and moving to the right. The computer prints a table of values showing the total distance for several positions of A.

When the total distance starts becoming larger, the computer repeats the calculations using positions of A closer to the one which gives the shortest network. The final result is the total length of the shortest network joining the four points.

```
100 REM *** SHORTEST NETWORK ***
110 INPUT "SIDE LENGTH? ";S:X1=S/2:X2=S
120 F=(X2-X1)/10:LD=1000000
130 FOR I=0 TO 10
140    X=X1+I*F
150    DIST=4*SQR((S-X)*(S-X)+S*S/4)+2*(X-S/2)
160    PRINT X,DIST
170    IF DIST<LD THEN LD=DIST:XMIN=X
180 NEXT I
190 PRINT:PRINT "A IS (";XMIN;", ";S/2;")"
200 PRINT "DISTANCE IS ";LD
210 PRINT:INPUT "PRESS C TO CONTINUE, RETURN
       TO STOP ";Y$
220 IF Y$="C" THEN PRINT:X1=XMIN-F:X2=XMIN+F:GOTO
       120
230 END
```

The solution to problems like this one has practical applications in the construction of such networks as railways, roads, power lines, and computer chips.

1. Use the program to find the length of the shortest network if the length of the side of the square is 10 units.

2. Use the result to construct an accurate diagram showing the shortest network.

3. Compare the length of the shortest network with the lengths of the networks shown at the top of the opposite page. Express the decrease in length as a percent in each case.

6-2 MIDPOINT OF A LINE SEGMENT

Performers on the high wire know that they must grip the long pole they carry for stability at its midpoint. The coordinates of the midpoint of a line segment are related to the coordinates of the endpoints.

Example 1. Find the coordinates of the midpoint, M, of the line segment joining $A(2, 1)$ and $B(8, 5)$.

Solution. Complete the right triangle ABC for which AB is the hypotenuse. MD and ME are the perpendiculars onto BC and AC respectively. It is clear from the diagram that the coordinates of M are the means of the coordinates of A and B.

x-coordinate of $M = \dfrac{2 + 8}{2}$

$= 5$

y-coordinate of $M = \dfrac{5 + 1}{2}$

$= 3$

The coordinates of M are $(5, 3)$.

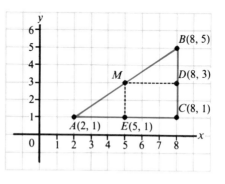

If M is the midpoint of a line segment having endpoints $P_1(x_1, y_1)$ and $P_2(x_2, y_2)$, then the coordinates of M are:
$$\left(\frac{x_1 + x_2}{2}, \frac{y_1 + y_2}{2}\right)$$

Example 2. Find the coordinates of the midpoint of the line segment joining $P(-5, 7)$ and $Q(2, -1)$.

Solution. $x\text{-coordinate} = \dfrac{-5 + 2}{2}$

$$= -\frac{3}{2}$$

$y\text{-coordinate} = \dfrac{7 + (-1)}{2}$

$$= 3$$

The midpoint of PQ is $\left(-\dfrac{3}{2}, 3\right)$.

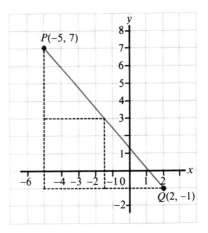

EXERCISES 6-2

(A)

1. State the coordinates of the midpoint of each line segment shown.

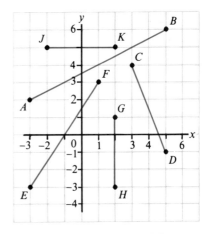

2. Find the coordinates of the midpoint of the line segment with the given endpoints.
   a) $A(0, 4), B(6, 4)$ b) $R(-2, 5), S(-2, -1)$
   c) $K(1, 1), L(7, 9)$ d) $F(5, 3), G(-3, 0)$
   e) $M(-6, 5), N(3, -2)$ f) $P(0, 7), Q(-4, -2)$
   g) $U(-3, -6), V(7, 5)$ h) $C(-9, 0), D(5, -4)$

3. On a grid, draw the triangle with vertices $J(0, 3)$, $K(8, 1), L(6, 9)$, and find the coordinates of the midpoint of each side.

(B)

4. The coordinates of the vertices of a rectangle are given. Draw the rectangle on a grid, and find the coordinates of the midpoints of its two diagonals. What do you notice?
   a) $A(1, 4), B(1, -2), C(11, -2), D(11, 4)$
   b) $P(6, 10), Q(-2, 6), R(4, -6), S(12, -2)$

5. A parallelogram has vertices $E(0, -3), F(7, -1), G(10, 4)$, and $H(3, 2)$. Draw the parallelogram on a grid and find the coordinates of the midpoints of its two diagonals. What do you notice?

6. A right triangle has vertices $A(-2, 8), B(6, 4)$, and $C(4, 0)$.
   a) Draw the triangle on a grid and find the coordinates of the midpoint, M, of the hypotenuse.
   b) Find the lengths of AM, BM, and CM. What do you notice?

7. A triangle has vertices $A(6, 8)$, $B(-2, 2)$, and $C(6, 2)$. The midpoints of AC and BC are M and N respectively.
   a) Graph the triangle and find the coordinates of M and N.
   b) Find the lengths of MN and AB. What do you notice?

Centroid
Median

8. A triangle has vertices $P(-2, 4)$, $Q(-4, -4)$, and $R(6, 0)$.
   a) Graph the triangle and draw its three medians.
   b) Find the lengths of the three medians of $\triangle PQR$.

9. Draw an example of a line segment AB which has one endpoint, A, on the x-axis and midpoint, M, on the y-axis. How are the coordinates of B related to those of A and M?

10. A is an endpoint and M the midpoint of a line segment. Locate A and M on a grid, and then find the coordinates of the other endpoint of the segment.
    a) $A(-2, 4)$, $M(2, -1)$
    b) $A(8, -1)$, $M(5, -5)$
    c) $A(3, 5)$, $M(-1.5, 1.5)$
    d) $A(-6, -4)$, $M(-3, -2)$

11. Find the coordinates of the three points that divide line segment AB into four equal parts when the coordinates of A and B are
    a) $(-4, 4)$, $(8, -12)$
    b) $(5, -7)$, $(-9, 5)$
    c) $(-2, -6)$, $(8, 4)$
    d) $(-5, -3)$, $(5, 3)$

12. Points P, Q, and R divide a line segment into four equal parts. Find the coordinates of the other endpoint if those of P and the adjacent endpoint are
    a) $P(5, 2)$, $(2, 4)$
    b) $P(-2, 1)$, $(-6, -2)$
    c) $P(4, -1.5)$, $(8, -5)$
    d) $P(-3, -6)$, $(-4, -8)$

Ⓒ

13. If a line segment has endpoints $A(x_1, y_1)$ and $B(x_2, y_2)$, find expressions for the coordinates of the points which divide AB into
    a) 3 equal parts
    b) 4 equal parts

14. A square has vertices $(4, 3)$, $(11, 6)$, $(8, 13)$, and $(1, 10)$.
    a) Find the mean of the x-coordinates and the mean of the y-coordinates of its vertices.
    b) Use the results of (a) as the coordinates of a point C and, by graphing, determine how C is related to the square.

15. Triangle ABC has vertices $A(-6, 2)$, $B(8, -2)$, $C(4, 6)$. Find the coordinates of its centroid.

INVESTIGATE

If you know the coordinates of the midpoints of the sides of a triangle, how can you find the coordinates of its vertices?

THE MATHEMATICAL MIND

The Invention of Coordinate Geometry

Coordinate geometry was developed over three hundred years ago to solve practical problems in astronomy, ballistics and navigation. It is one of the greatest mathematical achievements of all time because it provides a new method of solving problems in geometry. The basic idea involves using numbers and equations to represent points, lines and curves. In this way, problems in geometry can be solved using algebra and arithmetic. Two great French mathematicians are credited with inventing coordinate geometry.

Pierre de Fermat
1601–1665

René Descartes
1596–1650

René Descartes was a child of delicate health and developed a lifelong habit of staying in bed as late as he liked in the morning. He later regarded these hours as his most productive periods. In 1649 he was invited to tutor Queen Christina of Sweden, who insisted on beginning at 5 a.m. This inconsiderate demand and the rigors of the Stockholm winter contributed to his death the next year.

Pierre de Fermat was a lawyer who devoted his leisure time to the study of mathematics. He corresponded with many of the leading mathematicians of the time, and had considerable influence on their work. He made many important contributions to different branches of mathematics.

1. A triangle has vertices $P(4, 6)$, $Q(0, 0)$ and $R(10, 0)$. The midpoints of PQ and PR are M and N.
   a) Graph the triangle and find the coordinates of M and N.
   b) Find the lengths of MN and QR. What do you notice?

2. a) Repeat 1. using the triangle with vertices $P(2a, 2b)$ $Q(0, 0)$ and $R(2c, 0)$.
   b) Does this prove that the result is true for all triangles?

6-3 SLOPE OF A LINE SEGMENT

The pitch of a roof, the steepness of a ski run, or the gradient of a mountain road are all examples of *slope*.

In each case, the slope is the ratio of the rise to the run.

$$\text{Slope} = \frac{\text{rise}}{\text{run}}$$

Example 1. The diagrams below show how the rise and run of a water wave are defined. Oceanographers have found that a wave tends to fall over, or *break* when its slope becomes greater than $\frac{2}{7}$. For the waves shown, determine if either one should break.

a)

b)

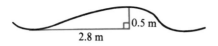

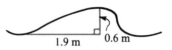

Solution. Find the slope of each wave.

a) $\text{Slope} = \dfrac{\text{rise}}{\text{run}}$

$= \dfrac{0.5}{2.8}$

$\doteq 0.178$

b) $\text{Slope} = \dfrac{\text{rise}}{\text{run}}$

$= \dfrac{0.6}{1.9}$

$\doteq 0.316$

Since $\frac{2}{7} \doteq 0.286$, the wave in (b) should break, and the one in (a) should not.

In a coordinate system, the slope of any segment can be found if the coordinates of any two points $P_1(x_1, y_1)$ and $P_2(x_2, y_2)$ on the line segment are known.

From P_1 to P_2:

• the rise is the difference in the y-coordinates: $y_2 - y_1$

• the run is the difference in the x-coordinates: $x_2 - x_1$

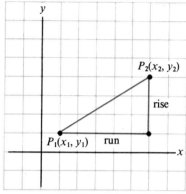

The slope of the line segment joining $P_1(x_1, y_1)$ and $P_2(x_2, y_2)$ is given by the formula:

$$\text{slope of } P_1P_2 = \frac{y_2 - y_1}{x_2 - x_1}, \ (x_2 \neq x_1)$$

Example 2. Graph the line segments and find their slopes.

    a) $A(2, 1)$, $B(5, 3)$ b) $M(-3, 4)$, $N(-1, -2)$

    c) $R(-2, 4)$, $S(5, 4)$ d) $J(1, -2)$, $K(1, 3)$

Solution.   a) Slope of $AB = \dfrac{3 - 1}{5 - 2}$

$$= \frac{2}{3}$$

b) Slope of $MN = \dfrac{(-2) - (4)}{(-1) - (-3)}$

$$= \frac{-6}{2}$$

$$= -3$$

c) Slope of $RS = \dfrac{4 - 4}{5 - (-2)}$

$$= \frac{0}{7}$$

$$= 0$$

d) Slope of $JK = \dfrac{3 - (-2)}{1 - 1}$

$$= \frac{5}{1 - 1}$$

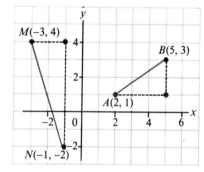

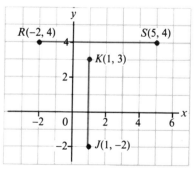

Note that the denominator in (d) equals 0 and division by 0 is not defined. Therefore, the slope of *JK* cannot be defined as a real number.

When we find the slope of a line segment it does not matter which point is taken as the first point and which is taken as the second point. In *Example 2a*, the slope of the segment could also be found as follows:

$$\text{Slope of } BA = \frac{1-3}{2-5}$$

$$= \frac{-2}{-3}$$

$$= \frac{2}{3}$$

Example 2 illustrates the following properties of slope.

Line segments *rising* to the right have *positive* slope.
Line segments *falling* to the right have *negative* slope.
The slope of any horizontal segment is zero.
The slope of any vertical segment is not defined as a real number.

EXERCISES 6-3

Ⓐ

1. Find the slope of the roof shown
   in the diagram.

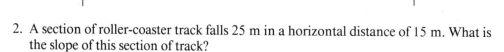

2. A section of roller-coaster track falls 25 m in a horizontal distance of 15 m. What is the slope of this section of track?

3. Find the slope of each line segment.

a)

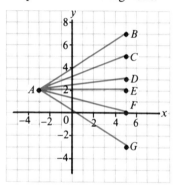

b)

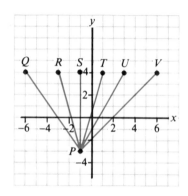

(B)

4. Graph these line segments and find their slopes.
   a) $A(-2, 7)$, $B(6, -4)$
   b) $C(3, -5)$, $D(8, 10)$
   c) $E(1, 6)$, $F(5, -4)$
   d) $G(-3, 7)$, $H(-3, -7)$
   e) $J(-4, -3)$, $K(8, 5)$
   f) $L(2, -7)$, $M(7, -7)$

5. The coordinates of the vertices of four triangles are given. Graph the triangles and find the slope of each side.
   a) $A(5, -1)$, $B(0, 4)$, $C(-2, -5)$
   b) $R(-3, 4)$, $S(6, 7)$, $T(2, -3)$
   c) $L(4, -2)$, $M(-4, 8)$, $N(4, 8)$
   d) $E(-2, -1)$, $F(-1, -6)$, $G(5, 6)$

6. A ladder, 2.6 m long, just reaches a window 2.4 m above the ground. What is its slope?

7. A new overpass is to be connected to an access road 250 m away by a road of uniform slope. If the overpass is 8 m above the access road, what will the slope of the connecting road be?

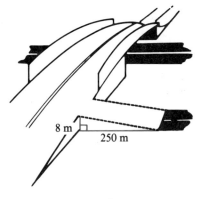

8 m
250 m

8. Guy wires supporting a broadcasting tower are fastened to the ground 20 m from its base. The first set of wires is attached to the tower part way up and have a slope of $\frac{7}{5}$. The second set is fastened to the top of the tower and each wire is 52 m in length.
   a) Find the length of the first set of guy wires.
   b) Find the slope of the second set of guy wires.

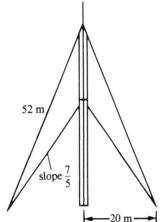

52 m

slope $\frac{7}{5}$

—20 m—

9. a) Can a triangle be drawn such that all three sides have positive slope?
   b) Can a quadrilateral be drawn such that three sides have positive slope? all four sides have positive slope?

10. Find the value of x if the line segment joining the given points has the given slope, and illustrate it on a grid.

　a)　$A(-1, 2)$, $B(x, 6)$　　slope $\dfrac{1}{2}$　　　　b)　$G(0, -2)$, $H(x, 3)$　　slope 1

　c)　$R(x, 0)$, $S(-2, 4)$　　slope $-\dfrac{2}{3}$　　　d)　$U(x, -3)$, $V(4, 9)$　　slope 3

11. Find the value of y if the line segment joining the given points has the given slope, and illustrate it on a grid.

　a)　$C(1, 3)$, $D(5, y)$　　slope $\dfrac{3}{4}$　　　　b)　$Q(0, y)$, $R(4, 6)$　　slope 2

　c)　$L(-2, 6)$, $M(5, y)$　　slope -1　　　　d)　$E(0, y)$, $F(4, -2)$　　slope $-\dfrac{3}{2}$

©

12. One endpoint of a line segment is $A(4, 6)$, the other is on the x-axis. Find the coordinates of the endpoint on the x-axis for the slope of the segment to be

　a)　1　　　　b)　2　　　　c)　3　　　　d)　$\dfrac{1}{2}$　　　　e)　-2　　　　f)　$-\dfrac{1}{2}$

13. One endpoint of a line segment is $B(-3, 4)$, and the other endpoint is on the y-axis. Find the coordinates of the endpoint on the y-axis so that the segment has these slopes.

　a)　3　　　　b)　2　　　　c)　1　　　　d)　$\dfrac{1}{2}$　　　　e)　$\dfrac{1}{4}$

　f)　0　　　　g)　-1　　　　h)　-2　　　　i)　-4　　　　j)　$-\dfrac{1}{2}$

14. Two line segments, with a common endpoint $(0, 4)$, have slopes 2 and $-\dfrac{1}{2}$. If the other endpoints are on the x-axis, find their coordinates.

15. A line segment has length 10, and its endpoints are on the coordinate axes. If the slope of the line segment is $-\dfrac{3}{4}$, find the possible coordinates of its endpoints.

 I N V E S T I G A T E

Since slope is defined as a ratio, it may be expressed in ratio form.

　　　　　　slope = rise : run

List some advantages and disadvantages of this form for writing slope.

6-4 SLOPES OF PARALLEL LINE SEGMENTS

In the diagram, line segments AB and CD are parallel.

Slope of $AB = \dfrac{5-3}{6-2}$

$\qquad = \dfrac{2}{4}$

$\qquad = \dfrac{1}{2}$

Slope of $CD = \dfrac{6-4}{3-(-1)}$

$\qquad = \dfrac{2}{4}$

$\qquad = \dfrac{1}{2}$

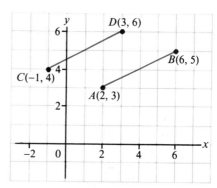

This example illustrates a fundamental property of slope.

If the slopes of two line segments are equal, the segments are parallel.

If two line segments are parallel, their slopes are equal.

Example 1. Determine whether or not the quadrilateral $A(0, -6)$, $B(2, -1)$, $C(-1, 5)$, $D(-3, 0)$ is a parallelogram.

Solution. Draw the quadrilateral on a grid.

Slope of $AB = \dfrac{-1-(-6)}{2-0}$

$\qquad = \dfrac{5}{2}$

Slope of $DC = \dfrac{5-0}{-1-(-3)}$

$\qquad = \dfrac{5}{2}$

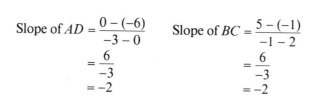

Slopes AB and DC are equal, therefore $AB \,||\, DC$.

Slope of $AD = \dfrac{0-(-6)}{-3-0}$

$\qquad = \dfrac{6}{-3}$

$\qquad = -2$

Slope of $BC = \dfrac{5-(-1)}{-1-2}$

$\qquad = \dfrac{6}{-3}$

$\qquad = -2$

Slopes AD and BC are equal, therefore $AD \,||\, BC$.
Since both pairs of opposite sides are parallel, quadrilateral $ABCD$ is a parallelogram.

Example 2. Given the points: $P(2, -5)$, $Q(-2, 1)$, and $R(3, -1)$. Find the coordinates of a point, S, on the y-axis such that line segment RS is parallel to segment PQ.

Solution. Graph the points P, Q, and R. Let $S(0, y)$ be the point on the y-axis.

Slope of $PQ = \dfrac{1 - (-5)}{-2 - 2}$

$= \dfrac{6}{-4}$

$= -\dfrac{3}{2}$

Slope of $RS = \dfrac{y - (-1)}{0 - 3}$

$= \dfrac{y + 1}{-3}$

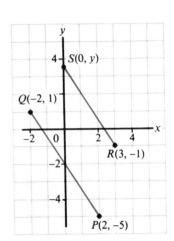

Since $PQ \parallel RS$, the slopes are equal:

$\dfrac{y + 1}{-3} = -\dfrac{3}{2}$

$2(y + 1) = 9$

$2y + 2 = 9$

$y = 3.5$

The coordinates of the required point are $(0, 3.5)$.

EXERCISES 6-4

1. Two line segments which appear to be parallel are shown. State the slopes of the segments and determine which line segments are parallel.

a)

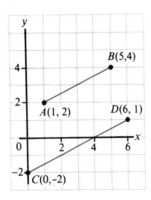

b)

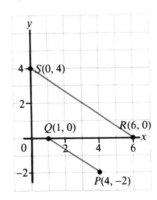

c)

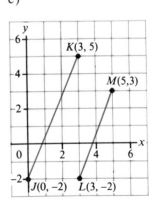

2. Graph each of the line segments and determine their slopes. Which of the line segments are parallel?

   a) $A(-2, -1)$, $B(1, 5)$ and $C(2, -1)$, $D(4, 3)$
   b) $E(-3, 2)$, $F(5, 5)$ and $G(0, 0)$, $H(5, 2)$
   c) $R(-1, 4)$, $S(7, -2)$ and $T(3, 4)$, $U(9, 0)$

3. Draw each quadrilateral on a grid, and determine whether or not it is a parallelogram.

   a) $A(5, 3)$, $B(-3, -3)$, $C(-2, -8)$, $D(6, -2)$
   b) $P(-6, 1)$, $Q(-2, -6)$, $R(10, 2)$, $S(7, 9)$
   c) $J(-4, 5)$, $K(-2, -1)$, $L(6, -4)$, $M(4, 2)$

Ⓑ

4. A triangle has vertices $A(2, 5)$, $B(-4, 1)$, and $C(6, -3)$. The midpoints of AC and BC are M and N respectively.

   a) Graph the triangle and find the coordinates of M and N.
   b) Find the slopes of MN and AB. What do you notice?
   c) Let P be the midpoint of AB, and find the slopes of PM, BC, PN, and AC. What do you notice?

5. A quadrilateral has vertices $A(-4, 0)$, $B(8, 2)$, $C(2, 8)$, and $D(-2, 4)$.

   a) Graph the quadrilateral and locate the midpoints of the four sides.
   b) Draw the quadrilateral formed by the midpoints in (a). What kind of quadrilateral does it appear to be?
   c) Use slopes to confirm your prediction in (b).

6. Given the points $A(-2, 0)$, $B(6, 4)$ and $C(-3, 4)$. Find the coordinates of a point D on the y-axis such that line segment CD is parallel to AB.

7. The points $A(6, 3)$, $B(2, 9)$ and $C(2, 3)$ are given. Find the coordinates of a point D such that CD is parallel to AB when D is on the

   a) y-axis   b) x-axis

8. The following are slopes of parallel segments. Find the value of k.

   a) $\dfrac{2}{3}, \dfrac{4}{k}$ b) $\dfrac{3}{2}, \dfrac{k}{-4}$ c) $\dfrac{-1}{5}, \dfrac{2}{k}$ d) $\dfrac{4}{7}, \dfrac{-8}{k}$

   e) $\dfrac{k}{4}, 2$ f) $\dfrac{-k}{5}, \dfrac{3}{2}$ g) $\dfrac{k}{2}, \dfrac{1}{3}$ h) $\dfrac{-k}{3}, \dfrac{-2}{7}$

Ⓒ

9. The coordinates of three vertices of a parallelogram are given. Find all possible coordinates of the fourth vertex.

   a) $A(-4, 1)$, $T(-3, -4)$, $G(5, 0)$ b) $W(-4, 4)$, $B(1, -2)$, $M(8, -5)$

10. The coordinates of the midpoints of the sides of a triangle are given. Find the coordinates of the vertices of the triangle.

   a) $(5, 0)$, $(2, 3)$, $(7, 3)$ b) $(-3, 3)$, $(-3, 8)$, $(5, 5)$

6-5 SLOPES OF PERPENDICULAR LINE SEGMENTS

In the previous section, we found that parallel line segments have the same slope. There is also a relationship between the slopes of perpendicular line segments. To discover what it is, we draw a right triangle and rotate it 90°.

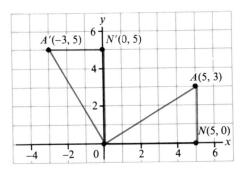

In the diagram, right triangle ONA is rotated 90° counterclockwise about $(0, 0)$ to $\triangle ON'A'$. The coordinates of A are $(5, 3)$. The coordinates of A' are $(-3, 5)$, and $OA \perp OA'$.

$$\text{Slope of } OA = \frac{3-0}{5-0} \qquad \text{Slope of } OA' = \frac{5-0}{-3-0}$$

$$= \frac{3}{5} \qquad\qquad\qquad = -\frac{5}{3}$$

The numbers $\frac{3}{5}$ and $-\frac{5}{3}$ are called *negative reciprocals*. The product of *negative reciprocals* is -1. This example suggests the relation between slopes of perpendicular line segments.

If the slopes of two line segments are negative reciprocals, the segments are perpendicular.

If two line segments are perpendicular, their slopes are negative reciprocals.

Example 1. A triangle has vertices $A(-2, 3)$, $B(8, -2)$ and $C(4, 6)$. Determine whether or not it is a right triangle.

Solution. Graph the triangle. From the graph, $\angle C$ appears to be a right angle. Calculate the slopes of AC and BC.

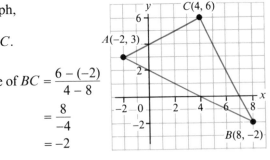

$$\text{Slope of } AC = \frac{6-3}{4-(-2)} \qquad \text{Slope of } BC = \frac{6-(-2)}{4-8}$$

$$= \frac{3}{6} \qquad\qquad\qquad\qquad = \frac{8}{-4}$$

$$= \frac{1}{2} \qquad\qquad\qquad\qquad = -2$$

Since $\left(\frac{1}{2}\right)(-2) = -1$, the slopes of AC and BC are negative reciprocals. Therefore, $AC \perp BC$, and $\triangle ABC$ is a right triangle.

Example 2. A line segment has endpoints $A(5, 4)$ and $B(1, -2)$. Find the coordinates of a point C such that line segment AC is perpendicular to AB.

Solution.   Draw segment AB on a grid.

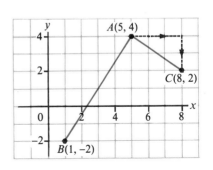

$$\text{Slope of } AB = \frac{-2 - 4}{1 - 5}$$

$$= \frac{-6}{-4}$$

$$= \frac{3}{2}$$

The slope of a line segment perpendicular to AB is $\frac{-2}{3}$. Begin at A. Move 3 to the right and 2 down. The point $C(8, 2)$ is a possible point.

In *Example 2*, $C(8, 2)$ is not the only point such that AC is perpendicular to AB. Other points may be found by moving 3 to the right and 2 down again, or by moving 3 to the left and 2 up.

EXERCISES 6-5

(A)

1. Two line segments which appear to be perpendicular are shown. State the slopes of the segments and determine if the segments are perpendicular.

a)

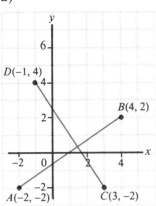

b)

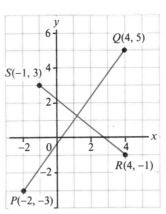

c)

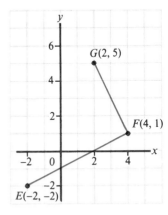

2. Find the slope of a line segment perpendicular to a segment with the given slope.

a) $\frac{2}{3}$ b) $\frac{5}{8}$ c) $-\frac{3}{4}$ d) $-\frac{1}{2}$ e) $-\frac{1}{3}$

3. Which pairs of numbers are slopes of perpendicular line segments?

a) $\frac{3}{4}, -\frac{4}{3}$ b) $\frac{2}{3}, \frac{3}{2}$ c) $\frac{4}{5}, -\frac{4}{5}$ d) $-4, \frac{1}{4}$ e) $3, \frac{1}{3}$ f) $2, -\frac{1}{2}$

4. Graph each line segment and determine its slope. Which line segments are perpendicular?
   a) $A(0, 0)$, $B(6, 4)$ and $C(5, -1)$, $D(1, 5)$
   b) $H(-3, 1)$, $I(6, 4)$ and $J(2, 0)$, $K(0, 6)$
   c) $L(5, -3)$, $M(1, 4)$ and $N(1, -1)$, $O(6, 2)$

5. Draw each triangle on a grid and determine whether or not it is a right triangle.
   a) $D(-2, 2)$, $E(-6, 2)$, $F(-6, -1)$ b) $A(3, 0)$, $B(-4, 4)$, $C(-1, -2)$
   c) $P(-3, 1)$, $Q(3, -3)$, $R(7, 3)$ d) $K(3, 2)$, $L(-5, -1)$, $M(-2, -8)$

Ⓑ——

6. Draw each quadrilateral on a grid and determine whether or not it is a rectangle.
   a) $A(5, 4)$, $B(-4, -2)$, $C(-2, -5)$, $D(7, 1)$
   b) $J(-3, 2)$, $K(-2, -3)$, $L(6, -2)$, $M(5, 3)$
   c) $P(5, 1)$, $Q(-4, 4)$, $R(-6, -2)$, $S(3, -5)$

7. Find the slope of a line segment parallel to the given segment.
   a) $A(0, 4)$, $B(2, 0)$ b) $C(-1, 1)$, $D(3, 3)$ c) $E(4, -2)$, $F(-1, 3)$
   d) $G(0, 1)$, $H(-5, -1)$ e) $J(2, 3)$, $K(-1, 3)$ f) $K(3, 5)$, $M(3, -2)$

8. Find the slope of a line segment perpendicular to each segment in *Exercise 7*.

9. The following are slopes of perpendicular line segments. Find the value of k for each.
   a) $3, k$ b) $\dfrac{-1}{2}, k$ c) $\dfrac{k}{2}, 2$ d) $\dfrac{k}{3}, -3$ e) $\dfrac{k}{4}, -4$

   f) $\dfrac{k}{2}, \dfrac{1}{4}$ g) $\dfrac{6}{k}, \dfrac{-2}{3}$ h) $\dfrac{3}{5}, \dfrac{k}{6}$ i) $\dfrac{1}{3}, \dfrac{k}{2}$ j) $\dfrac{-1}{7}, \dfrac{k}{5}$

10. In each of the following, a line segment AB is given. Graph the segment, and find the coordinates of a point C such that line segment AC is perpendicular to AB.
    a) $A(3, 2)$, $B(6, 8)$ b) $A(0, 5)$, $B(5, 3)$ c) $A(1, 3)$, $B(1, -2)$
    d) $A(-2, 4)$, $B(4, 1)$ e) $A(0, 0)$, $B(7, 2)$ f) $A(4, 3)$, $B(-2, 3)$

11. A line segment has endpoints $C(6, 2)$ and $D(8, 5)$. P is a point such that line segment PC is perpendicular to CD. Find the coordinates of P if P is on the
    a) x-axis   b) y-axis

12. a) Graph the quadrilateral with vertices $A(-2, 7)$, $B(-3, -1)$, $C(4, -5)$ and $D(5, 3)$, and find the lengths of all four sides.
    b) What kind of quadrilateral is $ABCD$?
    c) Find the coordinates of the midpoint of each diagonal.
    d) Find the slope of each diagonal.
    e) What can you conclude from (c) and (d)?

13. *A*, *B*, and *C* are three vertices of a rectangle. Plot the points on a grid, and find the
    coordinates of the fourth vertex.
    a) *A*(2, −1), *B*(5, −3), *C*(7, 0)   b) *A*(1, 8), *B*(3, −2), *C*(6, 6)
    c) *A*(−4, 7), *B*(−6, 4), *C*(3, −2)   d) *A*(2, 4), *B*(−2, −2), *C*(1, −4)

14. In the diagram, *ABCD* is a square. Find the
    coordinates of *C* and *D* if the coordinates of
    A and *B* are
    a) *A*(1, 0), *B*(0, 4)
    b) *A*(3, 0), *B*(0, 7)
    c) *A*(9, 0), *B*(0, 1)
    d) *A*(*a*, 0), *B*(0, *b*)

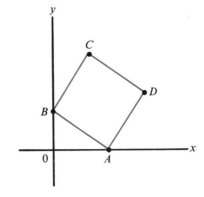

15. The line segment joining *R*(8, 6) and *S*(4, 8) is the shortest side of a right triangle
    RST. If *T* is a point on the *x*-axis, find the possible coordinates of *T*.

16. Two vertices of an isosceles triangle are (−5, 4) and (3, 8). The third vertex is on the
    x-axis. Find the possible coordinates of the third vertex.

17. The coordinates of two vertices of a square are given. Find the possible coordinates
    of the other two vertices.
    a) (0, 0), (2, 5)   b) (3, 1), (0, 5)

18. The diagram shows right triangle *OAB*
    with squares drawn on the three sides.
    Points *P*, *Q*, and *R* are the centres of
    the three squares.
    a) Draw the diagram on a grid.
    b) Show that the segments *AP* and *QR*
        are perpendicular and equal in
        length.
    c) Show that the line segments *BQ*,
        PR, *OR*, and *PQ* are also
        perpendicular and equal in length.

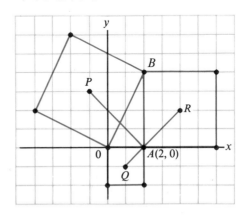

INVESTIGATE

Investigate whether the relations in *Exercise 18* are true for other right
triangles.

PROBLEM SOLVING

Use a Graph

At noon the Mahabir family left for their summer cottage 230 km away.
During the trip their average speed was 73 km/h.
a)   They stopped for gas at 1:20 p.m. How far had they travelled by then?
b)   When did they arrive at the cottage?

Understand the problem

• Did the family travel at 73 km/h at every
  moment during the trip?
• What is meant by average speed?

Think of a strategy

• Draw a graph to represent the journey.

Carry out the strategy

• Draw a graph of distance travelled against time taken.
• Label the horizontal axis *time* and the vertical axis *distance travelled*.

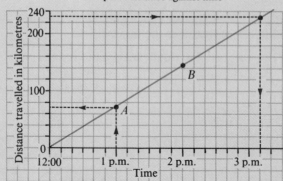

Graph of distance against time

• After 1 h, the family had driven about 73 km. Mark point *A*. After 2 h,
  they had driven about 146 km. Mark point *B*.
  Draw a line through O, A, and B. Using the line, we find that

  a) the family had travelled about 100 km when they stopped for gas

  b) the family arrived at the cottage at about 3:10 p.m.

Look back

• If it were possible to draw a graph showing the position of the car at all
  times during the trip, how would it differ from the graph above?

Solve each problem

1. A 43 km bike-a-thon started at noon. Naheed's average speed for the distance was 18 km/h.
   a) She stopped for refreshment at 12:35. How far had Naheed travelled by then?
   b) When did she finish the bike-a-thon?

2. At 10:00 the MacPhersons left for their summer cottage 270 km away. The first part of the trip was on a highway where they averaged 85 km/h. At 11:30 they stopped for one hour to have lunch. After lunch they completed the trip on a gravel road where they averaged 40 km/h.
   a) How far had the MacPhersons travelled when they stopped for lunch?
   b) When did they arrive at the cottage?

3. Car A leaves Winnipeg at 10 a.m. for Regina at an average speed of 80 km/h.
   a) Draw a graph showing how far Car A travelled during the first six hours.
   b) At noon Car B leaves Winnipeg for Regina on the same highway at an average speed of 100 km/h. Add this information to the graph in part a).
   c) Use the graph to determine when Car B overtakes Car A.

4. Car A leaves Edmonton for Calgary at an average speed of 80 km/h. At the same time Car B leaves Calgary for Edmonton at an average speed of 100 km/h. The two cities are 300 km apart, and both cars travel along the same highway. When they meet, how far are they from Edmonton?

5. A water tank has two taps, A and B. Line A on the graph shows how the tank drains if only tap A is open. Line B shows how the tank drains if only tap B is open.
   a) How long does it take to drain if only tap A is open?
   b) How long does it take to drain if only tap B is open?
   c) Use the graph to find how long it would take to drain the tank if both taps were open.

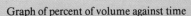
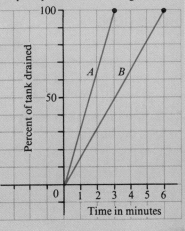

Graph of percent of volume against time

6. Using a power mower, Janet can mow a lawn in 30 min. Using a hand mower, Boris can mow the same lawn in 45 min. How long would it take them to mow the lawn if they worked together?

MATHEMATICS AROUND US

The Line of Best Fit—Long Distance Telephone Calls

One of the most expensive telephone calls you can make is to Australia. The table shows the cost of some typical calls.

Time (min)	4	6	9	11
Cost ($)	12.75	18.25	26.50	32.00

QUESTIONS

1. Plot the data in the table on a grid showing how the cost depends on the length of the call. Draw a straight line through the plotted points.

2. Use the graph to determine the cost of a call lasting
   a) 3 min   b) 5 min   c) 13 min

3. Use the graph to determine how long you could talk for
   a) $20   b) $25   c) $30

4. a) In which of the first three questions did you use interpolation?
   b) In which of the first three questions did you use extrapolation?

5. To call Australia, there is a fixed charged for the first 3 min, and a charge for each additional minute.
   a) What is the charge for the first 3 min?
   b) What is the charge for each additional minute?

Review Exercises

1. Find the length of the line segment with the given endpoints.
   a) $(-6, 3), (9, 3)$
   b) $(4, 11), (4, -3)$
   c) $(3, 7), (-7, -3)$
   d) $(-8, 9), (-3, 4)$
   e) $(5, 2), (1, -6)$
   f) $(-5, 3), (3, -5)$

2. A rectangle has vertices $(-2, -4), (6, -4), (6, 2), (-2, 2)$. Find the
   a) lengths of the sides
   b) perimeter
   c) lengths of the diagonals
   d) area

3. On a grid, draw a triangle with the given vertices and name each type of triangle.
   a) $A(-3, 2), B(0, -2), C(4, 1)$
   b) $P(-3, 7), Q(5, 3), R(7, 7)$

4. Find the coordinates of the midpoint of the line segment with these endpoints.
   a) $(3, -8), (3, 12)$
   b) $(5, -1), (-11, -1)$
   c) $(2, 6), (-10, -12)$
   d) $(5, -3), (13, -7)$
   e) $(-2, 8), (5, 4)$
   f) $(3, 7), (4, -2)$

5. A triangle has vertices $K(3, 7), L(-5, 1), M(7, -5)$.
   a) Find the coordinates of the midpoint of each side.
   b) Find the length of the median from L to KM.

6. On a grid, draw the triangle with vertices $D(-4, 4), E(2, -2), F(4, 6)$. Then find the
   a) length of each side
   b) coordinates of the midpoint of each side
   c) slope of each side

7. Find the slope of the line segment with the following endpoints.
   a) $(3, 8), (-1, -2)$
   b) $(8, -6), (-3, -6)$
   c) $(-3, 8), (4, -5)$
   d) $(-7, 2), (5, 10)$
   e) $(6, -3), (-8, 7)$
   f) $(2, -6), (-3, 9)$

8. A triangle has vertices $P(-3, 4), Q(-2, 2)$ and $R(6, 2)$. If S and T are the midpoints of PR and QR respectively, find the
   a) slopes of ST and PQ
   b) lengths of ST and PQ

9. If $M(3, 2)$ is the midpoint of AB, find the coordinates of B if the coordinates of A are
   a) $(5, -2)$
   b) $(-1, 4)$
   c) $(-2, -3)$
   d) $(0, 0)$

10. Find the coordinates of the midpoint of the longest side of the triangle with vertices $A(3, 8), B(2, 1), C(10, 7)$. How far is this point from each vertex?

11. The vertices of a quadrilateral are $P(1, 4), Q(7, 6), R(11, 2)$ and $S(3, -6)$. Show that the midpoints of the sides of the quadrilateral are the vertices of a parallelogram.

12. A line segment JK has slope $-\frac{2}{3}$, and joins $J(-3, 6)$ to a point K on the x-axis. Find the coordinates of the point K and the point where JK intersects the y-axis.

13. Find the value of *a* if the line segment joining the given points has the given slope.

   a) $P(-2, -1), Q(a, 2)$ slope $\frac{3}{4}$ b) $C(3, -2), D(-5, a)$ slope $-\frac{3}{8}$

14. A triangle has vertices $A(5, 7), B(-3, 4), C(2, -5)$.
   a) Find the slopes of AB and AC.
   b) Find the slope of a line segment through A parallel to BC.
   c) Find the slope of the median from B to AC.

15. Determine whether or not the quadrilateral $A(-1, 4), B(-3, -2), C(3, -1), D(4, 5)$ is a parallelogram.

16. A triangle has vertices $P(-4, -2), Q(6, 4), R(-7, 3)$. Show that $\angle QPR$ is a right angle.

17. State the slope of a line segment parallel to a segment with the given slope.

   a) $-\frac{3}{5}$ b) 4   c) $-\frac{7}{4}$ d) 0.3   e) -8

18. Find the slope of a line segment perpendicular to each segment given in *Exercise 17*.

19. Find the value of *k* if each of the following are slopes of parallel line segments; perpendicular line segments.

   a) $\frac{2}{3}, \frac{10}{k}$ b) $\frac{-1}{2}, \frac{4}{k}$ c) $-\frac{1}{3}, \frac{k}{4}$ d) $\frac{k}{5}, -0.6$

20. Find the slopes of line segments that are parallel to and perpendicular to the given line segments.
   a) $A(2, -3), B(-5, 3)$ b) $P(5, 2), Q(-1, 6)$ c) $M(-3, 7), N(-3, -5)$

21. Determine whether or not the quadrilateral $A(-2, 2), B(-1, 3), C(5, -2), D(4, 3)$ is a parallelogram or a rectangle.

22. Given the points $P(1, 4), Q(-1, -2)$ and $R(4, -3)$. Find the coordinates of a point S such that RS is parallel to PQ and S is on the
   a) *x*-axis   b) *y*-axis

23. Use the points given in *Exercise 22* to find the coordinates of a point S such that RS is perpendicular to PQ and S is on the
   a) *x*-axis   b) *y*-axis

24. In a game of "Flags" one team's flag is located at $A(8, 3)$, and the other team's is at $B(-4, -3)$. If the playing field is a rectangle with vertices $P(-7, 2), Q(-5, -6), R(11, -2)$ and $S(9, 6)$, find the
   a) distance between the flags
   b) coordinates of the midpoint of the segment joining the flags
   c) perimeter of the playing field
   d) length of the diagonals of the field
   e) coordinates of the midpoint of each diagonal

A volcano provides striking evidence that the temperature of the Earth's crust increases as the depth below the surface increases. How is the temperature related to the depth? (See *Example 2* in Section 7-3.)

7-1 THE SLOPE OF A LINE

In the previous chapter, slopes of line segments were determined using the coordinates of the endpoints. We now extend the concept of the slope of a segment to the slope of a line.

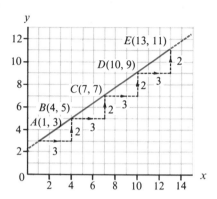

Starting at $A(1, 3)$ on a grid, move 3 units to the right and 2 units up to point B. Then move 3 units to the right and 2 units up to C. Continue in this way to D and E. We observe that A, B, C, D and E all lie on a line.

Choose any two segments of this line, say, AB and BD, or AD and CE and find their slopes:

$$\text{Slope of } AB = \frac{5-3}{4-1}$$
$$= \frac{2}{3}$$

$$\text{Slope of } BD = \frac{9-5}{10-4}$$
$$= \frac{2}{3}$$

$$\text{Slope of } AD = \frac{9-3}{10-1}$$
$$= \frac{2}{3}$$

$$\text{Slope of } CE = \frac{11-7}{13-7}$$
$$= \frac{2}{3}$$

The fact that these slopes are all equal to $\frac{2}{3}$ suggests that the slope of every segment of the line is $\frac{2}{3}$. Similar results apply for other lines.

Constant Slope Property
The slopes of all segments of a line are equal.

The constant slope property allows us to define the slope of a line to be the slope of any segment of the line. For example, the slope of the line shown above is $\frac{2}{3}$.

Example 1. Find the slope of the line shown.

Solution. Locate two points on the line such as $R(-1, 2)$ and $S(3, 5)$. Find the slope of the segment joining them.

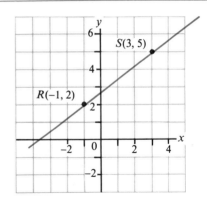

$$\text{Slope of } RS = \frac{5 - 2}{3 - (-1)}$$

$$= \frac{3}{4}$$

The slope of the line is $\frac{3}{4}$.

The constant slope property can be used to draw a line passing through a given point and with a given slope.

Example 2. On a grid, draw a line through $K(4, -2)$ with slope $-\frac{1}{3}$.

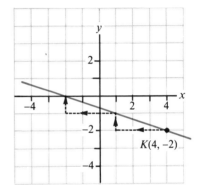

Solution. Starting at $K(4, -2)$, move 3 units to the left and 1 unit up (or, 3 units to the right and 1 unit down). Repeat two or three times to obtain several points on the line. Then draw the line through these points.

In the previous chapter, we found the relations between the slopes of parallel line segments and between the slopes of perpendicular line segments. Since the slope of a line is equal to the slope of any segment of the line, the same relations must be true for lines.

If the slopes of two lines are equal, the lines are parallel. Conversely, if two lines are parallel, their slopes are equal.

If the slopes of two lines are negative reciprocals, the lines are perpendicular. Conversely, if two lines are perpendicular, their slopes are negative reciprocals.

Example 3. On the same axes as in *Example 2*, draw lines through $L(2, 2)$ parallel to, and perpendicular to, the line drawn in *Example 2*.

Solution.   a)   The line in *Example 2* has slope $-\frac{1}{3}$. A line parallel to this line also has slope $-\frac{1}{3}$. Starting at $L(2, 2)$, repeat the steps of *Example 2* to locate points on the line.

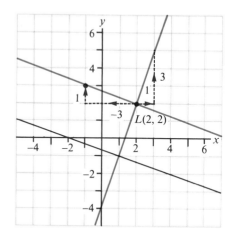

b)   A line perpendicular to the line in *Example 2* has slope 3. Starting at L, move 1 unit to the right and 3 up (or, 1 unit to the left and 3 down), and repeat. Draw the line through these points.

EXERCISES 7-1

Ⓐ

1. State the slope of the line.

a)

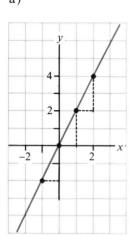

b)

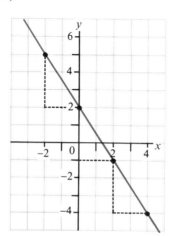

c)

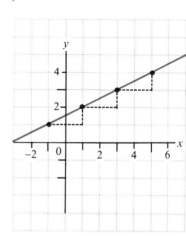

2. On the same axes, draw lines through $E(0, 4)$ with these slopes.

   a) 3   b) 2   c) 1   d) $\dfrac{1}{2}$ e) $\dfrac{1}{3}$

   f) 0   g) $-\dfrac{1}{2}$ h) –1   i) –2   j) $-\dfrac{1}{4}$

   k) –3   l) not defined by a real number

3. a) On a grid, draw a line through $A(0, -3)$ with slope $\dfrac{2}{3}$.

   b) On the same axes, draw three lines parallel to the line in (a); one through $B(0, 0)$, one through $C(0, 3)$, and one through $D(0, 6)$.

   c) On the same axes, draw lines perpendicular to the line in (a), through A, B, C, and D.

4. On a grid, draw a line through
   a) $A(0, 3)$ with slope   i) 1   ii) –1

   b) $R(2, 1)$ with slope   i) $\dfrac{2}{3}$ ii) $-\dfrac{3}{2}$

   c) $L(1, -3)$ with slope   i) $-\dfrac{1}{2}$ ii) 2

   d) $C(5, 4)$ with slope   i) 0   ii) not defined by a real number

Ⓑ

5. On a grid, draw a line through the following points.
   a) $W(3, 5)$ i) with slope $-\dfrac{2}{3}$ ii) perpendicular to the line in (i)

   b) $G(0, 2)$ i) with slope 1   ii) perpendicular to the line in (i)

   c) $T(-2, -1)$ i) with slope 3   ii) perpendicular to the line in (i)

   d) $Q(3, 1)$ i) undefined slope   ii) perpendicular to the line in (i)

6. a) Draw a line through $E(4, 1)$ with slope $\dfrac{3}{2}$.

   b) On the same axes, draw two lines through $F(0, 3)$; one parallel to the line in (a), the other perpendicular to the line in (a).

7. a) Draw a line through $J(-2, 5)$ with slope -2.

   b) On the same axes, draw one line through $K(5, 1)$ parallel to the line in (a) and another line perpendicular to the line in (a).

8. Graph the three points and find the slopes of segments AB, BC, and AC. When you compare their slopes, what do you notice?

   a) $A(0, 1)$, $B(3, 3)$, $C(9, 7)$

   b) $A(-6, 1)$, $B(-2, -1)$, $C(4, -4)$

   c) $A(8, 5)$, $B(-4, 1)$, $C(3, 4)$

9. Points which lie on the same line are called *collinear*. In the diagram, three points A, B, C appear to be collinear.

   a) Find the slopes of AB, BC, and AC.

   b) Determine whether or not the three points are collinear.

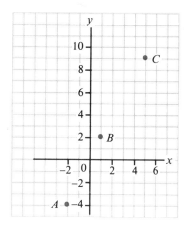

10. Are the following points collinear?
    a) $D(-4, 4)$, $E(0, 2)$, $F(6, -1)$

    b) $J(5, 9)$, $K(1, 4)$, $L(-2, 1)$

    c) $R(-3, -3)$, $S(2, 1)$, $T(11, 8)$

11. a) Graph the line through $P(-4, -2)$ and $Q(6, 4)$.

    b) Draw the lines perpendicular to PQ through P and then through Q.

    c) How are the lines you drew in (b) related?

ⓒ

12. On April 14, 1981, the first American space shuttle, *Columbia*, returned to Earth. At one point in its reentry, it was travelling at approximately 1080 km/h and dropping at 4200 m/min. What was the slope of the reentry path to two decimal places?

13. The points $A(-2, 3)$ and $B(4, 5)$ are two vertices of a right triangle ABC, in which C is on the y-axis. Determine the possible coordinates of C if
    a) $\angle A = 90°$ b) $\angle B = 90°$ c) $\angle C = 90°$

7-2 DIRECT VARIATION

If a ship travels at a steady speed of 50 km/h, then the distance, d, that is travelled is related to the elapsed time, t. The table and the graph show this relationship.

Elapsed time, t (h)	Distance travelled, d (km)
1	50
2	100
3	150
4	200

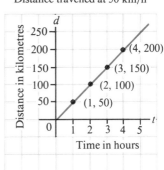

Distance travelled at 50 km/h

The table and graph show that when t is doubled, d is doubled. When t is tripled, d is also tripled, and so on. For this reason, we say that d *varies directly* as t.

The pattern of the numbers in the table suggests that the relation between t and d can be expressed by a formula. In each case, the distance travelled is 50 times the elapsed time. That is, the numbers in the table satisfy the formula:

$$d = 50t$$

where 50 is the speed of the ship, in kilometres per hour.

If y varies directly as x:

the graph of the relation between x and y is a straight line passing through the origin.

the equation relating the variables has the form $y = mx$, where m is called the *constant of proportionality*.

Example 1. In the table, y varies directly as x.

a) By what number are the x-values multiplied to give the corresponding y-values?

b) Complete the table.

c) Write the equation relating x and y.

d) What is the constant of proportionality?

e) Graph the relation between x and y.

x	y
2	▪
5	▪
6	12
▪	16
▪	17

Solution.

a) Since $y = 12$ when $x = 6$, the x-values are all multiplied by 2 to give the corresponding y-values.

b)

x	y
2	4
5	10
6	12
8	16
8.5	17

c) The equation relating x and y is $y = 2x$.

d) The constant of proportionality is 2.

e) The graph is shown.

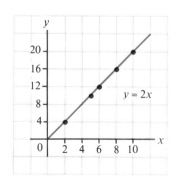

Example 2. Your distance, d, from a flash of lightning is related to the time interval, t, between your seeing the flash and hearing the thunderclap. It can be expressed by the formula: $d = 0.35t$, where d is in kilometres and t is in seconds.

    a) If the time interval is 2.5 s, how far are you from the lightning?

    b) If you are 4.0 km from the lightning, what is the time interval?

    c) Describe the graph of the relation between d and t.

    d) Draw the graph of the relation.

Solution.   a) Substitute 2.5 for t in the formula:

$$d = 0.35t$$

$$= 0.35 \times 2.5$$

$$= 0.875$$

When the time interval is 2.5 s, you are about 0.88 km from the lightning.

    b) Substitute 4.0 for d in the formula:

$$d = 0.35t$$

$$4.0 = 0.35t$$

$$t = \frac{4.0}{0.35}$$

$$\doteq 11.4$$

If you are 4.0 km from the lightning, the time interval is approximately 11.4 s.

    c) The graph of the relation is a straight line through the origin.

    d) The graph is shown.

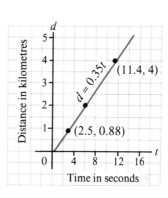

EXERCISES 7-2

Ⓐ

1. If y varies directly as x, how is y affected if x is doubled? x is halved?

2. In each of the following, y varies directly as x.
   a) By what number are the x-values multiplied to give the corresponding y-values?

   b) State the missing numbers.

   c) State the relation between x and y.

i)

x	y
1	■
2	10
3	■
4	■
5	■

ii)

x	y
1	■
2	■
3	■
4	−12
5	■

iii)

x	y
2	■
4	■
6	■
8	■
10	5

iv)

x	y
2	■
4	■
6	9
8	■
10	■

3. For the graph shown,
   a) state the missing numbers in the table of values.

   b) by what number are the x-coordinates multiplied to give the corresponding y-coordinates?

   c) state an equation for the relation between x and y.

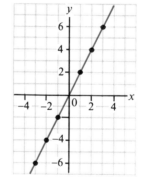

x	y
−3	■
−2	■
−1	■
0	■
1	■
2	■
3	■

4. In each of the following, y varies directly as x.
   a) Find the missing numbers.

   b) Write the equation relating x and y.

   c) Graph the relation between x and y.

i)

x	y
−6	■
■	−2
0	■
3	2
9	■

ii)

x	y
■	2
■	1
■	0
4	■
6	−3

iii)

x	y
0	■
3	2
6	■
9	■
12	■

iv)

x	y
■	0
2	■
4	10
8	■
■	30

(B)

5. The depth of water in a tub varies directly as the length of time the taps are on. If the taps are left on for 4 min, the depth of water is 24 cm.

   a) By what number is the time multiplied to give the water depth?

   b) Find the depth of the water if the taps are left on for 5 min.

   c) Find the length of time the taps were left on if the depth of the water is 42 cm.

   d) Write the equation relating depth to time.

   e) Graph the relation between depth and time.

6. At any given moment during daylight, the lengths of the shadows of objects vary directly as their heights. A tree 10 m tall casts a shadow 16 m long.

   a) By what number are the heights multiplied to give the shadow lengths?

   b) How tall is a tree that casts a shadow 24 m long?

   c) Write the equation relating shadow length to height.

   d) Graph the relation between shadow length and height.

7. For the bike-a-thon, Steven had pledges totalling $1.40 per kilometre.

   a) How much would he collect if he covered 20 km?

   b) How far would he have to ride to collect $40.00?

   c) Write the equation relating the amount collected to the distance covered.

   d) Graph the relation between the amount collected and the distance covered.

(C)

8. The number of tonnes of garbage collected in a city varies directly as the population. A city of 200 000 people generates 125 t of garbage per day. How many tonnes of garbage would you expect to be generated per day in a city with a population of

   a) 50 000?   b) 500 000?   c) 3 200 000?

9. In the diagram shown, the inner circle and the shaded region have equal areas.

   a) Find the equation relating x and y.

   b) Does y vary directly as x? Explain.

10. A square with a side length x is inscribed in a semicircle of radius r. Show that r varies directly as x, and state the constant of proportionality.

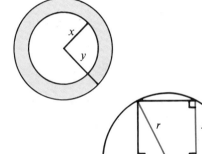

7-3 PARTIAL VARIATION

The cost of publishing a school yearbook consists of two parts:

• **a fixed part**, which represents the cost of setting the type and making the printing plates. This cost is the same no matter how many copies of the yearbook are printed.

• **a variable part**, which represents the cost of the paper, ink, and the operation of the presses. This cost varies directly as the number of copies of the yearbook to be printed.

If the fixed cost is $1000 and the variable cost is $200 for every hundred copies, the table and graph below show how the total cost is related to the number of copies that are printed.

Number of copies, n, in hundreds	Total cost, T, in dollars
0	1000
1	1200
2	1400
3	1600
4	1800
5	2000
6	2200

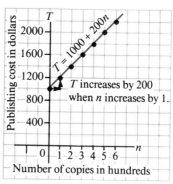

Although the graph is a straight line, it does not represent direct variation. If the number of copies is doubled, the total cost is *not* doubled. However, from the given information we can write the equation which relates T and n.

$$T = 1000 + 200n$$

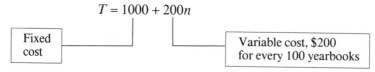

We say that *T varies partially* as *n*.

> If y varies partially as x:
>
> the graph of the relation between x and y is a straight line which does not pass through the origin
>
> the equation relating the variables can be written in the form $y = mx + b$, where m and b are constants, and $b \neq 0$

Example 1. A car's rate of fuel consumption averages 8.0 L/100 km.

a) If the fuel tank contains 60 L of gasoline to begin with, make a table of values relating n, the number of litres of gasoline left in the tank, to d, the distance travelled in hundreds of kilometres.

b) Draw a graph of the relation in (a).

c) Write the equation relating n and d.

d) When the car has travelled 280 km, about how much fuel is left in the tank?

Solution. a)

Distance in hundreds of kilometres (d)	Litres of fuel left in tank (n)
0	60
1	52
2	44
3	36
4	28
5	20
6	12
7	4

Increasing distance by 100 km...

...reduces amount of fuel by 8 L.

b)

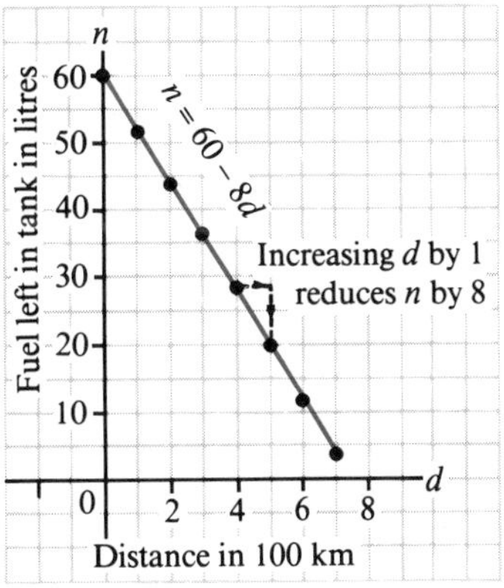

$n = 60 - 8d$

Increasing d by 1 reduces n by 8

c) The equation relating n and d is: $n = 60 - 8d$.

d) Substitute 2.8 for d: $n = 60 - 8(2.8)$
$$= 60 - 22.4$$
$$= 37.6$$

There is about 37.6 L of fuel left in the tank after the car has travelled 280 km.

Example 2. The temperature of the Earth's crust increases as the depth below the surface increases, as shown on the graph.

   a) Find the equation relating the depth, d, in kilometres, to the temperature, T, in degrees Celsius.

   b) What is the temperature at a depth of 3.2 km?

   c) At what depth is the temperature 60°C?

Solution.   a) The graph shows that the temperature at the surface ($d = 0$) is 20°C, and that the temperature increases 10°C for an increase in depth of 1 km. Therefore, the equation relating d and T is:

$$T = 10d + 20$$

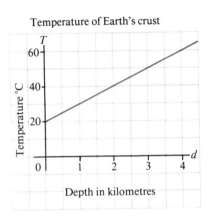

Temperature of Earth's crust

Depth in kilometres

   b) Substitute 3.2 for d:

$$T = 10(3.2) + 20$$

$$= 52$$

At a depth of 3.2 km, the temperature is 52°C.

   c) Substitute 60 for T:
$$60 = 10d + 20$$
$$40 = 10d$$
$$d = 4$$

The temperature is 60°C at a depth of 4 km.

EXERCISES 7-3

Ⓐ

1. The relation between x and y is given by $y = 4x - 3$.
   a) Draw the graph of this relation.
   b) Find y when $x = 7$.
   c) Find x when $y = 45$.

2. The graph represents a partial variation between x and y.
   a) Construct a table of values.
   b) Find y when $x = 5$.
   c) Find x when $y = 12$.
   d) Find the equation relating x and y.

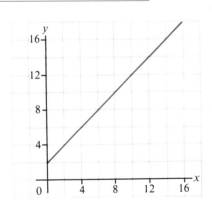

3. The graph represents the cost of printing election pamphlets.

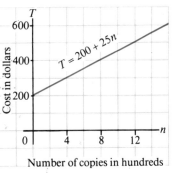

   a) Construct a table of values for n and T, where n is the number of pamphlets, in hundreds, and T is the cost, in dollars.

   b) In this printing job, what is the fixed cost and what is the variable cost?

   c) What is the cost of printing 2500 pamphlets?

   d) How many pamphlets can be printed for $500?

4. The fuel left (n litres) in the tank of a car after the car has been driven d hundreds of kilometres is given by the equation $n = 72 - 9d$.

   a) Construct a table of values for this relation.

   b) Graph the relation.

   c) How much fuel is left after 560 km?

   d) How far has the car been driven if 30 L of fuel remain?

Ⓑ

5. Water rates in the Township of Woolwich consist of a service charge of $2.00 plus $0.56 for each 100 units used.

   a) Construct a table of values relating the water charge, C, to n, the number of units of water used.

   b) Draw the graph of this relation.

   c) Write the equation relating n and C.

   d) If the water bill is $8.72, how many units were used?

6. The cost, C, of photofinishing varies partially as the number of exposures, n, on a roll.

   a) Graph this relation.

   b) Find the equation relating n and C.

Photofinishing
12 exposures—$7.00
24 exposures—$11.00
36 exposures—$15.00

7. The annual cost of owning a car varies partially as the distance driven. The cost is $3700 for 10 000 km, and $7450 for 25 000 km.

   a) Graph this relation.

   b) What is the fixed cost of owning a car?

   c) Determine the equation relating the total cost to the distance driven.

   d) Find the annual cost if 15 000 km are driven.

Ⓒ

8. A set of rectangles are all 5 cm wide. Graph the relation between the perimeter and the length of these rectangles. Express the relation as an equation.

MATHEMATICS AROUND US

The Line of Best Fit—Growing Vegetables Underground

It is very costly to transport vegetables to isolated mining communities. One proposal to reduce this cost is to grow vegetables in abandoned mine shafts. Since the Earth becomes hotter closer to its core, the temperature in a mine shaft increases as you go down the shaft.

A vegetable-growing experiment has been conducted in a mine shaft near Sudbury, Ontario. The table gives the temperature at different depths in the shaft.

QUESTIONS

1. Plot the data in the table on a grid showing how the temperature depends on the depth. Draw a straight line which is as close as possible to the plotted points.

2. Lettuce and tomatoes are grown at the 1249 m level. Use the graph to determine the temperature at that level.

3. Cucumbers are grown at the 1707 m level. What is the temperature at that level?

4. a) In which of the above questions did you use interpolation?

   b) In which of the above questions did you use extrapolation?

Depth (m)	Temperature (°C)
500	3.5
800	9.5
1000	14.5
1500	24.0

INVESTIGATE

In previous sections, equations of straight lines were graphed by making a table of values. There is another method of graphing these equations, which depends on obtaining information about the graph from the numbers in the equation.

Equations of the Form $y = mx$

1. a) Use a table of values to graph the following equations on the same axes:

$$y = x \qquad y = 2x \qquad y = \frac{1}{2}x \qquad y = 0x$$

$$y = -x \qquad y = -2x \qquad y = -\frac{1}{2}x$$

   b) Compare the graphs drawn in (a). How are they the same? How are they different?

2. a) Find the slope of each line you drew in 1.
   b) Compare each slope with the corresponding equation. What do you notice?

3. Each equation you graphed in 1 has the form:

$$y = mx$$

What does this number tell you about the graph?

Equations of the Form $y = mx + b$

4. a) Use a table of values to graph each set of equations on the same axes:

i) $y = 2x + 5$ $y = -\frac{1}{2}x + 5$ ii) $y = 2x + 5$ $y = 2x - 1$
$\quad y = x + 5$ $y = 2x + 3$ $y = 2x - 3$
$\quad y = \frac{1}{2}x + 5$ $y = -x + 5$ $y = 2x + 1$ $y = 2x - 5$
$\qquad\qquad\qquad\quad\; y = -2x + 5$
$\quad y = 0x + 5$

   b) Compare the graphs drawn in (a). How are they the same? How are they different?

5. a) Find the slope of each line you drew in 4.
   b) Compare each slope with the corresponding equation. What do you notice?

6. Each equation you graphed in 4 has the form:

$$y = mx + b$$

What does this number tell you about the graph?

What does this number tell you about the graph?

7-4 THE EQUATION OF A LINE: PART I

One method of graphing a linear equation is to construct a
table of values. Consider the equation $y = 2x + 3$.

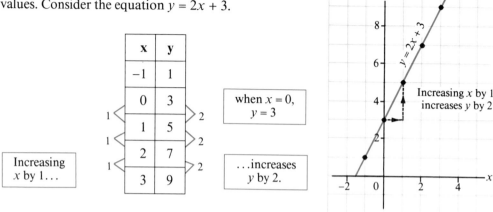

x	y
−1	1
0	3
1	5
2	7
3	9

Increasing
x by 1...

1 ⟩ 2
1 ⟩ 2
1 ⟩ 2

when x = 0,
y = 3

...increases
y by 2.

The table and graph suggest another method for graphing a linear
equation. This method is based on two numbers:

The slope

This is the coefficient
of *x* when the
equation is in the
form $y = mx + b$.
In this case, the slope is 2.

The y-intercept

This is the value of *y*
when $x = 0$. In this case,
the *y*-intercept is 3.

$$y = 2x + 3$$

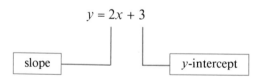

slope   *y*-intercept

The graph of the equation $y = mx + b$ has slope m and y-intercept b.

The equation $y = mx + b$ is called the *slope y-intercept form* of the
equation of a line. We can draw the graph of an equation in this form
without making a table of values.

Example 1. Graph these equations.

a) $y = \dfrac{2}{3}x - 5$
b) $y = -2x + 4$

Solution. a) The slope is $\dfrac{2}{3}$ and the y-intercept is -5.

Begin at $(0, -5)$. Move 3 to the right and 2 up. This is a point on the line. Other points on the line can be obtained by continuing in this way, or by moving 3 to the left and 2 down.

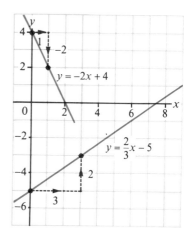

b) The slope is -2 and the y-intercept is 4. Begin at $(0, 4)$. Move 1 to the right and 2 down. This is a point on the line. Other points on the line can be obtained by continuing in this way, or by moving 1 to the left and 2 up.

We can also find the equation of a line in the slope y-intercept form when its graph is given.

Example 2. Find the equations of the lines shown on the grid.

Solution. The slope and the y-intercept of each line can be read from their graphs.

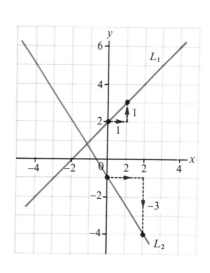

L_1 has a slope of 1 and a y-intercept of 2.

Its equation is $y = 1x + 2$ or,

$$y = x + 2$$

L_2 has a slope of $-\dfrac{3}{2}$ and a y-intercept of -1.

Its equation is $y = -\dfrac{3}{2}x - 1$

EXERCISES 7-4

Ⓐ

1. State the slope and the y-intercept for these lines.

   a) $y = 3x + 5$

   b) $y = -2x + 3$

   c) $y = \frac{2}{5}x - 4$

   d) $y = -\frac{1}{2}x + 6$

   e) $y = -4x - 7$

   f) $y = \frac{3}{8}x - \frac{5}{2}$

   g) $y = \frac{4}{3}x - 2$

   h) $y = \frac{9}{5}x + 1$

2. Write the equation of the line that has

   a) $m = 2, b = 3$

   b) $m = -1, b = 4$

   c) $m = \frac{2}{3}, b = -1$

   d) $m = -\frac{4}{5}, b = 8$

   e) $m = -3, b = \frac{5}{2}$

   f) $m = 0, b = 3$

3. For each line, state the slope, the y-intercept, and the equation.

   a)

   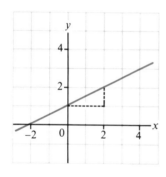

   b)

   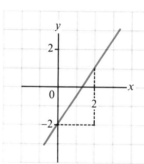

   c)

   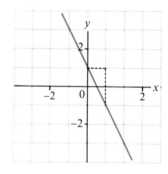

4. Find the equation of each line.

   a)

   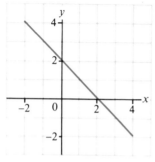

   b)

   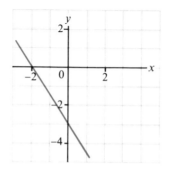

   c)

   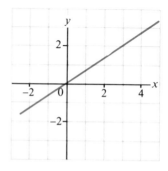

5. Graph these equations.

   a) $y = \frac{2}{5}x + 3$

   b) $y = \frac{3}{4}x - 2$

   c) $y = -\frac{1}{2}x + 1$

   d) $y = -\frac{3}{2}x - 1$

   e) $y = 2x - 3$

   f) $y = -x + 5$

   g) $y = -3x + 2$

   h) $y = 0x - 4$

Ⓑ

6. a) Graph the line $y = -\dfrac{1}{2}x + 3$.

   b) What are the coordinates of the point where the line in (a) intersects the x-axis?

   c) Find the length of the segment between the x- and y-axes.

   d) Shade in the triangle formed by the line and the x- and y-axes. Find its area and its perimeter.

7. Given the lines $y = 2x + 4$ and $y = -x + 7$.
   a) Graph the lines and find the coordinates of their point of intersection.

   b) Shade in the triangle formed by the two lines and the x-axis, and find its area.

8. The equations of the three sides of a triangle are $y = 2x - 4$, $y = -\dfrac{1}{2}x + 6$, and $y = -3x + 1$. Graph the lines on the same axes and find the coordinates of the vertices of the triangle.

9. The equation of a line is $y = 3x + b$. Find the value of b if the line passes through the point
   a) $R(2, 1)$ b) $K(-1, 4)$ c) $A(3, -2)$ d) $B(-2, 2)$

10. The equation of a line is $y = mx + 2$. Find the value of m if the line passes through the point
   a) $D(12, 5)$ b) $S(1, -3)$ c) $E(-2, 6)$ d) $A(-5, 1)$

Ⓒ

11. The equations of the sides of a square are $y = 2x + 10$, $y = 2x - 10$, $y = -\dfrac{1}{2}x + 5$, and $y = -\dfrac{1}{2}x - 5$.

   a) Graph the lines on the same axes.

   b) Find the coordinates of the centre of the square.

   c) Find the equations of the lines through the centre of the square, which are parallel to the sides.

12. The equations of three sides of a square are $y = x + 4$, $y = -x + 6$, and $y = -x + 10$.
   a) Graph the lines on the same axes.

   b) Find a possible equation for the fourth side.

13. Find the equation of the line which passes through the point of intersection of the lines $y = 2x - 5$ and $y = -x + 4$, and is also

   a) parallel to the line $y = \dfrac{2}{3}x + 4$ b) perpendicular to the line $y = \dfrac{3}{4}x - 1$

 PROBLEM SOLVING

Draw a Diagram

A student survey gives this data.

60% of those surveyed have seen movie *A*.
40% have seen movie *B*.
30% have seen movie *C*.

30% have seen both *A* and *B*.
20% have seen both *A* and *C*.
15% have seen both *B* and *C*.

10% have seen all three movies.

What percent of the students have seen at least one of the three movies?

Understand the problem

- Why do the percents have a total of more than 100%?
- What does 'at least one' mean?

Think of a strategy

- Draw a diagram to illustrate the findings of the survey.

Carry out the strategy

- Draw a loop to represent each movie. Inside the loops, write the number of students who watched each movie. Since 10% of the students have seen all three movies, mark 10 in the central region.

- Fill in the data for students who have seen two movies; this includes the students who have seen all three. Since 30% of the students saw *A* and *B*, mark a total of 30 in the overlapping region of *A* and *B*.

- Fill in the data for the students who have seen one movie; this includes the students who have seen two and three movies. Since 60% of the students saw *A*, there is a total of 60 in loop *A*.

- The total of the numbers in the loops, 20 + 20 + 5 + 10 + 10 + 5 + 5, or 75, gives the percent of the students who have seen at least one movie.

Look back

- What percent of the students have not seen any of the movies?
- What percent of the students have seen exactly two of the movies?
- What percent of the students have seen exactly one movie?

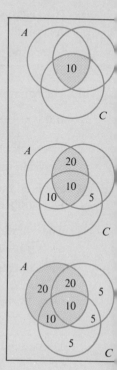

Solve each problem

1. The students in Mr. Crenshaw's class must take at least one of these subjects: French, Music, or Geography. Here is a list of how many students take which subjects.

   14 students take French   7 students take French and Music
   18 students take Music   3 students take French and Geography
   10 students take Geography 5 students take Music and Geography
   2 students take all three subjects

   How many students are in Mr. Crenshaw's class?

2. Four strips of colored cardboard, each measuring 2 cm by 10 cm, are used to make the border for a picture. If none of the cardboard is wasted, what are the possible dimensions of the picture?

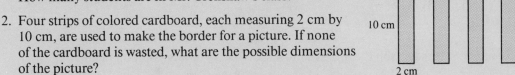

3. The equations of two sides of a rectangle are $y = \frac{1}{2}x + 3$ and $y = -2x + 13$.

   The centre of the rectangle is $R(1, 1)$. Find the equations of the other two sides of the rectangle.

4. Larry drew some triangles with their longest sides 6 cm. The lengths of the other two sides, in centimetres, were whole numbers. What is the greatest number of different triangles Larry could have drawn?

5. A ladder 10 m long leans against a vertical wall. The base of the ladder is 3 m from the wall. If the ladder slips so that the base is 6 m from the wall, how far down the wall does the top of the ladder fall? Give the answer to the nearest tenth of a metre.

6. How many positive integers less than 1000 are divisible by 3 or by 5?

7. Give an example of an equation of a line which has equal x- and y-intercepts.

8. The equation of a line is $y = -\frac{4}{3}x + 8$. Find the perimeter of the triangle formed by this line and the coordinate axes.

9. The radius of the Earth is 6170 km. Mount Everest, at 8850 m above sea level, is the highest point on Earth. The lowest point is the Marianas Trench, at 11 000 m below sea level. If these irregularities were preserved to scale on a relief globe 30 cm in diameter, what would be
   a) the height of the point corresponding to Mount Everest?
   b) the depth of the point corresponding to the Marianas Trench?
   Give the answers to the nearest hundredth of a centimetre.

7-5 THE EQUATION OF A LINE: PART II

In the preceding section, we found the equation of a line when its slope and *y*-intercept were known. If other information about the line is known, we can find its equation using the constant slope property.

Given the slope and a point on the line

There is only one line with a given slope which passes through a given point. The next example shows how its equation can be found.

Example 1.   Find the equation of the line with slope $\frac{2}{3}$ which passes through the point $A(-1, 3)$.

Solution.   First, graph the line as shown. Let $P(x, y)$ be any point on the line.

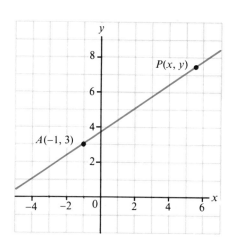

$$\text{Slope of } AP = \frac{y - 3}{x - (-1)}$$

$$= \frac{y - 3}{x + 1}$$

$$\text{Slope of the line} = \frac{2}{3}$$

Since these slopes are equal:

$$\frac{y - 3}{x + 1} = \frac{2}{3}$$

$$2(x + 1) = 3(y - 3)$$

$$2x + 2 = 3y - 9$$

$$2x - 3y + 11 = 0$$

The equation of the line is $2x - 3y + 11 = 0$.

In *Example 1*, the equation was written in the form $Ax + By + C = 0$. This is the *standard form* of the equation of a line.

Given two points on the line

There is only one line which passes through two given points. We find its equation by first finding its slope and then using the constant slope property.

Example 2. Find the equation of the line that passes through the points $R(1, 4)$ and $S(4, -2)$.

Solution. First, graph the line as shown.

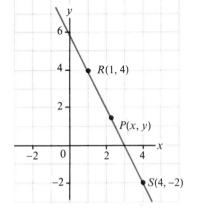

Slope of $RS = \dfrac{-2 - 4}{4 - 1}$

$= \dfrac{-6}{3}$

$= -2$

Let $P(x, y)$ be any point on the line.

Slope of $RP = \dfrac{y - 4}{x - 1}$ Slope of $RS = -2$

Since these slopes are equal:

$\dfrac{y - 4}{x - 1} = -2$

$-2(x - 1) = y - 4$

$-2x + 2 = y - 4$

$-2x - y + 6 = 0$, or $2x + y - 6 = 0$

The equation of the line is $2x + y - 6 = 0$.

The equation in *Example 2* can be checked by substituting the coordinates of the two given points in the equation of the line:

Using point $R(1, 4)$:

L.S. $= 2x + y - 6$ R.S. $= 0$
$= 2(1) + 4 - 6$
$= 0$

Using point $S(4, -2)$:

L.S. $= 2x + y - 6$ R.S. $= 0$
$= 2(4) - 2 - 6$
$= 0$

The equation is correct since it is satisfied by the coordinates of both points.

Property of Equations of Lines

The coordinates of every point on a line satisfy the equation of the line.

The coordinates of any point not on a line do not satisfy the equation of the line.

EXERCISES 7-5

Ⓐ

1. For each line shown, $P(x, y)$ is any point on the line. Find

   a) an expression for the slope of the segment AP

   b) the slope of the line

   c) the equation of the line

   i)   ii)   iii)

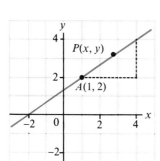
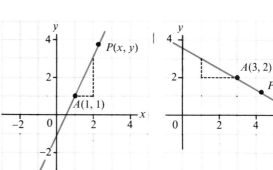

2. The coordinates of a point and the slope of a line are given. Draw a graph of the line through the point with the given slope and find the equation of the line.

   a) $A(2, 5)$, 3   b) $R(-4, 2)$, 7   c) $K(6, -8)$, -4 d) $G(-4, -5)$, 2

   e) $M(-10, 3)$, $-\dfrac{3}{5}$ f) $B(5, -2)$, $\dfrac{2}{3}$ g) $W(-3, 7)$, $-\dfrac{7}{2}$ h) $C\left(\dfrac{1}{2}, \dfrac{3}{4}\right)$, 0

3. Which of the following points lie on the line $3x - 2y + 12 = 0$?

   a) $(3, -2)$ b) $(-4, 0)$ c) $(0, -6)$ d) $(0, 6)$

   e) $(2, 9)$ f) $(-2, 3)$ g) $(4, 12)$ h) $(3, 10)$

4. Which of the following lines pass through the point $(-4, 2)$?

   a) $x + y - 2 = 0$ b) $x - y + 6 = 0$ c) $3x - y + 14 = 0$

   d) $x + 2y = 0$ e) $x - 2y - 8 = 0$ f) $2x + 5y - 2 = 0$

5. The coordinates of two points are given. Draw the line through the points and find the equation of the line. Check that the coordinates of the points satisfy the equation.

   a) $A(2, 2)$, $B(4, 3)$ b) $R(3, 4)$, $S(-3, 0)$ c) $F(-1, 5)$, $G(2, -1)$

   d) $M(3, -3)$, $N(-6, 0)$ e) $C(0, 2)$, $D(4, 1)$ f) $W(-4, 7)$, $V(3, 5)$

6. Find the equation of the line through these points.

   a) $E(2, 1)$ and $F(5, 7)$

   b) $S(-3, 2)$ and $T(1, -10)$

   c) $A(5, -2)$ and $B(7, 5)$

   d) $L(-1, -3)$ and $M(4, 7)$

   e) $Q(4, -1)$ and $R(-2, -5)$

   f) $C(-7, -12)$ and $D(-4, -4)$

   g) $U(3, 7)$ and $V(7, -5)$

   h) $G(-6, -2)$ and $H(-8, 2)$

Ⓑ

7. A triangle has vertices $R(0, 5)$, $S(3, 0)$ and $T(5, 6)$. Draw the triangle on a grid and find the equations of the three sides.

8. Find the equation of these lines.

   a) slope 3, through $M(2, 1)$

   b) slope $-\dfrac{2}{5}$, through $R(-1, 4)$

   c) through $A(-1, 3)$ and $B(3, -1)$

   d) through $K(2, 5)$ and $L(-1, 3)$

   e) slope $\dfrac{3}{4}$, through $F(4, 0)$

   f) slope -2, through $N(0, 5)$

   g) through $S(0, 4)$ and $T(-2, 0)$

   h) slope $-\dfrac{1}{3}$ and y-intercept 2

9. A square has vertices $A(0, 4)$, $B(-6, 0)$, $C(-2, -6)$ and $D(4, -2)$. Draw the square on a grid and find the equations of the

   a) four sides

   b) two diagonals

10. The equation of a line is $3x + 2y + k = 0$. Find the value of k if the line passes through

    a) $(2, -1)$

    b) $(-4, 3)$

    c) $(5, 2)$

    d) $(0, 4)$

    e) $\left(\dfrac{1}{3}, \dfrac{1}{2}\right)$

11. The equation of a line is $2x - 5y + k = 0$. Find the value of k if the line passes through

    a) $(3, 0)$

    b) $(-1, 4)$

    c) $(-7, -2)$

12. In $\triangle ABC$, M is the midpoint of side AB. Find the equation of the line

    a) BC

    b) through A parallel to BC

    c) through M parallel to BC

    d) through M perpendicular to AB

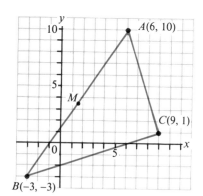

Ⓒ

13. a) Draw the design on a grid, as
    shown, starting with the black
    square with vertices (1, 1), (1, 2),
    (2, 2), and (2, 1).

   b) Find the equations of the following
      lines: AB, CD, EF, GH.
      What do they have in common?

   c) Find the equations of the following
      lines: AI, CJ, KL, MN. Show that
      they all pass through the same
      point. What are the coordinates of
      that point?

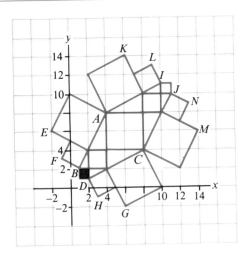

14. a) On a grid, draw the line segment joining $S(-3, 3)$ and $T(7, 7)$.

   b) Draw the perpendicular bisector of segment ST.

   c) Find the equation of the perpendicular bisector.

15. Graph $\triangle ABC$ using vertices $A(-3, 1)$, $B(5, -1)$ and $C(9, 9)$. Draw the
   a) median from A to the midpoint of BC

   b) altitude from C to AB

   c) perpendicular bisector of AC

16. Find the equations of the lines drawn in *Exercise 15*.

17. $P(-6, -4)$, $Q(6, 2)$, $R(-2, 8)$ are the vertices of a triangle. Find the
   a) equations of the three sides

   b) equation of the perpendicular bisector of each side

   c) point of intersection, A, of the perpendicular bisectors, and the lengths of the
      segments AP, AQ, and AR

18. $P(-1, 3)$, $Q(0, 6)$, $R(3, 5)$, $S(3, 0)$ are the vertices of a quadrilateral.
   a) Find the equations of the diagonals.

   b) Is PR the perpendicular bisector of QS?

   c) Is QS the perpendicular bisector of PR?

   d) Is $PQRS$ a rhombus? a parallelogram?

7-6 INTERPRETING THE EQUATION $Ax + By + C = 0$

In previous sections, equations of lines satisfying certain conditions
were found, and the results were written in the standard form,
$Ax + By + C = 0$. When the equation of a line is given in this form,
certain information about its graph can be obtained from it.

Finding the intercepts

The x-intercept of a line is the x-coordinate of the point where the line
intersects the x-axis. Similarly, the y-intercept is the y-coordinate of the
point where the line intersects the y-axis. The diagram suggests the
method of finding these intercepts.

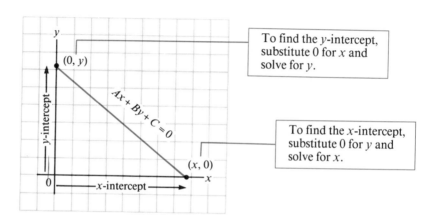

To find the y-intercept,
substitute 0 for x and
solve for y.

To find the x-intercept,
substitute 0 for y and
solve for x.

Example 1.   Given the line with equation $2x - 3y - 10 = 0$.

     a) Find the x-intercept

     b) Find the y-intercept

     c) Graph the line

Solution.   a) Substitute 0 for y:

$$2x - 3(0) - 10 = 0$$
$$2x = 10$$
$$x = 5$$

The x-intercept is 5.

b) Substitute 0 for x:

$$2(0) - 3y - 10 = 0$$
$$-3y = 10$$
$$y = \frac{-10}{3}$$

The y-intercept is $-3\frac{1}{3}$.

c)   Use the information to graph the line.

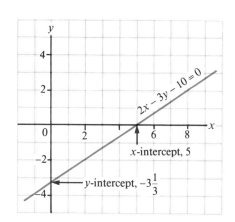

The solution for *Example 1* illustrates a disadvantage of using intercepts to graph a line. If either or both of the intercepts is not an integer, the graph may be inaccurate. An accurate graph can be obtained by making a table of values or by using the following method.

Finding the slope and the *y*-intercept

When the equation of a line is given, its slope may be found by solving the equation for *y*.

Example 2.   Given the line with equation $4x + 3y - 15 = 0$.
a)   Find the slope and the *y*-intercept
b)   Graph the line

Solution.   a)   Solve the equation for *y*:

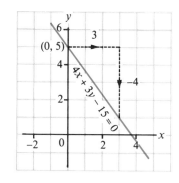

$$4x + 3y - 15 = 0$$
$$3y = -4x + 15$$
$$y = -\frac{4}{3}x + 5$$

From the equation in this form, we see that the slope of this line is $-\frac{4}{3}$, and the *y*-intercept is 5.

b)   Use the above information to graph the line.

Special cases of the equation $Ax + By + C = 0$

When one or more of A, B, or C are zero, the line has certain special properties.

Example 3. Graph these lines.

  a) $x - 3y = 0$

  b) $2y + 4 = 0$

  c) $3x - 12 = 0$

Solution.

a) Solve the equation for y:
$$3y = x$$
$$y = \frac{1}{3}x$$

This line has slope $\frac{1}{3}$ and y-intercept 0. From its graph we see that it passes through the origin.

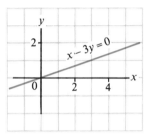

b) Solve the equation for y:
$$2y = -4$$
$$y = -2$$
This equation may be written as $y = 0x - 2$.

From this slope y-intercept form, we see that the line has a y-intercept of -2 and a slope of 0. It is a horizontal line 2 units below the x-axis. The equation $y = -2$ indicates that every point on the line has a y-coordinate of -2.

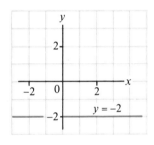

c) The equation $3x - 12 = 0$ cannot be written in slope y-intercept form. When it is written in the form $x = 4$, it indicates that every point on the line has an x-coordinate of 4. The line is a vertical line 4 units to the right of the y-axis.

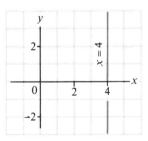

The equation $Ax + By = 0$ represents a line through the origin.
The equation $y = k$ represents a horizontal line.
The equation $x = k$ represents a vertical line.

EXERCISES 7-6

Ⓐ

1. For each line, state the *x*-intercept, the *y*-intercept, and the slope.

a)   b)   c)

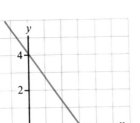 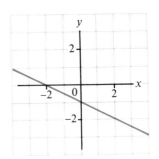

2. Which lines have an *x*-intercept of 3?
   a) $x + 2y - 3 = 0$ b) $2x - 3y - 4 = 0$ c) $2x + 5y - 6 = 0$

3. Which lines have a *y*-intercept of –2?
   a) $x + y + 2 = 0$ b) $3x + 4y + 8 = 0$ c) $2x + 3y - 6 = 0$

4. Find the *x*- and *y*-intercepts, and graph the line.
   a) $x - y - 5 = 0$ b) $3x + y - 9 = 0$ c) $x - 2y + 4 = 0$

   d) $2x - 3y + 12 = 0$ e) $4x - 3y - 24 = 0$ f) $2x + 5y - 6 = 0$

5. Find the slope of each line.
   a) $2x + y - 6 = 0$ b) $x - y + 3 = 0$ c) $3x - 2y + 8 = 0$

   d) $x - 3y - 7 = 0$ e) $4x - 2y - 9 = 0$ f) $2x - 8y - 3 = 0$

6. For each line find the slope and *y*-intercept and graph the line.
   a) $3x - 4y - 12 = 0$ b) $5x - 2y - 10 = 0$ c) $2x + y - 3 = 0$

   d) $3x + 5y + 20 = 0$ e) $x + 2y - 5 = 0$ f) $4x - 7y + 15 = 0$

Ⓑ

7. Graph the line.
   a) $3x - 2y = 6$ b) $2x + y = 4$ c) $5x - 2y = 10$

   d) $4x - 3y + 12 = 0$ e) $x - 2y - 8 = 0$ f) $5x + 3y - 6 = 0$

8. Graph the line.
   a) $x - 2y = 0$ b) $2x + y = 0$ c) $3x - y = 0$ d) $3x + 2y = 0$

   e) $2y - 6 = 0$ f) $3x + 6 = 0$ g) $x = 4$ h) $y = -5$

9. Compare each line listed with the graph of
   $2x - 3y + 6 = 0$.

   Which have the same x-intercept?
   y-intercept?   slope?

   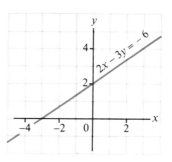

   a) $2x - 3y + 12 = 0$ b) $x + y + 6 = 0$
   c) $3x + 2y - 8 = 0$ d) $3x - 2y + 18 = 0$
   e) $4x - 6y - 9 = 0$ f) $2x - y + 4 = 0$

10. Compare each line listed with the line $x + 2y - 4 = 0$. Which have the same
    x-intercept? y-intercept?   slope?

    a) $x - y + 2 = 0$ b) $3x + 6y + 5 = 0$ c) $2x - y - 8 = 0$
    d) $2x + 4y - 9 = 0$ e) $4x - 3y + 6 = 0$ f) $5x - 7y - 20 = 0$

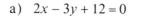

11. The equations of two adjacent sides of a square are $2x + y - 8 = 0$ and
    $x - 2y - 4 = 0$. The vertex of the square which does not lie on either of these sides
    is $A(-2, 2)$.

    a) Draw the square on a grid.

    b) Find the equations of the other two sides of the square.

12. The equations of the sides of a parallelogram are $x + 2y = 8$, $x - 2y = 8$, $x + 2y = 0$,
    and $x - 2y = -8$.

    a) Draw the parallelogram on a grid.

    b) Find the equations of the two diagonals.

13. The equations of the sides of a triangle are $2x + 3y = 18$, $5x + y + 7 = 0$, and
    $3x - 2y = 14$.

    a) Graph the lines on the same axes, and find the coordinates of the vertices of
        the triangle.

    b) Find the lengths of the sides of the triangle.

    c) What are the slopes of the sides?

    d) What kind of triangle is it?

    e) Find the area and the perimeter of the triangle.

INVESTIGATE

Given the line $Ax + By + C = 0$. Find expressions for the slope, the y-intercept,
the x-intercept.

7-7 WORKING WITH PARALLEL AND PERPENDICULAR LINES

Since we can determine the slope of a line from its equation, we can tell, without graphing, whether two given lines are parallel or perpendicular.

Example 1. The equations of four lines are given. Which lines are parallel? Which lines are perpendicular?

a) $3x + 4y - 24 = 0$ b) $3x - 4y + 10 = 0$

c) $4x + 3y - 16 = 0$ d) $6x + 8y + 15 = 0$

Solution.   Solve each equation for y to determine the slopes of the lines:

a) $3x + 4y - 24 = 0$ b) $3x - 4y + 10 = 0$

$\qquad 4y = -3x + 24$ $\qquad -4y = -3x - 10$

$\qquad y = -\dfrac{3}{4}x + 6$ $\qquad y = \dfrac{3}{4}x + \dfrac{5}{2}$

The slope is $-\dfrac{3}{4}$.   The slope is $\dfrac{3}{4}$.

c) $4x + 3y - 16 = 0$ d) $6x + 8y + 15 = 0$

$\qquad 3y = -4x + 16$ $\qquad 8y = -6x - 15$

$\qquad y = -\dfrac{4}{3}x + \dfrac{16}{3}$ $\qquad y = -\dfrac{3}{4}x - \dfrac{15}{8}$

The slope is $-\dfrac{4}{3}$.   The slope is $-\dfrac{3}{4}$.

The slopes of the lines in (a) and (d) are equal. Therefore, the lines $3x + 4y - 24 = 0$ and $6x + 8y + 15 = 0$ are parallel.

The slopes of the lines in (b) and (c) are negative reciprocals. Therefore, the lines $3x - 4y + 10 = 0$ and $4x + 3y - 16 = 0$ are perpendicular.

To find the equation of a line, two facts about the line must be known. One of these facts might be that the line is parallel or perpendicular to a given line.

Example 2. Find the equation of the line through $A(-1, 5)$ which is perpendicular to the line $3x - 2y - 12 = 0$.

Solution. Draw a graph showing the given point and line. To graph the line, solve the equation for y:

$$-2y = -3x + 12$$

$$y = \frac{3}{2}x - 6$$

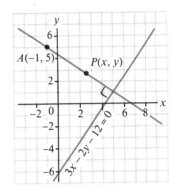

The line has slope $\frac{3}{2}$ and y-intercept -6.

Since the required line is perpendicular to it, its slope must be $-\frac{2}{3}$.

Let $P(x, y)$ be any point on the line.

$$\text{Slope of } AP = \frac{y - 5}{x + 1}$$

Since these slopes are equal:

$$\frac{y - 5}{x + 1} = -\frac{2}{3}$$

$$3(y - 5) = -2(x + 1)$$

$$3y - 15 = -2x - 2$$

$$2x + 3y - 13 = 0$$

The equation of the required line is $2x + 3y - 13 = 0$.

EXERCISES 7-7

Ⓐ

1. Which of these lines are parallel to the line $3x + y - 6 = 0$?
   a) $3x - y - 2 = 0$ b) $3x + y + 9 = 0$ c) $2x + 3y - 6 = 0$

   d) $6x + 2y - 9 = 0$ e) $x + 3y - 6 = 0$ f) $9x + 3y + 20 = 0$

2. Which of these lines are perpendicular to the line $2x - 3y + 12 = 0$?
   a) $3x + 2y - 6 = 0$ b) $2x - 3y - 12 = 0$ c) $3x - 2y - 15 = 0$

   d) $4x + 6y - 11 = 0$ e) $6x + 4y + 15 = 0$ f) $2x + 3y - 8 = 0$

3. Which of these lines are parallel or perpendicular to the line $5x - 2y - 10 = 0$?
   a) $5x - 2y + 8 = 0$ b) $2x + 5y - 12 = 0$ c) $5x + 2y - 10 = 0$

   d) $2x - 5y - 6 = 0$ e) $4x + 10y + 5 = 0$ f) $10x - 4y + 15 = 0$

(B)

4. The three equations represent the sides of a triangle. Determine if the triangle is a right triangle.
   a) $y = 2x + 3$, $x + 2y - 2 = 0$, $3x + 2y + 7 = 0$
   b) $3x - 5y = 10$, $4x + 2y - 9 = 0$, $5x - 3y + 8 = 0$
   c) $4x + 7y - 12 = 0$, $3x - 6y - 11 = 0$, $2x + y - 17 = 0$

5. Find the equation of the line with y-intercept 3 that is parallel to these lines.
   a) $2x - y + 7 = 0$ b) $x + 4y - 2 = 0$ c) $x - 2y - 1 = 0$

6. Find the equation of the line with y-intercept 3 that is perpendicular to these lines.
   a) $3x + 2y + 8 = 0$ b) $x - 2y + 6 = 0$ c) $x + 3y - 2 = 0$

7. Find the equation of the line parallel to the line $4x - 3y + 12 = 0$ that
   a) has y-intercept -2 b) passes through $(3, -2)$
   c) passes through $(-6, 0)$ d) has y-intercept 2

8. Find the equation of the line through $(4, 1)$ that is

   a) parallel to $y = 3x + 2$ b) parallel to $y = -\dfrac{3}{4}x - 1$

   c) perpendicular to $y = -\dfrac{3}{4}x - 1$ d) parallel to $2x + y - 4 = 0$

   e) perpendicular to $5x - 3y + 12 = 0$ f) perpendicular to $3x + 8y = 7$

(C)

9. The equations of two sides of a rectangle are $x - 2y + 8 = 0$ and $2x + y + 6 = 0$. The vertex which does not lie on either of these lines is $A(6, 2)$. Find the equations of the two sides passing through A.

10. The equations $2x - 3y + 6 = 0$, $3x + 2y - 30 = 0$, $2x - 3y - 20 = 0$, and $3x + 2y - 4 = 0$ represent the sides of a square. Find the equations of the lines through the centre of the square, which are parallel to the sides.

11. Find the equation of the line which passes through the point of intersection of the lines $x + 4y - 7 = 0$ and $2x - y + 4 = 0$, and is
    a) parallel to $3x - 5y + 15 = 0$ b) perpendicular to $6x + 2y - 18 = 0$

INVESTIGATE

$A_1x + B_1y + C_1 = 0$ and $A_2x + B_2y + C_2 = 0$ are two lines. What relations exist among A_1, B_1, C_1, A_2, B_2, and C_2 if the lines are:
a) parallel (but not coincident)? b) coincident? c) perpendicular?

1. State the slopes of the lines shown on the graph.

2. a) On a grid, draw a line through $A(-3, 2)$ with slope $\dfrac{2}{5}$.

   b) Draw a line through $C(-2, -1)$ which is parallel to the line in (a); perpendicular to the line in (a).

3. On the same axes, draw lines through $P(5, 2)$ with these slopes.

   a) $\dfrac{2}{3}$ b) $-\dfrac{1}{4}$ c) $-\dfrac{5}{7}$

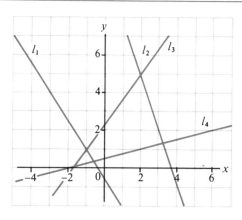

4. Determine whether or not the points $R(8, 5)$, $S(1, -2)$ and $T(5, 2)$ are collinear.

5. If y varies directly as x and $x = 20$ when $y = 15$, find

   a) the equation relating x and y b) x when $y = 60$

   c) y when $x = 30$ d) the constant of proportionality

6. The distance a train travels at constant speed varies directly as the time. If a train travels 275 km in $2\frac{1}{2}$ h, how far will it travel in $1\frac{1}{2}$ h? How long will it take to travel 605 km?

7. The relation between x and y is given by $y = 2x - 3$. Draw the graph. Find

   a) y when $x = 40$ b) x when $y = 37$

8. The annual cost of operating a motorcycle varies partially as the distance driven. The cost is $610 for 4000 km, and $850 for 10 000 km.

   a) Graph the relation between cost and distance.

   b) What is the fixed annual cost of owning a motorcycle?

   c) Determine the equation relating the total cost to the distance driven.

   d) Find the cost of driving 18 000 km in one year.

9. State the slope and the y-intercept for these lines.

   a) $y = 4x - 3$ b) $y = -\dfrac{5}{3}x + 7$ c) $y = -\dfrac{9}{4}x - 3$

10. Write the equation of the line that has

    a) $m = -\dfrac{1}{2}, b = -4$ b) $m = \dfrac{4}{3}, b = -6$ c) $m = -\dfrac{3}{2}, b = \dfrac{3}{4}$

11. Graph these equations.

    a) $y = \dfrac{2}{3}x - 1$ b) $y = -2x + 3$ c) $y = -\dfrac{4}{3}x + 1$ d) $y = x - 5$

12. a) Find the value of b if the line $y = \dfrac{3}{2}x + b$ passes through (4, 7); through $(-6, -4)$.

    b) Find the value of m if the line $y = mx - 3$ passes through (1, 5); through (4, 0).

13. Which of the following points lie on the line $2x - 5y + 4 = 0$?

    a) (3, 2)   b) (7, 4)   c) (−5, 1)   d) (8, 4)   e) $\left(\dfrac{1}{2}, 1\right)$

14. Which of the following lines pass through the point (−3, 4)?
    a) $2x + 3y - 5 = 0$ b) $3x - 2y + 17 = 0$ c) $5x + 2y + 7 = 0$

15. Find the equation of the line that passes through these points.
    a) (3, 5) and (−5, −3)   b) (−4, 7) and (5, −4)
    c) (2, 10) and (−2, −6)   d) (−8, 3) and (6, −5)

16. Find the equation of the line which passes through (5, 5) that is
    a) parallel to the line $3x + 4y = -16$
    b) perpendicular to the line $5x + 2y = 10$

17. A triangle has vertices $P(-3, -1)$, $Q(9, 3)$ and $R(3, 7)$. Find the equations of the
    a) sides of the triangle
    b) line through R, parallel to PQ
    c) line through R, perpendicular to PQ
    d) median from Q to the midpoint of PR

18. Find the x-intercept, the y-intercept, and the slope for each line.
    a) $2x - 5y + 10 = 0$ b) $4x + y - 12 = 0$ c) $3x - 7y - 14 = 0$

19. Graph each line without making a table of values.
    a) $2x - 3y + 12 = 0$ b) $3x + 5y = 0$ c) $5x + 2y - 15 = 0$
    d) $2y - 8 = 0$ e) $4x - 3y - 16 = 0$ f) $3x + 12 = 0$

20. For what value of k are the lines $3kx - 7y - 10 = 0$ and $2x + y - 7 = 0$ parallel? perpendicular?

21. The equations of the sides of a triangle are $4x - 3y + 9 = 0$, $x - 7y + 21 = 0$, and $3x + 4y - 37 = 0$. What kind of triangle is it?

1. Find the length of the line segment with these endpoints.
   a) $(5, 8), (-3, 2)$
   b) $(-5, 7), (-5, -11)$
   c) $(4, 8), (-8, -4)$
   d) $(2, -3), (9, 4)$
   e) $(-1, 0), (6, 0)$
   f) $(-5, 3), (0, 3)$

2. Find the perimeter of the triangle with vertices $A(2, 2)$, $B(5, 5)$ and $C(8, 2)$. What kind of triangle is $\triangle ABC$?

3. Determine whether or not $P(-4, 3)$, $Q(2, 1)$ and $R(11, -2)$ are collinear.

4. Find the coordinates of the midpoint of the line segment with these endpoints.
   a) $(5, -3), (9, -5)$
   b) $(-6, 3), (10, -7)$
   c) $(-3, 2), (1, -1)$
   d) $(-1, 7), (4, -2)$
   e) $(2, -3), (9, 4)$
   f) $(3, 6), (-5, -3)$

5. Find the slope of the line segment with these endpoints.
   a) $(-3, 7), (7, -3)$
   b) $(2, 8), (-6, 4)$
   c) $(8, -2), (-1, 6)$
   d) $(-5, -5), (10, 4)$
   e) $(-3, -2), (11, 5)$
   f) $(-9, 16), (-3, -8)$

6. The endpoints and slope of a line segment are given. Find the value of k.
   a) $(3, k), (-2, 4)$,   slope $\dfrac{2}{5}$
   b) $(2, 5), (k, -1)$,   slope $-\dfrac{3}{4}$
   c) $(5, -2), (-1, k)$, slope 0
   d) $(-3, -k), (1, -4)$, slope 4
   e) $(k, -3), (8, 7)$,   slope not defined by a real number

7. A triangle has vertices $A(3, 5)$, $B(1, -6)$, $C(-5, 4)$. Find the
   a) slope of AB.
   b) coordinates of the midpoint of BC.
   c) length of the median from A to BC.

8. Quadrilateral $ABCD$ has vertices $A(1, 5)$, $B(-3, -1)$, $C(7, -3)$ and $D(5, 3)$. Show that the midpoints of the sides of the quadrilateral are the vertices of a parallelogram.

9. Find the slopes of two line segments; one parallel to, the other perpendicular to the line segment with endpoints
   a) $(2, 7), (-3, 1)$
   b) $(-2, 4), (4, -3)$
   c) $(-3, -2), (2, 5)$

10. Given the points $A(2, 6)$, $B(5, 2)$ and $C(2, 2)$, find the coordinates of D on the y-axis such that CD is
    a) parallel to AB
    b) perpendicular to AB

11. Find the value of k if the following are slopes of parallel lines; perpendicular lines.
    a) $\dfrac{3}{4}, \dfrac{6}{k}$
    b) $-\dfrac{5}{2}, \dfrac{k}{5}$
    c) $\dfrac{4}{k}, \dfrac{2}{3}$
    d) $\dfrac{k}{6}, \dfrac{3}{2}$
    e) $\dfrac{k}{2}, \dfrac{1}{4}$

12. Find the equation relating x and y, and the missing numbers if

    a) y varies directly as x b) y varies partially as x

x	y
5	-2
10	▥
▥	-8
40	▥
80	▥

x	y
0	▥
1	9
3	▥
4	▥
6	19

13. State the slope and y-intercept.

    a) $y = -2x + 7$ b) $3x - 4y = 12$ c) $x + y = -2$

    d) $5x + 2y = -6$ e) $5 - 4x - 2y = 0$ f) $-2x - y + 3 = 0$

14. Write the equation of the line that has

    a) slope $-\dfrac{2}{3}$, y-intercept 4   b) slope $\dfrac{6}{5}$, y-intercept -3

15. Find the equation of the line that passes through

    a) $(4, 8)$ and $(-3, 6)$ b) $(-5, 10)$ and $(4, -6)$ c) $(0, -2)$ and $(5, -3)$

16. Find the equation of the line which passes through $(-1, 2)$ and is

    a) parallel to the line $2x + 5y = 10$ b) perpendicular to the line $3x - 5y = 15$

17. Find the equation of these lines through

    a) $(-3, 2)$ with slope $-\dfrac{3}{5}$ b) $(-2, 5)$ and parallel to the x-axis

    c) $(-3, 5)$ and $(6, 2)$ d) $(5, 2)$ and perpendicular to the x-axis

18. Graph these lines.

    a) $3x + 2y - 18 = 0$ b) $5x - 3y - 15 = 0$ c) $2x + 5y + 10 = 0$

19. The equations of six lines are given. Find as many pairs of lines as you can that are parallel; perpendicular.

    a) $x - 2y - 10 = 0$ b) $4x - 3y - 12 = 0$ c) $6x + 8y - 24 = 0$

    d) $2x + y - 4 = 0$ e) $2x - 4y - 12 = 0$ f) $x - 2y - 5 = 0$

A car averages 12.5 L/100 km in city driving and 7.5 L/100 km on the highway. If you know how much fuel was used, and how far it was driven, how can you determine the distance driven on the highway? (See *Example 2* in Section 8-9).

8-1 SOLVING SYSTEMS OF LINEAR EQUATIONS BY GRAPHING

Sales personnel at a sporting goods store are given a choice of two methods of remuneration:

Plan A
A monthly salary of $200 plus a 2% commission on all sales.

Plan B
No monthly salary, but a 5% commission on all sales.

Which is the better plan for the employee? This question can be answered using graphs. Let x represent the total monthly sales.

Plan *A*
The monthly remuneration is:
$$y = 200 + 0.02x$$

Plan *B*
The monthly remuneration is:
$$y = 0.05x$$

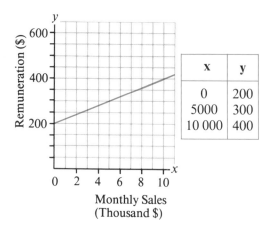

x	y
0	200
5000	300
10 000	400

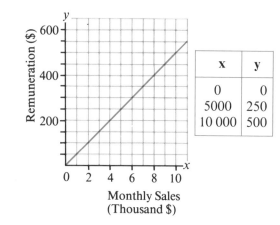

x	y
0	0
5000	250
10 000	500

When the two plans are graphed on the same grid, the two lines intersect. The point of intersection indicates that Plan A is the better plan if sales are less than about $7000. If sales are greater than $7000, then Plan B is better.

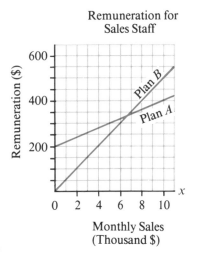

Remuneration for Sales Staff

A pair of linear equations, considered together, is called a *linear system*. To solve a linear system means to find all the ordered pairs (x, y) which satisfy *both* equations. These may be found by graphing both equations on the same grid. If the lines intersect, the coordinates of the point of intersection satisfy both equations. This gives the solution of the linear system.

Example. Solve the following linear system graphically.

$$x - 2y = 6 \quad \dots \text{①}$$
$$3x + y = 11 \quad \dots \text{②}$$

Solution. Make a table of values for each equation.

For $x - 2y = 6$

x	y
6	0
2	-2
0	-3

For $3x + y = 11$

x	y
0	11
1	8
2	5

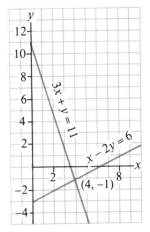

Graph each equation on the same grid. The only point common to both lines is the point of intersection, $(4, -1)$. The solution of the linear system is $(4, -1)$.

Check. Substitute $x = 4$ and $y = -1$ in *both* equations ① and ②.

L.S. $= x - 2y$	R.S. $= 6$	L.S. $= 3x + y$	R.S. $= 11$
$= 4 - 2(-1)$		$= 3(4) + (-1)$	
$= 4 + 2$		$= 12 - 1$	
$= 6$		$= 11$	

The solution $(4, -1)$ is correct.

It is not always possible to obtain the exact solution of a linear system by graphing. If the lines do not intersect on the grid lines, it is necessary to estimate the solution. The exact solution can only be found algebraically.

EXERCISES 8-1

1. Solve by graphing, and check.
   a) $x + y = 5$
      $3x - y = 3$
   b) $x - y = -2$
      $4x + 2y = 16$
   c) $x + y = 7$
      $3x + 4y = 24$
   d) $x - y = 2$
      $3x + y = -14$

   e) $x - y = 4$
      $2x + y = -4$
   f) $5x + 4y = 40$
      $5x + 6y = 50$
   g) $6x - 2y = -20$
      $4x + 2y = -10$
   h) $2x + 8y = 8$
      $-2x + y = 10$

2. Solve by graphing.
   a) $x - 2y = 10$
      $3x - y = 0$
   b) $4x - 6y = 4$
      $3x + 2y = -12$
   c) $10x + 2y = -5$
      $4x + 6y = 2$
   d) $5x - 2y = 8$
      $3x + y = -14$

(B)

3. Solve by graphing.
   a) $2x - y = 80$
      $x + 3y = -30$
   b) $3x + 2y = 60$
      $3x - 5y = -150$
   c) $x + y = -5$
      $2x + y = 20$
   d) $x + 2y = -6$
      $3x + 2y = -34$

4. Solve by graphing.
   a) $x + y = 4$
      $x - y = 1$
   b) $x + 2y = 5$
      $x - 2y = 2$
   c) $2x - y = 8$
      $3x + 6y = 2$
   d) $2x - 3y = 0$
      $4x + 6y = 6$

   e) $3x - 6y = 180$
      $2x + 3y = 30$
   f) $2x + 3y = 2$
      $4x - 3y = 1$
   g) $5x + 4y = 2$
      $2x - 3y = -15$
   h) $2x + 3y = 3$
      $3x - 5y = 25$

(C)

5. a) Solve the following system by graphing.
$$x + 2y = 8$$
$$3x - y = 3$$

   b) Form a new equation by *adding* the two equations in (a). Graph this equation on the same grid. What do you notice?

   c) Form another equation by *subtracting* the two equations in (b). Graph this equation on the same grid. What do you notice?

6. Solve by inspection.
   a) $x + y = 6$
      $2x + y = 8$
   b) $x - y = 1$
      $5x + 2y = 5$
   c) $x + y = -8$
      $2x + y = -11$
   d) $2x + y = 13$
      $x + 2y = 7$

 INVESTIGATE

If two lines are drawn on the same grid, do they always intersect at only one point? What other possibilities are there for two lines?

8-2 PROPERTIES OF LINEAR SYSTEMS

Linear systems have two basic properties which will be used later to develop algebraic methods to solve them.

Multiplying an Equation by a Constant

When we solve the following system graphically, the solution is found to be (4, 1).

$$3x - y = 11 \quad \ldots \text{①}$$
$$x + 2y = 6 \quad \ldots \text{②}$$

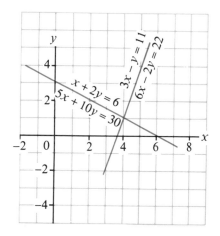

$3x - y = 11$

x	y
0	−11
5	4
3	−2

$x + 2y = 6$

x	y
0	3
6	0
2	2

Consider what happens if we multiply both sides of equation ① by 2 and both sides of equation ② by 5.

$$\text{①} \times 2: \quad 6x - 2y = 22 \quad \ldots \text{③}$$
$$\text{②} \times 5: \quad 5x + 10y = 30 \quad \ldots \text{④}$$

$6x - 2y = 22$

x	y
0	−11
5	4
3	−2

$5x + 10y = 30$

x	y
0	3
6	0
2	2

If we make tables of values for these equations, we see that they are the same as for equations ① and ②. The graphs of the new equations are the same lines as before. This illustrates a basic property of linear systems:

> Multiplying both sides of either equation of a linear system by a constant does not change the solution.

Adding or Subtracting the Equations

When we solved this system, the solution was found
to be (4, 1):

$$3x - y = 11 \quad \dots ①$$
$$x + 2y = 6 \quad \dots ②$$

Consider what happens if we *add* equations ① and ②.

$$\begin{array}{r} 3x - y = 11 \\ x + 2y = 6 \\ \hline 4x + y = 17 \end{array}$$

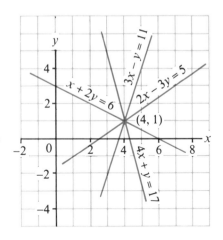

If we graph this equation on the same grid as
equations ① and ②, we see that the line
passes through the same point (4, 1).

$4x + y = 17$

x	y
3	5
4	1
5	−3

Consider what happens if we *subtract* equations ① and ②.

$$\begin{array}{r} 3x - y = 11 \\ x + 2y = 6 \\ \hline 2x - 3y = 5 \end{array}$$

If we graph this equation on the same grid as
equations ① and ②, we see that the line
also passes through (4, 1).

$2x - 3y = 5$

x	y
1	−1
4	1
7	3

This example illustrates another basic property of linear systems:

> Adding or subtracting the equations of a linear system does
> not change the solution.

The properties of linear systems allow us to combine the equations of a linear system without changing the solution.

Example.   Given the following linear system:

a)   Solve the system graphically.

b)   Give examples of two other linear systems which have the same solution.

$$3x + 2y = 18 \quad \ldots ①$$
$$x - y = 1 \quad \ldots ②$$

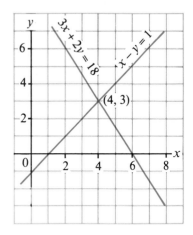

Solution.   a)   For $3x + 2y = 18$

x	y
6	0
0	9
2	6

For $x - y = 1$

x	y
1	0
0	-1
6	5

From the graph, the solution is (4, 3).

b)   Add equations ① and ②:

$$3x + 2y = 18$$
$$\underline{x - y = 1}$$
$$4x + y = 19$$

Subtract equations ① and ②:

$$3x + 2y = 18$$
$$\underline{x - y = 1}$$
$$2x + 3y = 17$$

This system has the same solution as the system in (a). We can check this by substituting 4 for x and 3 for y.

$$4x + y = 19$$
$$2x + 3y = 17$$

To obtain another linear system which has the same solution, we may multiply equations ① and ② by any constant before combining them. For example:

Multiply ① by 2: $6x + 4y = 36$
Multiply ② by 3: $\underline{3x - 3y = 3}$
Add: $9x + y = 39 \quad \ldots ③$

The system formed by equation ③ and equation ② has the same solution as the system in (a).

$$9x + y = 39$$
$$x - y = 1$$

EXERCISES 8-2

Ⓐ

1. State the equations formed by adding the equations; subtracting the equations.
   a) $5x + 2y = 10$ b) $2x - 3y = 12$ c) $x + 5y = 9$ d) $7x - 4y = -8$
       $x + y = 4$ $3x + 5y = 15$ $3x - 2y = -7$ $-9x + 2y = -12$

2. a) Write the equations formed by adding and by subtracting the equations of the linear system shown in each graph below.
   b) Check that the solution of the system is a solution of the equations found in (a).

   i)   ii)

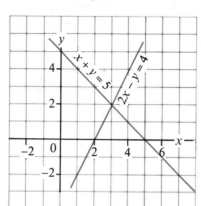
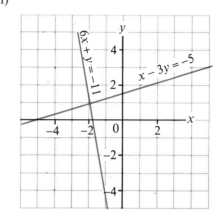

3. Given the linear system:
   $$2x + y = 5$$
   $$x - 3y = -8$$

   a) Solve the system graphically.
   b) Give an example of another linear system which has the same solution.
   c) Check that the solution found for the system in (a) is also the solution of the system in (b).

Ⓑ

4. Give an example of another linear system which has the same solution as each of the following systems.
   a) $2x + 7y = 9$ b) $5x - y = 17$ c) $x - 3y = -11$ d) $3x - 2y = 12$
       $6x - y = 5$ $x + 4y = -5$ $4x + 9y = 2$ $6x + 6y = 30$

5. a) Multiply by the numbers indicated and write the equations formed.

   i) $3x - y = -7$ ①   ii) $x + 2y = 8$ ①
      $x + 4y = 2$ ② $5x - 3y = 1$ ②
   Multiply ① by 2 and ② by 3.   Multiply ① by 3 and ② by 2.

   b) Write the equations formed by adding the equations found in (a).

   c) Write the equations formed by subtracting the equations found in (a).

8-3 SOLVING LINEAR SYSTEMS BY ADDITION OR SUBTRACTION

Solving linear systems by graphing is time-consuming and does not always give exact solutions. It is therefore important to develop algebraic methods to solve them. One method depends on the properties of linear systems illustrated in the previous section.

Example 1. Solve: $3x - 5y = -9$ ...①
                         $4x + 5y = 23$ ...②

Solution.   Since $-5y$ and $5y$ occur in both equations, we can *eliminate* y by adding the equations. According to the properties of linear systems, this will not change the solution.

$$3x - 5y = -9$$
$$4x + 5y = 23$$

Add: $\overline{7x \qquad = 14}$
                $x = 2$

Since the value of x is 2, we can find the value of y by *substituting* 2 for x in either ① or ②. Using ②:

$$4(2) + 5y = 23$$
$$5y = 23 - 8$$
$$5y = 15$$
$$y = 3$$

The solution of this linear system is (2, 3).

Check.   Substitute $x = 2$ and $y = 3$ in both equations ① and ②.

L.S. $= 3x - 5y$ R.S. $= -9$ L.S. $= 4x + 5y$ R.S. $= 23$
$ = 3(2) - 5(3)$ $ = 4(2) + 5(3)$
$ = 6 - 15$ $ = 8 + 15$
$ = -9$ $ = 23$

The solution (2, 3) is correct.

Sometimes it is necessary to multiply one, or both, of the equations by a constant before one of the variables can be eliminated by addition or subtraction. According to the properties of linear systems, this will not change the solution.

Example 2.   Solve: $x - 2y = 7$ ...①
$\qquad\qquad\qquad\quad 3x + 4y = 1$ ...②

Solution.   If we multiply ① by 3, the coefficients of x will be the same in both equations.

$$\begin{array}{ll} \text{Multiply ① by 3:} & 3x - 6y = 21 \\ \text{Subtract ②:} & \underline{3x + 4y = 1} \\ & -10y = 20 \\ & y = -2 \end{array}$$

Substitute -2 for y in equation ①:

$$\begin{array}{rcl} x - 2(-2) & = & 7 \\ x + 4 & = & 7 \\ x & = & 3 \end{array}$$

The solution of this linear system is $(3, -2)$.

If the value of the first variable found is not an integer, it may be easier to find the value of the other variable by elimination rather than by substitution.

Example 3.   Solve: $2x + 3y = 8$ ...①
$\qquad\qquad\qquad\quad 5x - 4y = -6$ ...②

Solution. $$\begin{array}{ll} \text{Multiply ① by 5:} & 10x + 15y = 40 \\ \text{Multiply ② by 2:} & \underline{10x - 8y = -12} \\ \text{Subtract:} & 23y = 52 \\ & y = \dfrac{52}{23} \end{array}$$

$$\begin{array}{ll} \text{Multiply ① by 4:} & 8x + 12y = 32 \\ \text{Multiply ② by 3:} & \underline{15x - 12y = -18} \\ \text{Add:} & 23x = 14 \\ & x = \dfrac{14}{23} \end{array}$$

The solution is $\left(\dfrac{14}{23}, \dfrac{52}{23}\right)$.

EXERCISES 8-3

(A)

1. For which linear systems is $(-1, 1)$ a solution?
   a) $5x + 6y = 1$
      $6x + 2y = -3$
   b) $3x + 4y = 1$
      $5x - 3y = -8$
   c) $3x - 4y = -6$
      $3x + 3y = 1$
   d) $7x - 3y = 10$
      $6x + 5y = -1$

2. Solve and check.
   a) $2x + 3y = 18$
      $2x - 3y = -6$
   b) $3x + 5y = 12$
      $7x + 5y = 8$
   c) $7x - 4y = 26$
      $3x + 4y = -6$
   d) $3x - 4y = 0$
      $5x - 4y = 8$
   e) $7x + 6y = 4$
      $5x - 6y = -28$
   f) $4x - 3y = 20$
      $6x - 3y = 24$
   g) $3x + 5y = 4$
      $3x + 2y = 7$
   h) $-5x + 2y = -1$
      $5x - 4y = -13$

3. Solve and check.
   a) $3x + y = 3$
      $2x + 3y = -5$
   b) $5x + 2y = 5$
      $3x - 4y = -23$
   c) $4x + 3y = 9$
      $2x - 7y = 13$
   d) $2x + 6y = 26$
      $5x - 3y = 11$
   e) $2x - 5y = -18$
      $8x - 13y = -58$
   f) $4x + y = -11$
      $3x - 5y = 9$
   g) $6x - 5y = -2$
      $2x + 3y = 18$
   h) $3x - 10y = 16$
      $4x + 2y = 6$

(B)

4. Solve.
   a) $8x - 3y = 38$
      $4x - 5y = 26$
   b) $3x + 4y = 29$
      $2x - 5y = -19$
   c) $6a - 5b = \dfrac{4}{3}$
      $10a + 3b = 6$
   d) $3s + 4t = 18$
      $2s - 3t = -5$
   e) $2m - 5n = 29$
      $7m - 3n = 0$
   f) $5x + 8y = -2$
      $4x + 6y = -2$
   g) $6x - 2y = 21$
      $3y + 4x = 1$
   h) $3c + 7d = 3$
      $4d - 5c = 42$

5. Solve.
   a) $7x + 6y = 2$
      $x + 8y = -4$
   b) $8x - y = 16$
      $2x - 3y = 2$
   c) $5x = y$
      $-x + 3y = 3$
   d) $3x + 2y = 8$
      $x - 12y = -10$
   e) $3x - y = 5$
      $2x + 3y = 10$
   f) $4x + 3y = 3$
      $3x - 2y = -19$
   g) $\dfrac{x}{3} + \dfrac{y}{2} = \dfrac{1}{6}$
      $x - 6y = 8$
   h) $\dfrac{1}{2}x - \dfrac{2}{3}y = 6$
      $\dfrac{1}{4}x + \dfrac{1}{3}y = -1$

6. Solve.
   a) $\dfrac{1}{3}x + \dfrac{1}{4}y = 0$
      $x + y = -1$
   b) $\dfrac{1}{2}x - \dfrac{1}{3}y = 1$
      $x + \dfrac{1}{4}y = 2$
   c) $\dfrac{2}{3}x + \dfrac{1}{5}y = -2$
      $\dfrac{1}{3}x - \dfrac{1}{2}y = -7$
   d) $\dfrac{x}{4} + \dfrac{y}{2} = 0$
      $x + y = 2$
   e) $\dfrac{1}{3}x + \dfrac{1}{2}y = -\dfrac{1}{2}$
      $\dfrac{1}{5}x - \dfrac{1}{3}y = \dfrac{27}{5}$
   f) $\dfrac{3}{4}x + \dfrac{y}{3} = \dfrac{11}{2}$
      $\dfrac{2x}{5} - \dfrac{3y}{2} = -\dfrac{21}{10}$

7. Solve.
    a) $x + 2y = 8$ b) $2x - y = 19$ c) $2x + 3y = 12$ d) $2x + 3y = 32$
    $y + x = 5$ $3y - 5x = -46$ $4y - 3x = -1$ $2y + 22 = 3x$
    e) $3y - 7x = x$ f) $3x - 10 = 4y$ g) $y + 2x = 10 + 4y$ h) $2(x - 2y) = 26 - 5y$
    $3x - 1 = y$ $6y + 2x = 11$ $4(x + y) = 42 - y$ $3(y - x) = -2(y - 7)$

Ⓒ

8. a) Solve this linear system by graphing.

$$7x - 11y = -22$$
$$2x + 3y = 18$$

   b) Solve the system in (a) by addition or subtraction, and give the solution correct to two decimal places.
   c) Compare the results of (a) and (b). What do you notice?

9. Consider the following linear system.

$$2x - 3y = 10$$
$$-4x + 6y = -20$$

   a) Check that the ordered pairs $(2, -2)$, $(5, 0)$, and $(8, 2)$ are all solutions.
   b) Find two more ordered pairs that are solutions.
   c) Attempt to find the solution by the method of addition or subtraction. Why does this system have infinitely many solutions?

10. Consider this linear system.

$$2x - 3y = 10$$
$$-4x + 6y = -30$$

   a) Attempt to find the solution by the method of addition or subtraction.
   b) Does the system have a solution? Explain.

11. For what values of m and n is $(5, -3)$ the solution for each of the linear systems given?
    a) $mx - y = 23$ b) $mx + ny = 12$ c) $mx + ny = -11$ d) $3mx + 4ny = 30$
    $nx + y = 12$ $mx - ny = 18$ $2mx - 3ny = 8$ $2mx - 5ny = 20$

12. Solve for x and y.
    a) $px + qy = r$ b) $ax + by = c$ c) $mx + y = p$
       $px - qy = s$ $x + y = b$ $nx - y = l$

    d) $lx + my = m$ e) $px + qy = r$ f) $bx + ay = 2ab$
       $mx + ly = l$ $x + y = 0$ $ax + by = a^2 + b^2$

13. Solve for x and y.

    a) $\dfrac{x}{a} + \dfrac{y}{b} = 3$ b) $(a - b)x + (a + b)y = 2(a^2 - b^2)$
                                                    $x + y = 2a$
       $\dfrac{x}{a} - \dfrac{y}{b} = 1$

8-4 SOLVING LINEAR SYSTEMS BY SUBSTITUTION

In the preceding section, a linear system was solved by adding or subtracting equations to eliminate one of the variables. Another way to
eliminate a variable is to use substitution.

Example 1. Solve: $2x - y = 13$ ...①
$4x + 3y = 1$ ...②

Solution. Choose equation ① and express y in terms of x.
$$2x - y = 13$$
$$y = 2x - 13 \quad ...③$$
Substitute this expression for y in equation ② and solve for x:
$$4x + 3(2x - 13) = 1$$
$$4x + 6x - 39 = 1$$
$$10x = 40$$
$$x = 4$$
Substitute 4 for x in ③ and solve for y:
$$y = 2(4) - 13$$
$$= -5$$
The solution of the linear system is $(4, -5)$.

It makes no difference which variable is chosen for elimination.
However, if one has a coefficient of 1 or -1, its choice makes for easier
work since fractions are avoided. In the next example, x is eliminated
because it has a coefficient of 1 in one of the equations.

Example 2. Solve: $x + 6y = 9$ ...①
$3x - 2y = -23$ ...②

Solution. Choose equation ① and express x in terms of y.
$$x + 6y = 9$$
$$x = 9 - 6y \quad ...③$$
Substitute $9 - 6y$ for x in ② and solve for y:
$$3(9 - 6y) - 2y = -23$$
$$27 - 18y - 2y = -23$$
$$-20y = -50$$
$$y = \frac{5}{2}$$

Substitute $\frac{5}{2}$ for y in ③ to find the value of x:

$$x = 9 - 6\left(\frac{5}{2}\right)$$
$$= 9 - 15$$
$$= -6$$
The solution is $\left(-6, \frac{5}{2}\right)$.

Check. Substitute $x = -6$ and $y = \dfrac{5}{2}$ in both equations ① and ②.

L.S. $= x + 6y$ R.S. $= 9$ L.S. $= 3x - 2y$ R.S. $= -23$

$\qquad = -6 + 6\left(\dfrac{5}{2}\right) \qquad\qquad\qquad = 3(-6) - 2\left(\dfrac{5}{2}\right)$

$\qquad = -6 + 15 \qquad\qquad\qquad\qquad\; = -18 - 5$

$\qquad = 9 \qquad\qquad\qquad\qquad\qquad\quad = -23$

The solution is correct.

EXERCISES 8-4

Ⓐ

1. For which of the given linear systems is $(-2, 5)$ a solution?

a) $\begin{aligned} 3x + y &= 1 \\ 2x + 3y &= 11 \end{aligned}$
b) $\begin{aligned} 5x - 3y &= -5 \\ 3x + 2y &= 4 \end{aligned}$
c) $\begin{aligned} -5x - 3y &= -5 \\ 3x + 2y &= 4 \end{aligned}$
d) $\begin{aligned} \dfrac{3}{2}x + \dfrac{2}{5}y &= -1 \\ \dfrac{5}{4}x - \dfrac{3}{10}y &= -4 \end{aligned}$

2. Solve by substitution.

a) $\begin{aligned} x + y &= 9 \\ 2x + y &= 11 \end{aligned}$
b) $\begin{aligned} x + y &= 1 \\ 3x - y &= 11 \end{aligned}$
c) $\begin{aligned} x - y &= 7 \\ 2x + y &= -10 \end{aligned}$
d) $\begin{aligned} 3x + y &= 7 \\ 5x + 2y &= 13 \end{aligned}$

e) $\begin{aligned} 2x + 3y &= 11 \\ 5x - y &= -15 \end{aligned}$
f) $\begin{aligned} 4x + y &= -5 \\ 2x + 3y &= 5 \end{aligned}$
g) $\begin{aligned} 3x + 2y &= 19 \\ 2x - 3y &= -9 \end{aligned}$
h) $\begin{aligned} 5y + 2x &= -2 \\ 5x - 2y &= 24 \end{aligned}$

Ⓑ

3. Solve by substitution and check.

a) $\begin{aligned} 3x - 4y &= -15 \\ 5x + y &= -2 \end{aligned}$
b) $\begin{aligned} 2x + y &= 2 \\ 3x - 2y &= 10 \end{aligned}$
c) $\begin{aligned} 3m - n &= 5 \\ 5m - 2n &= 8 \end{aligned}$
d) $\begin{aligned} 4s - 3t &= 9 \\ 2s - t &= 5 \end{aligned}$

e) $\begin{aligned} 5v + u &= -17 \\ 3u - 4v &= 6 \end{aligned}$
f) $\begin{aligned} x + 5y &= -11 \\ 4x - 3y &= 25 \end{aligned}$
g) $\begin{aligned} \dfrac{x}{2} + \dfrac{y}{2} &= 7 \\ 3x + 2y &= 48 \end{aligned}$
h) $\begin{aligned} \dfrac{a}{2} + \dfrac{b}{3} &= 1 \\ \dfrac{a}{4} + \dfrac{2b}{3} &= -1 \end{aligned}$

4. Solve.

a) $\begin{aligned} 3x + 6y &= 4 \\ x - 2y &= 1 \end{aligned}$
b) $\begin{aligned} 7x + y &= 13 \\ 3x - 2y &= 8 \end{aligned}$
c) $\begin{aligned} 4x + 6y &= 1 \\ x + y &= 4 \end{aligned}$
d) $\begin{aligned} 5x + 3y &= 5 \\ 2x + y &= 8 \end{aligned}$

e) $\begin{aligned} 9x + 2y &= 2 \\ 1 - y &= 4x \end{aligned}$
f) $\begin{aligned} 8x + 4y &= 1 \\ 7x &= -2y \end{aligned}$
g) $\begin{aligned} 9x + 6y &= 4 \\ 8x + 3y &= 9 \end{aligned}$
h) $\begin{aligned} 2x + 8y &= 1 \\ x &= 2y \end{aligned}$

Ⓒ

5. For what values of m and n is $(-1, 2)$ the solution of each linear system?

a) $\begin{aligned} mx + 3y &= 1 \\ 2x + ny &= -4 \end{aligned}$
b) $\begin{aligned} mx + ny &= 3 \\ 4x + ny &= -2 \end{aligned}$
c) $\begin{aligned} mx + ny &= 1 \\ mx + 5y &= 7 \end{aligned}$
d) $\begin{aligned} 2mx + ny &= 6 \\ 3mx - 2ny &= 2 \end{aligned}$

8-5 NUMBER OF SOLUTIONS OF A LINEAR SYSTEM

In the preceding sections, the linear systems always had one solution.
This is given by the point of intersection of the corresponding lines.
But not every linear system has one solution. We can see this by solving
certain systems graphically.

Example 1. Solve by graphing: $3x + y = 12$ ...①
$\qquad\qquad\qquad\qquad\qquad\quad 6x + 2y = 6$ ...②

Solution. Make a table of values for each equation:
For $3x + y = 12$ $\qquad\qquad$ For $6x + 2y = 6$

x	y
0	12
4	0

x	y
0	3
1	0

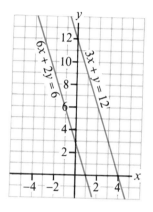

Graph each equation on the same grid. The lines
appear to be parallel. Therefore, the system has
no solution.

In *Example 1*, we can see from the equations that there is no solution. If equation ① is multiplied by 2, the result is $6x + 2y = 24$. No
ordered pair can satisfy this equation and also equation ②.

Example 2. Solve by graphing: $3x + y = 12$ ...①
$\qquad\qquad\qquad\qquad\qquad\quad 6x + 2y = 24$ ...③

Solution. If equation ① is multiplied by 2, the result is equation
③. Therefore, the graphs of the two equations coin-
cide, and there is only one line. Any point on this
line has coordinates which satisfy both equations.
This linear system has infinitely many solutions.

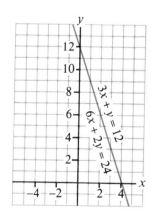

When we solve a linear system there are three possibilities:

Intersecting Lines   **Parallel Lines**   **Coincident Lines**

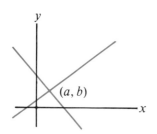   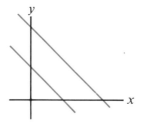   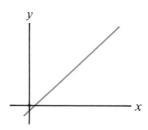

(a, b) is the only
solution.   There is no solution.

There are infinitely
many solutions.

Example 3. Given the equation $x - 2y = 8$. Write a second equation to form a linear system with

a) infinitely many solutions   b) no solution   c) one solution.

Solution.   a) Multiply *both* sides of the given equation by any non-zero number, say 3: $3x - 6y = 24$

This linear system has infinitely many solutions.
$$x - 2y = 8$$
$$3x - 6y = 24$$

b) Multiply *either* side of the given equation by any number, say 2:
$$x - 2y = 16$$
This linear system has no solution.

$$x - 2y = 8$$
$$x - 2y = 16$$

c) Write any equation in which the left side is not a multiple of the left side of the given equation: $x + 3y = 12$
This linear system has one solution.

$$x - 2y = 8$$
$$x + 3y = 12$$

In *Example 3c* we can say that the linear system has one solution, without knowing what the solution is.

EXERCISES 8-5

1. Determine whether the given linear system has infinitely many solutions, no solution, or one solution.

   a) $x + 2y = 6$
       $x + 2y = 2$
   e) $4x - y = 9$
       $3x + y = 5$

   b) $3x + 5y = 9$
       $6x + 10y = 18$
   f) $7x - 2y = 20$
       $5x + y = 12$

   c) $2x - 5y = 30$
       $4x - 10y = 15$
   g) $x - 8y = 24$
       $2x - 16y = 30$

   d) $3x + 2y = 12$
       $6x + 4y = 24$
   h) $6x - 4y = 8$
       $9x - 6y = 12$

2. From the equations listed, write two different linear systems which have infinitely many solutions; no solution; one solution.

   a) $4x + 2y = 20$
   d) $2x + y = 10$

   b) $x - 3y = 12$
   e) $6x + 3y = 5$

   c) $5x - 15y = -60$
   f) $2x - 6y = 24$

B

3. Given the equation $3x - 4y = 12$, write a second equation to form a linear system which has
   a) infinitely many solutions   b) no solution   c) one solution

4. For which of the following linear systems is $(2, -3)$ a solution?

   a) $x - y = 5$
       $3x + 4y = -6$

   b) $2x + y = 7$
      $x - 3y = 10$

   c) $4x - y = 11$
       $-12x + 3y = -33$

   d) $5x - 3y = 19$
       $-2x + 4y = -16$

5. For which of the systems in *Exercise 4* is $(2, -3)$ the only solution?

C

6. In the equation $2x + 5y = 8$, the coefficients form a pattern:

   a) Write two equations with coefficients that form a pattern like this.
   b) Solve the system in (a).
   c) Repeat with other systems. What do you notice?

 INVESTIGATE

Write any linear system which has
a)   no solution   b)   infinitely many solutions.
Investigate what happens when the equations of the system are added or subtracted.

THE MATHEMATICAL MIND

A Scottish Prodigy

The problem of solving systems of equations originated with the ancient Greeks, who created puzzles for mental recreation, but they lacked the symbols to solve the problems systematically.

The Scottish mathematician, Colin Maclaurin, was one of the first to develop a systematic method of solving a system of equations in three or more variables. He was a child prodigy who graduated from university when he was only 11 years old, and became a professor of mathematics when he was a teenager. During his short lifetime he made many important contributions to mathematics.

Colin Maclaurin
(1698-1746)

To solve a system of equations such as the one below, we combine pairs of equations to eliminate one of the variables.

$$
\begin{aligned}
x + 3y + 4z &= 14 \quad \dots ① \\
x + 2y + 3z &= 11 \quad \dots ② \\
x + y + z &= 7 \quad \dots ③
\end{aligned}
$$

Consider equations ① and ②:

$$
\begin{array}{r}
x + 3y + 4z = 14 \\
x + 2y + 3z = 11 \\
\hline
y + z = 3
\end{array}
$$

Subtract:

Consider equations ① and ③:

$$
\begin{array}{r}
x + 3y + 4z = 14 \\
x + y + z = 7 \\
\hline
2y + 3z = 7
\end{array}
$$

Subtract:

Using this method, the given system of three equations in three variables has been reduced to a system of two equations in two variables:

$$
\begin{aligned}
y + z &= 3 \quad \dots ④ \\
2y + 3z &= 7 \quad \dots ⑤
\end{aligned}
$$

This system can be solved using previous methods. The solution is $y = 2$, $z = 1$. To find the value of x, substitute these values for y and z in any one of the three given equations. The result is $x = 4$. Therefore, the solution of the given system of equations is $x = 4$, $y = 2$, $z = 1$.

As with linear systems in two variables, we often need to multiply one or more of the equations by a constant before we can eliminate a variable. For example, this is necessary in the following system:

$$x + 2y + z = 4 \quad ...\text{①}$$
$$2x + y - 3z = 1 \quad ...\text{②}$$
$$-3x + y - z = -15 \quad ...\text{③}$$

Multiply ① by 2 and subtract ②:

$$2x + 4y + 2z = 8$$
$$2x + y - 3z = 1$$

Subtract: $\quad 3y + 5z = 7$

Multiply ① by 3 and add ③:

$$3x + 6y + 3z = 12$$
$$-3x + y - z = -15$$

Add: $\quad 7y + 2z = -3$

The given system of three equations in three variables is now reduced to a system of two equations in two variables:

$$3y + 5z = 7 \quad ...\text{④}$$
$$7y + 2z = -3 \quad ...\text{⑤}$$

Since Maclaurin's time, other mathematicians have developed efficient methods for solving systems of equations. As a result of their work, mathematicians today use computers to solve systems of equations.

1. a) Solve the above system of two equations in two variables.
   b) Substitute your answer to (a) in one of the original equations. What is the solution of the given system?

2. Solve.
   a) $x + 3y + 4z = 19$
      $x + 2y + z = 12$
      $x + y + z = 8$

   b) $x + 5y + 3z = 4$
      $2x + y + 4z = 1$
      $2x - y + 2z = 1$

   c) $4x + 2y - 3z = 7$
      $x + 3y + z = 2$
      $x + 4y - 2z = -9$

3. Solve and check.
   a) $5x + y + 2z = 13$
      $x + y - z = 0$
      $2x - 3y + z = -1$

   b) $2x + 8y + 3z = 13$
      $4x + 6y - 5z = 7$
      $x + 4y - 2z = 10$

   c) $3a + 4b + 2c = 3$
      $2a - b + 4c = 4$
      $2a + 3b = 4$

4. The sum of three numbers is 15. The sum of the first, the second, and twice the third is 20. The sum of the first, twice the second, and three times the third is 27. What are the numbers?

8-6 TRANSLATING WORDS INTO SYMBOLS

Linear systems can be used to solve problems. When the facts of the problem are translated into the language of algebra we can use two different variables. Study the following verbal expressions and their algebraic equivalents in terms of two variables.

Verbal	Algebraic
The tens digit of a two-digit number	x
The ones digit of a two-digit number	y
The number	$10x + y$
The number with the digits reversed	$10y + x$
The sum of the digits	$x + y$
A certain number of dimes	d
A certain number of quarters	q
The value of the dimes (in cents)	$10d$
The value of the quarters (in cents)	$25q$
The total value of the coins (in cents)	$10d + 25q$
The total number of coins	$d + q$

When two numbers are related in a problem, we can use a different variable to represent each one. Then we can use the relation between the numbers to write an equation.

Verbal	Equation
The sum of two number is 72.	$x + y = 72$
Two times one number plus three times another number is 24.	$2x + 3y = 24$
One number exceeds twice another number by 3.	$y = 2x + 3$
4 chocolate bars and 3 ice-cream cones cost \$6.30	$4x + 3y = 630$

EXERCISES 8-6

1. Two numbers are represented by x and y. Translate the following into algebra.
   a) the sum of the two numbers
   b) double the first number plus triple the second number
   c) five times the first number minus four times the second number
   d) the sum of one-half the first number and one-third of the second number

2. Ravi has x $2 bills and y $5 bills. Translate the following into algebra.
   a) the total value of the bills, in dollars
   b) the total number of bills

3. Simone has n nickels and d dimes. Translate the following into algebra.
   a) the value of the nickels, in cents
   b) the value of the dimes, in cents
   c) the total value of the coins, in cents
   d) the total number of coins

4. For the school concert there were a adult tickets and s student tickets. Translate the following into algebra.
   a) the total number of tickets
   b) the total value of the tickets at $4 per adult and $2 per student

5. The tens digit of a two-digit number is x and the ones digit is y. Translate the following into algebra.
   a) the number
   b) the number with the digits reversed
   c) the sum of the digits of the number
   d) the sum of the original number and the number with the digits reversed

6. The length of a rectangle is 10 cm greater than the width. Translate the following into algebra.
   a) the width of the rectangle
   b) the length of the rectangle
   c) the perimeter
   d) the area

7. The length of a rectangle is 3 cm less than double the width. Translate the following into algebra.
   a) the length of the rectangle
   b) the perimeter
   c) the area

Ⓑ

8. A racquet club charges an initiation fee of *x* dollars and a monthly fee of *y* dollars. Translate into algebra.
   a) the fee for two months   b) the fee for six months

9. Chun Kit invested an amount of *x* dollars for one year. Janet invested *y* dollars for one year. Translate the following into algebra.
   a) The interest Chun Kit earned at 6%.
   b) The interest Janet earned at 9%.
   c) The total interest Chun Kit and Janet earned.

Use two variables to represent each of the following algebraically. Then write an equation relating the variables.

10. Two numbers have a sum of 50.

11. The sum of five times one number and four times another number is equal to 40.

12. Four pencils and three pens cost $2.50.

13. Six adult tickets and four student tickets cost $18.

14. A number of nickels and dimes has a total value of $2.

15. Divide 10 into two parts.

16. One number exceeds another number by 15.

17. Two times one number exceeds five times another number by 10.

18. Two numbers such that seven more than the first number is double the second number.

19. One-quarter of one number is 3 more than one-half of a second number.

20. When one number is divided by another number the quotient is 7 and the remainder is 5.

INVESTIGATE

Choose any two different digits and form all possible 2-digit numbers using them. Then add the results, and divide by the sum of the digits. Do this with other pairs of digits. What do you notice about the sums? Can you show this?

8-7 SOLVING PROBLEMS USING EQUATIONS: PART I

To solve a problem using equations, the facts of the problem must be translated into algebraic symbols. If two different variables are used, then *two* different equations must be found. When the system of equations is solved, the problem can be answered.

Example 1. The sum of two numbers is 176, and their difference is 48. Find the numbers.

Solution. Let x represent the larger number. Let y represent the smaller number.

$$
\begin{array}{rl}
\text{The equations are:} & x + y = 176 \quad \text{...①} \\
& x - y = 48 \quad \text{...②} \\
\text{Add:} & 2x = 224 \\
& x = 112
\end{array}
$$

Substitute 112 for x in ①:
$$
\begin{aligned}
112 + y &= 176 \\
y &= 176 - 112 \\
&= 64
\end{aligned}
$$

The numbers are 112 and 64.

Check. The sum of the numbers is $112 + 64 = 176$.
The difference is $112 - 64 = 48$.
The solution is correct.

Example 2. The coin box of a vending machine contains $4.55 in dimes and quarters. If there are 23 coins altogether, how many of each kind are there?

Solution. Let x be the number of dimes, and y the number of quarters. Then the value of the dimes, in cents, is $10x$. The value of the quarters is $25y$.

$$
\begin{array}{ll}
\text{Since there are 23 coins:} & x + y = 23 \quad \text{...①}
\end{array}
$$

Since the total value of the
coins is $4.55, or 455 cents:
$$
\begin{aligned}
10x + 25y &= 455 \quad \text{...②} \\
\text{Multiply ① by 10:} \quad 10x + 10y &= 230 \\
\text{Subtract:} \qquad\qquad\quad 15y &= 225 \\
y &= 15
\end{aligned}
$$

Substitute 15 for y in ①:
$$
\begin{aligned}
x + 15 &= 23 \\
x &= 8
\end{aligned}
$$

There are 8 dimes and 15 quarters in the coin box.

Check.
Value of the dimes, in cents: $\quad 8 \times 10 = 80$
Value of the quarters, in cents: $\quad 15 \times 25 = 375$
Total value: $\qquad\qquad\qquad\qquad\qquad 455$ cents, or $4.55
The solution is correct.

Example 3.   Four chocolate bars and three ice-cream cones cost $5.30. Two chocolate bars and one ice-cream cost $2.20. Find the cost of a chocolate bar and the cost of an ice-cream cone.

Solution.   Let the cost of a chocolate bar be x cents. Let the cost of an ice-cream cone be y cents.

The equations are: $4x + 3y = 530$ ...①
$$2x + \ \ y = 220 \quad ...②$$
Multiply ② by 3: $6x + 3y = 660$
Subtract ①: $\underline{4x + 3y = 530}$
$$2x = 130$$
$$x = 65$$

Substitute 65 for x in ②: $2(65) + y = 220$
$$y = 220 - 130$$
$$= 90$$

A chocolate bar costs 65 cents and an ice-cream cone costs 90 cents.

Check.   Chocolate bars: $4 \times \$0.65 = \$2.60$ $2 \times \$0.65 = \$1.30$
Ice-cream cones: $3 \times \$0.90 = \underline{\$2.70}$ $1 \times \$0.90 = \underline{\$0.90}$
Total: $\$5.30$ Total: $\$2.20$

The solution is correct.

EXERCISES 8-7

1. The sum of two numbers is 25, and their difference is 7. Find the numbers.

2. Find two numbers which have a sum of 53 and a difference of 21.

3. When two numbers are added, the result is 182. When they are subtracted, the result is 48. What are the numbers?

4. Two numbers have a sum of 10. The first number plus three times the second number is 24. Find the numbers.

5. Corina has $31 in $2 and $5 bills. There are 11 bills in all. How many of each does she have?

6. Lucian has $1.15 in dimes and quarters. There are 7 coins altogether. How many of each does he have?

7. The coin box of a vending machine contains $6.20 in dimes and quarters. There are 32 coins in all. How many of each kind are there?

8. For a school play, Janis sold 6 adult tickets and 15 student tickets, and collected $48. Parviz sold 8 adult tickets and 7 student tickets, and collected $38. Find the cost of adult and student tickets.

9. Lorraine buys 6 cheap golf balls and 4 expensive ones for $12.50. Bob buys 4 cheap and 3 expensive balls for $9.00. What are the prices of the two kinds of balls?

Ⓑ

10. The sum of two numbers is 7. Three times one of the numbers is 15 more than the other number. Find the numbers.

11. The sum of two numbers is 19. Four times one of the numbers minus one is equal to the other number. What are the numbers?

12. Two numbers have a difference of 6. The sum of three times the smaller number and twice the larger is 25. What are the numbers?

13. Two numbers differ by 5. Four times the smaller number is 5 less than three times the larger. Find the numbers.

14. Ken has $1.95 in nickels and dimes. There are 3 more nickels than dimes. How many of each does he have?

15. Mirella has $4.80 in nickels and quarters. She has 6 more nickels than quarters. How many of each does she have?

16. The cost of 4 L of oil and 50 L of gasoline is $42.50. The cost of 3 L of oil and 35 L of gasoline is $30.30. Find the cost of 1 L of oil and 1 L of gasoline.

17. When Chana rented a car for 3 days and drove 160 km, the charge was $124. When she rented the same car for 5 days and drove 400 km, the charge was $240. What was the charge per day and the charge per kilometre?

18. The perimeter of a rectangle is 64 cm. Twice the width is 4 cm more than the length. Find the dimensions of the rectangle.

19. The perimeter of a rectangle is 46 cm. What are its dimensions if the length is 4 cm less than twice the width?

20. Divide 10 into two parts such that when the larger is doubled and the smaller is tripled, the sum is 22.

21. Divide 15 into two parts such that when the larger is divided by 3 and the smaller is divided by 2, the quotients are equal.

22. When three times one number is added to four times another, the result is 44. When five times the first number is added to two times the second, the result is 50. What are the numbers?

23. When one number is added to double another number, the result is 29. When double the first number is added to the second, the result is 17. Find the numbers.

24. A scientist worked for 6 days on a project and her assistant worked for 5 days, earning a total of $780. They earned $500 on the next project, which required 4 days' work from the scientist and 3 days' work from the assistant. How much did each earn per day?

25. Mr. Kwok paid $26.00 for movie tickets for himself and 8 children. On another occasion he paid $34.00 for himself, 3 adults, and 4 children. What are the prices of the theatre tickets for adults and children?

Ⓒ

26. The sum of two numbers is five times their difference. What is the quotient when the larger number is divided by the smaller?

27. If 1 is added to the numerator of a fraction, the result is equivalent to $\frac{3}{4}$. If 1 is added to the denominator of the same fraction, the result is equivalent to $\frac{2}{3}$. Find the fraction.

28. If 1 is added to the numerator of a fraction and 2 subtracted from the denominator, the result is equivalent to 2. If 1 is subtracted from the numerator of the same fraction and 2 added to the denominator, the result is equivalent to $\frac{1}{3}$. What is the fraction?

29. Bulldozer operators are paid $80 per day, and laborers are paid $40 per day. One day the payroll was $1400 and there were three times as many laborers as bulldozer operators. On the next day there were 32 workers and the payroll was the same. How many bulldozer operators were working on each day?

30. Find two numbers such that three times the second exceeds twice the first by 1, and the ratio of their sum to their difference is 9 : 2.

MATHEMATICS AROUND US

How Fast Do Glaciers Move?

The Columbia Icefield in Jasper National Park is the largest accumulation of ice in the Rocky Mountains. It is estimated that 6–10 m of snow falls in this region each year. Not all of this snow melts in the summer and, over the centuries, the accumulated snow has been pressed into ice.

The Athabasca Glacier flows from the rim of the Columbia Icefield, and can be seen by travellers from the Banff-Jasper highway. This glacier is about 5.3 km long, 1.2 km wide, and has a maximum thickness of approximately 300 m. However, the glacier is presently receding, because the ice is melting at the end at a faster rate than it can be resupplied from above.

There are two rates associated with the Athabasca Glacier which have been measured:
- The rate of flow of the ice down the mountain—about 10 cm per day;
- The rate of recession of the end of the glacier—about 12 m per year.

These rates depend on the season or on the location on the glacier where the measurements are made.

QUESTIONS

1. a) About how many years might it take ice at the top of the glacier to flow to the end?
   b) About how long would it take to flow the length of your classroom?
   c) About how far has it flowed since you were born?

2. a) About how far has the end of the glacier receded since you were born?
   b) About how long would it take to recede the length of your classroom?
   c) About how long might it take for the glacier to disappear?

3. If the ice stopped flowing down the mountain, what would be the rate of recession of the end of the glacier?

4. What important assumptions did you make in answering the above questions? Discuss the validity of these assumptions.

8-8 SOLVING PROBLEMS USING EQUATIONS: PART II

When solving problems using equations, remember that one variable requires one equation, and two variables require two equations.

Example 1. The sum of the digits of a two-digit number is 12. The number formed by reversing the digits is 54 more than the original number. What is the original number?

Solution. Let the tens digit be x and the ones digit be y.

Original number: $10x + y$

Number with digits reversed: $10y + x$

Since their difference is 54:

$$(10y + x) - (10x + y) = 54$$
$$9y - 9x = 54$$
$$y - x = 6$$
$$-x + y = 6 \quad \dots \text{①}$$

Since sum of digits is 12: $\quad \underline{x + y = 12 \quad \dots \text{②}}$

Add ① and ②: $\qquad\qquad\qquad 2y = 18$
$$y = 9$$

Substitute 9 for y in either ① or ②: $x = 3$

The original number is 39.

Check. $93 - 39 = 54$. The solution is correct.

Although a problem may ask for only one unknown to be found, it is often best to use two unknowns and two equations.

Example 2. A tennis club charges an initiation fee and a monthly fee. At the
end of 1 month a member had paid a total of $260, and at the end of 6
months she had paid a total of $435. What is the initiation fee?

Solution. Let x represent the initiation fee and y the monthly fee.

Amount paid after 1 month is $260: $x + 1y = 260$ ...①
Amount paid after 6 months is $435: $x + 6y = 435$ ...②

$$\begin{aligned} \text{Subtract ①:} \quad x + y &= 260 \\ 5y &= 175 \\ y &= 35 \end{aligned}$$

Substitute 35 for y in ①: $x + 35 = 260$
$$x = 225$$

The initiation fee is $225.

Check. The monthly fee is $35.

Amount paid after 1 month: $225 + $35 = 260
Amount paid after 6 months: $225 + 6 \times $35 = $225 + 210
$$= $435$$

The solution is correct.

Example 3. Barry invested $2000, part at 8% per annum and the rest at 10% per
annum. After one year the total interest earned was $190. How much
did he invest at each rate?

Solution. Let x represent the amount invested at 8%. The interest on this amount
in one year, in dollars, is $0.08x$. Let y represent the amount invested at
10%. The interest on this amount in one year, in dollars, is $0.10y$.

Total money invested: $x + y = 2000$ ...①
Total interest earned: $0.08x + 0.10y = 190$ ...②

$$\begin{aligned} \text{Multiply ② by 100:} \quad 8x + 10y &= 19\ 000 \\ \text{Multiply ① by 8:} \quad 8x + 8y &= 16\ 000 \\ \text{Subtract:} \quad 2y &= 3000 \\ y &= 1500 \end{aligned}$$

Substitute 1500 for y in ①: $x = 500$

Barry invested $500 at 8% and $1500 at 10%.

Check. Interest on $500 at 8%: $0.08 \times 500 = $\ 40$
Interest on $1500 at 10%: $0.10 \times 1500 = 150
Total interest earned: $\overline{$190}$

The solution is correct.

EXERCISES 8-8

1. The sum of the digits of a two-digit number is 14. The number formed by reversing the digits is 36 more than the original number. What is the original number?

2. The sum of the digits of a two-digit number is 13. The number formed by reversing the digits is 27 more than the original number. Find the original number.

3. The sum of the digits of a two-digit number is 7. The number formed by reversing the digits is 45 less than the original number. What is the original number?

4. A sports club charges an initiation fee and monthly fee. At the end of 5 months a member had paid a total of $170, and at the end of 10 months she had paid a total of $295. What is the initiation fee?

5. A tennis club charges an annual fee and an hourly fee for court time. One year, Tony played for 39 h and paid $384. Sandra played for 51 h and paid $456. Find the annual fee and the hourly fee.

6. Jennifer invested $500, part at 7% per annum and the rest at 10% per annum. After one year the total interest earned was $44. How much did she invest at each rate?

7. The tens digit of a two-digit number is 6 more than the ones digit. The sum of the number, and the number formed by reversing the digits, is 88. Find the number.

8. The sum of the digits of a two-digit number is 7. The number formed by reversing the digits is two more than double the original number. Find the original number.

9. When 20 bolts are placed in a box the total mass is 340 g. When there are 48 bolts in the box the total mass is 760 g. Find the mass of the box and the mass of each bolt.

10. A crate of 36 grapefruit has a total mass of 4 kg. When 12 grapefruit are removed the total mass becomes 3 kg. Find the mass of the crate and the mass of a grapefruit.

11. Vien invested $800, part at 9% per annum and the rest at 12% per annum. After one year the total interest earned was $79.50. How much did he invest at each rate?

12. Mee Ha invested $2500, part at 8% per annum, and the rest at 12% per annum. In one year, the two parts earned equal amounts of interest. How much did she invest at each rate?

13. Naomi invested $1000, part at 8% per annum and the rest at 10% per annum. In one year, the two parts earned equal amounts of interest. How much did she invest at each rate?

14. The sum of two numbers is 56. The larger exceeds twice the smaller by 2. What are the numbers?

15. The difference of two numbers is 22. Twice the smaller exceeds the larger by 17. Find the numbers.

16. The coin box of a vending machine contains half as many quarters as dimes. If the total value of the coins is $22.50, how many dimes are there?

17. A collection of dimes and quarters has a value of $5.20. If the number of quarters is 4 more than twice the number of dimes, how many dimes are there?

18. The ones digit of a two-digit number is 5 more than the tens digit. The number formed by reversing the digits is eight times the sum of the digits. Find the number.

19. The sum of the digits of a two-digit number is 6. The number formed by reversing the digits is equal to three times the ones digit. Find the original number.

20. Three footballs and one soccer ball cost $155. Two footballs and three soccer balls cost $220. Find the cost of a football and the cost of a soccer ball.

21. For the school play, adult tickets cost $5.00 and student tickets cost $3.00. Twice as many student tickets as adult tickets were sold. If the total receipts were $1650, how many of each kind of ticket were sold?

22. For the athletic banquet, adult tickets cost $15.00 and student tickets cost $10.00. If 140 tickets were sold, and the total receipts were $1600, how many student tickets were sold?

23. The cost of renting a car depends on the number of days it is rented and the distance it is driven. The cost for one day and 240 km is $39, and the cost for three days and 800 km is $125. What is the cost per day and the cost per kilometre?

24. Denise invested $2000, part at 7% per annum and the rest at 8% per annum. After one year, the interest earned on the 7% investment was $50 more than the interest on the 8% investment. How much did she invest at each rate?

25. Vito invested $500, part at 9% per annum and the rest at 11% per annum. After one year, the interest earned on the 9% investment was $20 less than the interest on the 11% investment. How much did he invest at each rate?

Ⓒ

26. A lifeguard earns an hourly rate for 20 h work in one week and an increased rate for overtime. One week Theresa worked 24 h and received $166.40. The next week she worked 27.5 h and received $200.00. Find her hourly rate and her overtime rate of pay.

27. In a three-digit number, the hundreds digit is equal to the tens digit, and is 2 more than the ones digit. The number formed by reversing the digits is 19 times the sum of the digits. Find the original number.

28. A two-digit number is equal to seven times the sum of its digits.
    a) Show that the tens digit must be double the ones digit.
    b) Show that the number formed by reversing the digits must be equal to four times the sum of the digits.

PROBLEM SOLVING

Use A Table

A power boat has two separate motors. When motor A is used, the boat will run for 3 h on a tank of fuel. When motor B is used, the boat will run for 4 h on the same amount of fuel. How long would a tank of fuel last if both motors were using it?

Understand the problem

- Is the capacity of the tank known?
- What should be assumed about the speed of the boat?
- How can all the information be organized?

Think of a strategy

- Summarize the given information in a table.

Carry out the strategy

- Introduce variables to represent the things we want to know. Let t represent the time the tank of fuel would last if both motors used it. Let V represent the capacity of the tank.

- Make a table with appropriate headings. For this problem, the columns are labelled amount of fuel consumed, rate of consumption, and time. The rows are labelled motor A and motor B.

	Fuel Consumed (L)	Rate Consumption (L/h)	Time (h)
Motor A		$\dfrac{V}{3}$	t
Motor B		$\dfrac{V}{4}$	t

- Insert the given information and the variables. Complete the table. Note that this formula can be used.

$$\begin{array}{c} \text{Amount of Fuel} \\ \text{Consumed} \end{array} = \begin{array}{c} \text{Rate of} \\ \text{Consumption} \end{array} \times \text{Time}$$

Use this formula to complete the table.

	Fuel Consumed (L)	Rate of Consumption (L/h)	Time (h)
Motor A	$\dfrac{Vt}{3}$	$\dfrac{V}{3}$	t
Motor B	$\dfrac{Vt}{4}$	$\dfrac{V}{4}$	t

- Write equation(s) to relate the variables. The total amount of fuel used is equal to the capacity of the tank.

$$\frac{Vt}{3} + \frac{Vt}{4} = V$$

Can you divide both sides of this equation by V?

- Solve the equation and answer the question. How long will the tank of fuel last if both motors are using it?

Look back

- Is it necessary to know the capacity of the tank?
- Is it possible to find the capacity of the tank from the given information?
- How much fuel does motor A use? How much does motor B use?
- Can you solve the problem using a system of two equations in two variables?

The Andersons travelled 880 km from St. John's to Halifax via Argentia. Part of the trip was by car at 80 km/h, and the rest by ferry at 16 km/h. If the total travelling time for the entire trip was 27 h, how many hours were spent by car, and how many by ferry?

Understand the problem

- What does the travelling time depend on?
- How can all the information be organized?

Think of a strategy

- Summarize the given information in a table.

Carry out the strategy

- Introduce variables to represent the things we want to know. Let x represent the time in hours by car. Let y represent the time in hours by ferry.
- Make a table with appropriate headings. For this problem, the columns are labelled distance, speed, and time. The rows are labelled car and ferry.

	Distance (km)	Speed (km/h)	Time (h)
Car		80	x
Ferry		16	y

- Insert the given information and the variables. Complete the table. Recall that distance, speed, and time are related by this formula:

  Distance = Speed × Time

	Distance (km)	Speed (km/h)	Time (h)
Car	$80x$	80	x
Ferry	$16y$	16	y

- Write two equations to relate the variables. Use the columns containing the variables.
  The total distance is 880 km. $80x + 16y = 880$ ...①
  The total travelling time is 27 h. $x + y = 27$ ...②
- Solve the equations and answer the question. How many hours did the Andersons spend travelling by car and by ferry?

Look back

- How far did the Andersons travel by car and by ferry?
- Is this total distance 880 km?

Solve each problem

1. On the return trip from Halifax to St. John's, the Andersons travelled 1540 km via Port aux Basques. Part of the trip was by car at 80 km/h, and the rest by ferry at 25 km/h. If the total travelling time for the entire trip was 22 h, how many hours were spent by car, and how many by ferry?

2. It is a 230 km journey to the Jacksons' cottage. Part of the trip is on gravel roads at 50 km/h and part is on paved roads at 80 km/h. If the total trip takes 4 h, how much time is spent on gravel roads, and how much is spent on paved roads?

3. As part of her physical fitness training, Brenda cycled at 30 km/h and then jogged at 8 km/h. The total time spent was 2 h, and she covered a total distance of 49 km. How much time did she spend jogging?

4. The school hockey team travelled 150 km to a tournament by bus. The bus drove at 90 km/h most of the way, but was delayed by a storm, when its speed was only 30 km/h. If the trip took 3 h, how far did the bus travel in the storm?

5. A farmer set out to travel on a 170 km stretch of lonely prairie highway at an average speed of 105 km/h. He was more than halfway across when his car broke down and he had to complete the journey on foot. He walked at 6 km/h, and the whole trip took 7 h. How long did he walk? How far did he walk?

6. A boat at constant power travels 60 km upriver in 3 h and returns in 2 h. What is the speed of the
   a) boat relative to the water?   b) current?

7. An aircraft travels 2000 km from Winnipeg to Montreal in 3.2 h and returns in 4 h. If the wind speed is constant, find the wind speed and the speed of the aircraft in still air.

8. A boat has two motors, one large and one small. If only the large motor is running, a tank of fuel lasts 2 h. If only the small motor is running, the tank of fuel lasts 4 h. How long will the fuel last if both motors are running?

9. A tank has two taps. If tap A is open, the tank drains empty in 10 min. If tap B is open, the tank drains empty in 6 min. How long would it take to drain the tank if both taps are open?

10. Machine A makes 50 records in 2 min, and machine B makes 50 records in 3 min. With both machines working, how long would it take to make 1000 records?

11. A butcher has supplies of lean beef containing 15% fat, and fat trim containing 100% fat. How many kilograms of lean beef and fat trim does she need to make 50 kg of hamburger, which is 25% fat?

8-9 SOLVING PROBLEMS USING EQUATIONS: PART III

Solving a problem using equations requires a combination of algebraic skill and a strategy for attacking the problem. One such strategy is to use a table.

Example 1. Candy A sells for $2.50/kg. Candy B sells for $5.00/kg. What quantities of each kind of candy should be used to make up a 100 kg mixture to sell for $4.00/kg?

Solution.

Candy	Value ($)	Price ($/kg)	Mass (kg)
A	$2.50x$	2.50	x
B	$5.00y$	5.00	y
Mixture	400	4.00	100

The second and fourth columns give the equations:

$$2.5x + 5y = 400 \quad \ldots \text{①}$$
$$x + y = 100 \quad \ldots \text{②}$$

Multiply ② by 5: $\qquad 5x + 5y = 500$
Subtract ①: $\qquad \underline{2.5x + 5y = 400}$
$$2.5x = 100$$
$$x = 40$$
Substitute 40 for x in ①: $\qquad y = 60$
The mixture should contain 40 kg of candy A and 60 kg of candy B.

Check.   40 kg at $2.50/kg: $100
60 kg of $5.00/kg: $300
100 kg of mixture: $400
The solution is correct.

Example 2. A car averages 12.5 L/100 km in city driving and 7.5 L/100 km on the highway. In a week of mixed driving, the car used 35 L of fuel and travelled 400 km. Determine the distance travelled in highway driving.

Solution. The calculation is simplified if the fuel consumption is expressed in litres per kilometre:
12.5 L/100 km = 0.125 L/km and 7.5 L/100 km = 0.075 L/km

Type of Driving	Fuel Consumed (L)	Fuel Consumption (L/km)	Distance (km)
City	$0.125x$	0.125	x
Highway	$0.075y$	0.075	y
Mixture	35		400

The second and fourth columns give the equations:

$$0.125x + 0.075y = 35 \qquad \ldots \textcircled{1}$$
$$x + \quad y = 400 \qquad \ldots \textcircled{2}$$

Multiply ① by 1000: $125x + 75y = 35\,000$
Multiply ② by 75: $\underline{75x + 75y = 30\,000}$
    Subtract: $50x = \ \ 5\,000$
$$x = \quad\ \ 100$$
Substitute 100 for x in ②: $y = \quad\ \ 300$

The car travelled 300 km in highway driving.

Check.   Fuel consumed in city: $0.125 \times 100 \text{ L} = 12.5 \text{ L}$
Fuel consumed on highway: $0.075 \times 300 \text{ L} = \underline{22.5 \text{ L}}$

Total fuel consumed: 35.0 L
The solution is correct.

Example 3.   A laboratory technician has acid solution in two concentrations, 50% and 100%. She wants to mix the right amount of each to make 400 mL of 60% acid solution by volume. How many millilitres of each solution is needed?

Solution.

	Volume of Acid (mL)	Concentration	Volume of Solution (mL)
50% solution	$0.50x$	0.50	x
100% solution	$1.00y$	1.00	y
60% solution	$(0.60)(400)$	0.60	400

The second and fourth columns give the equations:

$$0.5x + y = \ \ 240 \qquad \ldots \textcircled{1}$$
$$\underline{x + y = \ \ 400} \qquad \ldots \textcircled{2}$$
    Subtract: $- 0.5x = -160$
$$x = \ \ 320$$
Substitute 320 for x in ②: $y = \quad 80$

She needs 320 mL of 50% solution and 80 mL of 100% solution.

Check.   In the final solution, the volume of acid, in millilitres, is:
$$0.50(320) + 1.00(80) = 160 + 80$$
$$= 240$$

Concentration of final solution: $\dfrac{240}{400} \times 100\%$, or 60%

The solution is correct.

EXERCISES 8-9

1. Standard quality coffee sells for $18.00/kg and prime quality coffee sells for $24.00/kg. What quantity of each should be used to produce 40 kg of a blend to sell for $22.50/kg?

2. One grade of mixed nuts costs $8.50/kg, while a second grade costs $6.00/kg. How much of each grade should be used to produce 80 kg of a mixture costing $7.00/kg?

3. Pit-run gravel costs $55.00/m^3 and third-grade gravel costs $70.00/m^3. How much pit-run gravel is required for 100 m^3 of a mixture costing $64.00/m^3?

4. If oil costing $22.50/barrel is combined with oil costing $35.00/barrel, how much of each is required to create 1250 barrels costing $27.50/barrel?

5. A car averages 7.5 L/100 km in city driving and 5.0 L/100 km on the highway. In 300 km of highway and city driving it was found to have used 17.5 L of fuel.
   a) How far was the car driven on the highway?
   b) How much fuel did it use in the highway driving?

6. A 40% sugar solution is added to an 85% sugar solution to create 1800 mL of a 60% solution. How much 40% solution is used?

7. A car averages 9.0 L/100 km in city driving and 7.0 L/100 km on the highway. In 500 km of driving it used 43 L of fuel.
   a) How far was the car driven in the city?
   b) How much fuel did it use in city driving?

8. A car averages 8.5 L/100 km in city driving and 6.3 L/100 km on the highway. In 720 km of driving it used 55.7 L of fuel.
   a) How far was the car driven on the highway?
   b) How much fuel did it use in highway driving?

9. A 21% oil-gas mixture is to be formed by mixing 80% and 20% oil-gas mixtures. If 35 L are required, how much of each should be used?

10. A vinegar-water solution is used to wash windows. If 1200 L of a 28% solution are required, how much of 16% and 36% solutions should be used?

11. A 60% sulfuric acid solution will be mixed with a 95% sulfuric acid solution to produce 2700 mL of a 70% solution. How much of each is required?

12. Divide 48 into two parts such that when the larger number is divided by the smaller, the quotient is 3.

13. Find two numbers such that twice the first exceeds three times the second by 1, and three times the first exceeds twice the second by 14.

14. The distance from Cambridge to Ottawa is 480 km. Gerry is able to drive at 100 km/h on Highway 401 but can only average 60 km/h on Highway 7. If the trip takes 6 h, how far did he travel on Highway 401?

15. Sacha travels from Winnipeg to Calgary, a distance of 1210 km, by train and bus. The train travels at 90 km/h, and the bus travels at 80 km/h. If the total trip takes 14 h, how far did he travel by train?

16. A set of barbells consists of red and blue disks. Disks with the same color have the same mass. Using a balance, Lia found that 7 blue disks balance one red disk and a 5 kg mass, while 2 blue disks and a red disk balance a 4 kg mass. Find the masses of the red and blue disks.

17. Muskoka Tire and Rubber Company produces two grades of radial tires. The cheaper tire requires 3 kg of rubber and takes 3 h of labor for a total production cost of $54.00. The higher grade tire requires 2 kg of rubber and 5 h of labor for a total production cost of $63.00.
    a) What is the cost of 1 kg of rubber?
    b) What is the hourly labor cost?

18. A two-digit number is equal to four times the sum of its digits. If it is increased by 3, the resulting number is equal to three times the sum of its digits. Find the original number.

19. Find a two-digit number such that the tens digit is 3 more than the ones digit, and the number is 3 less than seven times the sum of the digits.

20. The coin box of a vending machine contains twice as many dimes as quarters. If the total value of the coins is $18.00, how many quarters are there?

21. A sum of $4200 was invested, part at 8% and the remainder at 11%. If $426.00 was earned in interest after one year, how much was invested at 11%?

22. Two sisters shared a $36 500 inheritance. Teri invested her share at 9%, while Tammy obtained 8.5% interest. After one year, their combined interest was $3200.00. How much did each sister invest?

23. A candy store merchant sells 25 kg of ju-jubes for $3.00/kg. If he uses one brand selling for $2.25/kg and a second brand selling at $3.75/kg, how much of each brand is required?

24. Korn King livestock feed costs $165.00/t. It consists of feed costing $150/t and feed costing $195/t. How much of each is required for 225 t of Korn King feed?

25. A 22-wheeler uses 36 L/100 km in city driving and 21 L/100 km on the highway. On a 2450 km trip, 585 L of fuel was used.
    a) How far was it driven in the city?
    b) How much fuel was required for the highway?

26. Brand *A* fertilizer is 32% phosphorus, while Brand *B* is 18% phosphorus. How much of each must be used to produce 56 t of a 24% mixture?

27. Sue and Bill paddle 20 km upstream in 4 h. The return trip takes 3 h. What is the speed of the canoe relative to the water, and what is the speed of the current?

28. In a running-swimming race, Richard ran at 12 km/h, and swam at 3 km/h. He completed the race in 1 h 45 min, and travelled 16.5 km. How far did he run?

29. Mr. Ramotar and Mr. Hunter share a driveway. Mr. Ramotar can clear it of snow with his snowblower in 30 min. Mr. Hunter, with a more powerful blower, can clear the driveway in 20 min. How long would it take them to clear the driveway working together?

30. An oil tanker can be filled in 18 h using one pump, and in 15 h using a different pump. If both pumps are used, how long would it take to fill the tanker?

31. A farmer can plow a certain field in 5 h. His daughter, using a larger plow, requires only 3 h. If both work together, how long will it take?

©——

32. Brian's average mark on three mathematics tests was 78. The mark on the first test was 86. His average for the first two tests was 3 more than the mark on the third test. What marks did Brian get on the second and third tests?

33. A two-digit number is equal to four times the sum of its digits. Show that it is also equal to twelve times the difference of its digits.

34. Hoi Ching drives to work in 35 min. If she increases her average speed by 5 km/h she saves 5 min. How far from work does she live?

35. Kevin says to the owner of store *A*: "If you lend me as much money as I have with me, I'll spend $10 in your store." The owner agrees. Kevin then goes on to stores *B* and *C* in turn and makes the same deal. He then has no money left. How much did he start with?

36. It is estimated that to complete an excavation would take 2 days using 4 bulldozers and 3 steam shovels, and 3 days using 5 bulldozers and one steam shovel. How many days would one bulldozer and one steam shovel take?

COMPUTER POWER

A Formula for Linear Systems

If there were many pairs of linear equations to be solved, it would be useful to have a formula to solve them. A program could be written for this formula, and the equations solved by computer. To find such a formula, we solve the linear system:

$$Ax + By = C \ldots ①$$
$$Dx + Ey = F \ldots ②$$

① × E:	$AEx + BEy = CE$	① × D:	$ADx + BDy = CD$
② × B:	$BDx + BEy = BF$	② × A:	$ADx + AEy = AF$
Subtract:	$AEx - BDx = CE - BF$	Subtract:	$BDy - AEy = CD - AF$

$$x(AE - BD) = CE - BF$$

$$x = \frac{CE - BF}{AE - BD}$$

$$y = \frac{CD - AF}{BD - AE}$$

$$= \frac{AF - CD}{AE - BD}$$

The solution of the above linear system is the ordered pair $\left(\dfrac{CE - BF}{AE - BD}, \dfrac{AF - CD}{AE - BD} \right)$, provided that $AE - BD \neq 0$. If $AE - BD = 0$, there may be no solution or infinitely many solutions.
A simple BASIC program for the above formula is as follows:

```
100 REM *** LINEAR SYSTEMS ***
110 INPUT "COEFFICIENTS OF EQUATION #1? ";A,B,C
120 INPUT "COEFFICIENTS OF EQUATION #2? ";D,E,F
130 Z=A*E-B*D
140 IF Z<>0 THEN PRINT "THE SOLUTION IS:";
    (C*E-B*F)/Z,(A*F-C*D)/Z
150 IF Z=0 THEN PRINT "THERE IS NO UNIQUE SOLUTION"
160 END
```

1. Use the program to solve.

   a) $3.3x - 4.2y = 12$
      $1.7x + 2.6y = 30$

   b) $86x + 49y = 97$
      $15x - 24y = -276$

   c) $9.3x + 1.6y = -8.2$
      $4.7x - 7.3y = 6.1$

   d) $26x - 34y = 105$
      $41x + 9y = 83$

   e) $243x + 155y = 528$
      $-62x + 417y = 166$

   f) $3.15x - 5.81y = 12.66$
      $8.69x + 4.07y = -19.22$

 PROBLEM SOLVING

Choose the Strategy

1. If a 20 cm pizza serves two people, how many people should a 40 cm pizza serve?

2. A ball is dropped from a height of 2.0 m. After each bounce it rises to 75% of its previous height.
   a) What height does the ball reach after 5 bounces?
   b) After how many bounces does it reach a height of only 20 cm?

3. How many different integers satisfy the inequality $x^2 \le 1\ 000\ 000$?

4. Every prime number except 2 belongs in one of these two lists.
$$\text{List A:}\quad 3,\ 7, 11, 19, 23, 31,\dots$$
$$\text{List B:}\ 5, 13, 17, 29, 37, 41,\dots$$
   Given any prime number, describe a simple procedure you could use to tell in which list it belongs.

5. Rectangle $OABC$ has vertices $O(0, 0)$, $A(6, 0)$, $B(6, 4)$, and $C(0, 4)$. Find the equation of the line through $D(0, 8)$ which divides the rectangle into two trapezoids with equal areas.

6. It took 3 h to drive 200 km to a summer cottage. Part of the trip was on a highway where the average speed was 100 km/h, and the rest was on a detour where the average speed was 50 km/h. Find the length of the detour.

7. A television program on gifted children began by featuring this puzzle.
$$91\quad 10\quad 1$$
$$87\quad 15\quad \blacksquare$$
   The viewers were asked to determine the number represented by $\blacksquare$. At the end of the program, the "answer" as determined by the producers was announced. They had not realized that there was more than one answer. Determine a possible missing number, and explain the pattern you used to find it.

8. What number is represented by $\blacksquare$ in each pattern?
   a) 3 6 1
      5 3 2
      1 2 $\blacksquare$
   b) 5 3 9
      4 2 7
      1 6 $\blacksquare$
   c) 1 3 5
      4 1 9
      3 1 $\blacksquare$

9. Find a number which has this property. If you add 3 to it, and if you add 4 to it, the product of the two numbers obtained is the same as adding 12 to it.

1. Solve by graphing.
   a) $x + y = -8$
      $x - 2y = 7$
   b) $2x + y = 8$
      $4x - 9y = 5$
   c) $x + 2y = -2$
      $-2x + y = 6$
   d) $x - 2y = -5$
      $-3x + y = 4$

2. Give examples of two other linear systems which have the same solution as the system:
$$2x + 5y = 8$$
$$x - 3y = -7$$

3. Solve by addition or subtraction.
   a) $3x - 4y = 1$
      $3x - 2y = -1$
   b) $3a + 2b = 5$
      $9a - 2b = 15$
   c) $3x - 4y = -2$
      $4x - 3y = -5$
   d) $2s + 3t = 6$
      $5s + 10t = 20$
   e) $3a + 2b = 5$
      $2a + 3b = 0$
   f) $x + 2y = 4$
      $\frac{5}{2}x - 13y = 10$
   g) $3a + 10b = -4$
      $4a - 5b = 13$
   h) $3x + 2y = 8$
      $\frac{7}{2}x + 3y = 8$

4. Solve by substitution.
   a) $x + 2y = 4$
      $3x + 2y = 0$
   b) $2x + y = 9$
      $x - y = 3$
   c) $2x + 3y = 9$
      $x - y = 3$
   d) $2x + 5y = -5$
      $x + y = 2$
   e) $4x + y = -6$
      $-2x + 3y = 24$
   f) $2y + x + 10 = 0$
      $y - 4x = 13$
   g) $y + 4x + 1 = 0$
      $y + 7 = 4x$
   h) $4x + 5y = -15$
      $x - 4y = 12$

5. Solve.
   a) $ax + by = 3c$
      $bx + ay = 2c$
   b) $px + qy = r$
      $qx - py = r$
   c) $mx + ny = 2mn$
      $x + y = 2(m + n)$

6. Determine whether the given linear system has one solution, no solution, or infinitely many solutions.
   a) $5x - 3y = 12$
      $2x + y = 18$
   b) $5x - 3y = 12$
      $10x - 6y = 24$
   c) $5x - 3y = 12$
      $10x - 6y = 3$

7. Give examples of two other systems which have the same solution as each of the systems given.
   a) $4x - y = 8$
      $3x + 2y = 6$
   b) $x + 5y = 6$
      $7x - 2y = 5$
   c) $2x + 5y = 8$
      $x - 3y = -7$
   d) $-6x + 7y = 23$
      $3x - 2y = 5$

8. Represent each of the following algebraically.
   a) Two numbers have a sum of 80.
   b) One number is 7 less than another number.
   c) The sum of three times one number and four times another number is 30.
   d) A number of nickels and dimes has a total value of $3.00.
   e) The perimeter of a rectangle with a length 5 cm greater than the width is equal to 40 cm.

9. The sum of two integers is 36. Their difference is 4. Find the integers.

10. The sum of the digits of a two-digit number is 12. The ones digit is 2 more than the tens digit. Find the number.

11. The sum of two integers is 63. The smaller is 11 more than one-third the larger. Find the integers.

12. Lynn has $3.55 in dimes and quarters. If there are 25 coins altogether, how many dimes are there?

13. From his paper route, Andy collected $5.55 in nickels and dimes. The number of nickels was 6 more than the number of dimes. How many nickels were there?

14. The sum of the digits of a two-digit number is 11. The number formed by reversing the digits is 45 more than the original number. What is the original number?

15. A 100 kg mixture of peanuts contains peanuts of two different kinds, one priced at $2/kg and the other at $2.40/kg. If the mixture is priced at $2.08/kg, how many kilograms of each kind of peanut does it contain?

16. One train leaves a station heading west. A second train, heading east, leaves the same station 2 h later and travels 15 km/h faster than the first. They are 580 km apart 6 h after the second train departed. How fast is each train travelling?

17. A salmon-fishing boat put out to sea early in the morning travelling with the tide. It took 20 min to cover the 6 km to the captain's favorite fishing grounds. The return trip was against the tide and took 36 min. What was the still-water speed of the boat and what was the speed of the tide?

18. Sterling silver is 92.5% pure silver. How many grams of pure silver and sterling silver must be mixed to obtain 100 g of a 94% silver alloy?

19. A company hired four skilled and eight unskilled workers to install a solar-heated swimming pool, paying them a total of $300. To install a similar pool, they hired seven skilled and six unskilled workers paying them $375. What was each type of worker paid for the job?

20. A thin 30 cm candle takes 3 h to burn from one end to the other. A thicker candle with the same length takes 5 h to burn from one end to the other. If the thicker candle is lit at 7 p.m., and the thin candle is lit 30 min later, at what time will the candles be at the same height?

Ore from Rock Island, R, is to be shipped to the countries of Martinesia and New Hampton. Where should the unloading ports, M in Martinesia and N in New Hampton, be built so that the length of the round trip, $R \rightarrow M \rightarrow N \rightarrow R$, is a minimum? (See *Example 2* in Section 9-7.)

9-1 TRANSFORMATIONS AS MAPPINGS

Whenever the shape, size, or position of a figure is changed, it has
undergone a *transformation*. Some common transformations are
illustrated below.

Translation

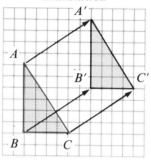

Rotation

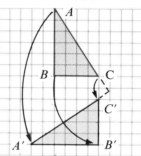

Reflection

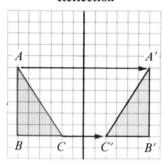

Enlargement

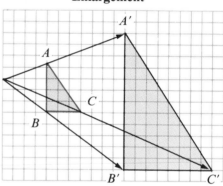

In each of the four diagrams there is a relation between corresponding points of the two triangles.

A maps onto A': $A \rightarrow A'$
B maps onto B': $B \rightarrow B'$
C maps onto C': $C \rightarrow C'$

A', B', and C' are the *images* of points A, B, and C.

A transformation maps every point P onto an image point P'.

Transformations can be represented as mappings of ordered pairs.
A *mapping rule* such as $(x, y) \rightarrow (x + 5, y - 2)$ can be used to find the
image of any point (x, y). This mapping rule states that the first coordinates are increased by 5, and the second coordinates are decreased by 2.

Example 1. Draw the image of the trapezoid with vertices $A(-2, 2)$, $B(0, 2)$, $C(0, 6)$, $D(-2, 4)$, under the transformation $(x, y) \rightarrow (x + 5, y - 2)$. Describe the transformation.

Solution. The table shows the coordinates of the images of the vertices of the trapezoid.

Point	Image
(x, y)	$(x + 5, y - 2)$
$A(-2, 2)$	$A'(3, 0)$
$B(0, 2)$	$B'(5, 0)$
$C(0, 6)$	$C'(5, 4)$
$D(-2, 4)$	$D'(3, 2)$

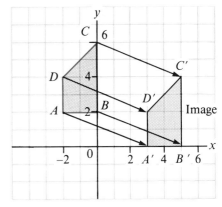

From the graph, the transformation appears to be a translation 5 units to the right and 2 units down.

The next example shows how the coordinates of a point can be found given the coordinates of its image.

Example 2. Under the transformation $(x, y) \rightarrow (-x, -y)$, the image of $\triangle ABC$ has vertices $A'(-3, 2)$, $B'(3, 6)$, $C'(-5, 6)$. Draw $\triangle ABC$ and $\triangle A'B'C'$, and describe the transformation.

Solution. Let (x, y) represent the coordinates of each of the vertices of $\triangle ABC$. Then $(-x, -y)$ represents the coordinates of the corresponding vertices of $\triangle A'B'C'$.

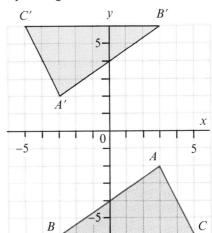

For A': $-x = -3$ and $-y = 2$
$x = 3$ $y = -2$
For B': $-x = 3$ and $-y = 6$
$x = -3$ $y = -6$
For C': $-x = -5$ and $-y = 6$
$x = 5$ $y = -6$

$\triangle ABC$ has vertices $A(3, -2)$, $B(-3, -6)$, and $C(5, -6)$. From the graph, the transformation appears to be a $\frac{1}{2}$-turn about $(0, 0)$.

EXERCISES 9-1

(A)

1. Find the image of the point (5, 2) under the following transformations.
   a) $(x, y) \rightarrow (x + 3, y - 2)$ b) $(x, y) \rightarrow (-x, y)$ c) $(x, y) \rightarrow (2x, y)$
   d) $(x, y) \rightarrow (x - 2, 3y)$ e) $(x, y) \rightarrow (-x + 10, y)$ f) $(x, y) \rightarrow (-3x, 1 - y)$
   g) $(x, y) \rightarrow (2x + 1, 2y - 1)$ h) $(x, y) \rightarrow (3x - 4, 5y + 1)$ i) $(x, y) \rightarrow (-5x + 2, 3 - y)$

2. a) Draw the square that has vertices $A(-1, 1)$, $B(3, 1)$, $C(3, 5)$, $D(-1, 5)$.
   b) Draw its image under the transformation $(x, y) \rightarrow (x + 5, y + 2)$.
   c) Describe the transformation.

3. a) Draw the parallelogram that has vertices $A(-2, 1)$, $B(4, 3)$, $C(5, 6)$, $D(-1, 4)$.
   b) Draw its image under the transformation $(x, y) \rightarrow (x, -y)$.
   c) Describe the transformation.

4. A triangle has vertices $P(1, -1)$, $Q(7, 2)$, $R(4, 6)$.
   a) Draw its image under the transformation $(x, y) \rightarrow (-x, -y)$.
   b) Describe the transformation.

(B)

5. Find the image of the point (2, 3) under the following transformations.
   a) $(x, y) \rightarrow (x + 1, y - 4)$ b) $(x, y) \rightarrow (y, x)$ c) $(x, y) \rightarrow (2x, -y)$
   d) $(x, y) \rightarrow (3 - x, 2y + 1)$ e) $(x, y) \rightarrow (y + 3, x - 3)$ f) $(x, y) \rightarrow (y - 1, -x + 5)$

6. Find the coordinates of the point that has the image (0, 6) under the following transformations.
   a) $(x, y) \rightarrow (x, -y)$ b) $(x, y) \rightarrow (x - 2, y - 2)$ c) $(x, y) \rightarrow (x, -y + 12)$
   d) $(x, y) \rightarrow (x, 2y)$ e) $(x, y) \rightarrow (2x, y - 1)$ f) $(x, y) \rightarrow (x + 4, 3y)$

7. A quadrilateral has vertices $J(1, -2)$, $K(5, -2)$, $L(5, 3)$, $M(2, 1)$. Draw its image under the transformation $(x, y) \rightarrow (-y + 2, x + 4)$.

8. A triangle has vertices $A(-2, -1)$, $B(4, -1)$, $C(5, 2)$. Draw its image under the transformation $(x, y) \rightarrow (x + y, 2x - y)$.

9. Find the coordinates of the point that has the image (-4, 8) under the following transformations.
   a) $(x, y) \rightarrow (x + 2, y - 3)$ b) $(x, y) \rightarrow (2x, 2y)$ c) $(x, y) \rightarrow (x, 4y)$
   d) $(x, y) \rightarrow (y, x)$ e) $(x, y) \rightarrow (y, -x)$ f) $(x, y) \rightarrow (5 - x, y)$

(C)

10. Draw the image of polygon $ABCDEO$ under each transformation, and describe the transformation.
   a) $(x, y) \rightarrow (x, y + 5)$ b) $(x, y) \rightarrow (x - 5, y)$
   c) $(x, y) \rightarrow (x, -y)$ d) $(x, y) \rightarrow (-x, -y)$
   e) $(x, y) \rightarrow (-y, x)$ f) $(x, y) \rightarrow (3x, y)$

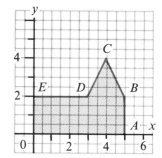

9-2 TRANSLATIONS

When a ship is launched, it slides down a specially-constructed ramp to the water. This motion illustrates a *translation*. When points and their images under a translation are plotted on a grid, certain properties of the translation become evident. The example below illustrates some of these properties.

Example 1. a) Plot the points $(-6, 3)$, $(-3, 5)$, $(-1, 6)$, $(1, 0)$, $(4, 4)$, and $(5, 1)$ and their images under the transformation $(x, y) \rightarrow (x + 3, y - 2)$.

  b) Join each point to its image. What do you notice?

Solution. a)

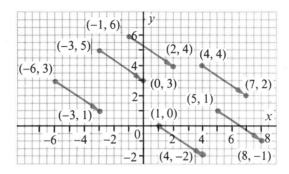

  b) The transformation is a translation 3 units to the right and 2 units down. The line segments appear to be equal in length and parallel.

The results of *Example 1* suggest the mapping rule for translations:

Mapping Rule for Translations
The transformation $(x, y) \rightarrow (x + h, y + k)$
represents a translation for all real values
of h and k.

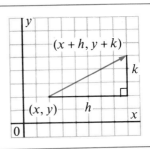

Under a transformation, some of the properties of a figure may be changed, while others remain the same. Those properties that remain the same are called *invariant*.

Example 2.   A square has vertices $A(6, 1)$, $B(8, 3)$, $C(6, 5)$, $D(4, 3)$.
   a)   On a grid, draw the image of the square under the translation
        $(x, y) \rightarrow (x - 5, \ y - 2)$.
   b)   Compare the square and its image with respect to side length and
        slopes of sides.

Solution.   a)   The image of square $ABCD$ is figure $A'B'C'D'$.
   b)   Length of BC: $\quad \sqrt{(6 - 8)^2 + (5 - 3)^2}$
   $$= \sqrt{8}$$
   $$= 2\sqrt{2} \text{ units}$$

Length of $B'C'$: $\quad \sqrt{(1 - 3)^2 + (3 - 1)^2}$
   $$= \sqrt{8}$$
   $$= 2\sqrt{2} \text{ units}$$

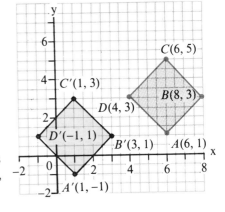

Therefore, line segment BC has the same length as its image, $B'C'$. Similarly, the other sides of the square can be shown to have the same lengths as their images. Under this translation, length is invariant.

Slope of BC: $\dfrac{5 - 3}{6 - 8} = -1$

Slope of $B'C'$: $\dfrac{3 - 1}{1 - 3} = -1$

Therefore, line segment BC is parallel to its image, $B'C'$. Similarly, the other sides of the square can be shown to be parallel to their images. Under this translation, slope is invariant.

Examples 1 and *2* illustrate these properties of translations:

> **Properties of Translations**
> The arrows from all points to their corresponding image points
> have the same length and the same direction.
> A translation preserves length and slope.

EXERCISES 9-2

Ⓐ

1. Find the missing points or mapping rule.

a)

Mapping Rule	Point	Image
$(x, y) \to (x - 2, y)$	$(5, -1)$	
$(x, y) \to (x, y + 3)$	$(-2, 1)$	
$(x, y) \to (x + 4, y)$		$(7, 2)$
$(x, y) \to (x - 3, y - 6)$		$(-2, -3)$
$(x, y) \to (x + 1, y + 6)$	$(-1, -5)$	

b)

Mapping Rule	Point	Image
	$(0, 0)$	$(4, -1)$
$(x, y) \to (x + 5, y + 1)$	$(4, -3)$	
	$(-2, 1)$	$(3, -1)$
$(x, y) \to (x, y - 2)$		$(-3, 0)$
	$(4, -2)$	$(1, 1)$

2. In the diagram, which of the images indicated are a translation image of the
shaded figure?

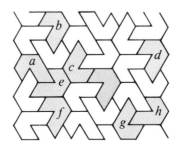

3. Copy each figure and draw its translation image.

a)   b)   c)

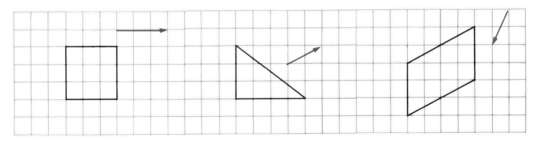

4. Given the translation $(x, y) \rightarrow (x - 2, y + 5)$.
   a) Find the images of the points $(0, 0)$, $(3, 1)$, and $(2, -6)$.
   b) Find the points that have $(0, 3)$, $(1, 7)$, and $(-3, 1)$ as their images.
   c) Graph all points and their images from (a) and (b), and join matching points with line segments.
   d) Determine the length and slope of each segment.

5. Copy the graph, and draw the image of parallelogram *ABCD* under each of the following translations.
   a) $(x, y) \rightarrow (x + 5, y + 2)$ b) $(x, y) \rightarrow (x - 8, y - 1)$
   c) $(x, y) \rightarrow (x + 2, y - 4)$ d) $(x, y) \rightarrow (x - 4, y + 2)$

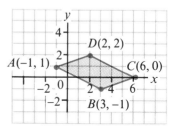

6. A triangle has vertices $A(-4, 2)$, $B(2, 2)$, $C(-4, 5)$. Draw the graph of the triangle and its image under the following transformations.
   a) $(x, y) \rightarrow (x + 5, y + 2)$ b) $(x, y) \rightarrow (x - 3, y - 4)$
   c) $(x, y) \rightarrow (x + 6, y - 3)$ d) $(x, y) \rightarrow (x - 3, y + 1)$

7. A square has vertices $A(1, 1)$, $B(4, 2)$, $C(3, 5)$ and $D(0, 4)$.
   a) Graph the square and its image under the translation which maps vertex *A* onto vertex *B*.
   b) Write the mapping rule for the translation.

8. Repeat *Exercise 7* for the translations which map vertex *A* onto
   a) vertex *C*   b) vertex *D*

9. A triangle has vertices $P(-3, 0)$, $Q(5, 4)$, $R(2, -2)$.
   a) Graph the triangle and its image under the translation $(x, y) \rightarrow (x + 8, y + 1)$.
   b) Compare the triangle and its image with respect to side length, slopes of sides, and area.

10. A quadrilateral has vertices $J(1, 3)$, $K(3, -1)$, $L(6, -2)$, $M(6, 4)$.
    a) Graph the quadrilateral and its image under the translation $(x, y) \rightarrow (x - 3, y - 2)$.
    b) Compare the quadrilateral and its image with respect to side length, slopes of sides, and area.

11. A parallelogram has vertices $A(-4, 0)$, $B(1, -1)$, $C(7, 2)$, $D(2, 3)$.
    a) Graph the parallelogram and its image under the translation $(x, y) \rightarrow (x + 2, y + 1)$.
    b) Compare the parallelogram and its image with respect to side length and slope of sides.

Ⓒ

12. a) Graph the line $y = 2x + 3$ and its image under the translation
$(x, y) \rightarrow (x, y + 2)$.
   b) Write a mapping rule for another translation in which the image of the line
$y = 2x + 3$ is the same as in (a).

13. a) Graph the line $x + y = 4$ and its image under the translation
$(x, y) \rightarrow (x + 1, y - 1)$.
   b) Write mapping rules for two other translations in which the image of the line
$x + y = 4$ is the same as in (a).

14. A square has vertices $A(2, 0)$, $B(5, 1)$, $C(4, 4)$, and $D(1, 3)$. A translation image of
the square has $(3, 2)$ as one of its vertices.
   a) How many different translations are there with this property?
   b) Write the mapping rule for each translation in (a).

INVESTIGATE

Copy the diagram and draw the
line segments joining matching
points PP', QQ', RR'.

Compare these segments with
respect to length and slope.

Describe a property of translations
that this example illustrates.

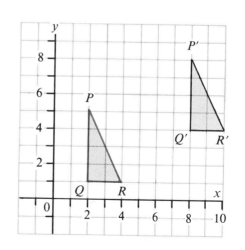

9-3 ROTATIONS

The "midnight sun" is a term used to describe the sun which never sets
on certain days in the summer above the Arctic Circle. As the Earth
turns on its axis, the sun appears to follow a path like the one shown in
the photograph. This motion illustrates a *rotation*. In two dimensions, a
rotation occurs when a figure is turned about a point, called the *rotation
centre*.

Example 1. A triangle has vertices $A(2, 0)$, $B(5, 0)$, $C(5, 2)$. On the same grid, draw
$\triangle ABC$ and its images under the following transformations. Describe each
transformation.

a) $(x, y) \rightarrow (-y, x)$ b) $(x, y) \rightarrow (-x, -y)$ c) $(x, y) \rightarrow (y, -x)$

Solution.

Point	Images		
(x, y)	$(-y, x)$	$(-x, -y)$	$(y, -x)$
$A(2, 0)$	$A'(0, 2)$	$A''(-2, 0)$	$A'''(0, -2)$
$B(5, 0)$	$B'(0, 5)$	$B''(-5, 0)$	$B'''(0, -5)$
$C(5, 2)$	$C'(-2, 5)$	$C''(-5, -2)$	$C'''(2, -5)$

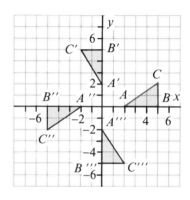

These transformations are rotations about
the origin through angles of 90°, 180°, and
270°, respectively.

The mapping rules for rotations depend on the position of the rotation centre, and on the angle of rotation. All rotations are considered to be counterclockwise.

Mapping Rules for Rotations About (0, 0)

90° rotation	180° rotation	270° rotation
$\left(\dfrac{1}{4}\text{-turn}\right)$	$\left(\dfrac{1}{2}\text{-turn}\right)$	$\left(\dfrac{3}{4}\text{-turn}\right)$

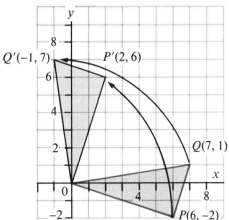

$(x, y) \rightarrow (-y, x)$ $(x, y) \rightarrow (-x, -y)$ $(x, y) \rightarrow (y, -x)$

Example 2. A triangle has vertices $O(0, 0)$, $P(6, -2)$, $Q(7, 1)$.
  a) Graph the triangle and its image under the transformation $(x, y) \rightarrow (-y, x)$.
  b) Compare the triangle and its image with respect to side length and slopes of sides.

Solution.   a)

Point (x, y)	Image $(-y, x)$
$O(0, 0)$	$O'(0, 0)$
$P(6, -2)$	$P'(2, 6)$
$Q(7, 1)$	$Q'(-1, 7)$

This transformation is a 90° rotation about $(0, 0)$, which is an invariant point.

  b) Length of PQ: $\sqrt{(7-6)^2 + (1+2)^2}$
            $= \sqrt{10}$ units

     Length of $P'Q'$: $\sqrt{(-1-2)^2 + (7-6)^2}$
            $= \sqrt{10}$ units

PQ has the same length as its image, $P'Q'$. Similarly, the other sides of the triangle can be shown to have the same lengths as their images. Under this rotation, length is invariant.

Slope of PQ: $\dfrac{1+2}{7-6} = 3$ Slope of $P'Q'$: $\dfrac{7-6}{-1-2} = -\dfrac{1}{3}$

PQ is perpendicular to its image, $P'Q'$. Similarly, the other sides can be shown to be perpendicular to their images. Slope is not necessarily preserved under a rotation.

Example 2 illustrates these properties of rotations:

Properties of Rotations

A rotation preserves length.

A rotation preserves the location of the rotation centre.

A rotation does not necessarily preserve slope.

EXERCISES 9-3

(A)

1. Copy and complete this table.

Object	After a $\frac{1}{4}$-turn	After a $\frac{1}{2}$-turn	After a $\frac{3}{4}$-turn	After a full turn
2	2	2		
		3		
			4	
			5	
		9		

2. Given the rotation $(x, y) \rightarrow (-y, x)$.
   a) Find the images of the points $(4, 1)$, $(0, 5)$, and $(-3, 2)$.
   b) Find the points that have $(2, 6)$, $(3, 0)$, and $(-1, -4)$ as their images.
   c) Graph all points and their images from (a) and (b).

3. In the diagram, which of the images indicated are the rotation image of the shaded figure?

4. A triangle has vertices $A(4, 1)$, $B(3, 4)$, $O(0, 0)$. On the same grid, graph the triangle and its images under these rotations.
   a) $(x, y) \rightarrow (-y, x)$ b) $(x, y) \rightarrow (-x, -y)$ c) $(x, y) \rightarrow (y, -x)$

5. A quadrilateral has vertices $P(-6, 5)$, $Q(-2, 1)$, $R(4, 1)$, $S(3, 5)$. On the same grid, graph the quadrilateral and its images under these rotations.
   a) $(x, y) \rightarrow (-y, x)$ b) $(x, y) \rightarrow (-x, -y)$ c) $(x, y) \rightarrow (y, -x)$

Ⓑ

6. Copy these diagrams and, with O as the rotation centre, draw the
   a) $\frac{1}{4}$-turn image   b) $\frac{1}{2}$-turn image
   i)   ii)   iii)

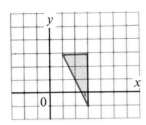
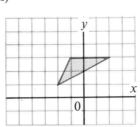
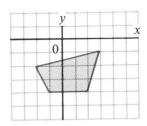

7. A triangle has vertices $P(2, 5)$, $Q(4, 5)$, $R(4, 1)$.
   a) Graph the triangle and its image under the rotation $(x, y) \rightarrow (-y, x)$.
   b) Compare the triangle and its image with respect to side length, slopes of sides, and area.

8. A rectangle has vertices $A(-1, -2)$, $B(7, 2)$, $C(5, 6)$, $D(-3, 2)$.
   a) Graph the rectangle and its image under the rotation $(x, y) \rightarrow (y, -x)$.
   b) Compare the rectangle and its image with respect to side length, slopes of sides, and area.

9. A triangle has vertices $J(5, 0)$, $K(7, 0)$, and $L(5, 3)$.
   a) Draw the triangle and its image under the transformation
      $(x, y) \rightarrow (-y + 3, \ x - 3)$.
   b) Describe the transformation.

10. A trapezoid has vertices $A(-3, 1)$, $B(-2, -2)$, $C(1, -1)$, $D(3, 3)$.
    Graph the trapezoid and its image under the following transformations.
    a) $(x, y) \rightarrow (-y + 6, x)$ b) $(x, y) \rightarrow (-x + 6, -y + 6)$ c) $(x, y) \rightarrow (y, -x + 6)$
    Describe each transformation.

Ⓒ

11. Graph the line $y = x$ and its image under the rotation $(x, y) \rightarrow (-y, x)$.

12. Graph the line $2x + y = 6$ and its image under the rotation $(x, y) \rightarrow (-x, -y)$.

13. Give an example of a rotation which preserves slope.

INVESTIGATE

1. In the diagram below, $\triangle P'Q'R'$ is the rotation image of $\triangle PQR$ under a $\frac{1}{4}$-turn
   about $C(7, 2)$.
   a) Copy the diagram, and draw the segments PP', QQ', RR' and their per-
      pendicular bisectors.
   b) Describe a property of rotations that is illustrated by (a).

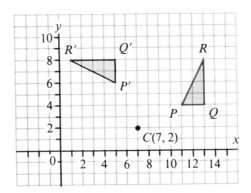

2. a) Draw the triangle with vertices $J(-1, 4)$, $K(5, -4)$, $L(7, -1)$ and its $\frac{1}{4}$-turn
      image about $(0, 0)$, $\triangle J'K'L'$.
   b) By extending the sides if necessary, measure the angles between JK and
      $J'K'$, JL and $J'L'$, KL and $K'L'$.
   c) Describe a property of rotations that is illustrated by (b).

9-4 REFLECTIONS

When we look in a mirror, we see a *reflection*. Unlike translations and rotations, there is no motion in two dimensions that produces the image of a figure under this transformation.

Example 1. A rectangle has vertices $A(2, 0)$, $B(6, 2)$, $C(5, 4)$, $D(1, 2)$. On the same grid, draw the rectangle and its images under the following transformations. Describe each transformation.

a) $(x, y) \rightarrow (x, -y)$ b) $(x, y) \rightarrow (-x, y)$

Solution.

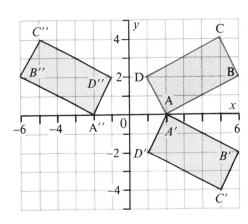

Point	Images	
(x, y)	$(x, -y)$	$(-x, y)$
$A(2, 0)$	$A'(2, 0)$	$A''(-2, 0)$
$B(6, 2)$	$B'(6, -2)$	$B''(-6, 2)$
$C(5, 4)$	$C'(5, -4)$	$C''(-5, 4)$
$D(1, 2)$	$D'(1, -2)$	$D''(-1, 2)$

These transformations are reflections in the x- and y-axes, respectively.

Example 2.   A triangle has vertices $P(5, 3)$, $Q(3, -1)$, $R(5, -1)$. On the same grid, draw
the triangle and its images under the following transformations. Describe
each transformation.

a) $(x, y) \rightarrow (y, x)$ b) $(x, y) \rightarrow (-y, -x)$

Solution.

Point	Images	
(x, y)	(y, x)	$(-y, -x)$
$P(5, 3)$	$P'(3, 5)$	$P''(-3, -5)$
$Q(3, -1)$	$Q'(-1, 3)$	$Q''(1, -3)$
$R(5, -1)$	$R'(-1, 5)$	$R''(1, -5)$

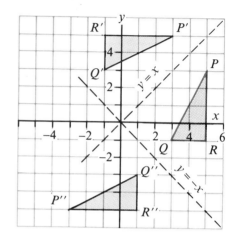

These transformations are reflections
in the lines $y = x$ and $y = -x$, respectively.

The mapping rules for reflections depend on which line is
the *reflection line*.

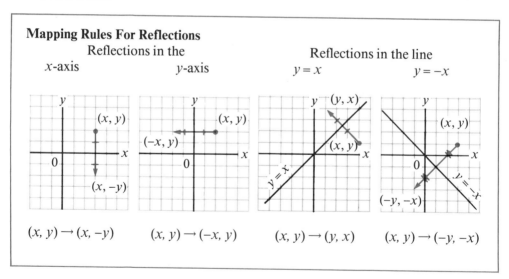

Mapping Rules For Reflections

Reflections in the

x-axis   *y*-axis

Reflections in the line

$y = x$ $y = -x$

$(x, y) \rightarrow (x, -y)$ $(x, y) \rightarrow (-x, y)$ $(x, y) \rightarrow (y, x)$ $(x, y) \rightarrow (-y, -x)$

Example 3.   A triangle has vertices $A(3, 7)$, $B(-4, 3)$, $C(3, 3)$.

a)   Graph the triangle and its image under the transformation
$(x, y) \rightarrow (y, x)$.

b)   Compare the triangle and its image with respect to side length and
slopes of sides.

Solution.   a)

Point (x, y)	Image (y, x)
$A(3, 7)$	$A'(7, 3)$
$B(-4, 3)$	$B'(3, -4)$
$C(3, 3)$	$C'(3, 3)$

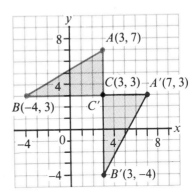

b) Length of AB:

$$\sqrt{(-4 - 3)^2 + (3 - 7)^2}$$
$$= \sqrt{65} \text{ units}$$

Length of $A'B'$:

$$\sqrt{(3 - 7)^2 + (-4 - 3)^2}$$
$$= \sqrt{65} \text{ units}$$

AB has the same length as its image, $A'B'$. Similarly, the other sides of the triangle can be shown to have the same lengths as their images. Under this reflection, length is invariant.

Slope of AB: $\dfrac{3 - 7}{-4 - 3} = \dfrac{4}{7}$ Slope of $A'B'$: $\dfrac{-4 - 3}{3 - 7} = \dfrac{7}{4}$

The side AB is not parallel to its image. Slope is not preserved under this reflection.

In the diagram of *Example 1*, to move from A to B to C is to move in a counterclockwise direction. To move from A' to B' to C' is to move in a clockwise direction. We say that a reflection reverses *orientation*. This reversal does not occur with translations or rotations.

Example 2 illustrates these properties of reflections:

Properties of Reflections

A reflection preserves length.

A reflection preserves the location of points on the reflection line.

A reflection does not preserve slope or orientation.

EXERCISES 9-4

Ⓐ

1. Copy the diagram and draw the reflection image in the given line.

   a)   b)   c)

2. Copy the diagram and draw the reflection image in the given line.

   a)   b)   c)

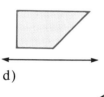

   d)   e)   f)

3. In the diagram, which of the images indicated are a reflection image of the shaded figure?

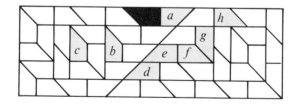

4. Given the reflection $(x, y) \rightarrow (-x, y)$.
   a) Find the images of the points $(1, 3)$, $(4, -2)$, and $(-1, 5)$.
   b) Find the points that have $(2, -3)$, $(-1, 2)$, and $(3, 0)$ as their images.
   c) Graph all points and their images from (a) and (b).

5. Draw the image of $\triangle PQR$, shown on the graph, under the following reflections.
   a) $(x, y) \rightarrow (y, x)$ b) $(x, y) \rightarrow (-y, -x)$
   c) $(x, y) \rightarrow (-x, y)$ d) $(x, y) \rightarrow (x, -y)$

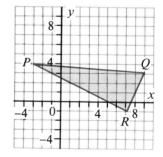

6. A triangle has vertices $A(3, 1)$, $B(7, 1)$, $C(7, 3)$. Graph the triangle and its image under the following reflections.
   a) $(x, y) \rightarrow (-x, y)$
   b) $(x, y) \rightarrow (x, -y)$
   c) $(x, y) \rightarrow (y, x)$
   d) $(x, y) \rightarrow (-y, -x)$

Ⓑ

7. A triangle has vertices $J(2, 2)$, $K(10, 6)$, $L(0, 6)$.
   a) Graph the triangle and its image under the reflection $(x, y) \rightarrow (x, -y)$.
   b) Compare the triangle and its image with respect to side length, slopes of sides, and area.

8. A square has vertices $A(0, 2)$, $B(-5, 0)$, $C(-3, -5)$, $D(2, -3)$.
   a) Graph the square and its image under the reflection $(x, y) \rightarrow (-y, -x)$.
   b) Compare the square and its image with respect to side length, slopes of sides, and area.

9. A triangle has vertices $P(2, 4)$, $Q(-1, 3)$, and $R(1, -1)$.
   a) Graph the triangle and its image under the transformation $(x, y) \rightarrow (-x + 6, y)$.
   b) Describe the transformation.

10. A parallelogram has vertices $E(-2, 1)$, $F(-3, -2)$, $G(3, 0)$, $H(4, 3)$.
    a) Graph the parallelogram and its image under the transformation $(x, y) \rightarrow (y + 3, x - 3)$.
    b) Describe the transformation.

11. A quadrilateral has vertices $P(2, 3)$, $Q(4, -1)$, $R(8, 1)$, $S(7, 4)$.
    a) Graph the quadrilateral and its image under the transformation $(x, y) \rightarrow (-y - 1, -x - 1)$.
    b) Describe the transformation.

12. The vertices of a triangle are $A(1, 4)$, $B(3, -2)$, $C(5, 1)$.
    a) Draw the image of $\triangle ABC$ under a reflection in the line
       i) $x + 2 = 0$. Call it $\triangle A'B'C'$
       ii) $y + 3 = 0$. Call it $\triangle A''B''C''$
    b) Draw the image of $\triangle A'B'C'$ in the line $y + 3 = 0$.
    c) Draw the image of $\triangle A''B''C''$ in the line $x + 2 = 0$.

Ⓒ

13. A quadrilateral has vertices $A(1, -1)$, $B(2, -5)$, $C(5, -5)$, $D(6, -3)$.
    a) Graph the quadrilateral and its image under the transformation $(x, y) \rightarrow (x + 9, -y)$.
    b) Show that the transformation in (a) is neither a translation, nor a reflection, nor a rotation.
    c) What properties does this new transformation have?

14. Graph the line $y = 2x + 1$ and its image under the reflection $(x, y) \rightarrow (-x, y)$.

15. Graph the line $x + y = 3$ and its image under the reflection $(x, y) \rightarrow (x, -y)$.

16. In the diagram, $\triangle A'B'C'$ is a reflection image of $\triangle ABC$.
    a) Copy the diagram and draw the reflection line.
    b) Find the equation of the reflection line.
    c) Find the image of $P(-3, -2)$ under this reflection.

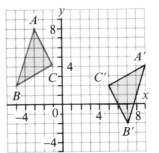

17. A reflection maps the point $(-3, -1)$, onto $(3, 5)$.
    a) Draw the reflection line and find the images of the points $(1, 5)$, $(2, -1)$, and $(4, -2)$ under the same reflection.
    b) Find the points that have $(3, 2)$, $(-4, 6)$, and $(-1, -3)$ as images under the same reflection.
    c) Write the equation of the reflection line.

INVESTIGATE

1. In the diagram, $\triangle P'Q'R'$ is the reflection image of $\triangle PQR$ in the line $y = -2x + 17$.
    a) Copy the diagram and draw the segments joining matching points PP' and QQ'.
    b) Show that the reflection line is perpendicular to both PP' and QQ' and bisects both PP' and QQ'.
    c) Describe the property of reflections that is illustrated in (b).

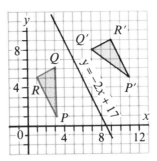

2. a) Draw the triangle with vertices $A(-3, 6)$, $B(1, 2)$, $C(2, 5)$ and its reflection image in the line $x = 4$.
    b) Extend AB and $A'B'$ to meet at P, AC and $A'C'$ to meet at Q, BC and $B'C'$ to meet at R.
    c) What property of reflections is illustrated in (b)?

| $0 < k < 1$ | $k = 1$ | $k > 1$ |

9-5 DILATATIONS

Not all transformations preserve length. The simplest that does not is a dilatation. A *dilatation* enlarges or reduces all dimensions of a figure by a factor k, called the *scale factor*. We assume that the scale factor is positive.

Example 1. A rectangle has vertices $P(2, 3)$, $Q(-2, 3)$, $R(-2, -2)$, $S(2, -2)$. On the same grid, draw the rectangle and its images under the following transformations. Describe each transformation:

a) $(x, y) \rightarrow (2x, 2y)$

b) $(x, y) \rightarrow \left(\frac{1}{2}x, \frac{1}{2}y\right)$

Solution.

	Images	
Point (x, y)	$(2x, 2y)$	$\left(\frac{1}{2}x, \frac{1}{2}y\right)$
$P(2, 3)$	$P'(4, 6)$	$P''(1, 1.5)$
$Q(-2, 3)$	$Q'(-4, 6)$	$Q''(-1, 1.5)$
$R(-2, -2)$	$R'(-4, -4)$	$R''(-1, -1)$
$S(2, -2)$	$S'(4, -4)$	$S''(1, -1)$

Both transformations are dilatations. The first is an enlargement with scale factor 2. The second is a reduction with scale factor $\frac{1}{2}$.

The results of *Example 1* suggest the mapping rule for dilatations.

Mapping Rule for Dilatations

The transformation $(x, y) \rightarrow (kx, ky)$ represents a dilatation with scale factor k, and dilatation centre $(0, 0)$. We assume that $k > 0$.

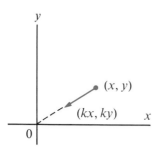   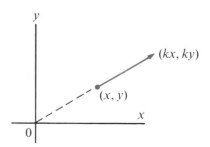

If $0 < k < 1$, the dilatation is a reduction.

If $k > 1$, the dilatation is an enlargement.

Example 2. A triangle has vertices $A(1, 3)$, $B(5, 5)$, $C(6, 3)$.

    a) Graph $\triangle ABC$ and its image under the transformation $(x, y) \rightarrow (2x, 2y)$.

    b) Compare the triangle and its image with respect to side length, slopes of sides, and area.

    c) Investigate the lines joining matching points.

Solution.   a)

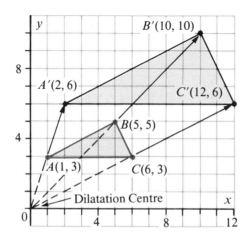

b) Length of AB:

$$\sqrt{(5-1)^2 + (5-3)^2}$$
$$= \sqrt{16 + 4}$$
$$= \sqrt{20}$$
$$= 2\sqrt{5} \text{ units}$$

Length of $A'B'$:

$$\sqrt{(10-2)^2 + (10-6)^2}$$
$$= \sqrt{64 + 16}$$
$$= \sqrt{80}$$
$$= 4\sqrt{5} \text{ units}$$

$A'B' = 2AB$. Similarly, $B'C' = 2BC$ and $A'C' = 2AC$.

Slope of AB: $\dfrac{5-3}{5-1} = \dfrac{1}{2}$ Slope of $A'B'$: $\dfrac{10-6}{10-2} = \dfrac{1}{2}$

Therefore, $A'B' \parallel AB$. Similarly, $B'C' \parallel BC$ and $A'C' \parallel AC$.

Area of $\triangle ABC$:

$$\frac{1}{2} bh = \frac{1}{2}(5)(2)$$
$$= 5 \text{ units}^2$$

Area of $\triangle A'B'C'$:

$$\frac{1}{2} bh = \frac{1}{2}(10)(4)$$
$$= 20 \text{ units}^2$$

Area of $\triangle A'B'C' = 4 \times$ Area of $\triangle ABC$.

c) Join AA', BB', and CC'. It appears that the lines joining matching points pass through the origin. We can prove this using slope.

Slope of OA: $\dfrac{3-0}{1-0} = 3$ Slope of OA': $\dfrac{6-0}{2-0} = 3$

Therefore O, A, A' are collinear. Similarly, O, B, B' are collinear, and O, C, C' are collinear. This shows that lines joining matching points intersect at the same point. This point is called the *dilatation centre*.

Example 2 illustrates these properties of dilatations.

Properties of Dilatations

A dilatation preserves slope.

A dilatation preserves the location of the dilatation centre.

A dilatation does not preserve length or area (except when $|k| = 1$).

Lines joining matching points pass through the dilatation centre.

EXERCISES 9-5

1. A triangle has vertices $A(-1, 2)$, $B(4, 2)$, $C(3, 5)$.
   a) Graph $\triangle ABC$ and its image under the transformation $(x, y) \rightarrow (2x, 2y)$.
   b) Compare the triangle and its image with respect to side length, slopes of sides, and area.
   c) Determine the scale factor and the dilatation centre.

2. A triangle has vertices $A(2, 2)$, $B(4, 2)$, $C(2, -2)$.
   a) Graph $\triangle ABC$ and its image, $\triangle A'B'C'$, under the transformation $(x, y) \rightarrow (3x, 3y)$.
   b) Join AA', BB', CC' and extend to meet at $O(0, 0)$.
   c) Calculate the lengths of the segments OA', OA, OB', OB, OC', OC and the ratios $\dfrac{OA'}{OA}, \dfrac{OB'}{OB}, \dfrac{OC'}{OC}$.
   d) Calculate the lengths of the segments $A'B'$, AB, $B'C'$, BC, $A'C'$, AC and the ratios $\dfrac{A'B'}{AB}, \dfrac{B'C'}{BC}, \dfrac{A'C'}{AC}$.
   e) What is the scale factor?

3. A triangle has vertices $P(3, 6)$, $Q(12, 6)$, $R(9, 12)$.
   a) Graph $\triangle PQR$ and its image, $\triangle P'Q'R'$, under the dilatation $(x, y) \rightarrow \left(\dfrac{1}{3}x, \dfrac{1}{3}y\right)$.
   b) What is the geometric effect of this dilatation?
   c) Calculate the lengths of the segments OP', OP, OQ', OQ, OR', OR and the ratios $\dfrac{OP'}{OP}, \dfrac{OQ'}{OQ}, \dfrac{OR'}{OR}$.
   d) Compare $\triangle PQR$ and its image with respect to side length and slopes of sides.
   e) What is the scale factor?

4. A rectangle has vertices $A(2, 0)$, $B(2, 3)$, $C(4, 3)$, $D(4, 0)$.
   a) Graph the rectangle and its dilatation image with $(0, 0)$ as the dilatation centre and 3 as the scale factor.
   b) What is the geometric effect of this dilatation?
   c) Measure the lengths of the line segments OB', OB, OC', OC and calculate the ratios $\dfrac{OB'}{OB}, \dfrac{OC'}{OC}$.
   d) Compare rectangle $ABCD$ and its image with respect to side length and area.

B

5. Copy the diagram. With (0, 0) as the dilatation centre, draw the dilatation image of △ABC with a scale factor of

a) 2.0   b) 1.5   c) 0.5

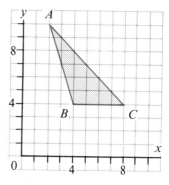

6. In the diagram below, determine the scale factor, k, for each of the following dilatations.

a) $A \rightarrow B$ b) $A \rightarrow C$ c) $B \rightarrow C$

d) $C \rightarrow A$ e) $C \rightarrow B$ f) $B \rightarrow A$

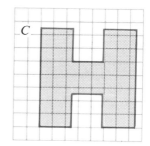

7. An object, a dilatation centre, and an image point are given. Copy each diagram and complete the image.

a)   b)

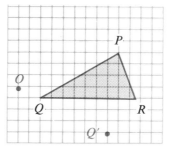

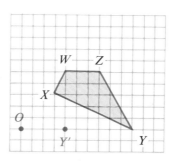
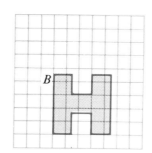

8. A trapezoid has vertices $A(2, 2)$, $B(8, 2)$, $C(8, 6)$, $D(4, 6)$.

a) Graph the trapezoid and its image under the dilatation $(x, y) \rightarrow \left(\frac{1}{4}x, \frac{1}{4}y\right)$.

b) What is the geometric effect of this dilatation?

c) What is the scale factor?

9. a) Trace △*PQR* and draw its dilatation images using a
   scale factor of 2 and dilatation centres at *P*; at *Q*; at *R*.

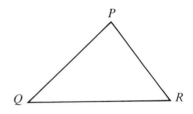

   b) For each part of (a), what is the ratio of the area of
   the image triangle to the area of △*PQR*?

10. The coordinates of the vertices of four polygons are given. Draw each polygon on a
   separate grid and show the positions of its dilatation images for the scale factors
   indicated. In each case, (0, 0) is the dilatation centre.

   a) (−1, 4), (2, 1), (5, 2)   i) $k = 2$ ii) $k = 3$

   b) (−4, −2), (2,4), (6, −3)   i) $k = \dfrac{3}{2}$ ii) $k = \dfrac{1}{2}$

   c) (0, 0), (9, 0), (0, 6)   i) $k = \dfrac{2}{3}$ ii) $k = \dfrac{4}{3}$

   d) (0, 0), (4, 0), (6, 6), (0, 4)   i) $k = \dfrac{1}{2}$ ii) $k = \dfrac{3}{2}$

©

11. The diagram shows a pattern using a trapezoid. The pattern is unusual because
   dilatations of the trapezoid can be seen in it.

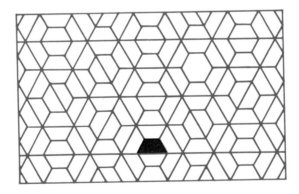

   a) Find three successive images of the shaded trapezoid and compare each image
   and the shaded trapezoid with respect to their perimeters and their areas.
   b) Explain how the pattern illustrates the properties of a dilatation.

12. Graph the line $x + y = 3$ and its image under the dilatation $(x, y) \rightarrow (2x, 2y)$.

13. Graph the line $y = 2x + 3$ and its image under the dilatation $(x, y) \rightarrow (2x, 2y)$.

MATHEMATICS AROUND US

The Pantograph

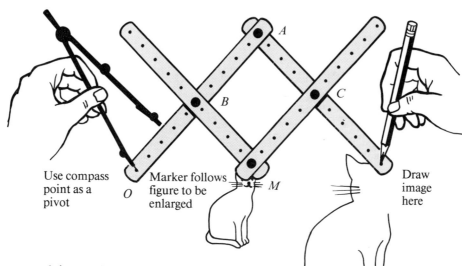

Use compass point as a pivot

O

Marker follows figure to be enlarged

A

B

C

M

Draw image here

The pantograph is a device for enlarging or reducing figures. The one shown in the illustration is set to reproduce images with scale factor 2. It can be adjusted for other scale factors by choosing other pivot points for *B* and *C*.

A working model of a pantograph can be made from four strips of thin cardboard pivoted together with dressmakers' snap fasteners. Convenient dimensions for the cardboard strips are 13 cm by 1 cm. To allow the pantograph to move freely at the pivots, use only the part of the snap fastener shown. To make the marker, *M*, fix the head of a pin to a snap fastener with epoxy cement and cut off the excess when the cement is dry.

Use for points *A*, *B*, and *C*.

Use for marker *M*.

QUESTIONS

1. Make a pantograph and use it to draw an enlargement of a figure.

2. How would you adjust the pantograph to make enlargements with scale factors other than 2?

3. How would you make reductions with the pantograph?

4. Investigate the effect of interchanging the positions of the compass point, *O*, and the marker, *M*.

5. Explain the pantograph's principle of operation.

9-6 IMAGES OF LINES

The diagram shows the line $2x - 3y + 6 = 0$. Assume that every point on this line is translated 4 units to the right and 2 units down. We can graph the image line by locating the images of any two points on the line, such as $A(-3, 0)$ and $B(0, 2)$. Under the translation, $A(-3, 0) \rightarrow A'(1, -2)$ and $B(0, 2) \rightarrow B'(4, 0)$. The image line passes through the points $A'(1, -2)$ and $B'(4, 0)$.

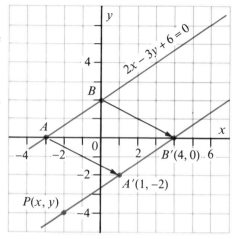

To find the equation of the image line, we find the equation of the line passing through A' and B'.

Let $P(x, y)$ be any point on the image line.

Slope of $A'P$: $\dfrac{y + 2}{x - 1}$ Slope of $A'B'$: $\dfrac{0 + 2}{4 - 1} = \dfrac{2}{3}$

By the constant slope property, these slopes are equal:

$$\frac{y + 2}{x - 1} = \frac{2}{3}$$
$$2x - 2 = 3y + 6$$
$$2x - 3y - 8 = 0$$

The equation of the image line is $2x - 3y - 8 = 0$.

The above example illustrates a general method for finding the equation of the image of a line under certain transformations.

To find the equation of the image of a line under a translation, reflection, rotation or dilatation:

Step 1. Find the coordinates of any two points on the line.

Step 2. Find the coordinates of the images of these two points.

Step 3. Find the equation of the line passing through the two image points.

Example 1. a) Graph the line $2x + y - 6 = 0$.
  b) Graph the image of the line in (a) under the rotation $(x, y) \rightarrow (-y, x)$.
  c) Find the equation of the image line.

Solution. a) Two points on the line are $A(3, 0)$ and $B(0, 6)$. Draw the line AB.
  b) Under the given rotation, $A(3, 0) \rightarrow A'(0, 3)$ and $B(0, 6) \rightarrow B'(-6, 0)$. Draw the image line $A'B'$.

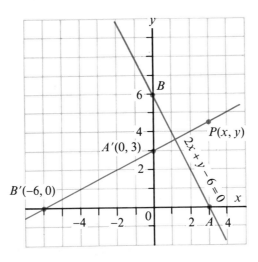

  c) Let $P(x, y)$ be any point on the image line.

Slope of $A'P$: $\dfrac{y - 3}{x - 0}$ Slope of $A'B'$: $\dfrac{0 - 3}{-6 - 0} = \dfrac{1}{2}$

By the constant slope property,
$$\frac{y - 3}{x} = \frac{1}{2}$$
$$x = 2y - 6$$
$$x - 2y + 6 = 0$$

The equation of the image line is $x - 2y + 6 = 0$.

In *Example 1*, the equation of the image line could have been found using the slope and the y-intercept. This method is illustrated in the following example.

Example 2. Find the equation of the image of the line $y = \frac{1}{2}x - 4$ under a reflection in the x-axis.

Solution. Graph the given line using the slope, $\frac{1}{2}$, and the y-intercept, -4.

From the graph, two points on the line are $A(0, -4)$ and $B(8, 0)$. Under a reflection in the x-axis, $A(0, -4) \rightarrow A'(0, 4)$ and $B(8, 0) \rightarrow B'(8, 0)$. Draw the image line $A'B'$.

From the diagram, this line has slope $-\frac{1}{2}$ and y-intercept 4.
Therefore, the equation of the image line

is $y = -\frac{1}{2}x + 4$.

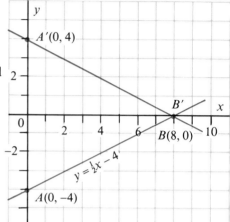

EXERCISES 9-6

Ⓐ

1. a) Graph the line $2x + y - 4 = 0$ and its image under the translation $(x, y) \rightarrow (x + 4, y - 2)$.
   b) Find the equation of the image line.

2. Graph the line $3x - 4y - 12 = 0$ and its image under the following translations. Find the equation of each image line.
   a) $(x, y) \rightarrow (x - 2, y - 5)$ b) $(x, y) \rightarrow (x + 3, y - 3)$
   c) $(x, y) \rightarrow (x - 1, y + 4)$ d) $(x, y) \rightarrow (x + 5, y + 2)$

3. Find the equation of the image of the line $3x - 5y - 15 = 0$ under the following translations.
   a) $(x, y) \rightarrow (x + 2, y + 4)$ b) $(x, y) \rightarrow (x - 1, y + 3)$
   c) $(x, y) \rightarrow (x - 5, y)$ d) $(x, y) \rightarrow (x - 3, y - 1)$

4. Find the equation of the image of the following lines under the translation $(x, y) \rightarrow (x + 3, y - 2)$.
   a) $2x + 7y - 12 = 0$ b) $y = 3x + 7$
   c) $4x - 9y + 18 = 0$ d) $2x + 5y - 20 = 0$

5. a) Graph the line $2x + y - 12 = 0$ and its reflections in the x-axis and y-axis.
   b) Find the equations of the two reflected lines.

6. Repeat *Exercise 5* for the following lines.
   a) $3x - y - 6 = 0$ b) $2x + 5y - 10 = 0$
   c) $4x + 7y - 28 = 0$ d) $-5x + 8y - 20 = 0$

Ⓑ

7. Find the equation of the image of the line $x + 2y - 4 = 0$ under these translations and graph each image line.
   a) $(x, y) \rightarrow (x - 2, y + 4)$ b) $(x, y) \rightarrow (x, y + 3)$ c) $(x, y) \rightarrow (x + 2, y + 2)$

8. a) Graph the line $y = 2x + 3$ and its reflection in the line $y = x$.
   b) Find the equation of the reflected line.

9. Repeat *Exercise 8* for the following lines.
   a) $y = -5x + 1$ b) $y = \frac{2}{3}x - 1$ c) $y = -\frac{1}{4}x + 2$
   d) $7x - 3y - 6 = 0$ e) $x + y - 7 = 0$ f) $x - y - 5 = 0$

10. Find the equation of the image of the line $y = x + 5$ under a reflection in the
    a) x-axis   b) y-axis   c) line $y = x$ d) line $y = -x$

11. Find the equation of the image of the line $3x - y + 6 = 0$ under the following rotations.
    a) $90°$ about $(0, 0)$ b) $180°$ about $(0, 0)$ c) $270°$ about $(0, 0)$

Ⓒ

12. a) On the same axes, graph the two lines L_1 and L_2.
    $$L_1\colon 3x - 2y - 6 = 0 \quad \text{and} \quad L_2\colon 3x - 2y - 12 = 0$$
    b) Find the mapping rules for three different translations such that L_2 is the image of L_1.

13. The line $x + y + 3 = 0$ is the image of the line $x + y - 3 = 0$ under a certain reflection. What is the equation of the reflection line?

14. Under a certain transformation, the line $2x - 5y + 10 = 0$ is the image of the line $2x - 5y - 10 = 0$. Describe a possible transformation which has this effect, assuming that the transformation is a
    a) translation   b) reflection   c) rotation

INVESTIGATE

In how many different ways can a line and its image coincide under a
a) reflection?   b) rotation?   c) translation?

COMPUTER POWER

Images of Lines

This program can be used to find the equation of the image of a line with equation $Ax + By + C = 0$ (where A, $B \neq 0$) under the transformations studied in this chapter. When a menu appears, press one of the numbers from 1 to 9 to select the desired transformation.

```
100 REM *** IMAGES OF LINES ***
110 HOME: INPUT "ENTER COEFFICIENTS A, B, C: ";A,B,C:AB=A*B
120 PRINT:PRINT "1 - TRANSLATION"
130 PRINT "2 - REFLECTION IN X-AXIS":PRINT "3 - REFLECTION IN Y-AXIS"
140 PRINT "4 - RELFECTION IN Y = X":PRINT "5 - REFLECTION IN Y = -X"
150 PRINT "6 - 90 DEGREE ROTATION":PRINT "7 -  180 DEGREE ROTATION"
160 PRINT "8 - 270 DEGREE ROTATION":PRINT "9 - DILATATION"
170 PRINT:INPUT "CHOOSE 1 - 9: ";N
180 IF N=1 THEN PRINT:INPUT "ENTER H AND K: ";H,K
190 IF N=1 THEN X=-C/A+H:Y=K:U=H:V=-C/B+K
200 IF N=2 THEN X=-C/A:Y=0:U=0:V=C/B
210 IF N=3 THEN X=C/A:Y=0:U=0:V=-C/B
220 IF N=4 THEN X=0:Y=-C/A:U=-C/B:V=0
230 IF N=5 THEN X=0:Y=C/A:U=C/B:V=0
240 IF N=6 THEN X=0:Y=-C/A:U=C/B:V=0
250 IF N=7 THEN X=C/A:Y=0:U=0:V=C/B
260 IF N=8 THEN X=0:Y=C/A:U=-C/B:V=0
270 IF N=9 THEN PRINT:INPUT "ENTER SCALE FACTOR: ";K
280 IF N=9 THEN X=-C/A*K:Y=0:U=0:V=-C/B*K
290 D=(V-Y)*AB:E=(X-U)*AB:F=(U*Y-X*V)*AB:P=D:Q=E
300 R=P-INT(P/Q)*Q
310 IF R<>0 THEN P=Q:Q=R:GOTO 300
320 PRINT:PRINT "COEFFICIENTS FOR IMAGE LINE ARE:"
330 PRINT D/Q,E/Q,F/Q
340 END
```

1. Use the program to find the equation of the image of $3x - y + 6 = 0$ under
   a) the translations $(x, y) \rightarrow (x + 4, y - 2)$ and $(x, y) \rightarrow (x - 3, y + 2)$.
   b) reflections in the x-axis, the y-axis, the line $y = x$, and the line $y = -x$.
   c) rotations about $(0, 0)$ of $90°$, $180°$, and $270°$.
   d) the dilatations $(x, y) \rightarrow (5x, 5y)$ and $(x, y) \rightarrow (-3x, -3y)$

9-7 APPLICATIONS OF TRANSFORMATIONS

Transformations are a powerful tool for solving certain types of problems. The following examples show how transformations can be used to solve problems which would be difficult to solve by other methods.

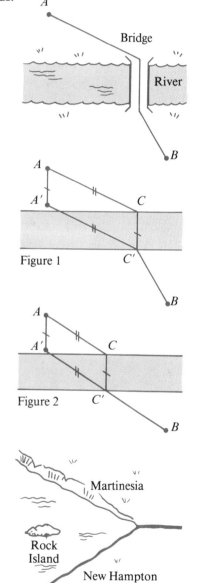

Example 1. A university students' residence is located at A. The athletic complex is located on the other side of the river at B. If a bridge is to be built perpendicular to both banks of the river, where should it be located so that the length of the path from A to B is a minimum?

Solution. Let C and C' denote the ends of the bridge. Locate A', the image of A under a translation that maps C onto C'. Since length is invariant under a translation, $AC = A'C'$.

Also, $AA' = w$ and $CC' = w$, where w is the width of the river. The length of the path from A to C to C' to B is $AC + w + C'B$.

This length is also equal to $A'C' + w + C'B$. The path is shortest when $A'C' + C'B$ is a minimum. This occurs when C' is located such that $A'C'B$ is a straight line, as shown in *Figure 2*. That is, the position of the bridge is found by translating A a distance w perpendicular to the river bank to obtain A'. Then C' is the point where $A'B$ intersects the opposite bank.

Example 2. Ore from Rock Island, R, is to be shipped to the countries of Martinesia and New Hampton. Where should unloading ports, M in Martinesia and N in New Hampton, be built so that the length of the round trip, $R \rightarrow M \rightarrow N \rightarrow R$, is a minimum?

Solution.   Let R' and R'' denote the images of R when reflected in the shorelines of Martinesia and New Hampton respectively. The round trip distance, $RM + MN + NR$, is equal to $R'M + MN + NR''$. Clearly, this is a minimum when R', M, N, and R'' lie on a straight line. The locations of the unloading ports are found by first finding R' and R'' and then joining them. M and N are the points of intersection of $R'R''$ with the shoreline.

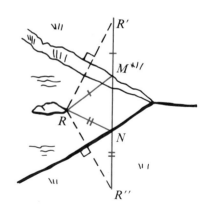

EXERCISES 9-7

Ⓐ

1. A contractor must install a fountain at B. The nearest water supply is at A. Copy the diagram and locate the position of the perpendicular cut that must be made across the sidewalk for the length of piping required to connect A and B to be a minimum.

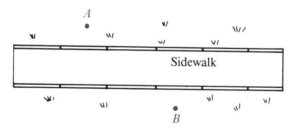

A

Sidewalk

B

2. Plot the points $A(2, 9)$ and $B(12, 6)$. If N is a point on the x-axis, find the
   a)   coordinates of N for the distance $AN + NB$ to be a minimum
   b)   minimum distance from A to N to B.

Ⓑ

3. In a race, runners must start at post P, run to the fence and then finish at post Q. Copy the diagram and find the point on the fence for the total distance run to be a minimum.

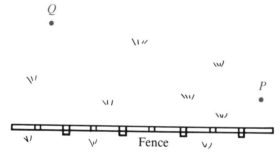

Q

P

Fence

4. Plot the points $A(3, 6)$ and $B(6, 3)$ on a grid. Calculate the length of the shortest path from A to the

   a) x-axis to B b) y-axis to B
   c) y-axis to the x-axis to B

5. The diagram shows the layout of a race at an athletic event. Runners must touch both fences before running toward the finish.

   a) Which fence should be touched first?
   b) Use the scale to calculate the shortest possible route from start to finish.

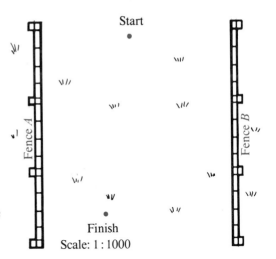

6. In a race, runners start from a post P, touch fence l_1, then fence l_2 and return to post P. Copy the diagram below (left) and locate the points on l_1 and l_2 for the total distance run to be a minimum.

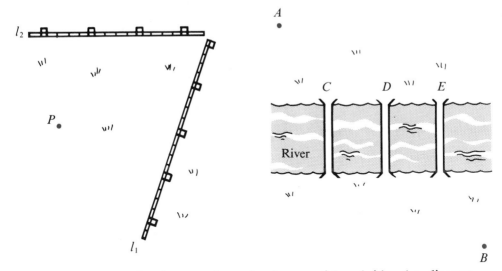

7. A race from A to B involves crossing a river by one of three bridges (see diagram above, right).
   a) Which bridge should be used for the distance run to be a minimum?
   b) Using a scale of $1 : 10\ 000$, how long is the race?

©

8. a) Plot the points $A(2, 1)$ and $B(12, 8)$ on a grid and shade the strip $4 \le y \le 6$. Points $C(x, 4)$ and $D(x, 6)$ are the endpoints of a segment parallel to the y-axis.
   b) Find x for the length of the path $ACDB$ to be a minimum.
   c) Find the minimum length of the path $ACDB$.

Transform, Solve, Transform

The main platform for a midway ride rotates about O. One of the cars, P, rotates about its centre, C, which is 3 m from O. What is the mapping rule for a 90° rotation counterclockwise about C? (Assume that it is at the beginning of the ride before the main platform moves.)

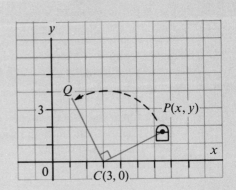

Understand the problem

- Why should you assume that the main platform is not moving?

Think of a strategy

- Transform to a simpler rotation problem and solve that.

Carry out the strategy

- Translate P 3 units to the left. The image of P is $P'(x - 3, y)$.

- Use the mapping rule for a 90° rotation about $(0, 0)$. The image of P' is $P''(-y, x - 3)$.

- Translate P'' 3 units to the right. The image of P'' is $Q(-y + 3, x - 3)$.

- Therefore, the mapping rule is $(x, y) \rightarrow (-y + 3, x - 3)$.

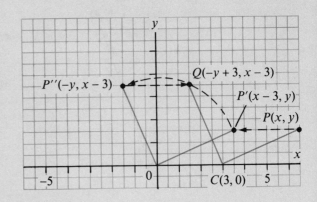

Look Back

- Check by repeating the above method for a point such as $R(5, 3)$, instead of $P(x, y)$. Then apply the mapping rule. Do the results agree?

Solve each problem

1. a) Find the mapping rule for a 180° rotation counterclockwise about $P(0, 3)$.
   b) Use the mapping rule to find the image of the triangle with vertices $A(0, 2)$, $B(-4, 3)$, and $C(0, 5)$.
   c) Check by graphing $\triangle ABC$ and its image.

2. The first step in finding the mapping rule for a reflection in the line $x = 2$ is to transform to a simpler problem.
   a) Which of the following is the simpler problem that is needed?
      i) Reflect in the line $x = -2$.
      ii) Reflect in the line $x = 0$.
      iii) Reflect in the line $y = 2$.
      iv) Reflect in the line $y = x$.
   b) Find the mapping rule for a reflection in the line $x = 2$.
   c) Use the mapping rule to find the image of the triangle with vertices $A(3, -2)$, $B(6, 0)$, and $C(5, 3)$.
   d) Check by graphing $\triangle ABC$ and its image.

3. Under a certain reflection, the image of $\triangle PQR$ has vertices $P'(-1, 8)$, $Q'(2, 7)$, and $R'(1, 4)$.
   a) Draw $\triangle PQR$ and $\triangle P'Q'R'$ on the same grid.
   b) Identify the reflection.
   c) Find the mapping rule for the reflection.
   d) Check the mapping rule using $\triangle PQR$ and $\triangle P'Q'R'$.

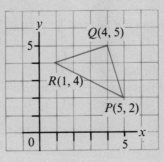

4. a) Find the mapping rule for a dilatation with a scale factor of 2 and a dilatation centre $T(0, 6)$.
   b) Use the mapping rule to find the image of the rhombus with vertices $A(0, 2)$, $B(3, 3)$, $C(4, 6)$, and $D(1, 5)$.
   c) Show the results of (b) on a grid.
   d) Join matching points, and verify that the dilatation centre is $(0, 6)$, and that the scale factor is 2.

5. Under a certain dilatation, the image of rectangle $ABCD$ has vertices $A'(11, 4)$, $B'(11, 10)$, $C'(-1, 10)$, and $D'(-1, 4)$.
   a) Draw rectangles $ABCD$ and $A'B'C'D'$ on the same grid.
   b) What are the coordinates of the dilatation centre?
   c) Find the mapping rule for the dilatation.
   d) Check the mapping rule using rectangles $ABCD$ and $A'B'C'D'$.

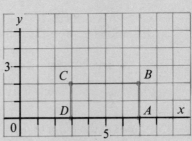

Review Exercises

1. Find the image of the point (4, 6) under the following transformations.
   a) $(x, y) \rightarrow (x + 4, y - 3)$
   b) $(x, y) \rightarrow (-y, -x)$
   c) $(x, y) \rightarrow (-x + 8, -y + 12)$
   d) $(x, y) \rightarrow (y + 3, x - 3)$

2. Find the coordinates of the point having the image (3, 8) under the following transformations.
   a) $(x, y) \rightarrow (x - 3, y - 3)$
   b) $(x, y) \rightarrow (2x, y - 5)$
   c) $(x, y) \rightarrow (y - 4, x + 2)$
   d) $(x, y) \rightarrow (y + 1, -x + 3)$

3. A triangle has vertices $A(-3, 3)$, $B(4, 3)$, $C(-3, 6)$. Graph the triangle and its image under these transformations.
   a) $(x, y) \rightarrow (x + 3, y + 2)$ b) $(x, y) \rightarrow (x - 2, y - 3)$ c) $(x, y) \rightarrow (x - 4, y - 6)$

4. Graph the line $y = 2x + 1$ and its image under the transformation $(x, y) \rightarrow (x + 1, y - 1)$. Find the equation of the image line.

5. A triangle has vertices $P(5, 2)$, $Q(2, 5)$, $R(0, 0)$. On the same grid, graph the triangle and its images under the following transformations. Describe each transformation.
   a) $(x, y) \rightarrow (-y, x)$
   b) $(x, y) \rightarrow (-x, -y)$

6. Graph the line $x + 2y = 3$ and its image under the transformation $(x, y) \rightarrow (-y, -x)$. Find the equation of the image line.

7. A triangle has vertices $A(2, 2)$, $B(6, 2)$, $C(6, 5)$. On the same grid, graph the triangle and its image under the following transformations. Describe each transformation.
   a) $(x, y) \rightarrow (-x, y)$
   b) $(x, y) \rightarrow (-y, -x)$

8. Graph the line $x - y = 4$ and its image under the transformation $(x, y) \rightarrow (-x, y)$. What is the equation of the image line?

9. A triangle has vertices $K(3, 5)$, $L(-2, 4)$, $M(2, -4)$. Graph the triangle and its image under the transformation $(x, y) \rightarrow (-x + 4, y)$.

10. A triangle has vertices $P(3, 5)$, $Q(6, 2)$, $R(7, 6)$. Graph the triangle and its image under the transformation $(x, y) \rightarrow (x - 6, -y)$.

11. A triangle has vertices $A(-3, 2)$, $B(1, 4)$, $C(4, 1)$. Graph $\triangle ABC$ and its image under the dilatation $(x, y) \rightarrow (2x - 3, 2y + 1)$.

12. Graph the line $2x + 3y = 4$ and its image under the transformation $(x, y) \rightarrow \left(\dfrac{x}{2}, \dfrac{y}{2}\right)$. What is the equation of the image line?

13. A fly lands at the point (3, 8) on a grid. It walks to the y-axis, then to the x-axis, and finally stops at the point (6, 4). What is the shortest distance the fly could have walked?

1. Solve by graphing.
   a) $x + 2y = 6$
      $2x - 3y = 5$
   b) $3x + y = 6$
      $2x + 4y = -1$
   c) $3x - 2y = -10$
      $6x + 8y = -2$

2. Solve by addition or subtraction.
   a) $2x + 3y = 7$
      $3x - 2y = 4$
   b) $x + 3y = 4$
      $3x - y = -18$
   c) $2x + 5y = -4$
      $3x + 2y = 5$

3. Solve by substitution.
   a) $y = 7 - 2x$
      $3x - 2y = 7$
   b) $2x + y = -5$
      $3x + 5y = 3$
   c) $4x - 3y = 7$
      $x - 2y = 8$

4. Determine the number of solutions for each of the following systems of equations.
   a) $5x - 3y = 12$
      $2x + 7y = 20$
   b) $2x - 3y = 10$
      $-6x + 9y = 30$
   c) $4x - 7y = 10$
      $8x - 14y = 20$

5. Translate the following into algebra.
   a) Two numbers have a difference of 12.
   b) Three times the first number, increased by the second, is 10.
   c) One number is 4 less than twice another number.
   d) A handful of dimes and quarters has a value of $3.50.
   e) The sum of a two-digit number and the number formed by reversing the digits is 77.

6. Sheila bought 7 baseball tickets, some at $8.50, the rest at $6.00. If she spent $49.50, how many of each did she purchase?

7. Two numbers have a sum of 26. Three times the first exceeds twice the second by 3. Find the numbers.

8. If the length of a rectangle is decreased by twice the width, the result is 8 cm. The perimeter is 40 cm. Find the dimensions.

9. The sum of the digits of a two-digit number is 10. The number formed by reversing the digits exceeds the original number by 36. Find the number.

10. Yasser invests $4500, part at 7%, the balance at $8\frac{1}{2}$%. After one year, the interest earned on the 7% investment was $150 less than the interest earned on the $8\frac{1}{2}$% investment. How much was invested at each rate?

11. Jeremy drives 1150 km and uses 122 L of fuel. His car averages 11.5 L/100 km in city driving, and 10.0 L/100 km in highway driving. How far did he drive on the highway?

12. A quadrilateral has vertices $A(2, 2)$, $B(3, -1)$, $C(6, -2)$, $D(6, 2)$. Graph the quadrilateral and its image under the following transformations.
    a) $(x, y) \rightarrow (x - 5, y + 3)$ b) $(x, y) \rightarrow (2x + 1, -3y)$
    c) $(x, y) \rightarrow (-y, x)$ d) $(x, y) \rightarrow (x, -y + 3)$

13. Find the images of $\triangle ABC$ that result from a
    a) translation   b) rotation   c) reflection   d) dilatation

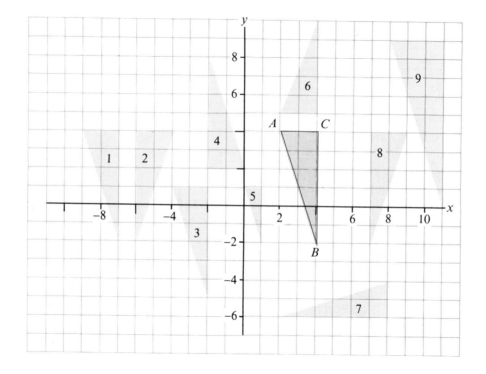

14. What kind of a transformation is represented by each of the following?
    a) $(x, y) \rightarrow (2x, 2y)$ b) $(x, y) \rightarrow (x - 2, y + 7)$
    c) $(x, y) \rightarrow (x, -y)$ d) $(x, y) \rightarrow (-y, x)$
    e) $(x, y) \rightarrow (x + 3, y + 1)$ f) $(x, y) \rightarrow (-x, y)$

15. Graph the line $3x + 2y = 6$ and its image under each of these transformations.
    a) $(x, y) \rightarrow (x + 5, y - 2)$ b) $(x, y) \rightarrow (-y, x)$
    c) $(x, y) \rightarrow (x, -y)$ d) $(x, y) \rightarrow (2x, 2y)$

16. Find the shortest distance from $A(4,2)$ to the x-axis to the y-axis to $B(2,4)$.

10 Reasoning and Geometry

In previous work you may have investigated the angles related to parallel lines. In Section 10-6, you will learn how to explain why certain angles are equal.

MATHEMATICS AROUND US

Recognizing Geometric Figures

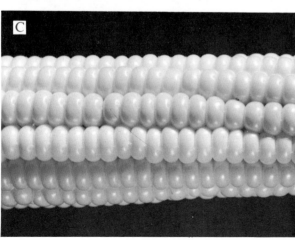

1. Describe what you see in each picture on these two pages. State as many things about it as you can.

2. What do these pictures have in common?
   a) B and C
   b) A and D
   c) D and F
   d) E and G
   e) E and F
   f) D and H
   g) F and H
   h) C and E

3. Which picture(s) illustrate the following?
   a) parallel lines
   b) a trapezoid
   c) a rectangle
   d) an isosceles triangle
   e) congruent triangles
   f) a circle
   g) a right triangle
   h) a parallelogram
   i) a polygon

4. Make a collection of pictures showing geometry in the world around us. Use photos you take yourself, or pictures from magazines and newspapers.

10-1 INDUCTIVE REASONING

If we examined many different snowflakes, we would likely find that
none of them are exactly alike. We might then conclude that no two
snowflakes are ever exactly alike. But we can never be certain because
we would have to examine every snowflake that ever existed.

If we observe that the same result occurs over and over again, we
may conclude that it will always occur. This kind of reasoning is called
inductive reasoning. We use inductive reasoning to conclude that two
snowflakes are never exactly alike.

Example 1. Suppose you multiply an odd number by an even number:
$$23 \times 14 = 322 \qquad 17 \times 24 = 408 \qquad 57 \times 32 = 1824$$
The products are all even numbers. What conclusion might you make?

Solution. The product of an odd number and an even number is even.

Example 2. Suppose you draw some intersecting lines.

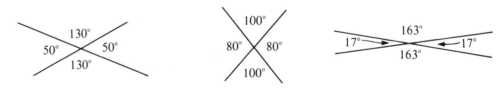

The angles opposite each other are equal. What conclusion might you make?

Solution. When two lines intersect, the opposite angles are equal.

When we use inductive reasoning, we can never be certain that the
conclusion is *always* true. In *Example 1*, we cannot be certain that
every time we multiply an odd number by an even number the product
is even. In *Example 2*, we cannot be certain that the opposite angles are
equal for *every* pair of intersecting lines.

EXERCISES 10-1

Ⓐ

1. Suppose you use a calculator to multiply the following 2-digit numbers.

$$28 \times 16 = 448 \qquad 35 \times 29 = 1015 \qquad 68 \times 75 = 5100$$

The products all have either 3 digits or 4 digits.
   a) Check this by multiplying other pairs of 2-digit numbers.
   b) What conclusion might you make?

2. Suppose you add consecutive odd numbers starting at 1.

The results are all perfect squares.
   a) Check this by continuing the pattern.
   b) What conclusion might you make?

$$1 + 3 = 4$$
$$1 + 3 + 5 = 9$$
$$1 + 3 + 5 + 7 = 16$$

Ⓑ

3. a) Draw a semicircle with diameter AB.

   b) Mark any point C on the semicircle and measure $\angle ACB$.

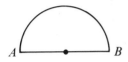

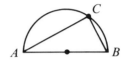

   c) Do this for other points on the semicircle.
   d) What conclusion might you make?

4. In each triangle, M is the midpoint of AB, and N is the midpoint of AC.

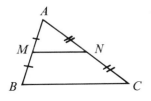
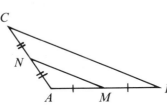
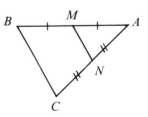

   a) How does MN compare with BC in each case?
   b) What conclusion might you make?

Ⓒ

5. a) Draw any quadrilateral $ABCD$. By measuring, locate the midpoints of its four sides.
   b) Join the midpoints to form another quadrilateral. What kind of quadrilateral is it?
   c) Do this for at least one more quadrilateral.
   d) What conclusion might you make?

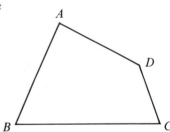

Look for a Counterexample

Many natural numbers can be written as the sum of consecutive numbers. Here are some examples.

$$9 = 2 + 3 + 4$$
$$15 = 1 + 2 + 3 + 4 + 5$$
$$22 = 4 + 5 + 6 + 7$$

$$29 = 14 + 15$$
$$39 = 12 + 13 + 14$$
$$74 = 17 + 18 + 19 + 20$$

Determine whether or not *every* natural number can be written as the sum of consecutive numbers.

Understand the problem

- Are the examples sufficient to solve the problem?
- Is it possible to check every natural number?

Think of a strategy

- Try to find an example of a natural number which *cannot* be written as the sum of consecutive numbers.

Carry out the strategy

- Try some more numbers.

$$12 = 3 + 4 + 5$$
$$17 = 8 + 9$$
$$26 = 5 + 6 + 7 + 8$$

$$30 = 9 + 10 + 11$$
$$40 = 6 + 7 + 8 + 9 + 10$$
$$100 = 18 + 19 + 20 + 21 + 22$$

- Start at any number and try to express it as a sum of consecutive numbers. If this is possible, continue with the next number, and so on.

$$5 = 2 + 3$$
$$6 = 1 + 2 + 3$$
$$7 = 3 + 4$$
$$8 = ?$$

- The number 8 cannot be expressed as the sum of consecutive numbers. Therefore, not every natural number can be written as the sum of consecutive numbers.

Look back

- An example which shows that a possible conclusion is false is called a *counterexample*. The number 8 is a counterexample which shows that not every natural number can be written as the sum of consecutive numbers.

Solve each problem

1. Each example suggests a possible conclusion. Give a counterexample to show that the conclusion is false.

   a)
   $$6 = 1^2 + 1^2 + 2^2 \qquad 59 = 1^2 + 3^2 + 7^2$$
   $$14 = 1^2 + 2^2 + 3^2 \qquad 61 = 3^2 + 4^2 + 6^2$$
   $$24 = 2^2 + 2^2 + 4^2 \qquad 89 = 2^2 + 2^2 + 9^2$$

   Possible conclusion: Every natural number can be written as the sum of three perfect squares.

   b)

    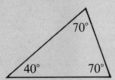 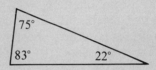

   Possible conclusion: In every triangle the three angles are all less than 90°.

   c)

   Possible conclusion: Every square has two horizontal sides and two vertical sides.

2. For which of the following statements is the diagram shown a counterexample?
   a) If a quadrilateral has four equal angles, it has four equal sides.
   b) The length of a rectangle is always double its width.
   c) The opposite sides of a parallelogram are equal.

3. Decide whether each statement is true or false. If it is false, give a counterexample.
   a) A number which is not positive is negative.
   b) If 1 is added to an odd number, the result is always an even number.
   c) The square of a number is always greater than the number.
   d) If two angles are acute, their sum is less than 180°.
   e) The altitude of a triangle always lies inside the triangle.
   f) Every rectangle is a square.
   g) Every square is a rectangle.

THE MATHEMATICAL MIND

A Famous Example of Intuitive Reasoning

For centuries people believed that the Earth was flat, and that the stars revolved around it. They rejected the ideas that the Earth was round and that it moves around the sun, because these ideas are contrary to intuition. By *intuition* we mean an instinctive knowledge or feeling without attention to reasoning.

When we use our intuition, we can never be certain that our conclusions are correct. For example: Suppose three lines l_1, l_2, and l_3 are such that $l_1 || l_2$ and $l_2 || l_3$. Our intuition might tell us that l_1 should be parallel to l_3. In this case the conclusion is correct, as we can see from a diagram.

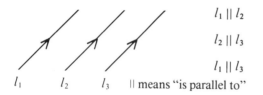

$l_1 || l_2$

$l_2 || l_3$

$l_1 || l_3$

$l_1 \quad l_2 \quad l_3$ || means "is parallel to"

But suppose three lines l_1, l_2, and l_3 are such that $l_1 \perp l_2$ and $l_2 \perp l_3$. Our intuition may suggest that l_1 is perpendicular to l_3. But in this case our intuition is incorrect, l_1 is *not* perpendicular to l_3. The diagram shows that l_1 and l_3 are parallel.

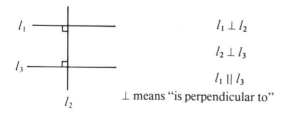

$l_1 \perp l_2$

$l_2 \perp l_3$

$l_1 || l_3$

$\perp$ means "is perpendicular to"

Use your intuition to answer Questions 1-3, and then reason out the answers.

1. A bottle and a cork together cost $2.10. If the bottle costs $2 more than the cork, how much does the cork cost?

2. Naomi's average in English, History, and Biology is 80%. She calculates that if she receives a mark of 60% in French, her average for the four subjects will be 70%. Is this correct?

3. A car travels 240 km at 80 km/h and then returns at 60 km/h. What is the average speed for the entire trip?

4. a) Suggest how people first became convinced that the Earth was round.

   b) List as many different ways as you can to explain, to someone living today, that the Earth is round.

10-2 DEDUCTIVE REASONING

To promote sales between 12 noon and 2 p.m., a pizza restaurant offers to give your pizza free of charge if it takes more than 5 min to bring it to your table after you order it. When this family was there, the following statements were true:

1. It was between 12 noon and 2 p.m.

2. It took more than 5 min to bring the pizza to their table.

They concluded that they would receive the pizza free of charge, and they did.

When we make a conclusion based on statements that we accept as true, we are using *deductive reasoning*. Here are some other examples of deductive reasoning.

Example 1. Suppose you add two odd numbers together.

$$3 + 7 = 10 \qquad 25 + 13 = 38 \qquad 437 + 129 = 566$$

Explain why the sums are always even.

Solution. Let $2m + 1$ and $2n + 1$ represent the odd numbers, where m and n are natural numbers. Then their sum is:

$$2m + 1 + 2n + 1 = 2(m + n + 1)$$

Since 2 is a factor of the sum, the sum is always even.

In *Example 1* we have *proved* that the sum of two odd numbers is always an even number, even for numbers we have not added. This illustrates the power of deductive reasoning. When we use deductive reasoning, we are certain that the conclusion is true.

Example 2.   *ABCD* is a square and △*ABE* is an equilateral triangle. Explain why △*BCE* is isosceles.

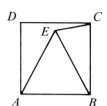

Solution.   Since *ABCD* is a square: $AB = CB$ ...①
Since *ABE* is an equilateral triangle: $AB = EB$ ...②
Comparing ① and ②, we see that: $CB = EB$
Therefore, △*BCE* is isosceles.

In *Example 2*, certain geometrical words were used. The definitions of these words are given below.

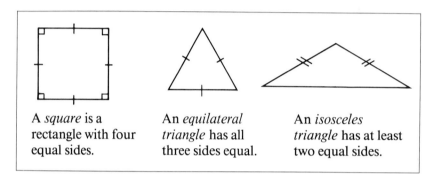

A *square* is a rectangle with four equal sides.

An *equilateral triangle* has all three sides equal.

An *isosceles triangle* has at least two equal sides.

EXERCISES 10-2

Ⓐ

1. Use deductive reasoning to complete the conclusion.

   a)   All students are teenagers. Lynn is a student.

   Conclusion: Lynn is a ▨▨▨▨▨.

   b)   All musicians have long hair. Sharon is a musician.

   Conclusion: Sharon has ▨▨▨▨▨.

   c)   If it is raining, the ground is wet. It is raining.

   Conclusion: The ground is ▨▨▨▨▨.

   d)   If the temperature goes above 5°C, the rink will melt.

   The temperature is 8°C.

   Conclusion: The rink will ▨▨▨▨▨.

   e)   A square is a rectangle. A rectangle has four right angles.

   Conclusion: A square has ▨▨▨▨▨.

   f)   Parallel lines never meet. Lines l_1 and l_2 are parallel.

   Conclusion: l_1 and l_2 ▨▨▨▨▨.

2. Use deductive reasoning to state a conclusion.
   a) Anyone who jogs regularly will be fit. Manuel jogs regularly. Therefore, ...
   b) If you take English, your writing will improve. Jennifer takes English. Therefore, ...
   c) A square has four equal sides. Some rectangles are squares. Therefore, ...
   d) A right angle measures 90°. $\angle ABC$ is a right angle. Therefore, ...

Ⓑ

3. Decide if the conclusion follows logically from the statement.
   a) All mathematics students can compute. Lisa is a mathematics student. Therefore, Lisa can compute.
   b) Some students like pizza. Sophie is a student. Therefore, Sophie likes pizza.
   c) An isosceles triangle has at least two equal sides. An equilateral triangle has three equal sides. Therefore, an equilateral triangle is isosceles.
   d) A square has four equal sides. $ABCD$ has four equal sides. Therefore $ABCD$ is a square.

4. If $\angle ABD = \angle CBD$, explain why $\angle ABD = 90°$.

5. $PQRS$ is a square and $\triangle PST$ is an equilateral triangle. Explain why $\triangle PQT$ is isosceles.

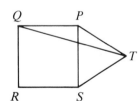

6. Explain why the sum of two even numbers is always even.

7. Explain why the product of two odd numbers is always odd.

8. Alec, Ahmad, Carlos, Dan, and Eddie are on the school basketball team. List the boys in order of increasing height if
   a) there are at least two boys shorter than Alec
   b) Dan is shorter than Carlos
   c) Ahmad is not the shortest boy
   d) Dan is taller than Alec

Ⓒ

9. $JKLM$ is a square and $\triangle JXK$ and $\triangle KYL$ are both equilateral. Prove that $\triangle KXY$ is isosceles.

10. What is the most important difference between inductive and deductive reasoning?

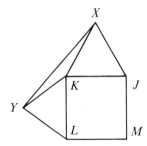

10-3 THE OPPOSITE ANGLE THEOREM

In geometry, we often make conclusions from diagrams. For example, consider the measures of the angles formed when two lines intersect.

We might use inductive reasoning to conclude that the angles opposite each other are equal. But we cannot draw all possible pairs of intersecting lines to examine every pair. How can we be sure that the opposite angles are equal, even for diagrams we have not drawn? We can do this by using deductive reasoning, as follows:

This diagram represents any two intersecting lines.

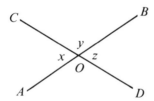

Since $\angle AOB$ is a straight angle: $x + y = 180°$ ...①
Since $\angle COD$ is a straight angle: $y + z = 180°$ ...②

Comparing ① and ②: $x + y = y + z$
$$x = z$$

Therefore, $\angle AOC = \angle DOB$. In the same way, we can explain why $\angle AOD = \angle COB$.

We have now *proved* that whenever two lines intersect, the opposite angles are equal. It is not necessary to draw a diagram and measure the angles. Since we have proved that this is true, and since it turns out to be useful later, we call it a *theorem*.

Opposite Angle Theorem
When two lines intersect, the opposite angles are equal.

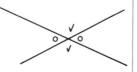

Example.   Find the value of x in the diagram below.

> **Think:**
> The three angles above the horizontal line add up to 180°. We can find the middle angle using the Opposite Angle Theorem.

Solution.   By the Opposite Angle Theorem, $\angle FGA = 75°$.
Since $\angle EGB$ is a straight angle:

$$x + 75° + 40° = 180°$$
$$x = 180° - 115°$$
$$x = 65°$$

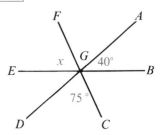

The above example can be solved in other ways. How many can you find?

EXERCISES 10-3

1. Name two pairs of opposite angles.
   a)

   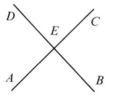

   b)

   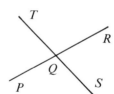

2. Find the values of x and y.
   a)

   b)

3. Find the values of x and y.
   a)

   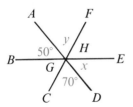

   b)

   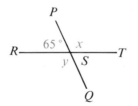

   c)

   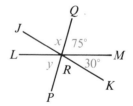

10-4 THE SUPPLEMENTARY ANGLE THEOREM

When a door is opened, two angles are formed; the angle it turned through, and the angle between the door and the wall behind it. Since these two angles add up to 180°, they are called supplementary angles.

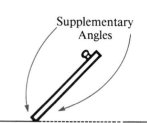

Supplementary
Angles

> Two angles with a sum of 180° are called *supplementary angles*. Each is the *supplement* of the other.

Example 1. Which angles are supplementary?
　　　　　a) 65° and 105°　　　　　　　　　　b) 123° and 57°

Solution.　a) 65° + 105° = 170°. These angles are not supplementary.
　　　　　b) 123° + 57° = 180°. These angles are supplementary.

Example 2. What is the supplement of 145°?

Solution.　To find the supplement of an angle, subtract it from 180°.
$$180° - 145° = 35°$$
　　　　　The supplement of 145° is 35°.

Suppose there are two doors in the room. Suppose also that each door is opened the same amount, that is $\angle① = \angle③$. Then, we might predict that $\angle②$ and $\angle④$ are equal. We can use deductive reasoning to explain why $\angle② = \angle④$.

Since $\angle①$ and $\angle②$ are supplementary:
$$\angle① + \angle② = 180°$$
$$\angle② = 180° - \angle①   \quad\dots①$$

Since $\angle③$ and $\angle④$ are supplementary:
$$\angle③ + \angle④ = 180°$$
$$\angle④ = 180° - \angle③   \quad\dots②$$

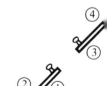

Comparing ① and ②, we see that the expressions on the right side are equal, since it is given that $\angle① = \angle③$. Therefore, $\angle② = \angle④$.

Supplementary Angle Theorem
If two angles are equal,
their supplements are equal.

$$\angle① = \angle②$$

EXERCISES 10-4

Ⓐ

1. Are the angles supplementary?
   a) 60° and 120°
   b) 75° and 115°
   c) 80° and 100°
   d) 43° and 137°
   e) 98° and 82°
   f) 50°, 60°, and 70°

2. What is the supplement of each angle?
   a) 60°
   b) 75°
   c) 150°
   d) 52°
   e) 90°

3. From the angles listed, find as many different pairs of supplementary angles as you can.

30°	55°	75°	80°	90°
100°	115°	125°	150°	180°

Ⓑ

4. From the view of a car (below, left), $\angle PQR = \angle JKL$. Explain why $\angle RQS = \angle LKM$.

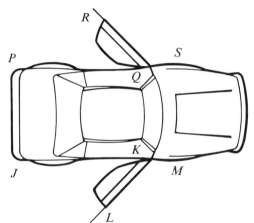

5. In the view of a church (above, right), $\angle ABC = \angle TUV$. Explain why $\angle CBD = \angle VUW$.

6. Explain why $\angle ABC = \angle ACB$.
   a)

   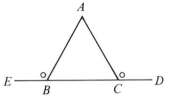

   b)

   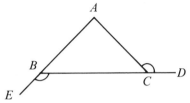

7. Two angles are supplementary. Find the angles if
   a) the angles are equal
   b) one angle is double the other

Ⓒ

8. Two angles are supplementary. Find the angles if one angle is n times the other.

9. Two angles have a sum of 90°. What is the sum of their supplements?

10-5 USING DEDUCTIVE REASONING IN GEOMETRY

As we have seen in the preceding section, we can use deductive reasoning to explain why many geometric properties are true. To do this, we need to know about definitions and axioms.

Definitions

These words have already been defined:

square   equilateral triangle   isosceles triangle   supplementary angles

Any definition involves other words which should also be defined. For example, consider the definition of a square:

A *square* is a rectangle with four equal sides. This definition contains the words "rectangle" and "sides". We are led to other definitions, such as the following:

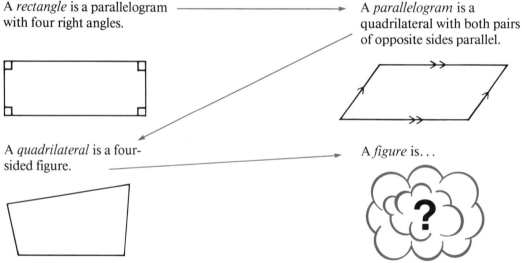

A *rectangle* is a parallelogram with four right angles.

A *parallelogram* is a quadrilateral with both pairs of opposite sides parallel.

A *quadrilateral* is a four-sided figure.

A *figure* is...

But we cannot continue doing this indefinitely. Therefore, there must always be some words which are *undefined*. Here are some words that we will accept as undefined.

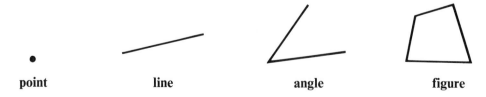

point   line   angle   figure

Although the diagrams suggest what the words mean, we will not attempt to define them.

Axioms

When we use deductive reasoning, we make conclusions based on given statements. There must always be some statements which we assume to be true, and which we cannot explain. Here are some examples of these kinds of statements:

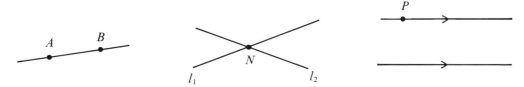

Only one line can be drawn through two different points.

Two intersecting lines meet at only one point.

Through any point there is only one line parallel to a given line.

Statements such as these are called *axioms*. Axioms are usually considered to be so obvious that they do not have to be explained. However, mathematicians tried for centuries to explain the last axiom above but without success.

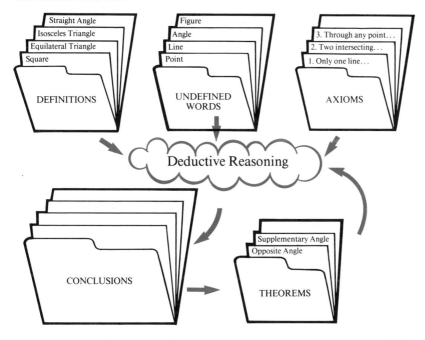

When we use deductive reasoning in geometry, we can use definitions, undefined words, and axioms to come to conclusions. Then any of the conclusions obtained can be used to form other conclusions. The ones which are the most useful for this purpose are called *theorems*.

EXERCISES 10-5

Ⓑ

1. A dictionary gives this definition for the word "line":

   A line is a long narrow mark.

   a) List three words in this sentence which should also be defined.
   b) Use a dictionary to look up the meaning of one of the words you selected in (a). List any other words encountered which should then be defined.

2. a) Decide which of the following words should be defined.

acute angle	obtuse angle	right angle	degree
triangle	vertex	octagon	plane
circle	radius	hypotenuse	polygon

   b) If you think the word should be defined, give a definition. If you think it should be undefined, draw a diagram to suggest its meaning.

3. a) Find at least five geometric words that were used in earlier sections of this chapter, but which were not explained.
   b) If you think the word should be defined, give a definition. If you think it should be undefined, draw a diagram to suggest its meaning.

4. Four geometric statements are given below. Two are usually taken as axioms, and two as theorems. Decide which are axioms and which are theorems.

   a) A line separates a plane into two half-planes.

   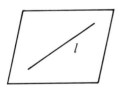

   b) The bisectors of the angles of a triangle meet at a point.

   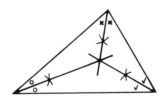

   c) In a right triangle, the square of the hypotenuse is equal to the sum of the squares of the other two sides.

   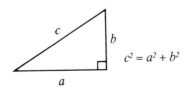

   $$c^2 = a^2 + b^2$$

   d) The shortest distance between two points is measured along a straight line.

   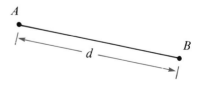

5. Explain the difference between an axiom and a theorem.

10-6 THE PARALLEL LINES THEOREM

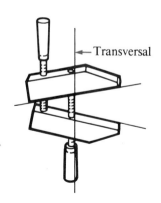

←— Transversal

In cabinetmaking, handscrews are very useful tools because they can be adjusted to different closing angles. They also illustrate a line intersecting two other lines in geometry. The jaws of the handscrew represent two lines, and the threaded screw represents a line intersecting them. Such a line is called a *transversal*, and it forms certain pairs of angles with the two lines.

When a transversal intersects two lines there are two pairs of *alternate angles* and there are four pairs of *corresponding angles*.

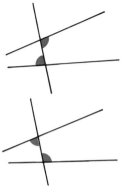

Alternate Angles

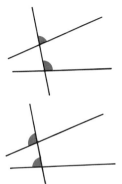

Corresponding Angles

Handscrews are usually set in the position shown, where the jaws are parallel. By measuring angles, you will find that when a transversal intersects two parallel lines, the alternate angles are equal and the corresponding angles are equal. We can use deductive reasoning to explain why these angles are equal, but we need the following axiom which is assumed to be true.

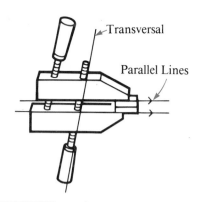

←—Transversal

Parallel Lines

Parallel Lines Axiom
If l_1 and l_2 are parallel lines, then
$$x + y = 180°.$$

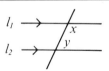

This diagram represents any two parallel lines intersected by a transversal.

By the Parallel Lines Axiom: $x + y = 180°$ ...①
Since $\angle ABC$ is a straight angle: $y + z = 180°$ ...②
Comparing ① and ②: $\quad x + y = y + z$
$$x = z \quad ...③$$

Therefore, the alternate angles are equal.

By the Opposite Angle Theorem: $z = w$ ...④
Comparing ③ and ④: $\quad x = w$

Therefore, the corresponding angles are equal.

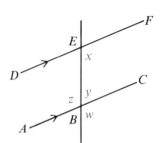

Parallel Lines Theorem

If a transversal intersects two parallel lines, then the

| alternate angles | corresponding angles |
| are equal. | are equal. |

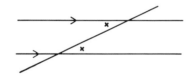 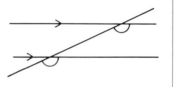

When we use the Parallel Lines Theorem, we must be able to recognize alternate and corresponding angles when they occur in different positions. Think of the letters Z and F.

Alternate angles form a Z pattern.   *Corresponding angles form an F pattern.*

Angles satisfying the Parallel Lines Axiom form a C-pattern.

          $x + y = 180°$

When we use these patterns, we must be sure that lines which look parallel are, in fact, known to be parallel.

Example 1. In the diagram, find the values of *x* and *y*.

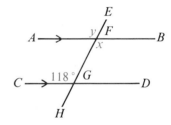

> **Think:**
> Angles marked *x* and 118° form a *Z*-pattern.
> Angles marked *y* and 118° form an *F*-pattern.

Solution. Since $AB \parallel CD$, alternate angles are equal.
Therefore, $x = 118°$.

Since $AB \parallel CD$, corresponding angles are equal. Therefore, $y = 118°$.

In *Example 1*, once we have found that $x = 118°$, we could use the Opposite Angle Theorem to find that $y = 118°$. This shows that results can be explained in different ways.

Example 2. Find the values of *x*, *y*, and *z* in the diagram below.

> **Think:**
> Angles marked *x* and 110° form a *C*-pattern. The angle marked *y* is opposite 55°. Angles marked *y* and *z* form a *Z*-pattern.

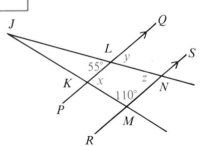

Solution. By the Parallel Lines Axiom: $x + 110° = 180°$
$$x = 70°$$

By the Opposite Angle Theorem: $y = 55°$

Since $PQ \parallel RS$, alternate angles are equal. $z = 55°$

EXERCISES 10-6

Ⓐ

1. In the figure given, name two pairs of alternate angles and four pairs of corresponding angles.

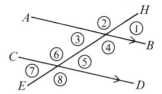

2. Find the values of *x* and *y*.
   a)

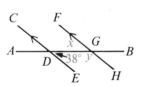

   b)

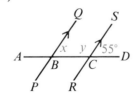

   c)

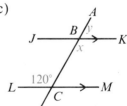

3. For the feather (below, left), if $\angle ABC = 40°$, find $\angle BDE$.

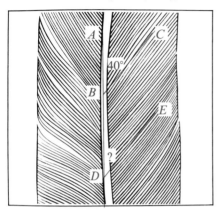

4. For the grain elevator (above, right), if $\angle PQR = 135°$, find $\angle QRS$.

5. Find the values of x, y, and z.

a)

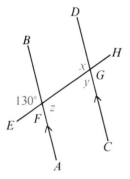

b)

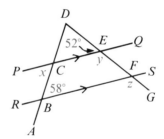

c)

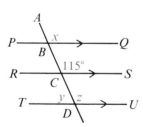

d)

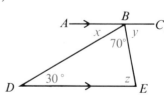

e)

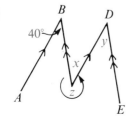

f)

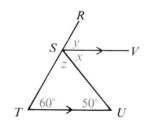

Ⓑ

6. If $AB \parallel CD$ and $XY \perp CD$, explain why $XY \perp AB$.

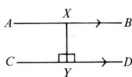

7. If $BE \parallel CD$ and $\angle C = \angle D$, explain why BE bisects $\angle ABD$.

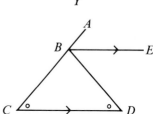

8. Find the measures of the angles indicated by the variables.
   a)

   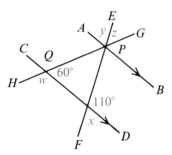

   b)

   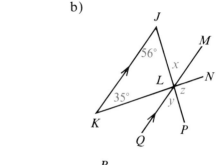

9. A pair of parallel mirrors is used in a periscope. This ensures that light rays entering the periscope at the top are parallel to those leaving at the bottom. In the diagram, name two different pairs of equal alternate angles.

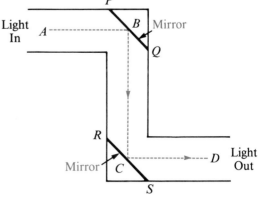

Ⓒ

10. Write definitions for
    a) parallel lines
    b) a transversal
    c) alternate angles
    d) corresponding angles

11. The Humber Estuary Bridge in England has the longest bridge span in the world. The towers are perfectly vertical, yet the tops of the towers are 3.6 cm farther apart than the bases. Explain how this can be so.

10-7 THE ANGLE SUM THEOREM

Set squares are often used in carpentry and drafting.
What is the sum of the angles in the set squares shown?

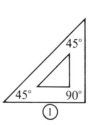
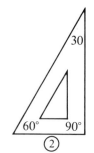

In ①: $45° + 45° + 90° = 180°$

In ②: $30° + 60° + 90° = 180°$

If we draw other triangles with different sizes and shapes and measure the angles, we will find that the sum of the angles is also 180°. But we cannot do this for all triangles. We can use deductive reasoning to explain why the sum is 180°, without drawing triangles and measuring angles.

In the diagram, $\triangle ABC$ represents any triangle. We draw a line through A, parallel to BC, and call it DE.

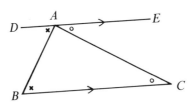

Since DE is parallel to BC:

$$\angle DAB = \angle B \quad \ldots① \qquad \text{(alternate angles)}$$

$$\angle EAC = \angle C \quad \ldots② \qquad \text{(alternate angles)}$$

Since $\angle DAE$ is a straight angle:

$$\angle DAB + \angle BAC + \angle EAC = 180°$$

Therefore, using ① and ②:

$$\angle B + \angle BAC + \angle C = 180°$$

This explains why the sum of the angles in $\triangle ABC$ is 180°.

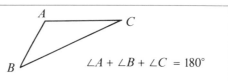

Angle Sum Theorem
In any triangle, the sum of the angles is 180°.

$$\angle A + \angle B + \angle C = 180°$$

Example 1. Find the value of x in the diagram below:

> **Think:**
> The angle marked x and $\angle ACB$ add to 180°.
> We can find $\angle ACB$ using the angles in $\triangle ABC$.

Solution. $\angle ACB + 60° + 40° = 180°$
                        $\angle ACB = \ \ 80°$

Since $\angle DCB$ is a straight angle:
                        $x + 80° = 180°$
                            $x = 100°$

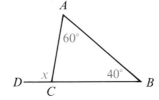

Example 2. In the diagram, $\angle AED = \angle ABC$. Explain why $\angle ADE = \angle ACB$.

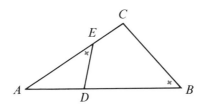

> **Think:**
> Visualize the triangles drawn separately.

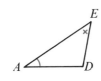 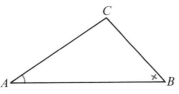

Solution.   Apply the Angle Sum Theorem to both triangles:

In $\triangle ADE$: $\angle A + x + \angle ADE = 180°$ ...①

In $\triangle ACB$: $\angle A + x + \angle ACB = 180°$ ...②

Comparing ① and ②, we see that $\angle ADE = \angle ACB$.

EXERCISES 10-7

Ⓐ

1. Find the value of *x*.

a)

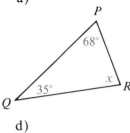

b)

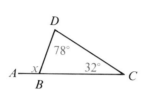

c)

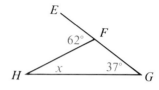

d)

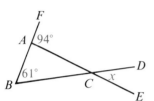

e)

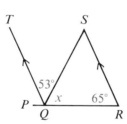

f)

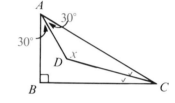

2. Find the values of *x* and *y*.

a)

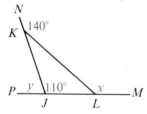

b)

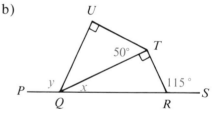

c)

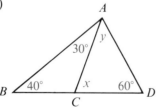

d)

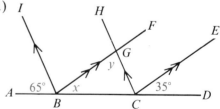

3. In the diagram below (left), explain why $\angle A + \angle B = 90°$.

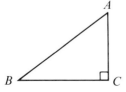

4. In the diagram above (right), explain why $\angle A = \angle E$.

Ⓑ

5. Two set squares are sometimes used in combination, as shown. What is the sum of the angles in quadrilateral *ABCD*?

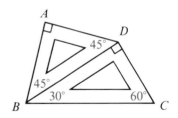

6. The diagram below (left) shows a cross section of a dam. Use the information in the diagram to determine ∠*DEF*.

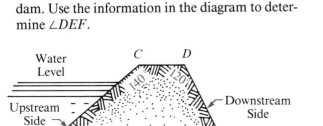

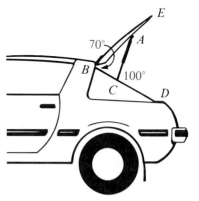

7. In the hatchback roof-support system (above, right), ∠*ABC* = 70° and ∠*ACD* = 100°. Find ∠*BAC* and ∠*CAE*.

8. △*ABC* is any triangle. The angle formed by extending one side, as shown, is called an *exterior angle* of the triangle. Explain why ∠*ACD* = ∠*A* + ∠*B*.

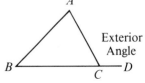

9. In the diagram below prove that ∠*EAB* + ∠*BCF* = ∠*B* + ∠*D*.

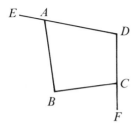

10. In the diagram below prove that ∠*E* = 90°.

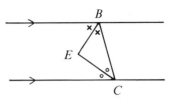

11. Find the sum of the shaded angles and state a probable conclusion based on the results.

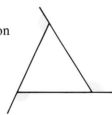

1. Suppose you write numbers ending in 5 as follows.

   $5 = 4 + 1$ $15 = 16 - 1$ $25 = 16 + 9$

   $35 = 36 - 1$ $45 = 49 - 4$ $55 = 64 - 9$

   You notice that these numbers can all be expressed as a sum or a difference of two perfect squares.
   a) Check this by expressing other numbers ending in 5 as a sum or a difference of two perfect squares.
   b) What conclusion might you make?

2. Use deductive reasoning to state a conclusion.
   a) Every artist is poor. Jeffrey is an artist.
   b) The opposite angles of a parallelogram are equal. *PQRS* is a parallelogram.
   c) A triangle with two equal sides is isosceles. $\triangle ABC$ has two equal sides.

3. Explain why the difference between two odd numbers is always even.

4. In each of *Exercises 1, 2,* and *3,* state whether you used inductive reasoning or deductive reasoning.

5. What is the supplement of each angle?
   a) 40°   b) 75°   c) 90°   d) 120°   e) 165°

6. Give examples of three undefined words. Why must there always be some words which are undefined?

7. Give an example of an axiom, and an example of a theorem.

8. Explain why $DE \perp AB$.   9. Explain why $\angle ABD = \angle ACE$.

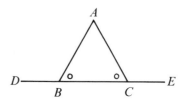

10. Find the value of *x*.
    a)   b)   c)

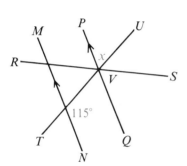

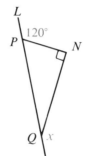

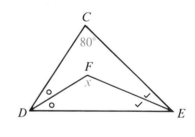

11 Congruence in Geometry

Many applications of mathematics involve right triangles. If we know the lengths of two sides of a right triangle, we can use the Pythagorean Theorem to calculate the length of the third side. In Section 11-4, you will learn how to prove the Pythagorean Theorem.

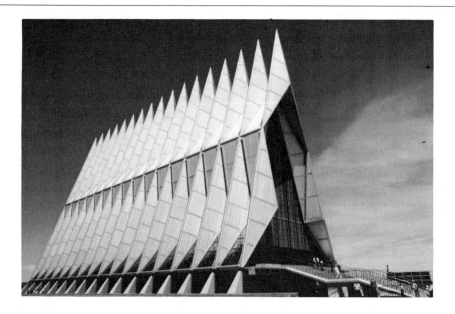

11-1 CONGRUENT TRIANGLES

This striking building is the U.S. Air Force chapel at Colorado Springs, Colorado. It appears to consist of many triangular sections which all have the same size and shape. For this reason, we say that the triangular sections are *congruent*.

If $\triangle ABC$ and $\triangle PQR$ are congruent, we write: $\triangle ABC \cong \triangle PQR$. This means that:

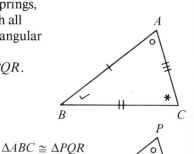

corresponding angles are equal.	corresponding sides are equal.
$\angle A = \angle P$	$AB = PQ$
$\angle B = \angle Q$	$BC = QR$
$\angle C = \angle R$	$AC = PR$

However, it is not necessary to know this much information to be certain that two triangles are congruent. The minimum conditions under which two triangles are congruent are called *congruence axioms*.

SSS Congruence Axiom
If three sides of one triangle are equal to three sides of another triangle, then the triangles are congruent.

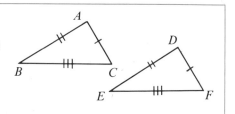

Example 1. In the diagram below, $PA = PB$ and $AC = BC$. Explain why
   a) $\triangle PAC \cong \triangle PBC$ b) $\angle APC = \angle BPC$

> **Think:**
> Two corresponding sides of each triangle are
> given to be equal. The third side, PC, is the same
> in each triangle.

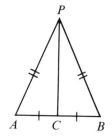

Solution.   a)   In $\triangle PAC$ and $\triangle PBC$, $PA = PB$
$$AC = BC$$
$$PC = PC$$
   Therefore, $\triangle PAC \cong \triangle PBC$ (SSS)

   b)   Since the triangles are congruent, $\angle APC = \angle BPC$.

> **SAS Congruence Axiom**
> If two sides and the contained angle
> of one triangle are equal to two sides
> and the contained angle of another
> triangle, then the triangles are congruent.

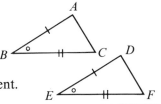

Example 2. In the diagram below, E is the midpoint of both AC and BD. Explain why
   $AB = CD$.

> **Think:**
> Not enough information is given to show that the
> triangles are congruent. But we can use the
> Opposite Angle Theorem to show that
> $\angle AEB = \angle CED$, and then the triangles will be
> congruent.

Solution.   By the Opposite Angle Theorem, $\angle AEB = \angle CED$.

   In $\triangle ABE$ and $\triangle CDE$, $AE = CE$
$$\angle AEB = \angle CED$$
$$BE = DE$$
   Therefore, $\triangle ABE \cong \triangle CDE$ (SAS)

   Since the triangles are congruent, $AB = CD$.

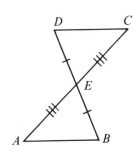

ASA Congruence Axiom
If two angles and the contained side
of one triangle are equal to two angles
and the contained side of another triangle, then the triangles are congruent.

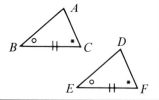

Example 3. In the diagram below, $BC = ED$, $\angle OBA = \angle OEF$, and $\angle OCB = \angle ODE$.
Explain why $\angle BOC = \angle EOD$.

> **Think:**
> If we can explain why $\angle OBC = \angle OED$, we can
> use ASA to show that $\triangle OBC \cong \triangle OED$.

Solution. By the Supplementary Angle Theorem, $\angle OBC = \angle OED$.

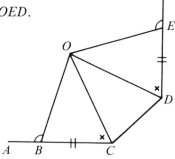

In $\triangle OBC$ and $\triangle OED$, $\angle OBC = \angle OED$
$$BC = ED$$
$$\angle OCB = \angle ODE$$
Therefore, $\triangle OBC \cong \triangle OED$ (ASA)

Since the triangles are congruent, $\angle BOC = \angle EOD$.

EXERCISES 11-1

1. a) Explain why $\triangle JKL \cong \triangle PQR$.
   b) List pairs of equal angles and
       equal sides.

2. a) Explain why the triangles are
       congruent.
   b) Explain why $\angle A = \angle B = \angle C$.

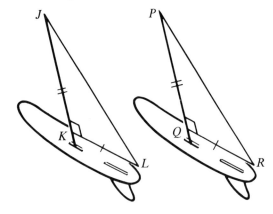

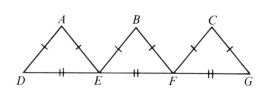

3. State why the triangles are congruent, and list pairs of equal angles and equal sides.

a)

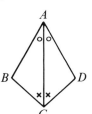

b)

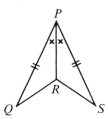

c)

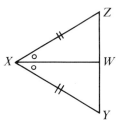

4. Find two congruent triangles and state the required congruence axiom.

a) i) ii) iii) b) i) ii) iii)

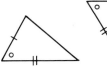

5. State a third condition necessary for congruence.

a)

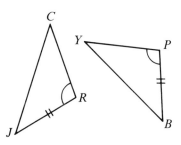

b)

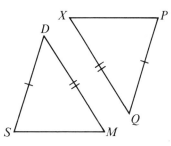

6. a) Explain why $\triangle ABC \cong \triangle ADC$.
   b) Explain why $BC = DC$.

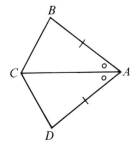

7. M is the midpoint of both crosspieces. Explain why $\triangle MPQ \cong \triangle MSR$.

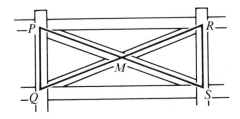

8. a) Explain why $\triangle PQS \cong \triangle RQS$.
   b) Explain why $\angle P = \angle R$.

9. a) Explain why $\triangle ABR \cong \triangle CBR$.
   b) Explain why $\angle A = \angle C$.

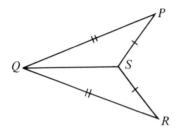

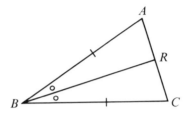

10. a) Explain why $\triangle ABD \cong \triangle CBD$.
    b) Explain why $AB = CB$.

11. Explain why $AD = BC$ and $\angle D = \angle C$.

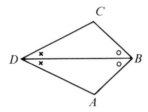

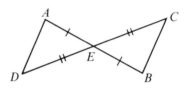

12. Explain why $CA = CD$ and $\angle A = \angle D$.

13. Explain why $\triangle PBC$ is isosceles.

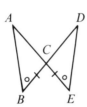

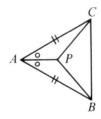

14. AB and CD are chords of equal length in a circle with centre O. Explain why $\angle AOB = \angle COD$.

15. If O is the centre of both circles, explain why $PQ = RS$.

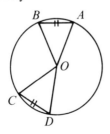

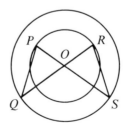

16. By measuring, an archaeologist finds that the angles and segments marked are equal. Explain why $AB = AD$.

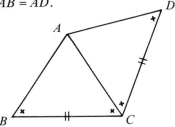

17. To bisect an angle, a carpenter places a try-square as shown. Explain why BD bisects $\angle ABC$.

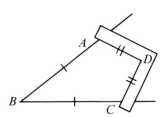

18. $\triangle ABC$ and $\triangle DBC$ are isosceles triangles with the same base BC. Prove that $\angle ABD = \angle ACD$.

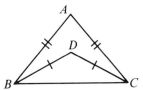

19. If $PQ \| ST$ and R is the midpoint of PT, prove that R is also the midpoint of QS.

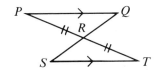

20. In quadrilateral $PQRS$, $PQ = RQ$ and $PS = RS$. If T is any point on the diagonal QS, prove that $PT = RT$.

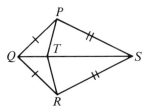

21. Prove that $AE = DB$.

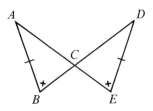

22. Prove that $KL = NM$.

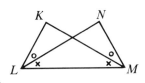

23. Prove that $BC = DE$.

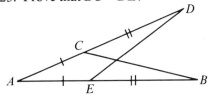

24. In $\triangle PQR$, S is the midpoint of QR and $PS \perp QR$. Prove that $\triangle PQR$ is isosceles.

25. In quadrilateral $PQRS$, $PQ = QR$ and the diagonal QS bisects $\angle Q$. Prove that $PS = RS$.

26. AB and CD bisect each other at point M. Prove that $AC = BD$.

27. If XY and WZ are diameters of a circle, prove that $XW = YZ$.

28. Circles with centres A and B intersect at C and D. Prove that $\angle ACB = \angle ADB$.

29. Draw $\triangle DEF$ in which $\angle D = \angle A$, $\angle E = \angle B$, $\angle F = \angle C$, but such that $\triangle DEF$ is *not* congruent to $\triangle ABC$. How does this explain that AAA is not a congruence axiom?

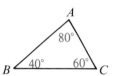

30. Draw $\triangle DEF$ in which $DE = AB$, $EF = BC$, $\angle F = \angle C$, but such that $\triangle DEF$ is *not* congruent to $\triangle ABC$. How does this explain that SSA is not a congruence axiom?

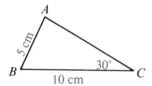

31. Prove the *Perpendicular Bisector Theorem*: Any point P on the perpendicular bisector of a line segment AB is equidistant from the endpoints A and B.

32. Prove the *Angle Bisector Theorem*: Any point P on the bisector of an angle ABC is equidistant from the arms AB and BC.

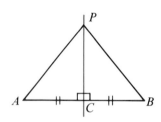

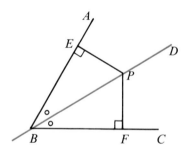

33. In $\triangle PQR$, $PQ = PR$, and S is the midpoint of QR. Prove that
    a) PS bisects $\angle QPR$
    b) $PS \perp QR$

INVESTIGATE

This equilateral triangle has been divided into three congruent figures. Show how to divide an equilateral triangle into

a) 2 congruent triangles
b) 3 congruent triangles
c) 4 congruent triangles
d) 6 congruent triangles

11-2 THE ISOSCELES TRIANGLE THEOREM

The *Chi-Chi-Cheemaun* is a ferry to Manitoulin Island in Ontario. Cars and trucks drive onto the ship through the upturned bow section, which resembles a triangle with two equal sides. If two sides of a triangle are equal, the triangle is called *isosceles*.

In the triangle in the photograph, $AB = AC$. By measuring, you can verify that the angles opposite these sides are equal:

$$\angle B = \angle C.$$

If you draw other isosceles triangles and measure the angles opposite the equal sides, you will find that they are equal. But you cannot do this for all isosceles triangles. The only way to be certain that the angles opposite the equal sides in *every* isosceles triangle are equal is to use deductive reasoning. We can explain why the angles are equal as follows:

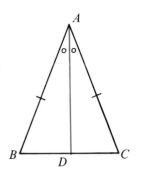

In the diagram, $\triangle ABC$ represents any isosceles triangle in which $AB = AC$.
We draw a line through A which bisects $\angle A$ and meets BC at D.

$$\text{In } \triangle ABD \text{ and } \triangle ACD, \ AB = AC$$
$$\angle BAD = \angle CAD$$
$$AD = AD$$
$$\text{Therefore, } \triangle ABD \cong \triangle ACD \quad \text{(SAS)}$$

Since the triangles are congruent, $\angle B = \angle C$.

Isosceles Triangle Theorem
In any isosceles triangle, the angles opposite the equal sides are equal.

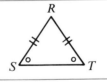

Example 1. Find the values of x and y in the diagram below.

> **Think:**
> The angle marked y equals $\angle DBC$, which is the supplement of $110°$. We can find x by using the Angle Sum Theorem.

Solution. Since $\angle ABC$ is a straight angle:
$$\angle DBC + 110° = 180°$$
$$\angle DBC = 70°$$
By the Isosceles Triangle Theorem,
$$y = 70°$$
By the Angle Sum Theorem,
$$x + 70° + 70° = 180°$$
$$x = 40°$$

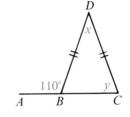

Example 2. In the diagram, $AB = AC$. Explain why $\angle ABE = \angle ACD$.

> **Think:**
> We can first show that $\angle ABC = \angle ACB$, and then we can use the Supplementary Angle Theorem.

Solution. By the Isosceles Triangle Theorem,
$$\angle ABC = \angle ACB$$
By the Supplementary Angle Theorem,
$$\angle ABE = \angle ACD$$

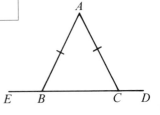

Example 3. A yield sign has the shape of an equilateral triangle. Prove that each angle is $60°$.

> **Think:**
> If we can explain why the angles are all equal, each one must be $\frac{1}{3}$ of $180°$, or $60°$.

Solution. By the Isosceles Triangle Theorem,
since $AB = BC, \angle A = \angle C$
and since $AB = AC, \angle B = \angle C$.

Therefore, $\angle A = \angle B = \angle C$.

By the Angle Sum Theorem, the sum of these angles is $180°$.
Therefore, each angle is $60°$.

EXERCISES 11-2

Ⓐ

1. Find the value of x.

 a)
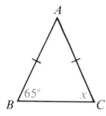

 b)
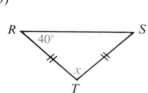

 c)
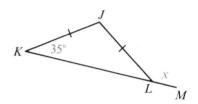

2. In this photograph of a church window, below (left), what is the measure of each angle?

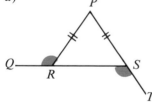

3. In the photograph above (right), if $\angle ABC = 135°$, explain why $\angle CDE = 135°$.

4. Explain why the shaded angles are equal.

 a)

 b)
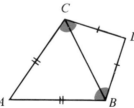

 c)
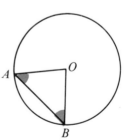

Ⓑ

5. Find the value of x.

 a)
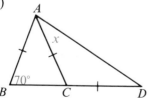

 b)
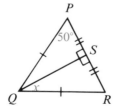

 c)
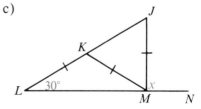

6. In the roof truss below, segments *AB*, *BC*, *CD*, *EB*, and *EC* all have equal lengths.
   Find   a) ∠*BEC*   b) ∠*ABE*   c) ∠*EAB*.

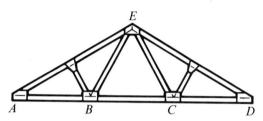

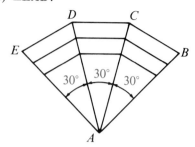

7. A floor plan of an auditorium is shown. If all three triangular sections are congruent, find ∠*BCD*.

8. In each of the following, *ABCD* is a square. Find the values of *x* and *y*.
   a)

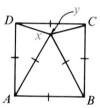

   b)

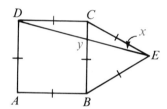

9. If *AB* = *AC* and *AB* || *DE*, explain why *BC* bisects ∠*ACE*.

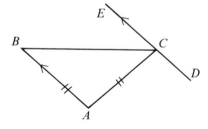

10. If *AB* = *AC* and *AE* || *BC*, explain why *AE* bisects ∠*CAD*.

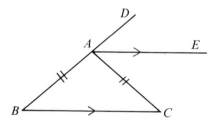

11. Prove that *AD* = *AE*.

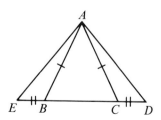

12. Prove that ∠*PTQ* = ∠*TRS* and that *PQ* = *TS*.

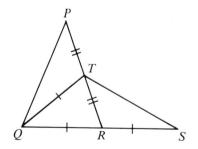

13. Two circles with centres A and B intersect at C and D. Prove that AB is the perpendicular bisector of CD.

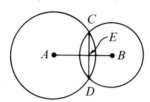

14. $\triangle ABC$ is an isosceles triangle, and $BD = EC$. Prove that $\triangle ADE$ is an isosceles triangle.

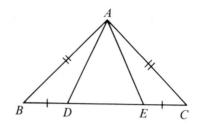

© ——————————————————————————————

15. XY and WZ are diameters of a circle. Prove that $\angle WXY = \angle WZY$.

16. In $\triangle ABC$, $\angle B = 90°$ and $AB = BC$. Side BC is extended to D such that $CD = AC$. Find the number of degrees in $\angle ADC$.

17. If 0 is the centre of the circle, prove that $\angle APB = 90°$.

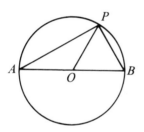

18. Find the values of x, y, and z.

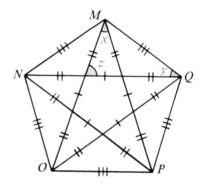

19. Explain why $\angle QSU = 45°$.

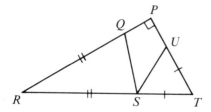

20. Explain why $\angle ADE = 3\angle ACE$.

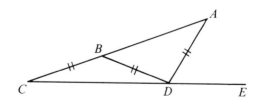

21. Any triangle is congruent to itself. If $AB = AC$, use the fact that $\triangle ABC$ is congruent to itself to prove that $\angle B = \angle C$.

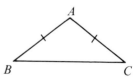

11-3 PROPERTIES OF A PARALLELOGRAM

This aerial photograph shows fields with a variety of shapes and sizes. Can you find examples which illustrate a rectangle? a square? a parallelogram?

> A *parallelogram* is a quadrilateral in which both pairs of opposite sides are parallel.

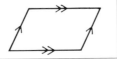

If you draw some parallelograms and measure their sides, you will find that the opposite sides appear to have the same length. But you cannot do this for all parallelograms. The only way to be certain that the opposite sides of a parallelogram have the same length is to use deductive reasoning.

ABCD represents any parallelogram. We join *AC* to create two triangles which we can prove are congruent.

Since $AB \| DC$, alternate angles are equal.
    Therefore, $\angle BAC = \angle DCA$

Since $AD \| BC$, alternate angles are equal.
    Therefore, $\angle ACB = \angle CAD$

In $\triangle ABC$ and $\triangle CDA$, $\angle BAC = \angle DCA$
        $AC = AC$
        $\angle ACB = \angle CAD$

    Therefore, $\triangle ABC \cong \triangle CDA$ (ASA)

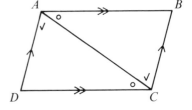

Since the triangles are congruent, $AB = CD$ and $BC = DA$. This proves that the opposite sides of a parallelogram have the same length.

We can obtain other properties of parallelograms from this diagram. Since the triangles are congruent, $\angle B = \angle D$. This proves that the opposite angles of a parallelogram are equal.

Also, by the Parallel Lines Axiom,
$$\angle BCD + \angle B = 180°$$
Therefore, the angles next to each other in a parallelogram are supplementary.

Some Properties of a Parallelogram

In any parallelogram,

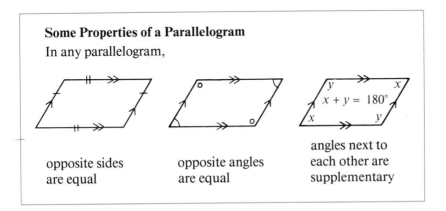

| opposite sides are equal | opposite angles are equal | angles next to each other are supplementary |

Example. Find the values of x and y in the diagram below.

> **Think:**
> The angle opposite the 55° angle is also equal to 55°, which allows us to find x. We can find y since it is next to the 55° angle.

Solution. Since $\angle BCD$ is opposite the 55° angle, $\angle BCD = 55°$.
Since $\angle DCE$ is a straight angle, $\qquad 55° + x = 180°$
$$x = 125°$$

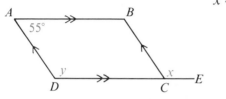

Since the angles marked y and 55° are next to each other:
$$55° + y = 180°$$
$$y = 125°$$

In the example, notice that the angles marked x and y are equal. Use a theorem studied previously to explain why they should be equal.

EXERCISES 11-3

Ⓐ

1. *ABCD* is a parallelogram. Find the values of *x* and *y*.

   a)

   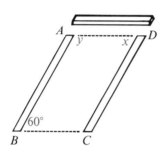

   b)

   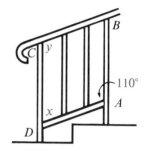

2. The measure of one angle of a parallelogram is given. Find the measures of the other three angles.

   a) 50°   b) 70°   c) 90°

3. Find the values of *x*, *y*, and *z*.

   a)

   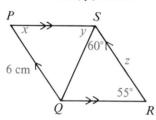

   b)

   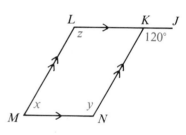

   c)

   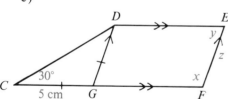

   d)

   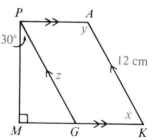

   e)

   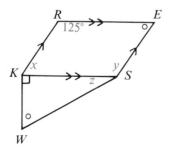

   f)

   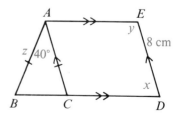

Ⓑ

4. In the diagram, *PT* = 8 cm and *ST* = 5 cm. Find the lengths of the diagonals *PR* and *SQ*.

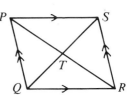

5. *ABCD* is a parallelogram. Its diagonals intersect at *M*.
   a) Explain why △*ABM* ≅ △*CDM*.
   b) Explain why *AM* = *CM* and *BM* = *DM*.
   c) What property of a parallelogram have you proved?

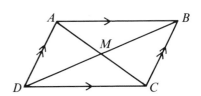

6. The shadow has the shape of a parallelogram. Find the measure of ∠*A* and the length of the railing.

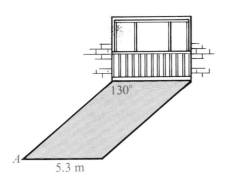

7. This *X* is made with two overlapping parallelograms. Find the measure of ∠*A*.

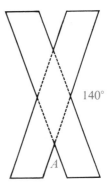

8. A *rectangle* is a parallelogram with four right angles.
   a) Explain why *AC* = *BD*.
   b) If the diagonals intersect at *M*, explain why *AM* = *MC*.
   c) What properties of a rectangle have you proved?

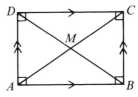

9. A *rhombus* is a parallelogram with four equal sides. The diagonals of rhombus *PQRS* intersect at *M*.
   a) Explain why ∠*SPR* = ∠*QPR* and ∠*SMP* = ∠*QMP*.
   b) What properties of a rhombus have you proved?

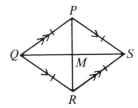

10. In the diagram, *PQRS* is a parallelo-
gram, and *M, N* are the midpoints of
PQ and *RS*. Prove that *MT* = *TN* and
QT = *TS*.

11. In the diagram, *EFGH* is a parallelogram, and *FR* = *FG*. Prove that
∠*FRG* = ∠*H*.

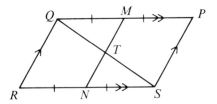

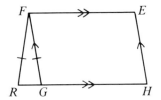

Ⓒ

12. A *square* is a quadrilateral with four equal sides and four
right angles. Prove that the diagonals of a square bisect
each other at right angles.

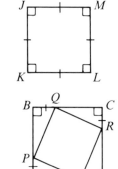

13. *ABCD* is a square. Points *P, Q, R, S* are located on the
sides as shown. Prove that quadrilateral *PQRS* is also
a square.

14. Use the Supplementary Angle Theorem and the Parallel
Lines Axiom to prove that the opposite angles of a parallelogram are equal.

15. Is it possible for two parallelograms to have corresponding sides equal but
corresponding angles not equal? Draw diagrams to support your answer.

16. a) Draw an example of a parallelogram whose diagonals bisect its opposite angles.
    b) Determine whether or not the diagonals of every parallelogram bisect its
       opposite angles.

 INVESTIGATE

Sketch these polygons, if possible.

1. A pentagon with 2 pairs of parallel sides.

2. A hexagon with
   a) 3 pairs of parallel sides
   b) 2 triplets of parallel sides

3. A quadrilateral with both pairs of opposite sides perpendicular.

4. A quadrilateral with one pair of opposite sides parallel and the other pair
   perpendicular.

THE MATHEMATICAL MIND

A Best Seller From Way Back

In 300 B.C., the city of Alexandria was the intellectual and cultural centre of ancient Greek civilization. A university was established there, and Euclid was the head of the mathematics department.

Euclid's *Elements* is one of the world's most famous books. More than 1000 editions have appeared in the last 500 years. In the *Elements*, Euclid organized the results in geometry, number theory, and algebra of mathematicians from 600 to 300 B.C. He showed that the theorems of what is now called *Euclidean geometry* can be deduced from ten axioms. Here are three of the axioms he used.

- Things which are equal to the same thing are equal to each other.
- If equals are added to equals, the sums are equal.
- All right angles are equal to one another.
Because it was the first organized source of mathematical knowledge, Euclid's *Elements* has probably had more influence on mathematical thinking than any other book. It has dominated the study of geometry for more than two thousand years.

- Euclid used the word "elements" to refer to the most important theorems. From Chapters 10 and 11, make a list of the theorems which might be considered to be the "elements" of geometry.

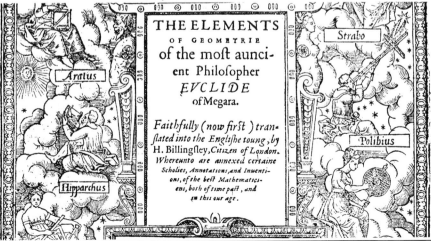

THE ELEMENTS
OF GEOMETRIE
of the moſt aunci-
ent Philoſopher
EVCLIDE
of Megara.

Faithfully (now firſt) tranſlated into the Engliſhe toung, by H. Billingſley, Citizen of London. Whereunto are annexed certaine Scholies, Annotations, and Inuentions, of the beſt Mathematiciens, both of time paſt, and in this our age.

Aratus

Hipparchus

Strabo

Polibius

11-4 PROVING THE PYTHAGOREAN THEOREM

Many applications of mathematics involve right triangles. Some of these are illustrated in the photographs on page 398. In any of these applications, if \ e know the lengths of two sides of a right triangle, we can use the *Pythagorean Theorem* to calculate the length of the third side.

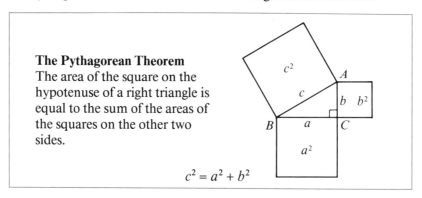

The Pythagorean Theorem
The area of the square on the hypotenuse of a right triangle is equal to the sum of the areas of the squares on the other two sides.

$$c^2 = a^2 + b^2$$

Since it has many applications, the Pythagorean Theorem is one of the most important of all mathematical theorems. As a result, over the last 2500 years, mathematicians have found hundreds of ways of proving it. The book, *The Pythagorean Proposition*, contains 370 of them. Here is one of the simplest explanations of the Pythagorean Theorem.

Step 1.

Let $\triangle ABC$ be a right triangle with side lengths a, b, and c. Draw square $CDEF$ as shown. Each side of this square has length $a + b$.

Step 2.

Locate points G, H, as shown, and draw quadrilateral $ABGH$. By the SAS congruence axiom, the four corner triangles are all congruent.

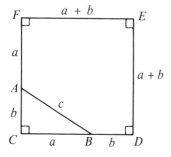

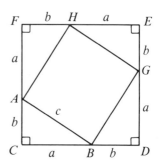

Step 3.

Since the triangles are congruent, the sides of quadrilateral *ABGH* are all *c* units long. Also, the angles marked *x* and *y* are equal in each triangle.

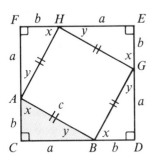

Step 4.

In △*ABC*, by the Angle Sum Theorem, $x + y + 90° = 180°$. Therefore, $x + y = 90°$. Since ∠*CBD* is a straight angle, ∠*ABG* = 90°. Therefore, quadrilateral *ABGH* is a square.

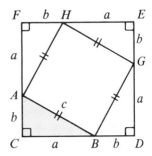

Step 5.

Area of square *CDEF* = Area of square *ABGH* + 4(Area of △*ABC*).

$$(a + b)^2 = c^2 + 4\left(\tfrac{1}{2}ab\right)$$
$$a^2 + 2ab + b^2 = c^2 + 2ab$$
$$a^2 + b^2 = c^2$$

This completes the proof of the Pythagorean Theorem.

Example. Find the value of *x* in the diagram below.

> **Think:**
> We can find *BE* using the Pythagorean Theorem.
> Then we can find *x* using congruent triangles.

Solution.

In △*ABE*, $BE^2 = 4^2 + 2^2$
$$= 20$$
$$BE = \sqrt{20}$$
$$= 2\sqrt{5} \text{ units}$$

In △*BEC* and △*DEC*, *BC* = *DC*
$$\angle BCE = \angle DCE$$
$$CE = CE$$

Therefore, △*BEC* ≅ △*DEC*   (SAS)

Since the triangles are congruent,
$$DE = BE$$
$$x = 2\sqrt{5} \text{ units}$$

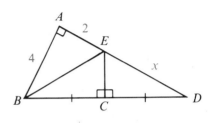

EXERCISES 11-4

Ⓐ

1. The two squares below are congruent to the corresponding squares in the diagram at the right.

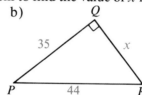

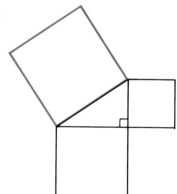

a) Trace and cut out the squares. Then cut the larger square along the lines. Rearrange the five pieces such that they all fit in the large square in the diagram.

b) Explain why this demonstrates the Pythagorean Theorem.

2. Use the Pythagorean Theorem to find the value of x rounded to two decimal places.

a)
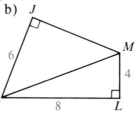

b)

c)
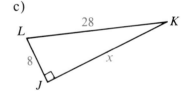

3. Find the perimeter of each figure, to the nearest tenth.

a)
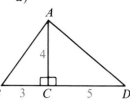

b)

c)
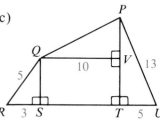

Ⓑ

4. Find the value of x rounded to one decimal place.

a)
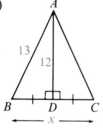

b)
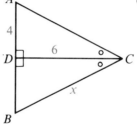

c)
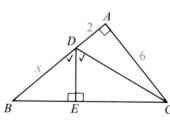

5. The shaded figure consists of five squares. Find the side length of the outer square.

6. The shaded figure consists of five squares. Find the radius of the circle.

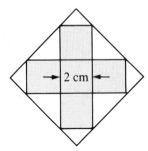

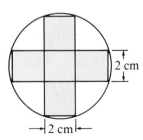

ⓒ

7. In the diagram, *ABDE* is a square. The four triangles inside the square are congruent to $\triangle ABC$.
   a) What is the side length of the shaded square?
   b) Find two different expressions for the area of the shaded square.
   c) Use the result in (b) to prove that $c^2 = a^2 + b^2$.

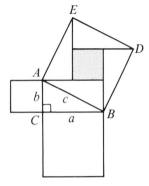

8. Two students were discussing the Pythagorean Theorem. Their discussion went as follows:

   Frank: "In these problems we had to find the value of x.

   In the first triangle I got $\sqrt{7}$ using the Pythagorean Theorem. Then I noticed that $4 + 3 = 7$. So a faster way to find the value of x is just to add the two given lengths and take the square root. This method gives the correct answer for the three other triangles too."

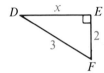

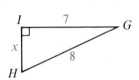

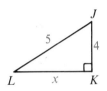

   Rhonda: "But your method doesn't work for all right triangles. I have found a counterexample."
   a) Find a counterexample to show that Frank's method does not work for all right triangles.
   b) Explain why Frank's method works for some right triangles but not for others.

Use Indirect Proof

In $\triangle ABC$, M is a point on BC such that $BM \neq CM$ and AM bisects $\angle A$. Prove that $AB \neq AC$.

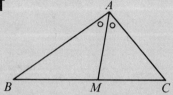

Understand the problem

- What information is given?
- What are you asked to prove?

Think of a strategy

- Instead of proving that $AB \neq AC$, assume that $AB = AC$, and see what happens.

Carry out the strategy

- Assume that $AB = AC$. Then, in $\triangle ABM$ and $\triangle ACM$,

$$AB = AC \quad \text{(assumption)}$$
$$\angle BAM = \angle CAM \quad \text{(given)}$$
$$AM = AM$$

Therefore, $\triangle ABM \cong \triangle ACM$ (SAS)

Since the triangles are congruent, $BM = CM$.

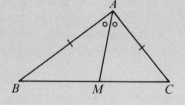

- Refer back to the original information.

BM cannot equal CM, since it was given that they are not equal. The only possible explanation for this contradiction is that the assumption that $AB = AC$ was incorrect. This means that $AB \neq AC$. Therefore, we have proved that $AB \neq AC$.

Look back

The above example was proved using *indirect proof*. To use an indirect proof, follow these steps.

Step 1.   Assume that the *opposite* of the desired result is true.

Step 2.   Show that a conclusion can be reached which contradicts the known facts.

Step 3.   Since there is a contradiction, what was assumed in *Step 1* is false. Therefore, the desired result must be true.

Complete each proof

1. In $\triangle PQR$, $\angle Q = 50°$ and $\angle R = 60°$. Prove that $PQ \neq PR$.

2. Prove that a triangle cannot have two
   a) right angles   b) obtuse angles

3. Prove that only one perpendicular can be drawn from the point, P, to the line, l.

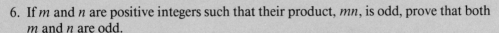

4. If n is an integer such that n^2 is odd, prove that n is odd.

5. If n is an integer such that n^2 is even, prove that n is even.

6. If m and n are positive integers such that their product, mn, is odd, prove that both m and n are odd.

7. In $\triangle ABC$, AM is the median from A to BC, and $\angle AMC = 60°$. Prove that $AB \neq AC$.

8. In $\triangle PQR$, PS is the altitude from P to QR, and $QS \neq RS$. Prove that $PQ \neq PR$.

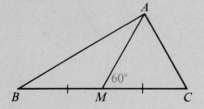
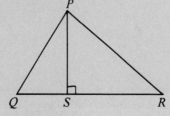

9. In $\triangle DEF$, G and H are the midpoints of DE and DF respectively, and $DF \neq DE$. Prove that EH and FG cannot bisect each other.

10. The ages in years, of Anjanee, Blair and Concetta, are three consecutive numbers. If only *one* of the following statements is true, prove that Anjanee is the oldest of the three.

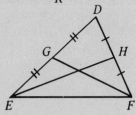

   • Blair is 2 years older than Anjanee.

   • Blair is 1 year older than Concetta.

   • Anjanee is 1 year older than Concetta.

   • Concetta is 1 year younger than Anjanee.

11-5 PROOFS USING TRANSFORMATIONS

The following properties of transformations have been demonstrated in earlier sections.

1. Length and angle measure are invariant under translations, rotations, and reflections.

2. If two lines are parallel, one may be mapped onto the other by a translation, a $\frac{1}{2}$-turn, or a reflection.

       Translation $\frac{1}{2}$-turn   Reflection

3. A line may be mapped onto itself by a translation, a $\frac{1}{2}$-turn, or a reflection.

       Translation $\frac{1}{2}$ turn   Reflection

4. The perpendicular bisector of any line segment AB is the reflection line of the reflection which maps $A \rightarrow B$ and $B \rightarrow A$.

5. If two lines intersect, one may be mapped onto the other by a reflection or a rotation.

             Reflection   Rotation

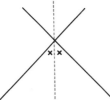
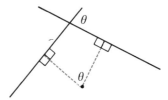

The bisector of the angle formed by the line and its image is the reflection line.

The angle formed by the line and its image is equal to the angle of rotation.

If we assume the above properties as axioms, we can use transformations to prove theorems and make deductions.

A Proof Using Reflection

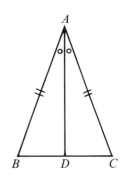

Example 1. Prove that the angles opposite the equal sides of an isosceles triangle are equal.

      Proof. In $\triangle ABC$, $AB = AC$ and the bisector of $\angle A$ meets BC at D. Under a reflection in AD, the line containing segment AB maps onto the line containing segment AC. Since $AB = AC$, $B \rightarrow C$. Therefore, $\angle B \rightarrow \angle C$. Since angle measure is invariant, $\angle B = \angle C$. That is, the angles opposite the equal sides of an isosceles triangle are equal.

A Proof Using Translation

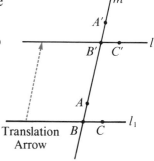

Example 2. Prove that if a transversal intersects two parallel lines, the corresponding angles are equal.

      Proof. Label the figure as shown. Under a translation parallel to the transversal, m, that maps line l_1 onto line l_2,

$$A \rightarrow A', \quad B \rightarrow B', \quad C \rightarrow C'$$

      Therefore, $\angle ABC \rightarrow \angle A'B'C'$. That is, corresponding angles are equal.

The next example illustrates a problem that is easier to solve by transformations than by other methods.

A Proof Using Rotation

Example 3. $\triangle ABC$ and $\triangle ECD$ are equilateral. Prove that $AD = BE$ and that $\angle AFB = 60°$.

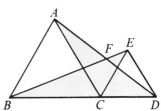

      Proof. Under a $60°$ rotation about C, $\triangle ACD \rightarrow \triangle BCE$. Therefore, $AD \rightarrow BE$ and AD intersects BE at $60°$. That is, $AD = BE$ because length is invariant under a rotation and $\angle AFB = 60°$.

EXERCISES 11-5

Proofs Using Translations

1. In quadrilateral $ABCD$, $AB\,||\,DC$ and $AB = DC$. Prove that $AD\,||\,BC$ and $AD = BC$.

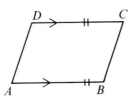

2. Line segments AD, BE, and CF (below, left) are equal and parallel. Prove that $\triangle ABC \cong \triangle DEF$.

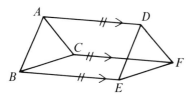

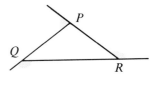

3. In $\triangle PQR$ (above, right), prove that the sum of the exterior angles is 360°.

Proofs Using Reflections

4. Prove that any point on the perpendicular bisector of a line segment is equidistant from the endpoints of the segment.

5. In the figure below, PR is the perpendicular bisector of QS. Prove that $\angle SPR = \angle QPR$.

6. In the figure below, $PT = QT$ and $RT = ST$. Prove that $\triangle PQS \cong \triangle QPR$.

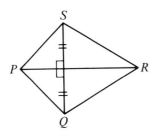

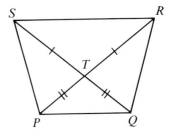

7. *ABCD* is a square and *AE = AF*. Prove that
   a) *CE = CF*   b) *BE = DF*

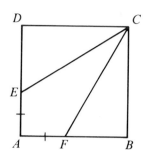
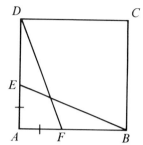

Proofs Using Rotations

8. Two lines intersect. Prove that the opposite angles are equal.

9. Prove that when a transversal intersects two parallel lines, the alternate angles are equal.

10. The diagonals of quadrilateral *ABCD* bisect each other. Prove that *ABCD* is a parallelogram.

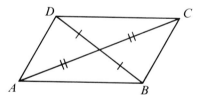

11. △*ABC* (below, left) is an equilateral triangle, and *BD = CE*. Prove that *AD = BE* and that ∠*BFD* = 60°.

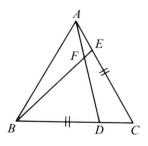
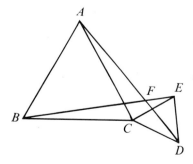

12. △*ABC* and △*ECD* (above, right) are equilateral triangles. Prove that *BE = AD* and that ∠*AFB* = 60°.

MATHEMATICS AROUND US

Geometric Figures and Their Properties

The photographs on this page illustrate some of the geometric properties studied in this chapter and Chapter 10.

1. Study the photographs carefully. Find examples which illustrate the following:
   - a) the Opposite Angle Theorem
   - b) the Supplementary Angle Theorem
   - c) the Parallel Lines Theorem
   - d) the Angle Sum Theorem
   - e) congruent triangles
   - f) the Isosceles Triangle Theorem
   - g) properties of a parallelogram
   - h) the Pythagorean Theorem
   - i) similar triangles
   - j) equilateral triangles

2. Find examples of as many geometric properties as you can in the photographs on pages 342 and 343 of Chapter 10.

Review Exercises

1. Find the values of x and y.

a)

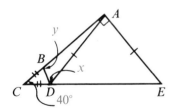

b)

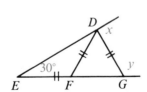

c)

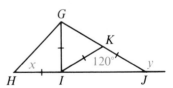

2. Prove that $\angle M = \angle K$.

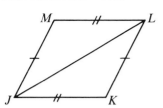

3. Prove that AD bisects $\angle A$.

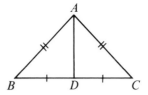

4. In $\triangle ABC$, $AB = BC$ and $\angle BCE = \angle BAD$. Prove that $EB = DB$.

5. In the figure, $PQ \parallel RS$ and T is the midpoint of PS. Prove that T is the midpoint of QR.

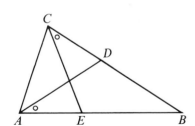

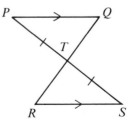

6. A bracket for a hanging plant consists of two metal strips attached at A. If the bracket is to be perpendicular to the wall, how far apart should the holes at B and C be?

7. In the figure, $\angle S = \angle P$, $PT = SR$, and $SQ \perp PR$. Prove that $SQ = PQ$.

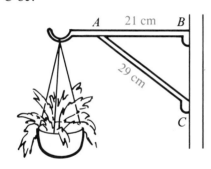

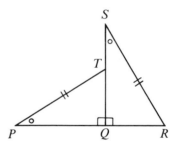

8. Prove that $PS = PT$.

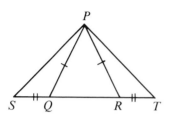

9. Prove that $\angle KML = \angle K + \angle L$.

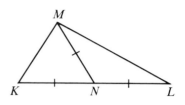

10. In $\triangle PQR$, $PR = QR$, S is the midpoint of PQ, and $\angle TSP = \angle USQ$. Prove that $ST = SU$.

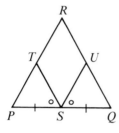

11. Explain why the area of $\triangle BFA$ is equal to the sum of the areas of $\triangle BDC$ and $\triangle AEC$.

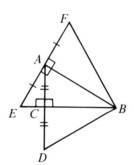

12. Find the values of x, y, and z.

a)

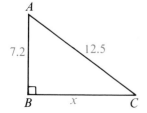

b)

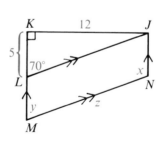
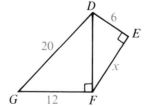

c)

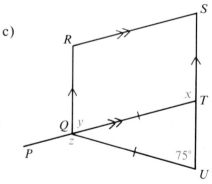

13. Find the value of x correct to one decimal place.

a)

b)

c)

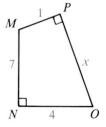

12 Three-Dimensional Geometry

This is the first photograph that was ever taken showing the whole Earth. How can the surface area and the volume of the Earth be found? (See the Example in Section 12-4.)

12-1 CONSTRUCTING CYLINDERS AND CONES

In the seventeenth and eighteenth centuries, a popular form of art, called *anamorphic art* was introduced. The pictures appear distorted, but they are not meant to be viewed in the normal manner. Instead, they are viewed by looking at their reflections in cylindrical and conical mirrors.

To construct a cylinder, a rectangle is used. The length of the rectangle is the circumference of the cylinder.

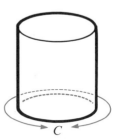

Example 1. Construct a cylinder with diameter 5.0 cm and height 8.5 cm.

Solution. Calculate the circumference of the base:

$$C = \pi d$$
$$\doteq 3.14(5.0)$$
$$\doteq 15.7$$

Use a ruler and a protractor to construct a rectangle with length 15.7 cm and height 8.5 cm. Cut out the rectangle and join the two shorter ends with tape to form the cylinder.

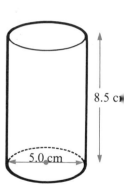

In *Example 1*, the cylinder had no top or bottom. If desired, these could be constructed and taped to the cylinder to form a closed cylinder.

To construct a cone, part of a circle is used. The radius of the circle is equal to the *slant height, s*, of the cone. It is necessary to calculate the angle, θ, corresponding to the part of the circle which forms the cone.

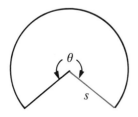
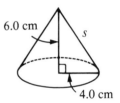

Example 2. Construct a cone with base radius 4.0 cm and height 6.0 cm.

Solution. **Step 1.** *Calculate the slant height.*

By the Pythagorean Theorem,

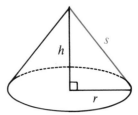

$$s = \sqrt{4^2 + 6^2}$$
$$= \sqrt{52}$$
$$\doteq 7.2$$

The slant height of the cone is approximately 7.2 cm.

Step 2. *Construct a circle with radius equal to the slant height, and calculate its circumference.*

Construct a circle with radius 7.2 cm.

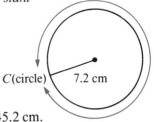

$$C(\text{circle}) = \pi d$$
$$\doteq 3.14(14.4)$$
$$\doteq 45.2$$

The circumference of the circle is about 45.2 cm.

Step 3. *Calculate the circumference of the base of the cone.*

Use the base radius, 4.0 cm:

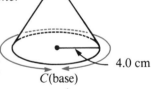

$$C(\text{base}) = 2\pi r$$
$$\doteq 2(3.14)(4.0)$$
$$\doteq 25.1$$

The circumference of the base is approximately 25.1 cm.

Step 4. *Use a proportion to calculate the angle at the centre of the circle, and construct it using a protractor.*

$$\frac{\theta}{360°} = \frac{C(\text{base})}{C(\text{circle})}$$

$$\theta = 360° \left(\frac{25.1}{45.2}\right)$$

$$\doteq 200°$$

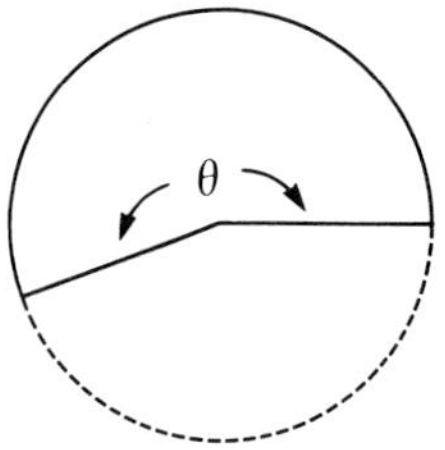

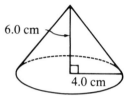

Step 5. *Cut the circle along the arms of the angle, and join with tape to make the cone.*

6.0 cm

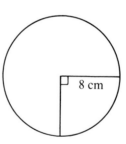

4.0 cm

EXERCISES 12-1

(A)

1. Construct the following diagrams using the dimensions given. Then cut out the figures and use tape to construct a cylinder and a cone.

a)

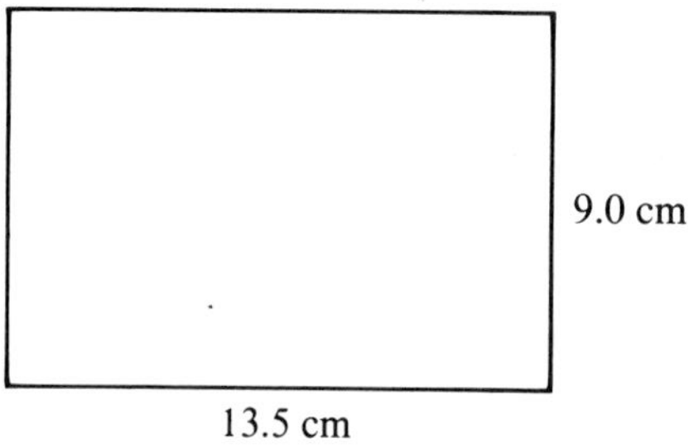

9.0 cm

13.5 cm

b)

8 cm

(B)

2. A cylinder has diameter 6.0 cm and height 7.5 cm.
   a) Calculate the circumference of the cylinder.
   b) Construct the cylinder.

3. Construct the cones shown.

a)

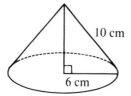

10 cm

6 cm

b)

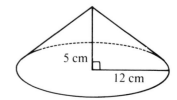

5 cm

12 cm

4. A semicircular piece of paper has a radius of 6 cm. Edges *OA* and *OB* are joined to form a cone.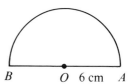
   a) Construct the cone.
   b) Calculate the base radius and the height of the cone, and check by measuring.

5. A square piece of paper measuring 20 cm on a side is used to form the curved surface of a cylinder. Circles cut from another piece of paper are used for the top and bottom. Find the
   a) radius of the cylinder
   b) total surface area, including the top and bottom

6. Repeat *Exercise 5*, assuming that the paper measures *x* cm on a side.

Ⓒ

7. A cone is constructed from a quarter-circle cut from a square piece of paper with sides of length 20 cm. A circle is then cut from another piece of paper for the base. Find the total surface area, including the base.

8. Repeat *Exercise 7*, assuming that the paper measures *x* cm on a side.

20 cm

9. One litre is often represented by a cube measuring 10 cm on each edge. Construct a cone which would fit inside the cube as shown.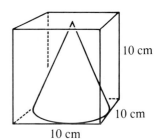

 INVESTIGATE

1. a) Construct two copies of this parallelogram, and cut them out.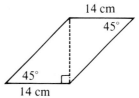
   b) Tape the edges of the parallelogram in two different ways to form cylinders, without any overlapping.
   c) Calculate the base diameter and height of each cylinder, and check by measuring.

2. a) Can every parallelogram be used to construct two cylinders in this way?
   b) Draw an example of a parallelogram for which the two cylinders would be congruent.

12-2 SURFACE AREA OF CYLINDERS AND CONES

It is impossible to make a flat map which shows the Earth's curved surface accurately. In the illustrations, imagine that the outlines of the continents on a globe are pierced with small holes. A light at the centre of the globe shines through the holes, forming a corresponding outline of the continents on the paper touching the globe. This suggests a method of finding the area of the curved surface of a cylinder or a cone.

Surface Area of a Cylinder

When the cylinder is unrolled, it forms a rectangle with length equal to the circumference of the cylinder. The area of the curved surface of the cylinder is equal to the area of the rectangle.

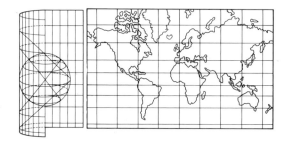

Example 1. Find the area of the curved surface of a cylinder with radius 15 cm and height 40 cm.

Solution. Find the circumference of the cylinder:
$$C = \pi d$$
$$\doteq 3.14(30)$$
$$\doteq 94.2$$
The area of the cylinder can now be found.
$$A \doteq 94.2(40)$$
$$\doteq 3768$$
The area of the curved surface of the cylinder is about 3800 cm².

In a similar manner, a formula can be developed for the surface area of a cylinder with base radius r and height h. The area of the curved surface is found by multiplying the circumference of the base by the height $A = (2\pi r)(h)$, or $2\pi rh$.

The area of the curved surface of a cylinder with base radius r and height h is given by the formula:

$$A = 2\pi rh$$

Example 2. Find the total surface area of a cylinder with diameter 30 cm and height 40 cm.

Solution. The total surface area includes both the base and the top.

Area of curved surface: Area of base:

A(curved) $= 2\pi rh$ A(base) $= \pi r^2$

$\doteq 2(3.14)(15)(40)$ $\doteq 3.14(15^2)$

$\doteq 3768$ $\doteq 706.5$

Total surface area: $3768 + 2(706.5) = 5181$. The total surface area of the cylinder is about 5200 cm².

Surface Area of a Cone

When the cone is unrolled, it forms part of a circle. The radius of the circle is the slant height of the cone. The area of the curved surface of the cone is equal to the area of the part circle.

 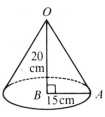

Example 3. Find the area of the curved surface of a cone with base radius 15 cm and height 20 cm.

Solution.

By the Pythagorean Theorem: Area of entire circle:

$OA^2 = OB^2 + BA^2$ $A = \pi r^2$

$= 20^2 + 15^2$ $\doteq 3.14(25^2)$

$= 625$ $\doteq 1962.5$

$OA = \sqrt{625}$

$= 25$

The area of the cone can be found from the proportion:

$$\frac{\text{Area of cone}}{\text{Area of circle}} = \frac{\text{Circumference of cone}}{\text{Circumference of circle}}$$

$$\frac{\text{Area of cone}}{1962.5} = \frac{2\pi(15)}{2\pi(25)}$$

$$\text{Area of cone} = 1962.5\left(\frac{15}{25}\right)$$

$$= 1177.5$$

The area of the curved surface of the cone is about 1180 cm².

In a similar manner, a formula can be developed for the surface area of a cone. If the base radius is r and the height is h, then by the Pythagorean Theorem, the slant height is $s = \sqrt{r^2 + h^2}$. This is the radius of the circle forming the curved surface.

$$\frac{\text{Area of cone}}{\text{Area of circle}} = \frac{\text{Circumference of cone}}{\text{Circumference of circle}}$$

$$\frac{\text{Area of cone}}{\pi s^2} = \frac{2\pi r}{2\pi s}$$

$$\text{Area of cone} = \pi s^2 \times \frac{r}{s}$$

$$= \pi r s$$

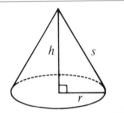

The area of the curved surface of a cone with base radius r and height h is given by the formula

$$A = \pi r s$$

where s is the slant height, $s = \sqrt{r^2 + h^2}$.

EXERCISES 12-2

Ⓐ

1. Find the area of the curved surface of each cylinder.

a)

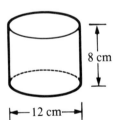

8 cm

⊢—12 cm—⊣

b)

2.5 cm

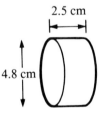

4.8 cm

c)

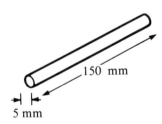

150 mm

5 mm

2. Find the total surface area of each cylinder.

a)

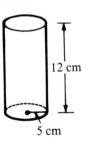

12 cm

5 cm

b)

1.5 m

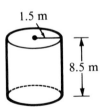

8.5 m

c)

45 cm

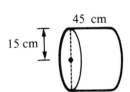

15 cm

3. Find the area of the curved surface of each cone.

a) b) c)

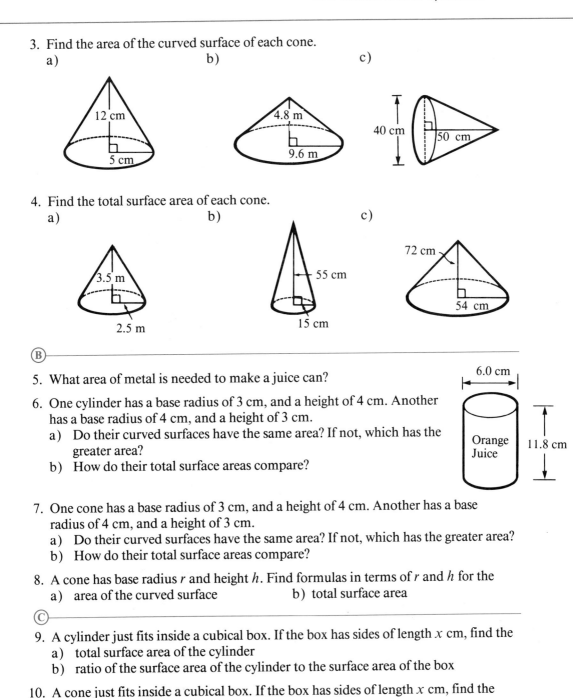

4. Find the total surface area of each cone.

a) b) c)

Ⓑ

5. What area of metal is needed to make a juice can?

6. One cylinder has a base radius of 3 cm, and a height of 4 cm. Another has a base radius of 4 cm, and a height of 3 cm.
   a) Do their curved surfaces have the same area? If not, which has the greater area?
   b) How do their total surface areas compare?

7. One cone has a base radius of 3 cm, and a height of 4 cm. Another has a base radius of 4 cm, and a height of 3 cm.
   a) Do their curved surfaces have the same area? If not, which has the greater area?
   b) How do their total surface areas compare?

8. A cone has base radius *r* and height *h*. Find formulas in terms of *r* and *h* for the
   a) area of the curved surface   b) total surface area

Ⓒ

9. A cylinder just fits inside a cubical box. If the box has sides of length *x* cm, find the
   a) total surface area of the cylinder
   b) ratio of the surface area of the cylinder to the surface area of the box

10. A cone just fits inside a cubical box. If the box has sides of length *x* cm, find the
   a) total surface area of the cone
   b) ratio of the surface area of the cone to the surface area of the box
   c) ratio of the surface area of the cone to the surface area of the cylinder in *Exercise 9a*

 INVESTIGATE

The Volume of a Cone

To investigate the volume of a cone, follow these steps. You will need an empty tin can, such as a soup can, a piece of paper, and some tape.

Step 1.

Roll the piece of paper into the shape of a cone, and adjust it such that it just fits in the tin can.

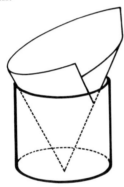

Step 2.

Secure the cone with tape so that it does not unroll. Mark the rim of the can on the cone, and cut off the excess.

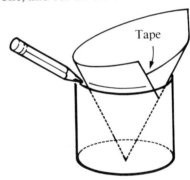

Step 3.

Suppose the cone were filled with water, and then emptied into the can. Estimate how many times this could be done until the can is full.

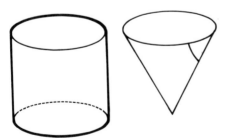

Step 4.

Check your estimate with water.

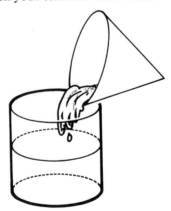

What probable conclusion can you make about the volume of a cone compared with the volume of a cylinder which has the same height and the same base radius?

12-3 VOLUME OF CYLINDERS AND CONES

Cylinders and cones can be seen everywhere.

The Peachtree Centre in Atlanta features a cylindrical hotel. Architects need to know how to find the volume of space enclosed using the base radius and the height.

Salt falling from a conveyor forms a conical pile. The volume of salt in the pile can be calculated using the base radius and the height.

Volume of a Cylinder

To determine the volume of a cylinder, think of filling it with unit cubes in layers. The area of the base is the number of cubes, including part cubes, which cover it. If this is multiplied by the number of layers, the result is the number of cubes, and part cubes, which fill the cylinder. The volume of the cylinder is the base area multiplied by the height $V = (\pi r^2)(h)$, or $\pi r^2 h$.

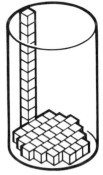

The volume of a cylinder with base radius r and height h is given by the formula:

$$V = \pi r^2 h$$

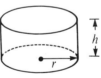

Example 1. The hotel in Peachtree Centre has a height of 320 m and a base diameter of 60 m. Calculate the volume of space enclosed by the hotel.

Solution. The radius of the base is 30 m. Substitute 30 for r and 320 for h in the formula:

$$V = \pi r^2 h$$
$$\doteq 3.14(30^2)(320)$$
$$\doteq 904\ 320$$

The volume of space enclosed by the hotel is about 900 000 m³.

Volume of a Cone

In the preceding investigation you found that there is a simple relationship between the volumes of certain cones and cylinders. If a cone and a cylinder have the same height and the same base radius, then the volume of the cone is one-third the volume of the cylinder.

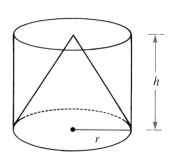

The volume of a cone with base radius r and height h is given by the formula:

$$V = \frac{1}{3}\pi r^2 h$$

Example 2. At a sawmill, a conical pile of wood chips has a base diameter of 20 m and a height of 8 m. Calculate the volume of wood in the pile.

Solution. The base radius is 10 m. Substitute 10 for r and 8 for h in the formula:

$$V = \frac{1}{3}\pi r^2 h$$

$$\doteq \frac{1}{3}(3.14)(10^2)(8)$$

$$\doteq 837$$

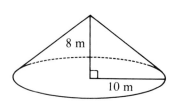

The pile contains about 837 m³ of wood. Allowing for air spaces, there should be about 800 m³ of wood in the pile.

EXERCISES 12-3

Ⓐ

1. Find the volume of each cylinder.
   a)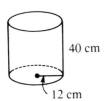
   40 cm
   12 cm
   b)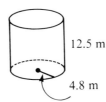
   12.5 m
   4.8 m
   c)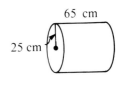
   65 cm
   25 cm

2. Find the volume of each cone.
   a)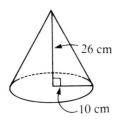
   26 cm
   10 cm
   b)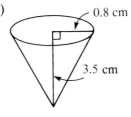
   0.8 cm
   3.5 cm
   c)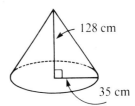
   128 cm
   35 cm

3. Find the volume of the cylinder or cone.
   a)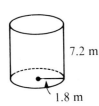
   7.2 m
   1.8 m
   b)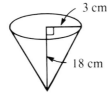
   3 cm
   18 cm
   c)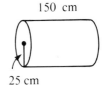
   150 cm
   25 cm

4. Find the missing data for each cylinder.

	Diameter	Radius	Base Area	Height	Volume
a)	10 cm			10 cm	
b)		4 cm		8 cm	
c)	1.2 m			0.6 m	

5. Hay is baled in rolls about 2.8 m in diameter and 4.0 m long. What volume of hay is in each roll?

6. Grain is discharged from a conveyor and forms a conical heap that has a diameter of 5.4 m and a height of 2.7 m. What is the volume of grain in the heap?

7. A cylindrical oil tank has a diameter of 12.0 m and a height of 9.4 m. Find the
   a) volume of the tank to the nearest ten cubic metres
   b) surface area of the tank

Ⓑ

8. A Canadian $100 gold coin has a diameter of 27.0 mm and a thickness of 2.16 mm. What is its volume?

9. A phonograph record has a diameter of 30.0 cm and a thickness of 1.7 mm. How many cubic metres of material are needed to make the first production run of 50 000 records?

10. A tanker develops a leak, and oil spreads in a circle around the ship to a distance of 1200 m, and a thickness of about 1.8 cm.
    a) What is the area of the oil spill?
    b) How many cubic metres of oil were spilled?
    c) If one barrel of oil is equivalent to 0.16 m³ and oil is worth $31.60 per barrel, what is the value of the oil lost?

11. A tin can has a base radius of 5.0 cm and a height of 20 cm. If 1 L of water is poured in, how deep will it be?

12. Calculate the volume of the cylinder formed if rectangle *ABCD* is rotated about side
    a) *AB*   b) *BC*

13. Calculate the volume of the cone formed if △*ABC* is rotated about side
    a) *AB*   b) *BC*

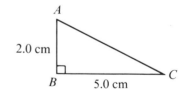

14. Calculate the volume of oil in a 320 km pipeline which has a diameter of 1.8 m.

15. A tunnel-boring machine may soon be used to make a tunnel beneath the English Channel to form a rail link between England and France. The tunnel will be about 37 km long.
    a) If the machine moves forward at six metres per hour, how many hours would it take to bore the tunnel, assuming there are no delays?
    b) If the diameter of the hole is 12 m, how many cubic metres of earth and rock would have to be removed?
    c) As the machine passes along, the wall of the tunnel is lined with concrete. How many square metres of wall must be lined?

16. How is the volume of a cylinder affected if
    a) its height is doubled?
    b) its base radius is doubled?
    c) both its height and base radius are doubled?

©————————————————————————————

17. A semicircular sheet of paper has a radius of 6 cm. Edges *OA* and *OB* are joined to
    form a cone.
    a) Find the radius of the base of the cone.
    b) Find the height of the cone.
    c) What is the volume of the cone?

18. A 90-degree sector is removed from a circular
    sheet of paper with a radius of 8 cm. Edges
    OA and *OB* of both pieces are then joined to
    form two cones.
    a) Find the radius of the base of each cone.
    b) Find the height of each cone.
    c) What is the volume of each cone?

19. A roll of black tape has an outside diameter of
    58 mm and an inside diameter of 32 mm.
    The tape is 19 mm wide and 10 m long. Find
    a) the volume of tape in the roll, in cubic
       millimetres
    b) the thickness of the tape
    c) a formula for the thickness of the tape if the outside diameter is *D*, the inside
       diameter is *d*, and the length is *l*.

20. A cylindrical tank with a height of 18 m can store a maximum of 12 700 m³ of oil.
    What is the diameter of the tank?

21. A cylindrical concrete pipe, 12.65 m long, has
    an inside diameter of 48 cm and an outside
    diameter of 80 cm. Find, to the nearest cubic
    metre, the volume of concrete needed to make
    the pipe.

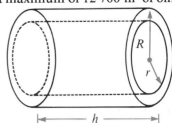

 INVESTIGATE

A rectangular piece of paper can be rolled into
a cylinder in two different directions. If there
is no overlapping, which cylinder has the greater
volume, the one with the long side of the rectangle
as its height, or the one with the short side of the
rectangle as its height?

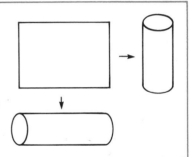

Use Spatial Visualization

A space shuttle launched a large solar panel which is designed to convert the sun's rays into electricity. The panel measures 31.5 m by 4.1 m, and contains many foldable sections. When the sections are folded on top of one another, they fit into the storage area shown below. How thick is the solar panel when all the sections are unfolded?

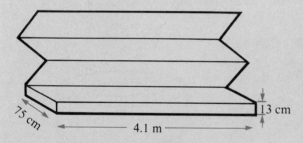

Understand the problem

- How do the dimensions of the solar panel compare with those of the storage area?

Think of a strategy

- Visualize the solar panel folded into layers 4.1 m long, and hinged along the 4.1 m side.

Carry out the strategy

- Since the sections are 75 cm wide, the number of sections required to reach a final length of 31.5 m is:
$$\frac{31.5 \text{ m}}{75 \text{ cm}} = \frac{3150}{75} \text{ or } 42$$
- There are 42 layers in the storage area. Since the total height is 13 cm, the thickness of each layer is:
$$\frac{13 \text{ cm}}{42} \doteq 0.3 \text{ cm or 3 mm.}$$
The solar panel is about 3 mm thick.

Look back

- What is the volume of the solar panel, when it is unfolded?
- How does this volume compare with the volume of the storage area?

Solve each problem

1. These seven objects can be put together to form a cube. What is the length of an edge of the cube?

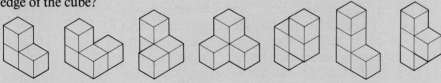

2. A rectangular block of wood measuring 5 cm by 5 cm by 10 cm is painted blue and then cut into 1 cm cubes. How many cubes will have no paint on them?

3. An open box is made from a square piece of tin by cutting 4 cm squares out of the corners and folding up the sides. If the box has a volume of 100 cm³, find the dimensions of the original piece of tin.

4. Calculate the distance between the parallel bars.

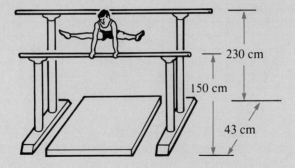

230 cm

150 cm

43 cm

5. In a steel mill, red-hot slabs of steel are pressed many times between heavy rollers. The drawings show two stages in rolling a slab.
   a) How long is this slab when its thickness has been reduced to 1 cm?
   b) A car body requires 20 m² of steel, 1 mm thick. How many cars can be made from the slab shown?

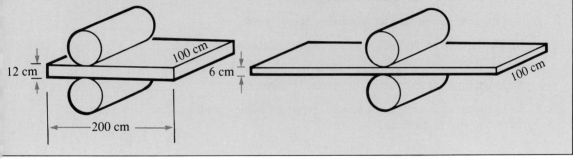

12 cm

100 cm

6 cm

100 cm

200 cm

INVESTIGATE

The Surface Area of a Sphere

To investigate the surface area of a sphere, Tony obtained an orange which was nearly spherical in shape. He carefully measured its diameter. It was approximately 6.9 cm. Then he found the surface area of the orange by peeling it and arranging the pieces on 1 cm graph paper. He pressed the pieces down to make them as flat as possible, and then traced around them, forming the irregular shapes shown. Each square represents 1 cm² on the diagrams.

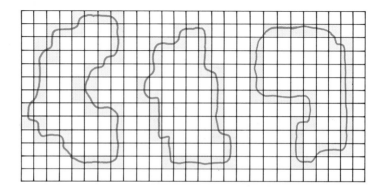

There are 95 squares fully inside. These have an area of 95 cm². All of these were on the orange. There are 108 squares partly inside. These have an area of 108 cm². About half of these were on the orange. Tony estimated that the area of the orange is approximately:

$$95 \text{ cm}^2 + \frac{1}{2}(108 \text{ cm}^2) = 95 \text{ cm}^2 + 54 \text{ cm}^2$$
$$= 149 \text{ cm}^2$$

1. Obtain an orange which is nearly spherical in shape, and which can be easily peeled. Measure its diameter as accurately as you can.

2. Peel the orange and find its area using Tony's method.

3. Divide the area by the *square* of the diameter. Record the result.

4. Repeat the investigation with a different orange, or include the results of other students. Find the average of the results in *Question 3*.

5. An orange is an example of a sphere. What probable conclusion can you make about the area of a sphere?

INVESTIGATE

The Volume of a Sphere

To investigate the volume of a sphere, follow these steps. You will need an old tennis ball, a 355 mL cardboard orange juice can, and a larger container, such as a large margarine tub. If the fuzz is worn off the ball, it should fit snugly in the can.

Step 1.

Measure the diameter of the ball. Carefully cut the can such that its height is equal to the diameter of the ball.

Step 2.

Place the can in the tub, and fill the can with water, without allowing it to overflow.

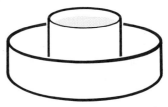

Step 3.

Soak the ball with water. Then slowly place it in the can, allowing the water to overflow into the tub. Push the ball right down to the bottom of the can.

Step 4.

Take the can out of the tub, remove the ball and empty the can. Then pour the water from the tub into the can. Measure the depth of the water.

1. The volume of the water in the can in *Step 4* should be the same as the volume of the ball. Which of the following fractions is closest to the fraction of the can that is filled with water?

$$\frac{1}{4} \qquad \frac{1}{3} \qquad \frac{1}{2} \qquad \frac{2}{3} \qquad \frac{3}{4}$$

2. What probable conclusion can you make about the volume of a sphere compared with the volume of the cylinder in which it fits?

12-4 SURFACE AREA AND VOLUME OF A SPHERE

For centuries people believed that the Earth was flat. They rejected the idea that it was round because it is contrary to intuition. In 1967, this first photograph, showing the whole Earth, was taken from a satellite. It clearly shows not only that the Earth is round, but that it appears to be a sphere. In fact, it is not a perfect sphere because every point on the Earth is not the same distance from its centre. It is slightly flatter at the poles.

A *sphere* is a set of points in space which are the same distance from a fixed point called the *centre*. A line segment joining the centre to any point on the sphere is called its *radius*. A line segment joining two points on a sphere and passing through the centre is called its *diameter*.

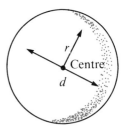

In a preceding investigation, you found that the surface area of a sphere is slightly more than 3 times the square of its diameter. This suggests that the surface area of a sphere with diameter d is πd^2. Since $d = 2r$, we may write

$$A = \pi(2r)^2$$

$$= 4\pi r^2$$

The surface area of a sphere with radius r is
$$A = 4\pi r^2$$

In another investigation, you found that the volume of a sphere is $\frac{2}{3}$ the volume of the cylinder in which it fits. If the sphere has radius r, the cylinder has base radius r and height $2r$. Therefore, the volume of the sphere is:

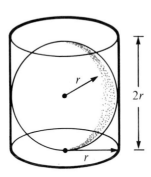

$$V = \frac{2}{3}(\text{volume of cylinder})$$

$$= \frac{2}{3}(\pi r^2 h)$$

$$= \frac{2}{3}(\pi r^2 (2r))$$

$$= \frac{4}{3}\pi r^3$$

The volume of a sphere with radius r is

$$V = \frac{4}{3}\pi r^3$$

Although the Earth is not a perfect sphere, we can use these formulas to estimate its surface area and volume.

Example.   The mean radius of the Earth is approximately 6365 km. Estimate the surface area and volume of the Earth.

Solution.   Substitute 6365 for r in the formulas:

$$A = 4\pi r^2 \qquad\qquad V = \frac{4}{3}\pi r^3$$

$$\doteq 4(3.14)(6365^2) \qquad \doteq \frac{4}{3}(3.14)(6365^3)$$

$$\doteq 5.1 \times 10^8 \qquad\qquad \doteq 1.1 \times 10^{12}$$

The surface area of the Earth is approximately 5.1×10^8 km^2, and its volume is approximately 1.1×10^{12} km^3.

EXERCISES 12-4

Ⓐ

1. Calculate the surface area and volume of each sphere.

   a)

   b)

   c)

2. Find the surface area and the volume of the balls listed.

Sport	Diameter of ball (cm)
Baseball	7.4
Golf	4.3
Table tennis	3.7
Volleyball	20.9

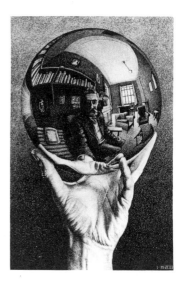

3. The Dutch artist, M.C. Escher, produced many striking prints and drawings. In this self-portrait he is seen holding a reflecting sphere in his hand. The diameter of the sphere is 20 cm. Find the surface area and the volume of this sphere.

Ⓑ

4. A squash ball has a radius of 2.0 cm. It comes in a box in the shape of a cube. Find the ratio of the

   a) surface area of the cube to the surface area of the ball

   b) volume of the cube to the volume of the ball

5. A basketball has a circumference of 75 cm. Find its

   a) radius   b) surface area   c) volume

6. Estimate the surface area and the volume of the

   a) moon, which has a radius of 1738 km

   b) sun, with a radius of 696 260 km

7. Which has the greater volume, a sphere with radius r, or a cube with edges of length r?

8. If a spherical balloon is blown up from a diameter of 20 cm to a diameter of 60 cm, by how many times has its
   a) surface area increased?   b) volume increased?

9. What happens to the surface area and volume of a sphere if the radius is doubled? tripled? multiplied by n?

10. Find formulas for the surface area and volume of a sphere with diameter d; circumference C.

Ⓒ

11. History was made in August, 1978, when three Americans made the first successful attempt to cross the Atlantic Ocean by balloon. It had the shape of a hemisphere on a cone. The overall height was 33.0 m, and its diameter was 19.6 m. How many
    a) cubic metres of helium were needed to fill the balloon?
    b) square metres of material were needed to make the balloon?

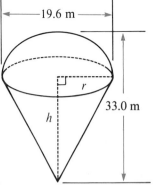

12. A spherical soap bubble containing a fixed volume of air lands on a flat surface and its shape changes to that of a hemisphere. Find the ratio of the
    a) radius of the hemisphere to the radius of the sphere
    b) surface area of the film in the hemisphere to the area of the film in the sphere

13. The Space Telescope is designed to operate in orbit, high above the Earth's atmosphere. The diagram shows that the Space Telescope can see seven times farther into space than ground observatories.
    a) Compare the volume of space that can be studied by the Space Telescope with that which can be studied by ground observatories.
    b) The unaided eye can see objects up to 600 000 light years away. Compare the volume of space that can be studied by ground observatories with the volume that can be studied by the unaided eye.

THE MATHEMATICAL MIND

Archimedes of Syracuse

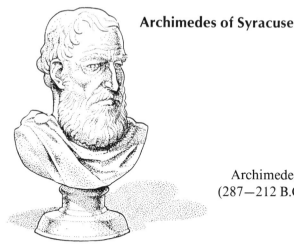

Archimedes
(287–212 B.C.)

Archimedes of Syracuse was the greatest mathematician of antiquity. His many accomplishments include the invention of a pump for raising water and a planetarium to show the motions of the sun, moon and planets. He showed how to use levers and pulleys to move heavy objects. Archimedes even contributed to the defense of Syracuse by designing catapults and military engines which were used against the Romans. He also set Roman ships afire by using mirrors to concentrate the sun's rays on their sails.

In 212 B.C., when the Romans attacked Syracuse, Archimedes was preoccupied with a diagram he had drawn in the sand. According to legend, he did not hear the approach of a Roman soldier, who killed him while he was concentrating on his diagram. In doing so, the soldier disobeyed his commander, who had ordered that Archimedes was not to be harmed.

In his work, *On the Sphere and the Cylinder*, Archimedes described many formulas he had derived for the areas and volumes of geometric solids. One of his results involves the relationships between the volumes and areas of a sphere and a cylinder which touches it.

If a sphere is inscribed in a cylinder:

The volume of the sphere is $\frac{2}{3}$ the volume of the cylinder.

The area of the sphere is $\frac{2}{3}$ the area of the cylinder.

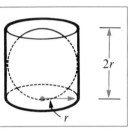

Archimedes was so pleased with this discovery that he requested that
the diagram be inscribed on his tombstone. His tombstone, with this
inscription, was uncovered in 1965 by a crew excavating the founda-
tions of a new hotel in Syracuse.

1. Verify that Archimedes' relationships between the areas and volumes of a sphere
   and the touching cylinder are correct.

2. In each diagram below, the cylinder has a height equal to the radius of its base. The
   second and third diagrams show a hemisphere and a cone inscribed in the cylinder.
   Find the volumes of the cylinder, hemisphere and cone. How are these volumes
   related?

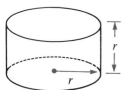 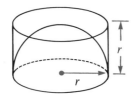 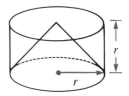

3. Archimedes was the first mathematician to attempt to compute π in a systematic
   way. He drew polygons to approximate a circle, and used formulas to calculate the
   perimeters of the polygons. Using this method, Archimedes determined that π lies
   between $3\frac{1}{7}$ and $3\frac{10}{71}$. Use a calculator to express these numbers in decimal form.
   Which is closer to π?

4. Archimedes is also famous for an essay in which he devised a way of representing
   very large numbers. In *The Sand Reckoner*, he described the problem of estimating
   the number of grains of sand that would fill a sphere with centre at the Earth and
   radius reaching to the sun. Using modern scientific notation, his answer was
   approximately 10^{51}. Check Archimedes' result as follows:
   a) Assume that a grain of sand is a sphere, estimate its radius, in millimetres. Then
      calculate the volume of the grain of sand.
   b) The distance to the sun is approximately 1.5×10^8 km. Calculate the volume of
      space enclosed by a sphere with centre at the Earth and radius reaching to the
      sun.
   c) Approximately how many grains of sand would fit inside this sphere? Make any
      necessary assumptions that seem reasonable.
   d) In Archimedes' time, people thought that the sun represented the edge of the
      universe. It is estimated today that the universe has a diameter of approximately
      10^{25} km. Approximately how many grains of sand would fill the observable
      universe?

COMPUTER POWER

Designing Package Sizes

When a new line of products is introduced, a manufacturer has a choice of package shapes and sizes. If a cylindrical package must hold 350 mL, the manufacturer can design the shape of the package in different ways.

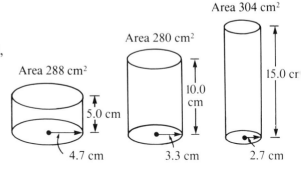

Area 288 cm²   Area 280 cm²   Area 304 cm²

5.0 cm   10.0 cm   15.0 cm

4.7 cm   3.3 cm   2.7 cm

These packages have the same volume, but a different total surface area. It may be desirable to design the package so that this area is as small as possible in order to minimize the cost of the package.

The program below directs the computer to display a table of values for a cylindrical package of given volume. The program provides for packages with and without tops. Input the volume, and an estimated initial and final height. The table will show the radius and the total surface area for several different heights between these. For the heights listed, the least surface area is also indicated. This will usually be close to the actual minimum surface area. By refining the initial and final heights, the dimensions of the package with a minimum surface area can be found as accurately as desired.

```
100 REM *** PACKAGE SIZES ***
110 PI=3.14159265:LOW=10^9
120 HOME:PRINT "1 - WITHOUT TOP":PRINT "2 - WITH TOP"
130 PRINT:INPUT "PRESS 1 OR 2: ";S
140 PRINT:INPUT "WHAT IS THE VOLUME? ";V
150 PRINT:INPUT "WHAT IS THE INITIAL HEIGHT? ";H1
160 INPUT "WHAT IS THE FINAL HEIGHT? ";H2
170 PRINT:PRINT "HEIGHT","RADIUS","AREA":PRINT
180 F=(H2-H1)/10
190 FOR I=0 TO 10
200     H=H1+I*F:R=SQR(V/(PI*H)):TSA=2*PI*R*H+S*PI*R*R
210     R=INT(100*R+0.5)/100:TSA=INT(100*TSA+0.5)/100
220     IF TSA<LOW THEN LOW=TSA
230     PRINT H,R,TSA
240 NEXT I
250 PRINT:PRINT "LEAST AREA: ";LOW
260 END
```

The program was run to find the minimum area for packages with tops to hold 350 mL. When initial and final heights of 1 and 11 were used, this was the display:

```
1 - WITHOUT TOP
2 - WITH TOP
PRESS 1 OR 2. 2
WHAT IS THE VOLUME? 350
WHAT IS THE INITIAL HEIGHT? 1
WHAT IS THE FINAL HEIGHT? 11
HEIGHT          RADIUS          AREA
1               10.56           766.32
2               7.46            443.79
3               6.09            384.2
4               5.28            307.64
5               4.72            288.29
6               4.31            279.11
7               3.99            275.46
8               3.73            275.08
9               3.52            276.74
10              3.34            279.72
11              3.18            283.59
LEAST AREA: 275.08
```

The minimum surface area is about 275.08 cm², and occurs when the height is 8 cm and the radius is 3.73 cm. For greater accuracy, the program can be repeated using initial and final heights of 7 and 9. Then the minimum surface area is found to be about 274.93 cm², when the height is 7.6 cm and the radius is 3.83 cm.

1. Find the dimensions of the package of minimum total surface area, including the top, with a volume of
   a) 500 mL   b) 1 L   c) 1.5 L

2. Find the dimensions of the package of minimum surface area, not including the top, with a volume of
   a) 500 mL   b) 1 L   c) 1.5 L

3. Carefully examine the results of 1 and 2. How are the radius and height of the package related if there is a minimum surface area and the top
   a) is included?   b) is not included?

MATHEMATICS AROUND US

Estimating the Size of a Molecule

A molecule is the smallest part of a compound which has all the properties of that compound. It is too small to be isolated and measured in the normal way. But the size of a molecule of a substance called stearic acid can be found by getting a drop of it to form a film on a water surface and treating the film as a cylinder one layer of molecules high. The height of the cylinder will be the size of a molecule of stearic acid.

Follow these steps:

Step 1.

Dissolve one drop of stearic acid in 1 L of benzene. Then calculate the volume of stearic acid in one drop of the solution.

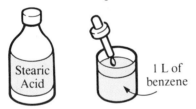

There are about 10 drops in 1 cm³ of liquid. Therefore, there are about 10 000 drops in the solution. Since one drop of stearic acid has a volume of about 0.1 cm³, the volume of acid in one drop of the solution is

$$\frac{0.1}{10\ 000}\text{cm}^3, \text{ or } 10^{-5} \text{ cm}^3$$

Step 2.

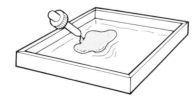

Put one drop of the solution on the surface of clean water. The benzene evaporates and

the stearic acid spreads out to form a circle 8.0 cm in diameter.

Step 3.

Calculate the thickness, h, of this layer using the formula for the volume of a cylinder, $V = \pi r^2 h$. Substitute 10^{-5} for V and 4.0 for r and solve the equation for h.

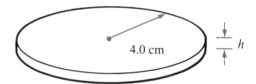

Since the film of stearic acid is one molecule thick, the height of the cylinder is an approximation to the size of a molecule of stearic acid.

QUESTIONS

1. Make the calculation in *Step 3* to find the size of a molecule of stearic acid in metres and in centimetres.

2. Gord dissolved one drop of oleic acid in 1 L of alcohol. He then put one drop of the solution on the surface of clean water. After the alcohol had dissolved in the water, there was a circular layer of oleic acid with a diameter of 10.6 cm.

   a) Calculate the size of a molecule of oleic acid.

   b) If Gord put two drops of the solution on the water, what would the diameter of the circular layer of acid be?

1. Find the dimensions of the rectangle required to construct each of the following cylinders.

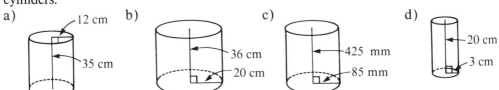

a) 12 cm, 35 cm b) 36 cm, 20 cm c) 425 mm, 85 mm d) 20 cm, 3 cm

2. Find the slant height and the angle required to construct each of the following cones.

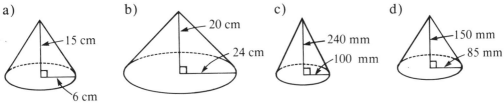

a) 15 cm, 6 cm b) 20 cm, 24 cm c) 240 mm, 100 mm d) 150 mm, 85 mm

3. Calculate the surface area including the top and bottom of each cylinder in *Exercise 1*.

4. Calculate the surface area of each cone in *Exercise 2*.

5. A semicircular piece of paper has a radius of 15 cm. Edges OA and OB are joined to form a cone. Calculate the
   a) base radius   b) height of the cone

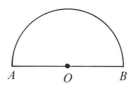

A O B

6. A rectangular piece of paper measuring 16 cm by 30 cm is used to form the curved surface of a cylinder.
   a) Find the radius of the cylinder if its height is 16 cm; 30 cm.
   b) Find the total surface area, including the top and bottom, in each cylinder.

7. Calculate the total surface area and the volume of a hockey puck if its diameter is 7.2 cm and its height is 2.3 cm.

8. Calculate the total surface area and the volume of a cylinder that has a height of
   a) 7 cm and a radius of 4 cm
   b) 8 mm and a radius of 4.5 mm
   c) 1.2 m and a radius of 1.4 m

9. A cylinder has the base shown. Find its total surface area and its volume if its height is

   a) 5 cm

   b) 7.5 cm

   c) 10 cm

2.3 cm

10. A cone has the base shown. Find its total surface area and its volume if its height is
    a) 8 cm

    b) 10 cm

    c) 12 cm

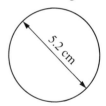

11. Mr. Wong builds a circular above-ground pool with walls of height 2.8 m and a
    diameter of 7.8 m. What is the volume of the pool to the nearest cubic metre?

12. Calculate the volume and surface area of a cylinder of cheese with a diameter of
    15 cm and a height of 12 cm.

13. One cylinder has a base radius of 3 cm, and a height of 4 cm. Another has a base
    radius of 4 cm, and a height of 3 cm. Do the cylinders have the same volume? If
    not, which has the greater volume?

14. One cone has a base radius of 3 cm, and a height of 4 cm. Another has a base
    radius of 4 cm, and a height of 3 cm. Do the cones have the same volume? If not,
    which has the greater volume?

15. Calculate the surface area and volume of a sphere of radius
    a) 9 cm   b) 125 mm   c) 6.5 cm

16. Find the surface area and volume of a basketball which is inflated to a diameter of
    24.2 cm.

17. Golf balls, with a diameter of 4.3 cm, are packed three to a box. If the box is 4.5 cm
    square and 13.2 cm long, find the
    a) volume of the three golf balls
    b) volume of air inside the box
    c) ratio of the volume of the balls to the volume of the box

18. Tennis balls, with a diameter of 5.8 cm are packed three to a cylindrical can. If the
    can is 6.0 cm in diameter and 17.7 cm high, find the
    a) volume of the three tennis balls
    b) volume of air inside the can
    c) ratio of the volume of the balls to the volume of the can

19. Find the total surface area and volume of each of the following.
    a)   b)   c)

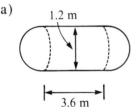

1.2 m

3.6 m

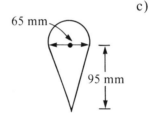

65 mm

95 mm

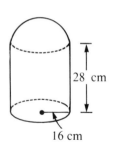

28 cm

16 cm

1. Suppose you add the cubes of consecutive numbers.
   The results are perfect squares.
   a) Check this by continuing the pattern.
   b) What conclusion might you make?

$$1 = 1$$
$$1 + 8 = 9$$
$$1 + 8 + 27 = 36$$
$$1 + 8 + 27 + 64 = 100$$

2. Explain why the sum of two odd numbers is always even.

3. Use inductive reasoning to state the next two numbers.
   a) 3, 5, 8, 13, 21,...
   b) 1, 3, 8, 16, 27,...

4. Use deductive reasoning to state a conclusion.
   a) Passengers must register 45 min before flight-time. Maria registered 20 min before flight-time. Therefore,....
   b) A rhombus has four equal sides. A square has four equal sides, Therefore,....

5. Find the values of x and y.

a)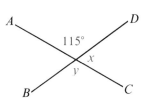

b)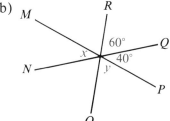

c)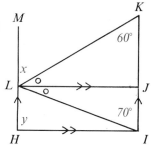

d)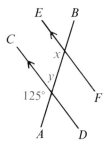

e)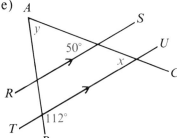

f)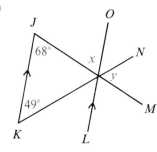

6. State the supplement of
   a) 42°   b) 78°   c) 60°

7. Find the values of x and y.

a)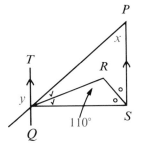

b)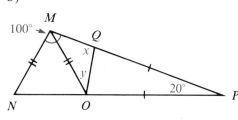

8. Prove that $AB = DE$.

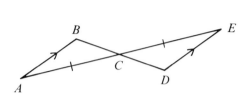

9. Prove that $\triangle PRS$ is isosceles.

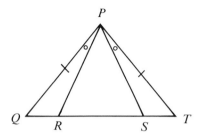

10. In parallelogram $JKLM$, P and Q are points on JL such that $JP = QL$. Prove that $\angle JKQ = \angle LMP$.

11. If $PS \| QR$ and PS bisects $\angle TPR$, prove that $\triangle PQR$ is isosceles.

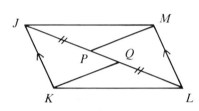

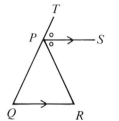

12. $\triangle ABC$ and $\triangle ADE$ are isosceles. Prove that $BC \| DE$.

13. List the properties of a parallelogram.

14. Find the value of x to two decimal places.

a)

b)

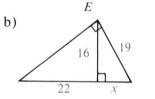

15. Construct a cone with base radius 6.0 cm and height 10.0 cm.

16. Construct a cylinder of diameter 12 cm and height 18 cm.

17. A square piece of paper measuring 24 cm on a side is used to construct an open cylinder. Find its radius and total surface area.

18. Find the surface area of a closed cylinder and a cone of radius
    a) 8.5 cm and height 15.0 cm   b) 12.9 cm and height 27.0 cm

19. Find the surface area and volume of a cylinder of radius 21 cm and height 35 cm.

20. Find the surface area and volume of a cone of diameter 26 cm and height 63 cm.

21. A gravel pit has a conical pile of crushed stone measuring 17.0 m in diameter and 12.6 m high. How many dump truck loads are in the pile if each dump truck carries 6.2 m³ per load?

22. Find the surface area and volume of a sphere of radius 45 cm.

The Vancouver Canucks joined the National Hockey League in 1970-1971. Has there been a trend to the number of goals the Canucks scored each season since then? (See Section 13-5)

13-1 INTERPRETING GRAPHS

The statements below are determined by using a branch of mathematics called statistics. *Statistics* deals with the collection, interpretation, and analysis of data for the purpose of drawing inferences and making predictions.

A recent study indicates that moderate exercise can significantly increase life expectancy.

According to an Air Canada survey, 75% of travellers prefer a wide-body aircraft over a narrow-body one.

Statistical information is often presented in graphs such as the following. Can you answer the questions that accompany each graph?

Bar Graphs

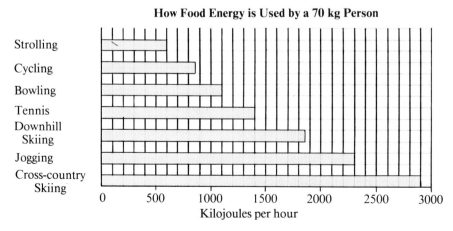

How Food Energy is Used by a 70 kg Person

Strolling
Cycling
Bowling
Tennis
Downhill Skiing
Jogging
Cross-country Skiing

Kilojoules per hour

Suppose you go cross-country skiing for 1 h each weekend in the winter. How many hours would you have to cycle each weekend in the summer to use the same amount of kilojoules?

    A *bar graph* is a graph in which the lengths of the bars represent certain quantities in a set of data. In the bar graph, a 70 kg person consumes approximately 850 kJ cycling for one hour.

Histograms

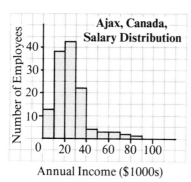

How many workers at Ajax earn less than $30 000 per year? About what percent of the workers is this?

    A *histogram* is a bar graph in which the bars represent a range of values. For example, in the histogram the third bar represents salaries between $20 000 and $30 000.

Line Graphs

There are two types of line graphs, as these examples show.

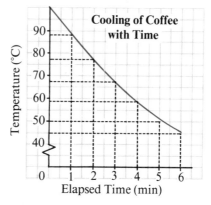

To make this graph, a point was plotted for each month and adjacent points were joined with line segments. This graph is called a *broken-line graph*, or a *frequency polygon*. The only points that represent actual data are the endpoints of the segments.
- What was the peak month for sales?
- What were the total sales?

To make this graph, the temperature of a cup of coffee was recorded every minute. This graph is called a *continuous-line graph*. Unlike a frequency polygon, all points on the graph represent actual values of the variables.

- How long did it take the temperature of the coffee to fall to 60°?

Circle and Rectangle Graphs

Origin of Travellers to British Columbia

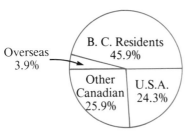

About what fraction of the travellers in British Columbia are Canadian?

How Visitors to British Columbia Spend 100 Travel Dollars

Transportation $25	Restaurants $22	Accommodation $20	Shopping $16	Recreation $9	Groceries $8

Find three items that account for 50% of the spending.

Circle and rectangle graphs can only be used to show a whole quantity divided into parts.

EXERCISES 13-1

Ⓐ

1. a) How much longer is the Trans-Canada highway than the Canada-U.S. border?
   b) If you drove from Whitehorse to St. John's, how much farther would you travel than the shortest air distance across Canada?

East-West Distances in Canada

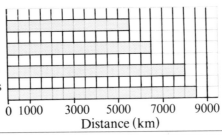

Shortest Air Distance
Canada-U.S. Border
Trans-Canada Highway
Whitehorse to St. John's by Horse and Ferry

0 1000   3000   5000   7000   9000
Distance (km)

Ⓑ

2. a) How many students competed in the Bell Canada Run?

   b) What percent of the students completed the run in 15 min or less?

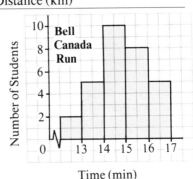

3. If the still-air temperature is −12°C,
   a) what is the wind-chill temperature when the wind speed is 20 km/h? 35 km/h?
   b) what wind speed gives a wind-chill temperature of −35°C?

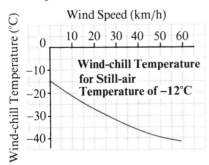

4. a) What is the optimum heartbeat rate for those whose age is 30? 45? 57?
   b) How old is the person whose optimum heartbeat rate is 145 beats/min? 135 beats/min?

Optimum Heartbeat Rate for Joggers

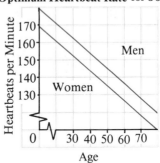

5. One year, Canada produced 24 million tonnes of wheat. How much wheat was produced in each of the three prairie provinces that year?

Canada's Wheat Production

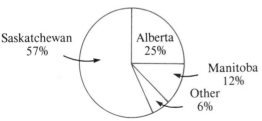

6. To make 25 kg of hot dogs,
   a) how much fat is needed?
   b) how much protein is needed?

Composition of a Hot Dog

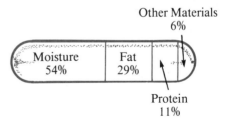

7. To make this graph, the sales were recorded at the end of each month and the cumulative total represented by points on the graph. What were the total sales for the six months? How many sales were there in March?

8. a) What change in the Consumer Price Index was recorded from 1972 to 1973? from 1982 to 1983?
   b) When did the greatest change occur?
   c) If the Consumer Price Index was 100.0 in 1981, what was it in 1982? 1983? 1985? 1986?

Percentage Change in Consumer Price Index (1971-1986)

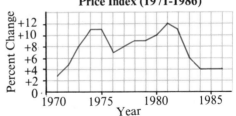

13-2 COLLECTING AND ORGANIZING DATA

To prepare the graphs in the preceding section, it was necessary to collect and organize data. This can be done in different ways.

Conducting a Poll or Questionnaire

In the last century, more than 1000 sightings of a man-like creature have been reported in western North America. This creature, if it actually exists, has come to be known as the *Sasquatch*. A similar creature, the *Abominable Snowman*, is supposed to inhabit the Himalayas. No one has seen the *Abominable Snowman*, but certain marks in the snow have been attributed to it.

How many people believe that creatures like the *Sasquatch* and the *Abominable Snowman* exist?

The only way to answer a question such as this is to conduct a poll. You might ask a number of people the question below.

"Do you believe that man-like creatures such as the *Sasquatch* and the *Abominable Snowman* really exist?"

Definitely exist	☐	Possibly exist	☐
Probably don't exist	☐	Definitely don't exist	☐

In one poll, 1067 people in 30 Canadian cities were asked this question in telephone interviews. The results of the survey are given in the following table and the bar graph.

Survey Results

Definitely exist	96
Possibly exist	352
Probably don't exist	181
Definitely don't exist	427
No opinion	11
	1067

**People's Belief in the Sasquatch
and the Abominable Snowman**

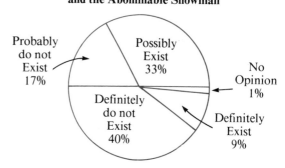

The survey results can also be used to draw a circle graph. To organize the data for drawing the circle graph, follow these steps:

Step 1. Divide each value by the total to express it as a decimal.

Step 2. Multiply the decimal in *Step 1* by 360°. The result is the number of degrees in the corresponding region on the circle graph. Round to the nearest degree.

The results of *Steps 1* and *2* and the complete circle graph are shown below. Notice that the decimal in *Step 1* can be multiplied by 100% to express the data in percent form.

Survey Results

Definitely exist	96	0.090	32°
Possibly exist	352	0.330	119°
Probably don't exist	181	0.170	61°
Definitely don't exist	427	0.400	144°
No opinion	11	0.010	4°
Totals	1067	1.000	360°

**People's Belief in the Sasquatch
and the Abominable Snowman**

Probably
do not
Exist
17%

Possibly
Exist
33%

No
Opinion
1%

Definitely
do not
Exist
40%

Definitely
Exist
9%

Conducting an Experiment

A different way to collect data is to conduct an experiment. A grade 10 class did this to investigate the following question:

> By keeping both feet on the floor, how high can you reach, to the nearest centimetre?

The students attached a measuring tape to a wall, then recorded how high each of them could reach, to the nearest centimetre. The results for 34 students are as follows:

Height Students Can Reach (cm)						
216	203	223	212	228	199	210
225	232	197	230	242	223	225
208	211	204	236	225	204	238
220	236	240	237	239	224	207
195	223	212	200	229	218	

This data can be organized and displayed in different ways:

To make a frequency table, the data must be arranged into classes, or groups. The heights are grouped into intervals of 10, such as 190-199, 200-209, and so on. *Frequency* means the number of students in each group.

Each row in the stem-and-leaf diagram below corresponds to several numbers. For example, the *stem* in the third row is 21, and the *leaves* are 6, 2, 0, 1, 2, 8. This row represents the numbers:

216   212   210   211   212   218

Frequency Table

Height (cm)	Tally	Frequency
190-199	lll	3
200-209	++++ l	6
210-219	++++ l	6
220-229	++++ ++++	10
230-239	++++ ll	7
240-249	ll	2

Stem-and-Leaf Diagram

Stem	Leaf
19	9 7 5
20	3 8 4 4 7 0
21	6 2 0 1 2 8
22	3 8 5 3 5 5 0 4 3 9
23	2 0 6 8 6 7 9
24	2 0

The data in the frequency table is used to draw the histogram and the frequency polygon. Since the exact heights for individual students cannot be determined from the frequency table, the frequency polygon is drawn as if all the students in each interval had the same height (the middle value of the interval). Thus the frequency polygon is obtained by plotting points corresponding to the midpoints of the tops of the bars of the histogram.

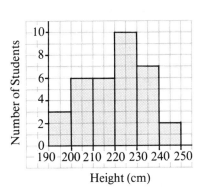

Height Students can reach

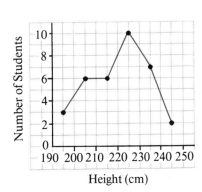

Height Students can reach

EXERCISES 13-2

(A)

1. a) How many students received a mark of 59? 67? 70?
   b) How many received a mark of 70 or higher?
   c) How many students wrote the test?

   Mathematics Test Marks

   ```
   4 | 7  5
   5 | 6  3  9
   6 | 7  2  6  4  8  7  5  7
   7 | 2  4  7  0  3  8  0
   8 | 1  6  4  7
   9 | 2
   ```

2. a) How many participants received a score of 32? 35? 45?
   b) How many received a score below 33?
   c) How many received a perfect score of 50?
   d) How many participants were there?

   Bicycle Rodeo Scores

   ```
   2 | 4  7  2
   3 | 2  0  6  1  7  6  9  6
   4 | 8  3  5  9  5  1
   5 | 0  0  0
   ```

3. a) How many students weigh 54 kg? 63 kg? 66 kg?
   b) How many weigh more than 70 kg? less than 55 kg?

   Students' Masses (kg)

   ```
   4 | 4  2  3
   4 | 6  9
   5 | 4  2  4
   5 | 7  5  8  5  7
   6 | 3  1  3  2  2  4  3
   6 | 6  5  8  8  7
   7 | 2  4  2
   7 | 8  5
   ```

4. a) What was the winning time?
   b) How many skiers completed the course in 249 s? 253 s?
   c) How many finished in less than 250 s?

   Ski Race Times

   ```
   23 | 5
   24 | 2  1  3
   24 | 6  9  5  8  6
   25 | 0  4  1  3  3  4  4
   25 | 5  6  8  5
   26 | 1  0  0
   26 | 6  5
   ```

5. The heights, in centimetres, of 27 students in Elmwood Collegiate are listed.
   a) Construct a stem-and-leaf diagram.
   b) Construct a histogram.

150	162	171	159	168	148	175	163	157
150	168	170	172	155	164	153	160	149
176	161	155	149	156	168	172	158	173

6. a) Construct a stem-and-leaf diagram for the geography marks given.
   b) Construct a histogram.

7. a) Construct a frequency table for the golf scores.
   b) Construct a histogram.

Students' Geography Marks

60	99	66	52	66	73	84	57
71	81	85	50	65	77	74	68
80	41	61	91	55	74	59	45
44	78	55	47	69	59	67	62

Amateur Golf Scores

87	79	75	85	97	67	92	96
69	99	89	93	84	104	94	106
95	68	78	98	79	102	72	71

Ⓑ

8. The average daily temperatures in Mariposa during April and May were:

−3	−3	1	2	3	−1	1	2	−1	2	6	7	9	8	3
8	9	12	14	15	10	8	11	14	17	17	18	13	16	19
12	5	5	11	13	18	19	15	9	13	9	16	13	20	20
16	14	11	13	18	23	23	17	14	14	20	23	23	25	24	24

   a) Construct a frequency table using 5° intervals.
   b) Construct a histogram.

9. The marks of 23 driver-education students on a test out of 35 were as shown.
   a) Construct a frequency table using 5-mark intervals.
   b) Construct a frequency polygon.

9	29	18	30	20	35	13	21
18	20	19	19	26	28	28	17
34	27	24	32	21	22	19

10. The points scored by 28 players in a basketball tournament are as follows:

| 13 | 15 | 11 | 10 | 16 | 13 | 17 | 13 | 10 | 13 | 14 | 11 | 16 | 14 |
| 16 | 14 | 12 | 15 | 18 | 17 | 11 | 14 | 15 | 15 | 13 | 16 | 15 | 15 |

Construct a frequency polygon for this data.

11. In Madrid, the average temperatures for the days in June were:

| 30 | 24 | 22 | 25 | 19 | 28 | 24 | 27 | 28 | 25 | 26 | 27 | 28 | 28 | 25 |
| 25 | 20 | 27 | 26 | 26 | 27 | 23 | 20 | 19 | 22 | 29 | 21 | 24 | 26 | 29 |

Construct a histogram for this data.

12. Construct a circle graph to illustrate the following data.

Purpose of Trips by Canadians to Foreign Destinations (Other Than U.S.) in 1984	
Business or employment	11.7%
Visiting friends and relatives	28.4%
Recreation, holidays	50.4%
Other or combined reasons	9.5%

13. Construct a circle graph to illustrate the following data.

Weekly Budget	
Item	**Amount ($)**
Apartment	100
Food	50
Recreation	15
Transportation	10

Conduct surveys among your classmates or in your school to investigate the following questions. Show the results in a circle graph.

14. Do you believe that water creatures such as the *Loch Ness monster* and *Ogopogo* actually exist?

15. Do you think that some of the stories one hears about flying saucers are true?

16. Do you believe that some people have extra-sensory powers such as mental telepathy?

17. Do you believe that intelligent life exists elsewhere in the universe?

Conduct surveys among your classmates or in your school to investigate the following. Show the results in a frequency table and a histogram.

18. The number of persons in your immediate family.

19. The distance you live from school.

Ⓒ

20. Construct circle graphs to illustrate the following data.

a) **Canadian Travellers Returning from Destinations Other than the U.S.A. in 1984**

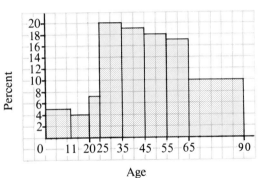

b) **Distribution of Company's Weekly Salaries**

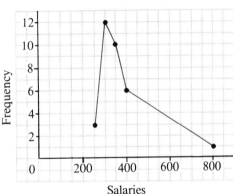

13-3 MEASURES OF CENTRAL TENDENCY

In the preceding sections, data was summarized using graphs. Another way to summarize data is to represent all the items by one number, such as an average.

The table gives the lengths of the drives of two golfers in a driving contest. Who hits a longer drive, on the average, Lise or Monique?

	Length of Drive (metres)						
Lise	260	302	268	260	250	288	291
Monique	285	257	282	252	290	280	250

The answer to the question depends on which of the following meanings of "average" is chosen.

> To find the *mean*, add the numbers and divide by the number of numbers.

For Lise's drives, the mean is:
$$\frac{260 + 302 + 268 + 260 + 250 + 288 + 291}{7} = \frac{1919}{7}$$
$$\doteq 274$$

For Monique's drives, the mean is:
$$\frac{285 + 257 + 282 + 252 + 290 + 280 + 250}{7} = \frac{1896}{7}$$
$$\doteq 271$$

To find the *median*, first arrange the numbers in order. If the number of numbers is odd, take the middle number. If it is even, take the mean of the two middle numbers.

Lise's drives,
in order are: 250   260   260   268   288   291   302

The median is 268.

Monique's drives,
in order are: 250   252   257   280   282   285   290

The median is 280.

To find the *mode*, look for the number which occurs most frequently. There may be more than one mode, or no mode.

For Lise's drives, the mode is 260. There is no mode for Monique's drives.

The mean, median, and mode are called *measures of central tendency*. They are usually calculated using larger sets of data than those for the golfers. To find the median of a large set of numbers, a stem-and-leaf diagram helps us to find the middle number.

Example.   A school's grade 10 students obtained the following marks on a mathematics examination. Find the median.

63 57 82 80 71 93 44 53 58 61 55
80 66 69 63 72 77 81 50 58 70 62
85 83 74 42 57 62 68 81 58 74 71
79 80 60 67 95 41 65 73 82 77 60
67 63 72 78 50 57 60 65 55 82 86
79 69 60 63 71 78 68 60 58 70

Solution.   Form the stem-and-leaf diagram.

```
4 | 4 2 1
5 | 5 7 7 8 5 8 3 7 8 0 8 0
6 | 3 5 0 6 2 5 8 9 0 3 0 7 0 3 7 9 2 0 1 8 3
7 | 0 1 0 3 8 4 1 7 1 9 2 4 7 9 2 8
8 | 1 0 2 2 0 5 3 2 0 6 1
9 | 3 5
```

Since there are 65 marks, the median is the 33rd mark when the marks are ordered. There are 32 lower marks and 32 higher marks. We see from the stem-and-leaf diagram that there are 36 marks in the 40's, 50's, and 60's. The median is therefore the fourth highest mark in the 60's. The highest four marks in this row, in order, are 68, 68, 69, 69. Therefore the median is 68.

EXERCISES 13-3

1. Find the mean, median, and mode.
   a) 5, 9, 4, 6, 2, 8, 7, 6, 3
   b) 24, 33, 25, 29, 32, 37, 25, 40, 38, 25, 33
   c) 3.7, 4.2, 7.1, 5.8, 6.3, 4.8, 5.2, 6.3, 5.4, 3.9
   d) 114, 92, 126, 85, 94, 109, 111, 88, 96, 107, 100, 105, 95, 90, 97, 99, 101
   e) 65, 52, 73, 86, 58, 47, 65, 78, 69, 58, 71, 67, 56, 57, 55, 58, 54, 59, 60, 70, 75, 55, 59, 61, 71, 85, 80, 81, 79, 66

2. The heights, in centimetres, of 13 players on a junior basketball team are as follows:

   172, 182, 178, 187, 183, 176, 182, 182, 178, 173, 177, 181, 176.

   Find the mean, median, and mode.

3. Bobolink Sports Equipment employs 16 people at a weekly salary of $200, 3 people at a weekly salary of $150, and 2 people at a salary of $750 per week. Find the mean, median, and mode salary paid by the company.

4. Find the mean, median, and mode.

   a) 3 | 7
      4 | 6 3 9
      5 | 5 2 8 5
      6 | 3 2

   b) 17 | 8 6
      18 | 3 0 2 3
      18 | 5 9 7 8 5
      19 | 2 1 4 3 2 2
      19 | 7 5 8

5. The batting averages of the Tillson Giants were:

   0.263, 0.309, 0.350, 0.207, 0.256, 0.278, 0.378, 0.283, 0.274, and 0.229.

   a) Find the mean   b) Find the median
   c) Would the mean necessarily be the team's batting average? Why?

6. A bowler had these scores after eight games of 5-pin bowling:

   299, 321, 317, 396, 245, 390, 340, 272.

   a) Find the mean score; the median score.
   b) In two more games, the bowler scored 173 and 216. Find the mean score and the median score for the ten games.

7. From the clipping, determine the
   a) total value of the prizes
   b) total number of prizes
   c) mean value of the prizes

8. The prizes in a lottery were as follows:

5 prizes of	$100 000
2 prizes of	$75 000
102 prizes of	$7 500
102 prizes of	$750
53 000 prizes of	$25

   Find the
   a) mean value of the prizes
   b) median value
   c) mode

   Which measure seems best to describe the average value of the prizes?

> ## Hello, young lovers.
> ## Did you win $5000?
> MONTREAL (CP)—A total of 770 winning numbers were drawn in a special Loto Canada "Sweetheart Draw" on Valentine's Day.
>
> In a departure from its usual million-dollar lottery, Loto Canada awarded 70 prizes of $5000 each and 700 prizes of $500 each. The winners were part of a Valentine's Day bonus program.

9. Your marks (out of 25) on five tests are 19, 18, 22, 17, and 23. What mark would you have to get on the next test to have a mean mark of at least 20 on the six tests?

Ⓒ

10. In 1980, George Brett of the Kansas City Royals almost became the first major league baseball player since 1941 to have a 0.400 batting average. By September 22, he had 162 hits in 411 times at bat. During the remaining games of the season, he had 13 hits in 38 times at bat.
    a) What was his batting average on September 22?
    b) What was his batting average for the entire season?
    c) How many more hits did he need to reach a 0.400 batting average?
    d) In 1941, Ted Williams had 185 hits in 456 times at bat. What was his batting average?

11. Find seven numbers that have a mean of
    a) 12 and a median of 13
    b) 62 and a median of 65
    c) 8, a median of 10, and a mode of 5
    d) 15, a median of 12, and a mode of 15

 INVESTIGATE

If some 1 kg masses are placed in different positions on this seesaw, how can you determine in advance whether the seesaw will balance?

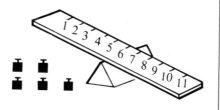

13-4 SCATTERPLOTS AND TRENDS

Is there any relation between the area of a lake and its depth? To investigate this question, consider the data below.

North America's Largest Lakes

Name	Area (km²)	Depth (m)
Superior	82 100	406
Huron	59 600	229
Michigan	57 800	281
Great Bear	31 200	446
Great Slave	28 700	614
Erie	25 700	64
Winnipeg	24 400	18
Ontario	19 000	244
Nicaragua	8 100	70
Athabasca	7 900	124

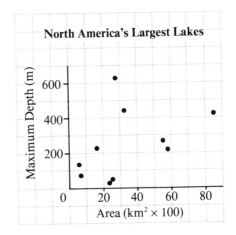

This data can be graphed on a grid as shown, where each point
represents one of the lakes. Such a graph is called a *scatterplot*. This
scatterplot shows that there is little relation between the area of a lake
and its depth. In other scatterplots, a trend is often evident.

Example.   An almanac listed the average high and
low temperatures for two months of the
year at 16 Canadian airports. This data
was used to make the scatterplot shown.
What conclusions might be made from
this scatterplot?

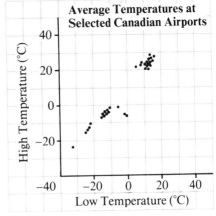

Solution.   There is a trend to the data. Airports with
higher low temperatures have higher high
temperatures. In addition, there are two
clusters, or groups, of data. In one cluster,
both temperatures are much higher than in
the other. This indicates that one of the
months was a summer month, while the
other was a winter month.

EXERCISES 13-4

Ⓐ

1. What conclusions can you make from each scatterplot?
   a) **Average Monthly Precipitation in Armstrong, Ontario**
   b) **Population of Major Canadian Cities and Metropolitan Areas**

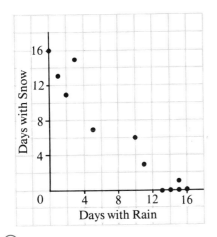

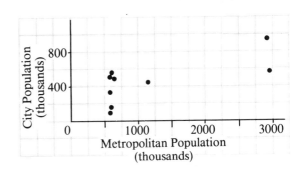

Ⓑ

In *Exercises 2* to *5*, draw a scatterplot for each set of data. What conclusions can you make from the scatterplot?

2. **New Car Sales in Canada (thousands of cars)**

Year		Year	
1950	325	1970	640
1955	387	1975	989
1960	448	1980	932
1965	709	1985	843

3. **British Columbia Unemployment**

Year	(%)	Year	(%)
1976	8.6	1981	6.7
1977	8.5	1982	12.1
1978	8.3	1983	13.8
1979	7.6	1984	14.7
1980	6.8	1985	14.2

4. **Fuel Consumption of Automobiles** (1986)

Make	Engine Size (L)	L/100 km
Chevrolet Chevette	1.6	5.7
Chevrolet Sprint	1.0	4.3
Chrysler Fifth Avenue	5.2	10.1
Ford Mustang	5.0	8.5
Honda Civic	1.5	6.2
Hyundai Pony	1.4	6.7
Jaguar XJ-S	5.3	12.5
Lincoln Continental	5.0	9.4
Plymouth Colt	1.5	5.8
Pontiac Grand Prix	5.0	9.6

5. **Passenger Aircraft Dimensions**

Type	Length (m)	Wingspan (m)
Boeing 707	46.6	44.4
Boeing 727	46.7	32.9
Boeing 737	30.4	28.3
Boeing 747	70.5	59.6
Boeing 757	47.3	37.9
Boeing 767	48.5	47.6
Concorde	62.1	25.5
DC-9	45.1	32.9
DC-10	55.6	50.4
Lockhead L-1011	54.2	47.4

13-5 MANIPULATING DATA: THE MEDIAN FIT LINE

The table and the scatterplot show the
number of goals scored by the Vancouver
Canucks during the regular season each
year since their entry into the National
Hockey League in 1970-71.

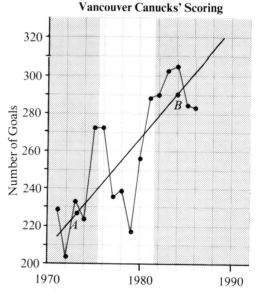

Vancouver Canucks' Scoring

Year	Goals	Year	Goals	Year	Goals
1971	229	1976	271	1982	290
1972	203	1977	235	1983	303
1973	233	1978	239	1984	306
1974	224	1979	217	1985	284
1975	271	1980	256	1986	282
		1981	289		

There is a definite trend toward greater goal production over time. We
can indicate this by drawing a straight line to represent the data, using
the following method.

Step 1. Divide the graph into three vertical regions, each containing
about the same number of points, as shown.

Step 2. In the *first* region, determine the median *x*-coordinate and the
median *y*-coordinate.
x-coordinates: 1971, 1972, 1973, 1974, 1975 Median: 1973
y-coordinates: 229, 203, 233, 224, 271 Median: 229

Step 3. Repeat *Step 2* in the *third* region.
x-coordinates: 1982, 1983, 1984, 1985, 1986 Median: 1984
y-coordinates: 290, 303, 306, 284, 282 Median: 290

Step 4. Draw a line through the points $A(1973, 229)$ and $B(1984, 290)$
with the median coordinates identified in *Steps 2* and *3*.

The line drawn in *Step 4* is called the *median fit line*. By extending
the line, we can predict how many goals the Vancouver Canucks might
score in a future year. For example, the line indicates that 315 goals
might be scored in 1988. Such a prediction must be made *assuming* that the trend indicated by the line
continues. Can you give reasons why the trend might not continue in
this example?

EXERCISES 13-5

Ⓐ

1. a) Copy the graph.

   b) Determine the median *x*-coordinate and the median *y*-coordinate in each shaded region.

   c) Draw the median fit line.

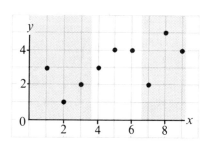

Ⓑ

For *Exercises 2* to *5*, use the data in *Exercises 2* to *5* on page 449.

2. a) Draw a median fit line for Canada's new car sales.
   b) Use the median fit line to predict the sales in 1990.

3. a) Draw a median fit line for British Columbia unemployment.
   b) Use the median fit line to predict the unemployment in 1990.

4. a) Draw a median fit line for automobile fuel consumption.
   b) Use the median fit line to predict the fuel consumption of a 6.8 L Rolls Royce engine.

5. a) Draw a median fit line for aircraft dimensions.
   b) Use the median fit line to predict the wingspan of an aircraft which is 80 m long.

6. a) Construct a scatterplot using the data in the table.
   b) Draw a median fit line.
   c) Use the median fit line to predict how many games the Vancouver Canucks might win in 1990.

Regular Season Games Won by the Vancouver Canucks

Year	Won	Year	Won	Year	Won
1971	24	1976	33	1982	30
1972	20	1977	25	1983	30
1973	22	1978	20	1984	32
1974	24	1979	25	1985	25
1975	38	1980	27	1986	23
		1981	28		

Ⓒ

7. Draw a median fit line for each set of data. Would this line be a good one to use to make a prediction? Explain.

a) **Persons Granted Canadian Citizenship (in thousands)**

Year		Year		Year	
1970	58	1975	138	1980	119
1971	64	1976	117	1981	94
1972	81	1977	124	1982	87
1973	105	1978	223	1983	90
1974	130	1979	157	1984	110

b) **Average Weekly Wages in British Columbia**

Year	Wages	Year	Wages
1940	$27.44	1965	$100.71
1945	34.72	1970	137.97
1950	47.70	1975	229.97
1955	66.00	1980	363.51
1960	82.85	1985	504.43

13-6 MANIPULATING DATA: SMOOTHING GRAPHS

The table and the scatterplot show the number of regular season games won by the Toronto Blue Jays each year since their entry into the American Baseball League in 1977.

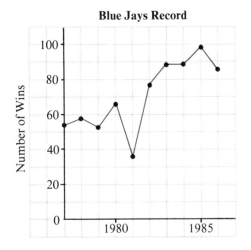

Blue Jays Record

Year	1977	1978	1979	1980	1981
Wins	54	59	53	67	37

Year	1982	1983	1984	1985	1986
Wins	78	89	89	99	86

The number of wins varies widely. There are three highs and two lows which are all reversed the next year, and which do not appear to be part of a general trend. If we were looking for a general trend, we would tend to overlook these individual highs and lows, unless they occur together over two or more years. To help us see the trend, we *smooth* the data as follows.

Step 1. Prepare another row in the table of values, for the smoothed data. The first and last numbers are the same as in the original table. For 1978, consider the wins in 1977, 1978, 1979. Their median is 54. Write this median in the space for 1978.

Year	1977	1978	1979	1980	1981	1982	1983	1984	1985	1986
Wins	54	59	53	67	37	78	89	89	99	86
Smoothed wins	54	54								86

Step 2. For 1979, consider the wins in 1978, 1979, 1980. Their median is 59. Write 59 in the space for 1979.

Year	1977	1978	1979	1980	1981	1982	1983	1984	1985	1986
Wins	54	59	53	67	37	78	89	89	99	86
Smoothed wins	54	54	59							86

Step 3. Repeat until the row is complete. The figure entered for each year is the median of the number of wins for the three years beginning with the previous year.

Year	1977	1978	1979	1980	1981	1982	1983	1984	1985	1986
Wins	54	59	53	67	37	78	89	89	99	86
Smoothed wins	54	54	59	53	67	78	89	89	89	86

Step 4. Plot the smoothed data and join the points with line segments.

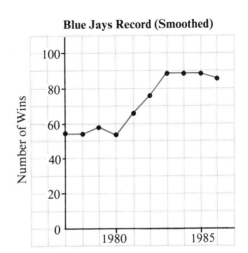

Blue Jays Record (Smoothed)

The smoothed graph suggests that the number of wins is levelling off around 85 to 90. If this trend continues, we would predict that the Blue Jays might win somewhere around 90 games in each future year.

EXERCISES 13-6

Ⓐ

1. Construct a smoothed set of values for each set of data.
   a) 3 7 6 2 8
   b) 2 6 8 3 5
   c) 12 23 18 15 31 27
   d) 39 35 22 27 24 17

Ⓑ

For *Exercise 2*, use the data in *Exercise 6* on page 451.

2. a) Construct a smoothed table of values for the number of games won by the Vancouver Canucks.
   b) Draw a smoothed graph and use it to predict the number of games that might be won in 1991.

For *Exercises 3* and *4*, use the data in *Exercises 2* and *3* on page 449.

3. a) Construct a smoothed table of values for new car sales.
   b) Draw a smoothed graph and use it to predict the sales in 1990.

4. a) Construct a smoothed table of values for B.C. unemployment.
   b) Draw a smoothed graph and use it to predict the unemployment in 1990.

COMPUTER POWER

The Median Fit Line

The program below can be used to calculate the coordinates of the two points which determine the median fit line.

```
100 REM *** THE MEDIAN FIT LINE ***
110 DIM X(30),Y(30)
120 INPUT "HOW MANY POINTS? ";H:PRINT
130 FOR I=1 TO H
140    PRINT:PRINT "ENTER COORDINATES OF POINT #";I
150    INPUT "SEPARATED BY A COMMA: ";X(I),Y(I)
160 NEXT I
170 PRINT:INPUT "HOW MANY POINTS IN REGIONS? ";N
180 M=INT((N+1)/2)
190 FOR K=1 TO 2
200    FOR I=1 TO M+1:FOR J=I+1 TO N
210       IF X(I)>=X(J) THEN F=X(I):X(I)=X(J):X(J)=F
220       IF Y(I)>=Y(J) THEN F=Y(I):Y(I)=Y(J):Y(J)=F
230    NEXT J:NEXT I
240    IF N/2<>INT(N/2) THEN X(M+1)=X(M):Y(M+1)=Y(M)
250    X=X(M)/2+X(M+1)/2:Y=Y(M)/2+Y(M+1)/2
260    PRINT:PRINT "POINT #";K;": (";X;", ";Y;")"
270    FOR I=1 TO N:X(I)=X(H-N+I):Y(I)=Y(H-N+I):NEXT I
280 NEXT K
290 END
```

1. a) Draw a scatterplot for this data.

   b) Find the coordinates of two points on the median fit line, and draw the median fit line.

   c) Predict the wheat production in the year 2000.

Canadian Wheat Production
(millions of tonnes)

Year		Year	
1930	11.4	1960	17.7
1935	7.7	1965	9.0
1940	14.7	1970	17.1
1945	8.6	1975	13.3
1950	12.7	1980	17.2
1955	14.1	1985	21.2

2. Investigate the effect of drawing a median fit line using
   a) more than one-third of the points in the left and right regions;
   b) less than one-third of the points in the left and right regions.

Smoothing Data

The method of smoothing data described in the preceding section involves the repetitive calculation of the median of three successive numbers. For this reason, the method is ideally suited to a computer. The program below can be used to smooth up to 30 points using this method.

```
100 REM *** SMOOTHING DATA ***
110 DIM Y(30)
120 INPUT "HOW MANY POINTS? ";N:PRINT
130 FOR I=1 TO N
140     PRINT "ENTER Y-COORDINATE OF POINT #";I;":"
150     INPUT Y(I)
160 NEXT I
170 PRINT:PRINT "SMOOTHED DATA FOLLOWS: ":PRINT
180 PRINT Y(1)
190 FOR I=2 TO N-1
200     A=Y(I-1):B=Y(I):C=Y(I+1)
210     IF A>B THEN D=A:A=B:B=D
220     IF B>C THEN D=B:B=C:C=D
230     IF A>B THEN D=A:A=B:B=D
240     PRINT B
250 NEXT I
260 PRINT Y(N)
270 END
```

3. a) Draw a scatterplot for the data below.
   b) Use the program to obtain smoothed data, and draw a smoothed graph.
   c) Does the graph show a general trend? Suggest a reason for the trend.
   d) Predict the number of tornadoes that might be reported in 1990; in the year 2000.

Number of Tornadoes Reported in Canada (1950-1981)

Year	Number of Tornadoes	Year	Number of Tornadoes	Year	Number of Tornadoes	Year	Number of Tornadoes
1950	11	1958	12	1966	35	1974	29
1951	7	1959	18	1967	20	1975	65
1952	15	1960	22	1968	56	1976	45
1953	31	1961	21	1969	61	1977	55
1954	14	1962	21	1970	36	1978	92
1955	11	1963	25	1971	34	1979	54
1956	21	1964	41	1972	24	1980	81
1957	22	1965	25	1973	56	1981	59

Eggs up 20¢...
Shoes cost 15% more...
Rents up only 3%...
Consumer Price Index for May, 133.2

13-7 COMPARING SAMPLES WITH POPULATIONS

Some of the statistics we see in newspapers and magazines come from samples. Each month a Consumer Price Index is calculated, which relates the current prices of goods and services to those in an earlier year; currently taken to be 1981. To determine the Consumer Price Index in any month, the prices of a sample of goods are determined. The sample reflects the items that people normally buy, including groceries, furniture, movie tickets, auto repairs, and haircuts. The sample also reflects prices in different regions of Canada.

A small group of items which is chosen to represent a larger group is called a *sample*. The larger group is called a *population*. Population does not necessarily refer to people. In the case of the Consumer Price Index, the population is the prices of all the goods and services sold in Canada.

Samples must be chosen carefully. They must be large enough and they must be representative of the population as a whole. This means that each element of the population should have an equal chance of being included in the sample. Such a sample is called a *random sample*.

The following example illustrates some methods of obtaining random samples in the classroom. A relatively small population is chosen in order that the results for the sample can be compared with the results for the population.

Example. These are the surnames of the students in Mr Scully's mathematics class. Use a random sample to estimate the mean, median, and mode for the number of letters in the surnames.

Balfour	Forsyth	Kennedy	Majic	Richardson	Thompson
Barnett	Francesconi	Keyes	Ng	Rucker	Triantafylidou
Borshay	Gianelia	Kilbank	Norris	Sarraude	Veerman
Burt	Gillis	King	Peressini	Sinclair	Walker
Dunlop	Hood	Lee	Perkins	Stelzer	Willoughby
Durocher	Karpenko	MacPherson	Reardon	Tabori	Zimnicki

Solution 1. *Using random draws.*

Write the data on slips of paper and put them in a box. Shake the box, and draw slips one at a time to form the desired sample. Using this method the following sample of six names was obtained:

Kennedy   Norris   Giannelia   Perkins   Stelzer   Gillis

The numbers of letters in these names are: 7, 6, 9, 7, 7, 6.
For this sample: Mean 7, Median 7, Mode 7.

Solution 2. *Using a pair of dice.*

Arrange the data as a 6 x 6 array, in any order. Roll two dice and record the corresponding item. Repeat until enough items have been identified to form the sample.

White Die

	⚀	⚁	⚂	⚃	⚄	⚅
⚀	Balfour	Forsyth	Kennedy	Majic	Richardson	Thompson
⚁	Barnett	Francesconi	Keyes	Ng	Rucker	Triantafylidou
⚂	Borshay	Giannelia	Kilbank	Norris	Sarraude	Veerman
⚃	Burt	Gillis	King	Peressini	Sinclair	Walker
⚄	Dunlop	Hood	Lee	Perkins	Stelzer	Willoughby
⚅	Durocher	Karpenko	MacPherson	Reardon	Tabori	Zimnicki

(Red Die labels the rows.)

Using this method, the following sample of six names was obtained:

Thompson   Rucker   Sarraude   Gillis   Dunlop   Willoughby

The numbers of letters in these names are: 8, 6, 8, 6, 6, 10
For this sample: Mean 7.3, Median 7, Mode 6.

If dice are used, this method is restricted to populations of 36 or less. For larger populations, playing cards, coins, and dice may be used.

Solution 3.   *Using random numbers.*

Using slips of paper, dice, and playing cards is awkward and time-consuming when it is necessary to obtain many samples. A more efficient method is to use random numbers. A very large set of single-digit numbers in which each number has an equal chance of occurring is called a set of *random numbers*. A table of random numbers is shown on the opposite page, or you can make your own by taking the last digits of the telephone numbers on any page of a telephone directory.

To use a random-number table to obtain samples, the items in the population must be numbered.

01	Balfour	10	Gillis	19	Majic	28	Sinclair
02	Barnett	11	Hood	20	Ng	29	Stelzer
03	Borshay	12	Karpenko	21	Norris	30	Tabori
04	Burt	13	Kennedy	22	Peressini	31	Thompson
05	Dunlop	14	Keyes	23	Perkins	32	Triantafylidou
06	Durocher	15	Kilbank	24	Reardon	33	Veerman
07	Forsyth	16	King	25	Richardson	34	Walker
08	Francesconi	17	Lee	26	Rucker	35	Willoughby
09	Giannelia	18	MacPherson	27	Sarraude	36	Zimnicki

Now start anywhere in the table and record 2-digit numbers in some systematic way. Numbers may be recorded horizontally or vertically, forwards or backwards. For example, starting at the 2nd number in the 5th row and proceeding horizontally, the following 2-digit numbers were obtained:

ⓐ27 ⓑ12 ⓒ09 ⓓ06   75 ⓔ19   09   75   80   91   68 ⓕ24

The circled numbers give this sample of six names:

Sarraude   Karpenko   Giannelia   Durocher   Majic   Reardon

The numbers of letters in these names are: 8, 8, 9, 8, 5, 7
For this sample: Mean 7.5, Median 8, Mode 8

The results of *Solutions 1, 2,* and *3* are, of course, only estimates of the actual mean, median, and mode of the population of 36 names. Compare the estimates with the actual values for the population of 36 names:

Mean 7.1, Median 7, Mode 7

As this example indicates, when a sample is chosen randomly, the mean, median and mode of the sample will usually be close to the mean, median, and mode of the population. But this will not always happen. In the above example, the sample chosen could contain the six shortest names, (mean 3.7) or the six longest ones, (mean 11.2). The chance that this will happen is about one in a million.

2250 Random Numbers

1	67983	60852	09916	43596	20363	53315	37287	07662	26401	28650
2	19010	91956	31795	41845	25190	06991	66521	93755	02166	79003
3	41830	13963	52289	51633	77785	31712	93500	19449	77822	36645
4	50115	21246	09195	09502	53413	26357	63992	52872	42570	80586
5	22712	09067	51909	75809	16824	41933	97621	68761	85401	03782
6	82806	82277	88300	29832	22806	92486	36042	34590	55743	85297
7	68885	23670	25151	14619	33069	05296	14748	43282	62802	30626
8	41971	29316	23695	60065	62854	01237	72575	98475	61743	66763
9	86818	10485	28018	57382	70220	77420	94651	05024	24716	63746
10	61411	17729	56740	10634	56007	05873	36764	41765	97918	49916
11	20240	11618	52392	19715	20334	01124	39338	73458	63616	72057
12	47935	98490	99047	20071	81921	13627	99672	26523	53766	01219
13	28555	86201	62668	98919	54425	52470	21863	38900	96199	02418
14	59767	56647	35868	12109	29037	72768	45163	69121	72091	48070
15	99784	67224	77465	88593	61371	05036	41838	02224	34532	14840
16	69823	11868	50659	64782	20491	11303	41774	80579	09599	00703
17	89585	58666	00566	73433	67326	86922	42271	45800	59208	94299
18	93707	06735	84194	51810	19421	68021	05152	06217	57168	95760
19	04063	28256	83450	70758	00038	24278	55795	30155	78395	65622
20	89294	03751	09422	22965	09888	95835	80131	65972	16145	59876
21	60301	16519	51348	36322	70572	48637	05309	08369	79567	67699
22	74006	15355	95718	91467	30481	31576	84764	67417	19343	01920
23	86117	80403	42385	64085	70178	07265	87005	48570	25755	81223
24	87860	70624	75971	40430	43435	34945	70220	32445	18369	01990
25	10484	39599	04817	06980	22037	43080	52425	77667	67793	92230
26	45635	80376	17981	83957	91343	18249	85861	90149	59239	10040
27	89884	99155	65450	31432	60782	51442	31091	91187	81633	54164
28	08854	49077	20318	73772	85867	61524	78601	92812	34536	97897
29	43755	12282	84744	58693	25640	66247	58618	40854	85560	00699
30	36381	94203	18050	28540	97769	63915	65191	04638	76462	13106
31	05478	49611	27465	72222	56456	82646	09667	43683	33611	15020
32	30900	37036	68577	43276	57609	88486	16952	46799	49171	19486
33	87097	50134	42000	51378	60900	70086	51319	51408	85037	15608
34	84951	45154	20051	46979	79305	46375	16686	96475	54604	14795
35	52243	19460	67237	95379	78426	75457	05919	05828	13052	51831
36	48397	03688	27314	19086	58154	56293	78283	87702	17610	97741
37	36108	73699	01494	88477	18706	86938	40590	38087	22757	04249
38	73798	17752	23699	42632	77518	34777	66590	12061	35079	14551
39	26577	40103	74102	06328	43037	77254	78000	61577	41810	85898
40	81004	57367	28642	02357	23267	76973	29206	69086	42603	49297
41	27346	40553	51131	02911	76081	81510	32041	12592	53089	16876
42	75820	17172	54381	10928	63101	20817	08819	00264	38508	94741
43	06940	77259	57591	56640	35761	81718	40979	88063	50261	66925
44	17772	34298	05693	26833	91346	57941	76006	78275	85258	45102
45	01458	47852	91481	69165	93122	30194	92266	29754	80002	19151

EXERCISES 13-7

Ⓐ

1. A survey is conducted to determine the average height of high school students. Which of the following methods should give a representative sample?
   a) Choose the first student in the class list for each home room.
   b) Use random numbers to choose 10 students from each grade.
   c) Choose the members of the school basketball team.

2. An airline wishes to estimate the percent of Canadians who have flown in an airplane at least once in the last year. The following methods of choosing a sample of Canadians are considered. Which method should give a representative sample?
   a) Choose people in airport waiting rooms.
   b) Choose people in hotel lobbies.
   c) Select people at random from the telephone book.

3. A tire manufacturer is establishing a quality control program. The following methods of choosing a sample of 100 tires are considered. Which method is more appropriate? Give reasons for your answer.
   a) Select the first 100 tires produced in one day.
   b) Select every 50th tire produced in a week's production of 5000 tires.

Ⓑ

4. The 36 members of Mrs. Lee's class measured their handspans to the nearest half centimetre, and recorded the results in a table.

   a) Use slips of paper, dice, or random numbers to obtain a sample of 8 handspans.

   b) For your sample, find the mean, the median, and the mode.

18.5	23.5	21.0	20.0	19.0	19.5
20.0	22.0	19.0	20.0	19.5	24.0
19.0	20.0	25.0	18.0	22.5	20.5
23.0	19.0	19.5	21.0	20.0	19.0
21.0	24.5	22.5	19.5	18.5	22.0
20.0	22.0	19.0	24.0	19.5	20.5

5. The 34 members of Mr. Thompson's class recorded their pulses. These are the results.
   a) Use slips of paper, dice, or random numbers to obtain a sample of 6 pulses.
   b) For your sample, find the mean, the median, and the mode.
   c) Compare your results in (b) with the results for the population of 34 students, which are given in the answer section.

78	76	68	72	80	70
78	75	78	66	70	74
82	70	74	72	92	74
72	88	68	78	68	78
86	66	90	90	74	
92	72	70	68	78	

6. The 33 students in Mrs. Raymond's class recorded their ages in days. These are the results:

5535	5572	5705	5362	5680	5700	5509	5429	5679	5771	5857
5451	5569	5729	5523	5681	5832	5383	5535	6051	5492	5923
5696	6139	5590	5758	5477	5622	5888	5658	5811	5502	5920

a) Obtain a random sample of 7 ages using any appropriate method.
b) For your sample, find the mean, the median, and the mode.
c) Compare your results in (b) with the results for the entire population of 33 students, which are given in the answer section.

7. In this book there are 99 text sections, numbered 1-1, 1-2, 1-3,...These are identified in the Table of Contents. The exercises in these sections are divided into groups A, B, and C.
a) Obtain a random sample of 10 sections using any appropriate method.
b) For each section in your sample record the number of A, B, and C exercises. Then find the mean, median, and mode for each type of exercise.

Ⓒ ───

8. Each day throughout the summer, a newspaper reported the donations to a Fresh-Air Fund to provide a holiday for needy children. The 100 donations for one day are shown below. They are arranged to facilitate obtaining random samples using a coin and a well-shuffled deck of playing cards.

		A	2	3	4	5	6	7	8	9	10	J	Q	K	
Heads	♠	30	100	50	20	24	50	50	35	70	25	10	100	20	
	♥	7	75	50	200	75	5	275	50	25	25	100	10	50	
	♦	10	100	10	25	25	1	40	15	50	50	50	35	100	Donations in
	♣	25	50	25	50	35	32	20	25	200	10	30	20	25	Dollars
Tails	♠	100	100	20	57	10	100	5	25	10	20	25	250		
	♥	25	25	15	100	30	20	25	50	5	25	20	50		
	♦	25	100	10	40	25	50	20	20	35	20	15	100		
	♣	25	25	200	10	25	150	20	25	50	25	150	25		

a) Flip a coin and draw a card from the deck. Use the headings in the table to obtain the corresponding contribution. Do this 10 times to obtain a random sample of 10 contributions.
b) For your sample, find the mean, the median, and the mode.
c) Compare your results in (b) with the results for the entire population of 100 contributions, which are given in the answer section.

 INVESTIGATE

Determine how the results of *Exercises 4* and *5* are affected if the samples are
a) smaller   b) larger than those specified.

MATHEMATICS AROUND US

Estimating Wildlife Populations

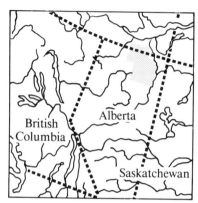

Wood Buffalo National Park

One of the world's largest surviving buffalo herds lives in Wood Buffalo National Park which is on the boundary between Alberta and the Northwest Territories. It is estimated that there are about 12 000 buffaloes in the park. This number is determined by scientists who use a *capture-recapture* sampling technique.

The capture-recapture sampling technique is based on the assumption that if enough members of a wildlife population are captured, tagged, and released, any sufficiently large sample of that population will contain the same proportion of tagged individuals as the entire population. One year, scientists captured, tagged, and released 300 buffaloes in Wood Buffalo National Park. The next year they captured 1000 buffaloes and found that 25 had tags. From this data, they estimated the number of buffaloes in the park as follows:

Let n represent the number of buffaloes in the park. Proportion of tagged buffaloes in the entire population:

$$\frac{300}{n}$$

Proportion of tagged buffaloes in the sample:

$$\frac{25}{1000}$$

If the sample is representative of the population, then:

$$\frac{25}{1000} = \frac{300}{n}$$

$$25n = 300\ 000$$

$$n = 12\ 000$$

There are about 12 000 buffaloes in the park.

QUESTIONS

1. a) What assumptions are made about the buffaloes in the park, and their movements, in the above calculation?

   b) What is the least number of buffaloes there could be?

2. A game warden nets and tags 250 lake trout in Fairy Lake. Two months later she nets 150 lake trout and finds that 30 of them are tagged. Estimate the number of lake trout in Fairy Lake.

3. Biologists, studying the migratory patterns of Canada geese, tag 1425 of the birds in the month of October. The next year, they capture 760 Canada geese and find that 285 are tagged. About how many Canada geese are in that region in October?

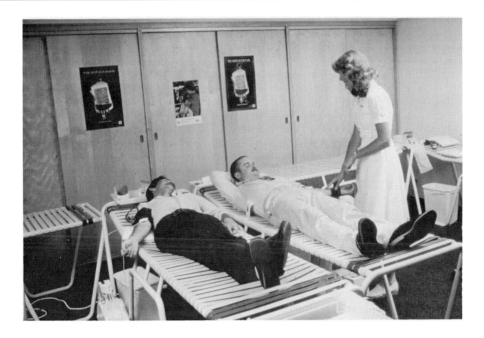

13-8 SAMPLING AND PREDICTING

One of the principal uses of statistics is to make predictions. For example, suppose it is necessary to know the number of Canadians with type O blood. It is clearly not possible to check the blood types of all Canadians. Instead, a sample is tested. From the results, the number of Canadians with type O blood can be predicted.

If, in a sample of 2000 Canadians, 900 have type O blood, the relative frequency of type O blood is $\frac{900}{2000}$, or 0.45.

In a population of 25 000 000, the number of Canadians with type O blood would be about:

$$0.45 \times 25\ 000\ 000, \text{ or } 11\ 250\ 000$$

If an outcome, A, occurs r times in n repetitions of an experiment, then the *relative frequency* of A is $\frac{r}{n}$.

The accuracy of a prediction depends on the sample being a random sample.

Example. A jar contains 3000 white, black, and red beads. The beads are thoroughly mixed and a sample of 60 taken. The sample is found to contain 17 white beads, 32 black beads, and 11 red beads. Estimate the number of beads of each color in the jar.

Solution. White: Relative frequency: $\dfrac{17}{60}$

Estimated number in jar: $\dfrac{17}{60} \times 3000$, or 850

Black: Relative frequency: $\dfrac{32}{60}$

Estimated number in jar: $\dfrac{32}{60} \times 3000$, or 1600

Red: Relative frequency: $\dfrac{11}{60}$

Estimated number in jar: $\dfrac{11}{60} \times 3000$, or 550

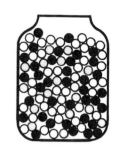

The answers given in the above example are only estimates of the number of beads of each color. If other samples are taken, the results may differ. For a more reliable estimate, it would be necessary to take several samples and find the mean of the results.

EXERCISES 13-8

(A)

1. A class tossed pennies a total of 36 000 times. Heads occurred 17 563 times. What was the relative frequency of heads?

2. A die was rolled 7200 times. The frequency of each outcome is shown in the table. What was the relative frequency of each outcome? Do you think it was a fair die? Explain.

Outcome	⚀	⚁	⚂	⚃	⚄	⚅
Frequency	1175	1225	1142	1168	1273	1217

3. A pair of dice was rolled 5350 times. A pair of 6s occurred 140 times. What was the relative frequency of a pair of 6s?

4. When a thumbtack is tossed, there are two possible outcomes. If the relative frequency of "point up" is found to be 0.62, what should the relative frequency of "point down" be?

point up   point down

(B)

5. a) Toss a coin 50 times and record the frequency of heads.
   b) Calculate the relative frequency of heads.
   c) Combine your results with those of other students to obtain the relative frequency of heads for a greater number of tosses.
   d) How does the relative frequency of heads compare with 0.5 as the number of tosses increases?

6. Choose 10 consecutive lines from a magazine story or newspaper article. Count the number of words and the number of syllables in each word. What is the relative frequency of words containing one syllable? more than two syllables?

7. a) Use a paper cup to shake and toss 5 coins. Record the number of heads.
   b) Repeat part (a) 19 times.
   c) Calculate the relative frequency of each outcome.
   d) Combine your results with other students' to obtain more accurate values.
   e) Based on these results, if 5 coins were tossed 1280 times, about how many times would you expect to get 1 head? 3 heads? 5 heads?

8. a) Toss two dice 25 times and record the results.
   b) Combine your results with those of at least three other students.
   c) Based on these results, if two dice were tossed 750 times, how many times would you expect them to show a sum of 7? a sum of 11? a product of 12?

9. A dental survey of 360 students in Glentown High School revealed that 135 of them had two or more cavities. If the total school enrolment is 1656, about how many students would you expect to have two or more cavities?

10. The table shows the blood types of a random sample of Inuits. Estimate the number of Inuits with each blood type in a population of 1850.

Blood Type	O	A	B	AB
Number of Inuits	75	59	14	8

(C)

11. In a random survey, 240 homeowners in each of towns *A* and *B* were asked if they used a water softener. 80 in town *A* and 66 in town *B* said they did. In which town should a manufacturer of water softeners concentrate his sales efforts if the populations of the towns are *A*, 4620; *B*, 5265? *A*, 8430; *B*, 7856?

12. A jar contains 1250 red, blue, and yellow marbles. Ten marbles are taken out at random and their colors recorded. This is done eight times, the marbles being returned to the jar after each draw. From the following table of results, estimate the number of marbles of each color in the jar.

Draw	1st	2nd	3rd	4th	5th	6th	7th	8th
Red	5	3	3	1	3	4	2	4
Blue	2	2	3	2	3	1	2	0
Yellow	3	5	4	7	4	5	6	6

13. a) Count the number of photographs on any 20 pages in this book.
    b) Use the result of (a) to predict the number of photographs in the whole book.
    c) Combine your results with those of others to obtain a more accurate prediction of the total number of photographs.

13-9 PROBABILITY

Every day we encounter statements such as the following:

"There is a 20% chance of rain tomorrow."

"The chance of winning a prize in the draw is 1 in 50."

This means that in the past, when weather conditions have resembled present conditions, there has been rain in 20% of the cases.

This means that the ratio of the number of winning tickets to the total number of tickets is $\frac{1}{50}$.

"The probability of drawing a spade from a well-shuffled deck of cards is 0.25."

This last statement follows from the fact that 13 of the 52 cards in a deck of cards are spades. If a card is drawn, there are 52 equally likely outcomes, of which 13 are favorable. We say that the probability of drawing a spade is $\frac{13}{52}$, and we write:

$$P(\text{spade}) = \frac{13}{52}$$
$$= \frac{1}{4}$$
$$= 0.25$$

Any outcome, or set of outcomes, of an experiment is called an *event*.

> If an experiment has n equally likely outcomes of which r are favorable to event A, then the *probability* of event A is:
>
> $$P(A) = \frac{r}{n}$$

Example 1. A card is drawn from a well-shuffled deck. Find the probability that the card is:

  a) a club   b) an ace   c) a red card   d) the 7♣

Solution. There are 52 cards and each has the same chance of being drawn.

  a) There are 13 clubs.   b) There are 4 aces.

$$P(\text{club}) = \frac{13}{52}$$ $$P(\text{ace}) = \frac{4}{52}$$

$$= \frac{1}{4}$$ $$= \frac{1}{13}$$

$$= 0.25$$ $$\doteq 0.077$$

  c) There are 26 red cards.   d) There is one 7♣.

$$P(\text{red card}) = \frac{26}{52}$$ $$P(7\clubsuit) = \frac{1}{52}$$

$$= \frac{1}{2}$$ $$\doteq 0.019$$

$$= 0.5$$

Example 2. If a die is thrown 300 times, about how many times should it show 5?

Solution. Since $P(5) = \frac{1}{6}$, the die should show 5 *about* $\frac{1}{6} \times 300$, or 50 times.

The result of *Example 2* does not mean that 5 is likely to appear 50 times. It means that the number of 5's should be around 50. The probability that 5 appears exactly 50 times is only about 0.06.

EXERCISES 13-9

Ⓐ

1. A card is drawn from a well-shuffled deck of cards. What is the probability that the card drawn will be
    a) a heart?   b) black?   c) a 5?
    d) a red jack?   e) an ace   f) a black 3, 6, or 9?

2. If one letter is selected at random from the word "mathematics", what is the probability that it will be
    a) an "m"?   b) an "e"   c) a vowel?
    d) a consonant?   e) an "o"?   f) a "t" or an "h"?

3. Nashila buys 3 tickets for a Student-Council Christmas draw. What is the probability of her winning if the number of tickets sold is
    a) 360?   b) 600?   c) 945?

4. A lottery issues 100 000 tickets. What is the probability of your winning if the number of tickets you hold is
    a) 1?   b) 10?   c) 120?   d) none?   e) 100 000?

5. A die is tossed. What is the probability that the die shows
   a) a 3?
   b) an even number?
   c) a perfect square?
   d) a prime number?

6. When the wheel is spun, what is the probability it will stop with the arrow pointing to
   a) a 4?
   b) an odd number?
   c) a prime number?
   d) a number divisible by 3?
   e) a number greater than 5?
   f) a number less than 8?
   g) a two-digit number?
   h) a one-digit number?

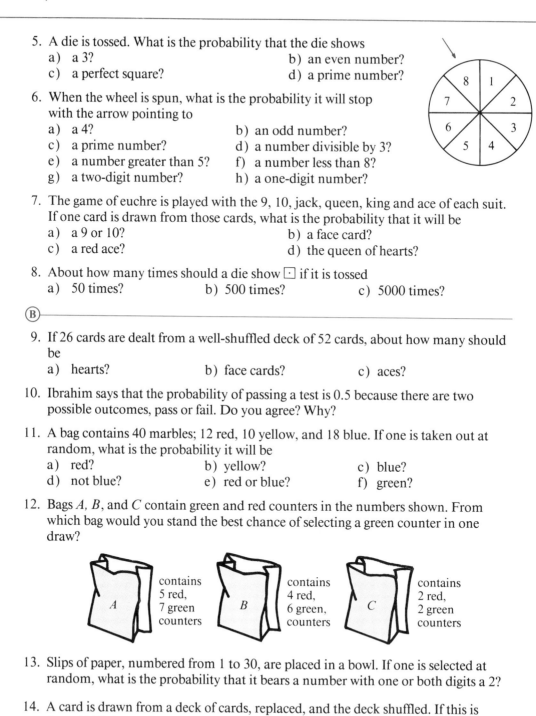

7. The game of euchre is played with the 9, 10, jack, queen, king and ace of each suit. If one card is drawn from those cards, what is the probability that it will be
   a) a 9 or 10?
   b) a face card?
   c) a red ace?
   d) the queen of hearts?

8. About how many times should a die show ⊡ if it is tossed
   a) 50 times?
   b) 500 times?
   c) 5000 times?

Ⓑ

9. If 26 cards are dealt from a well-shuffled deck of 52 cards, about how many should be
   a) hearts?
   b) face cards?
   c) aces?

10. Ibrahim says that the probability of passing a test is 0.5 because there are two possible outcomes, pass or fail. Do you agree? Why?

11. A bag contains 40 marbles; 12 red, 10 yellow, and 18 blue. If one is taken out at random, what is the probability it will be
    a) red?
    b) yellow?
    c) blue?
    d) not blue?
    e) red or blue?
    f) green?

12. Bags *A, B,* and *C* contain green and red counters in the numbers shown. From which bag would you stand the best chance of selecting a green counter in one draw?

A contains 5 red, 7 green counters

B contains 4 red, 6 green, counters

C contains 2 red, 2 green counters

13. Slips of paper, numbered from 1 to 30, are placed in a bowl. If one is selected at random, what is the probability that it bears a number with one or both digits a 2?

14. A card is drawn from a deck of cards, replaced, and the deck shuffled. If this is done 1000 times, about how many times should the card drawn be
    a) black?
    b) a queen?
    c) a diamond?
    d) the ace of spades?

15. In the game "In Between", the value of the third card dealt must be in between the first two in order to win. What is the probability of winning if the two cards already dealt are

a) a 2 and a 6?   b) a 5 and a queen?

c) a 7 and an 8?   d) the jack and a king?

16. The table shows the distribution of blood types among Canadians.

a) Determine the probability that a person selected at random will have

i) type AB blood

ii) either type A or type B blood

iii) neither type A nor type O blood

Blood Type	O	A	B	AB
Percent of Canadians	45%	40%	11%	4%

b) About how many Canadians in a sample of 100 000 would you expect to have type B blood?

c) A hospital tries to keep 35 bottles of type AB blood on hand. About how many bottles of type A should be kept on hand?

Ⓒ

17. The table shows how the blood types of donor and patient must be matched. The check marks indicate compatible combinations of blood types. Use this table and the one in the previous exercise to find the probability that a person selected at random may give blood to a person with

a) type A blood

b) type B blood

Patient

Donor		O	A	B	AB
	O	✓	✓	✓	✓
	A		✓		✓
	B			✓	✓
	AB				✓

18. Our calendar repeats itself every 400 years. There are 4800 months during this period. The 13th day of the month in each of these 4800 months occurs on the day of the week indicated by the following table.

Day of Week	Sun.	Mon.	Tue.	Wed.	Thu.	Fri.	Sat.
How often the 13th day of the month occurs on this day	687	685	685	687	684	688	684

a) Using the above table, find the probability that the 13th day of the month will occur on a Friday.

b) Is this probability greater than, less than, or equal to the probability of it falling on any other day of the week?

c) What is the probability that the first day of the month falls on a Sunday?

13-10 THE PROBABILITY OF TWO OR MORE EVENTS

Suppose that a coin and die are tossed. What is the probability that the coin shows heads and the die shows an even number?

The *tree diagram* shows that there are 12 possible outcomes. The event that the coin shows heads and the die shows an even number has three favorable outcomes: H2, H4, H6.

$P(\text{heads and even number}) = \dfrac{3}{12}$

$= \dfrac{1}{4}$

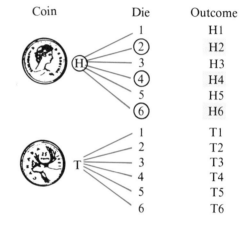

Another way of finding this probability is to notice that the number of outcomes involving heads is one-half the total number of outcomes, and the number of outcomes involving an even number is also one-half the total number of outcomes.

$P(\text{heads and even number}) = \dfrac{1}{2} \times \dfrac{1}{2}$

$= \dfrac{1}{4}$

The probability of two or more events is the product of the probability of each event.

Example 1. A die is tossed three times. What is the probability that it shows 5 or greater each time?

Solution. For each toss, $P(5 \text{ or greater}) = \dfrac{2}{6}$

$= \dfrac{1}{3}$

$P(5 \text{ or greater on all 3 tosses}) = \dfrac{1}{3} \times \dfrac{1}{3} \times \dfrac{1}{3}$

$= \dfrac{1}{27}$

When a die is tossed several times, the outcomes are independent of each other. Care must be taken in calculating the probability of two or more events when the outcomes are related.

Example 2. A bag contains 5 black balls and 5 red balls. Find the probability of drawing 2 red balls in succession if the first ball is
   a) replaced before drawing the second   b) not replaced

Solution.   a) *First draw*: There are 10 balls of which 5 are red.

$$P(\text{red}) = \frac{5}{10}$$

$$= \frac{1}{2}$$

Second draw: There are 10 balls of which 5 are red.

$$P(\text{red}) = \frac{5}{10}$$

$$= \frac{1}{2}$$

$$P(2 \text{ reds in succession}) = \frac{1}{2} \times \frac{1}{2}$$

$$= \frac{1}{4}$$

$$= 0.25$$

   b) $$P(\text{red on first draw}) = \frac{1}{2}$$

Second draw: There are 9 balls of which 4 are red.

$$P(\text{red on second draw}) = \frac{4}{9}$$

$$P(2 \text{ reds in succession}) = \frac{1}{2} \times \frac{4}{9}$$

$$= \frac{2}{9}$$

$$\doteq 0.22$$

EXERCISES 13-10

1. A coin and a regular tetrahedron (with faces marked 1, 2, 3, 4) are tossed. Draw a tree diagram to find the probability of getting a
   a) head and a 2
   b) tail and a perfect square

2. What is the probability of two tossed dice showing a sum of 12?

3. What is the probability of tossing four coins and getting four heads?

4. If it is equally likely that a child be born a girl or a boy, what is the probability that a family of
   a) three children will be all girls?   b) six children will be all boys?

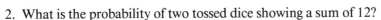

Ⓑ

5. A baseball player has a batting average of 0.300.
   a) What is the probability that the player has a hit each time he comes to bat?
   b) If he comes to bat four times in the next game, what is the probability that he has 4 hits? no hits?

6. A weather report gives the chance of rain on both days of the weekend as 80%. If this is correct, what is the probability that
   a) there is rain on both days?   b) it does not rain on either day?

7. A multiple-choice test has 4 questions. Each has 5 responses, only one of which is correct. If all the questions are attempted by guessing, what is the probability of getting all 4 right?

8. A bag contains 3 red balls and 5 green balls. Find the probability of drawing 2 green balls in succession if the first ball
   a) is replaced before drawing the second   b) is not replaced

9. Repeat the previous exercise for a bag containing
   a) 4 red balls and 6 green balls
   b) 5 red balls and 4 green balls
   c) 8 red balls and 12 green balls

10. A meal at a fast-food outlet has the following types of choices. If a choice is made at random, what is the probability that a meal will include a
    a) hamburger?   b) hot dog and a shake?   c) cheeseburger, a shake, and cookies?

    a hamburger, cheeseburger, or hot dog
    a soft drink or shake
    a sundae, a piece of pie, or cookies.

11. Two cards are drawn from a well-shuffled deck. Find the probability that they are both spades; both aces; both face cards if the first card is
    a) replaced before the second is drawn   b) not replaced

12. In the SCRABBLE® Crossword Game, the letters of the alphabet are distributed over 100 tiles as shown in the table. Two tiles are selected simultaneously from a full bag of tiles. What is the probability that they are both

    a) "B"?   b) "E"?   c) vowels?

Distribution of Tiles		
A—9	J—1	S—4
B—2	K—1	T—6
C—2	L—4	U—4
D—4	M—2	V—2
E—12	N—6	W—2
F—2	O—8	X—1
G—3	P—2	Y—2
H—2	Q—1	Z—1
I—9	R—6	Blank—2

13. The word "Mathematics" is spelled out with SCRABBLE® Crossword tiles and the tiles are put in a bag. What is the probability that two tiles drawn simultaneously will be both vowels? both consonants? both "M"?

©

14. In basketball, a player given a one-and-one foul shot is given a second shot only if the first is successful. Thus, the player can score 0, 1, or 2 points in this situation. If the player shoots with 75% accuracy, find the probability that she will score
    a) 0 points   b) 1 point   c) 2 points

15. What is the probability that two persons selected at random would both have birthdays in February? the same month? (What assumption are you making?)

16. Five dice are tossed simultaneously. Find the probability that
    a) they all show 6   b) no die shows 6
    c) no die shows 5 or 6   d) they all show the same number

17. Cards are dealt until a jack appears. What is the probability that the first jack is the
    a) second card?   b) third card?

18. Cards are dealt until a heart appears. What is the probability that the first heart is the
    a) second card?   b) third card?

19. What is the probability of getting two heads two times in a row when tossing two coins?

20. A rare astronomical event occurred on March 10, 1982. On that day, the nine planets were closer together than they have been in the last 500 years. Viewed from the sun, they were all located within a 98° arc, as illustrated. What is the probability that all nine planets will lie within a 98° arc?

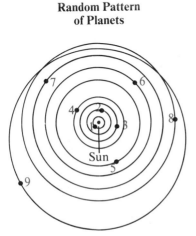

Random Pattern of Planets

1. Mercury
2. Venus
3. Earth
4. Mars
5. Jupiter
6. Saturn
7. Uranus
8. Neptune
9. Pluto

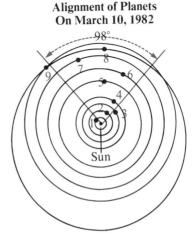

Alignment of Planets On March 10, 1982

   PROBLEM SOLVING

Consider All Cases

Janet and Barry toss a coin to decide who will pay for lunch in a restaurant. Barry offers to toss the coin three times. If heads come up exactly two times out of three, Barry will pay for lunch. Otherwise, Janet will pay. Is this fair? If not, whom does it favor?

Understand the problem

- What does "exactly two times out of three" mean?
- What are you asked to find out?

Think of a strategy

- List all the different ways the coin could fall when it is tossed three times.

Carry out the strategy

Case 1.   All three are heads.   H H H

Case 2.   Two out of three are heads.
This can happen in three ways.   H H T   H T H   T H H

Case 3.   One out of three is a head.
This can happen in three ways.   H T T   T H T   T T H

Case 4.   All three are tails.   T T T

- There are 8 possibilities. For only 3 of these possibilities will Barry pay for lunch, that is, H H T, H T H and T H H. It is not a fair deal for Janet who is more likely to end up paying!

Look back

- Would it be fair if Barry paid when heads came up at least two out of three times?
- What other condition could be equally fair?

Solve each problem

1. When deciding who will pay for lunch, Janet suggests tossing a coin 4 times. She says that if exactly one head or exactly one tail comes up, she will pay for lunch. Is this fair to Barry?

2. The left side of the equation below contains the digits from 1 to 9 in increasing order, and three plus or minus signs.
$$12 - 345 - 6 + 789 = 450$$
Find an equation like this one, in which the result is 100.

3. The left side of the equation below contains the digits from 1 to 9 in increasing order, and *only* addition signs.
$$12 + 3 + 4 + 56 + 7 + 8 + 9 = 99$$
   a) Find another example like this, in which the result is 99.
   b) Write a similar equation in which the digits from 1 to 9 are written in decreasing order and the result is also 99.

4. Decide whether the numbered statement is true, false, or neither true nor false.

   a) 1. Statement 3 in this list is true.
      2. Statement 3 in this list is false.
      3. Their is one spelling misteak in this list.

   b) 1. Statement 2 in this list is true.
      2. Statement 1 in this list is false.

5. Twelve congruent squares are arranged to form a rectangle. If the perimeter of the rectangle is 145.6 cm, find all the possible dimensions of the squares.

6. Imagine that you are eating lunch with a friend in a restaurant. To decide who will pay, your friend suggests tossing two dice with faces marked as shown. When the dice are tossed, the person whose die has the lower number pays for lunch. Your friend offers you the choice of one of the dice. Would you prefer to roll the red die or the white die?

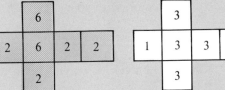

7. An equilateral triangle is divided into 16 congruent equilateral triangles. In the figure,
   a) how many triangles are there?
   b) how many rhombuses are there?
   c) how many parallelograms are there?

8. a) How many line segments of different lengths can be drawn joining two vertices of a cube?
   b) If the length of an edge of a cube is 1 unit, find the length of each segment in part (a).

1. This bar graph illustrates the modes of transportation of Grade 10 students at one secondary school.
   a) How many more students walk than travel by school bus?
   b) How many students travel by bicycle or car?
   c) How many students are there in Grade 10?

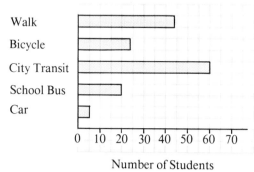

Travelling to School

Number of Students

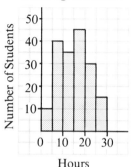

Hours per Week Spent Watching Television

2. The histogram shows the results of a survey of student television-viewing habits. From the histogram, determine how many students

   a) took part in the survey
   b) watch television 15 h per week or less
   c) watch more than 20 h

3. Mike works at a swimming pool during the summer. The various jobs are shown in the circle graph. If he works a 45 h week, how many hours are spent in

   a) life guarding
   b) instructing
   c) cashier and maintenance
   d) neither guarding nor instructing?

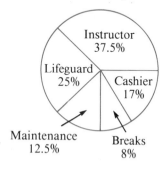

How Mike's Time at Work is Spent

Instructor 37.5%

Lifeguard 25%

Cashier 17%

Maintenance 12.5%

Breaks 8%

4. This stem-and-leaf diagram shows the marks obtained by students on a science test.

   a) How many students received a mark of 57? 67? 77?
   b) How many students received a mark of 76 or higher?
   c) What was the most frequently-occurring mark?
   d) How many students took the test?

4	8
5	7 3 8 7
6	0 4 2 7 6 7 3 8 7
7	8 6 0 5 9 3 4 4 2
8	0 7 3 8 6
9	1 4

5. From the set of final marks in Mathematics, construct a
   a) stem-and-leaf diagram
   b) frequency table using 10 mark intervals
   c) histogram

65	37	84	60	44	52	58	87
58	77	42	92	74	55	62	67
73	55	62	56	65	78	46	64
62	68	77	82	57	66	72	56

6. Construct a circle graph to illustrate the following data.

Favorite Sport	
Hockey	64
Football	52
Basketball	44
Tennis	36
Swimming	24
Soccer	20

7. Find the mean, median, and mode of the set of final marks in Mathematics in *Exercise 5*.

8. a) Construct a scatterplot for the data below.
   b) Draw a median fit line and use it to predict the number of immigrants in 1991.

9. a) Construct a scatterplot for the data below.
   b) Construct a smoothed table of values.
   c) Draw a smoothed graph.

   Immigration to Canada (thousands)

Year		Year		Year	
1971	122	1976	149	1981	129
1972	122	1977	115	1982	121
1973	184	1978	86	1983	89
1974	218	1979	112	1984	88
1975	188	1980	143	1985	84

   Canadian Interest Rates (Savings)

Year	(%)	Year	(%)	Year	(%)
1974	8.5	1978	7.1	1982	11.5
1975	8.0	1979	10.1	1983	6.9
1976	7.8	1980	11.2	1984	7.7
1977	6.0	1981	15.4	1985	6.1

10. The 32 students in Mrs. Wilson's class recorded their heights, to the nearest centimetre as follows.

168	156	172	164	175	182	191	162
158	164	148	176	155	176	174	180
167	178	176	190	175	181	167	174
171	186	180	176	165	170	182	162

    a) Obtain a random sample of six heights, using any appropriate method.
    b) For your sample find the mean, the median, and the mode.
    c) Compare your results in (b) with the results for the entire population of 32 students which are given in the answer section.

11. A pair of dice was rolled 5400 times. A pair of 6s occurred 144 times. What was the relative frequency of a pair of 6s?

12. A survey of 225 students at Richmond Secondary School revealed that 65 of the students received an allowance of $10 or more per week. If the total student population is 1350 students, how many would you expect to receive $10 or more per week in allowance?

13. A card is drawn from a well-shuffled deck of cards. What is the probability that the card drawn will be
    a) a diamond?　　　　b) red?　　　　　　　c) a 7?
    d) a black queen?　　 e) a 2, 5, or 8?　　　 f) a red 2, 5, or 8?

14. A bag contains 30 marbles; 6 red, 9 yellow, and 15 blue. If one is taken out at random, what is the probability that it will be
    a) red?　　　　　　　 b) yellow?　　　　　 c) blue?
    d) not yellow?　　　　e) yellow or blue?　　f) green?

15. A die is tossed. What is the probability that the die shows a
    a) 4?　　　　　　　　　　　　 b) number greater than 4?
    c) number less than 4?　　　　 d) number divisible by 3?

16. A bag contains 5 red balls and 7 yellow balls. Find the probability of drawing 2 yellow balls in succession if the first ball
    a) is replaced before drawing the second
    b) is not replaced

17. Two cards are drawn from a well-shuffled deck. Find the probability that they are both clubs; both kings; both red face cards if the first card
    a) is replaced before the second is drawn
    b) is not replaced

18. The letters in "Manitoba" are written on separate slips of paper and placed in a bag. What is the probability that two slips drawn simultaneously will both show
    a) vowels?　　　　　　b) consonants?　　　　　c) "a"?

19. A case of 150 flash cubes is known to contain 5 defective ones. If 2 cubes are taken from the box, what is the probability that both are defective?

20. The faces of two regular tetrahedrons are numbered 1 to 4. If they are tossed, what is the probability of the bottom faces

    a) being a pair?　　　　　　 b) having a total of 6?
    c) having a difference of 1?　 d) having a total of 9?

14 Trigonometry

Suppose you know the distance between two office towers. By taking measurements from the window of one tower, how can you find the height of the other tower? (See *Example 2* in Section 14-5).

14-1 SIMILAR TRIANGLES

In this photograph, the triangles have the same shape. For this reason, we say that the triangles are similar. If $\triangle ABC$ and $\triangle PQR$ are similar, we write $\triangle ABC \sim \triangle PQR$. This means that:

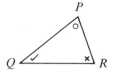

Corresponding angles are equal.

$\angle A = \angle P$

$\angle B = \angle Q$

$\angle C = \angle R$

Ratios of corresponding sides are equal.

$$\frac{AB}{PQ} = \frac{BC}{QR} = \frac{AC}{PR}$$

However, it is not necessary to know this much information to be certain that two triangles are similar. It is sufficient to know that two pairs of corresponding angles are equal. For example, if $\angle B = \angle Q$ and $\angle C = \angle R$, then since the sum of the angles in a triangle is 180°, $\angle A = \angle P$ and the triangles are similar.

If two angles of one triangle are equal to two angles of another triangle, then the triangles are *similar*, and corresponding sides have the same ratio.

$$\triangle ABC \sim \triangle DEF$$

and

$$\frac{AB}{DE} = \frac{BC}{EF} = \frac{AC}{DF}$$

Example 1. In $\triangle MRC$ and $\triangle JAQ$, $\angle R = \angle A$ and $\angle C = \angle Q = 90°$.

a) Explain why $\triangle MRC \sim \triangle JAQ$.

b) Use the dimensions given on the diagram to find the length of JQ.

Solution.

a) Since $\angle R = \angle A$, $\angle C = \angle Q$, and the sum of the angles in a triangle is $180°$, $\angle M = \angle J$. Therefore, $\triangle MRC \sim \triangle JAQ$.

b) Since $\triangle MRC \sim \triangle JAQ$:

$$\frac{MR}{JA} = \frac{RC}{AQ} = \frac{MC}{JQ}$$

Substitute the given lengths:

$$\frac{MR}{JA} = \frac{16.8}{22.4} = \frac{9.9}{JQ}$$

$$16.8JQ = 22.4(9.9)$$

$$JQ = \frac{22.4(9.9)}{16.8}$$

$$= 13.2$$

The length of JQ is 13.2 m.

Frequently, similar triangles overlap, as illustrated in the next example.

Example 2. A photographer took this photograph by standing 50 m from a smokestack and aligning it with the 360 m level of the CN tower. How high is the smokestack if it is 400 m from the tower?

Solution. Construct the following diagram, where x represents the height of the smokestack.

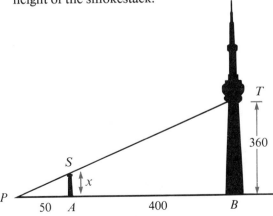

In △SPA and △TPB:

$$\angle SPA = \angle TPB$$
$$\angle SAP = \angle TBP$$

Therefore, △SPA ~ △TPB, and

$$\frac{SP}{TP} = \frac{PA}{PB} = \frac{SA}{TB}$$

$$\frac{50}{450} = \frac{x}{360}$$

$$450x = 50(360)$$

$$x = \frac{50(360)}{450}$$

$$= 40$$

The smokestack is 40 m high.

EXERCISES 14-1

Ⓐ

1. Write the ratios of corresponding sides.

a)

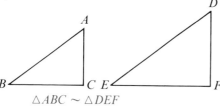

△ABC ~ △DEF

b)

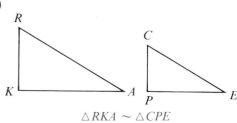

△RKA ~ △CPE

c)

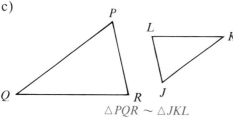

△PQR ~ △JKL

d)

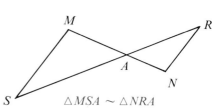

△MSA ~ △NRA

2. Write the ratios of corresponding sides, and then find the value of x.

a)

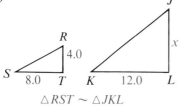

△RST ~ △JKL

b)

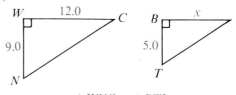

△WNC ~ △BTL

c)

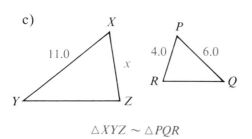

$\triangle XYZ \sim \triangle PQR$

d)

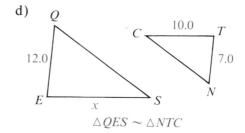

$\triangle QES \sim \triangle NTC$

3. Explain why $\triangle AEC \sim \triangle BED$.

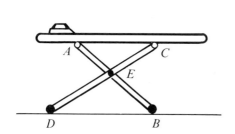

4. Explain why $\triangle PST \sim \triangle PQR$.

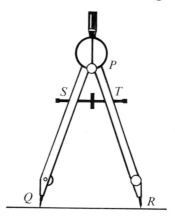

B

5. Explain why the triangles are similar, and then find the values of x and y.

a)

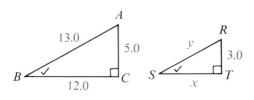

b)

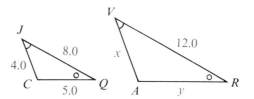

c)

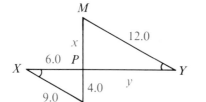

d)

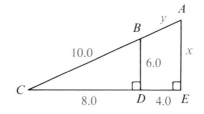

6. Find the values of *x* and *y*.

a)

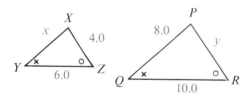
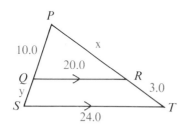

b)

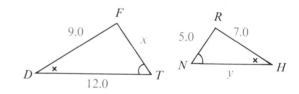
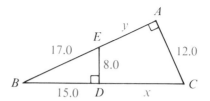

c)

d)

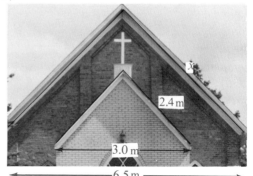

7. Find the distance marked *x* in each photograph below.

a)

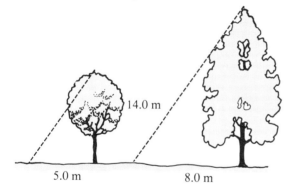

b)

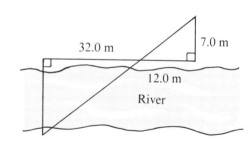

8. Two trees cast shadows as shown. How tall is the evergreen tree?

9. How far is it across the river?

10. How far is it across the pond?

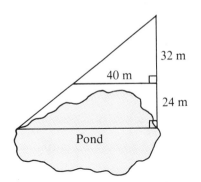

Pond

32 m

40 m

24 m

11. How high are the two supports for the conveyor?

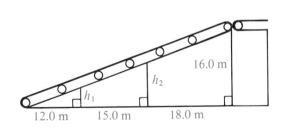

16.0 m

h_2

h_1

12.0 m   15.0 m   18.0 m

Ⓒ

12. Two triangles have vertices $A(-2, 6)$, $B(-6, 0)$, $C(2, 2)$ and $D(7, 6)$, $E(1, -3)$, $F(13, 0)$.
    a) Graph the triangles and calculate the lengths of all their sides.
    b) Determine the ratios of corresponding sides. Are the triangles similar?
    c) Measure the angles in each triangle. Are corresponding angles equal?

13. In $\triangle ABC$, $FE \parallel BC$ and $FD \parallel AC$. Explain why $\triangle AFE$, $\triangle FBD$ and $\triangle ABC$ are all similar to each other.

14. The diagram below shows the floor plan of an auditorium, which has 26 rows. Only the first row and every fifth row after the first are shown. There are 60 seats in the first row, and the rows are 1 m apart.
    a) How many seats are there in Row F? Row K? Row P? Row U? Row Z?
    b) Estimate the total number of seats in the auditorium.

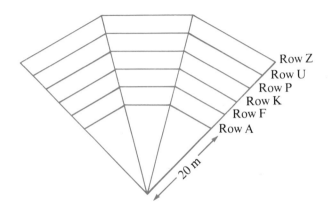

Row Z
Row U
Row P
Row K
Row F
Row A

20 m

15. △*ABC* is a right triangle in which ∠*A* = 90°.
    D is a point on the hypotenuse *BC* such that
    AD is perpendicular to *BC*. The lengths of the
    line segments on the diagram are represented
    by lower case letters, as shown.
    a) Explain why all three triangles on the dia-
       gram are similar to one another.
    b) Show that $c^2 = ax$ and $b^2 = ay$.
    c) Use the result of (b) to prove the Pythagorean
       Theorem.

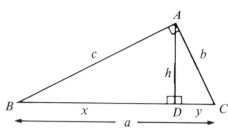

16. In the diagram of *Exercise 15*, how are *h*, *x*, and *y* related?

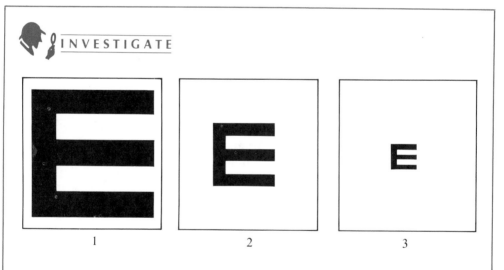

1	2	3

When testing a patient's eyes, one doctor uses these three cards. Card 2 is
placed 3.0 m from the patient. The other two cards are placed so that the
letter E on them will appear to be the same size to the patient as the E on
Card 2.

1. By taking measurements from the diagrams, predict how far Card 1 and Card 3
   should be placed from the patient, if the patient's vision is normal.

2. Trace the three cards and carry out the test with a partner. Do the results confirm
   your predictions in *Question 1*?

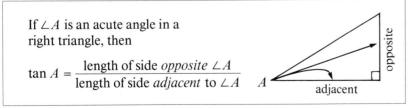

14-2 THE TANGENT RATIO IN RIGHT TRIANGLES

Many similar right triangles can be seen in this photograph. The diagram at the right shows four similar right triangles overlapping in the same way. The triangles are similar because they all have $\angle A$ in common, and therefore corresponding angles are equal. To check that the triangles are similar, we find the ratios of corresponding sides. We use the sides which are opposite $\angle A$ and the sides which are adjacent to $\angle A$.

$$\frac{BC}{AC} = \frac{3 \text{ m}}{4 \text{ m}} = 0.75 \qquad \frac{DE}{AE} = \frac{6 \text{ m}}{8 \text{ m}} = 0.75$$

$$\frac{FG}{AG} = \frac{9 \text{ m}}{12 \text{ m}} = 0.75 \qquad \frac{HI}{AI} = \frac{12 \text{ m}}{16 \text{ m}} = 0.75$$

The ratios are all equivalent. They depend only on the measure of $\angle A$, and not on the size of the triangles. We call this ratio the *tangent* of $\angle A$, and write it as tan A.

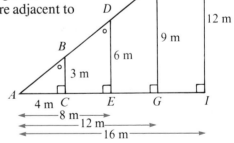

If $\angle A$ is an acute angle in a right triangle, then

$$\tan A = \frac{\text{length of side } opposite \ \angle A}{\text{length of side } adjacent \text{ to } \angle A}$$

Tangents of angles up to 90° can be obtained using the table on page 514, or a scientific calculator. The calculator must be in *degree mode*. Some calculators can be put in degree mode using the key DRG or d-r . Consult your manual if necessary.

Example 1.   Find tan 40°.

Solution.   *Using the table:*   *Using a scientific calculator:*

tan 40°   OR   Press: 40 tan

= 0.839   Result: 0.8390996

The table or a scientific calculator can also be used to find an angle when its tangent is known.

Example 2.   Find $\angle A$ to the nearest degree if

a) $\tan A = 1.319$ b) $\tan A = \dfrac{7}{8}$

Solution.   a)   *Using the table:*   *Using a scientific calculator:*

Find the value in the *tan*   OR   Press: 1.319 inv tan
column closest to 1.319.

or: 1.319 tan⁻¹

tan 52° = 1.280
tan 53° = 1.327   Result: 52.832411

To the nearest degree,   To the nearest degree,
$\angle A = 53°$. $\angle A = 53°$.

b)   Express $\dfrac{7}{8}$ as a decimal:

$$\frac{7}{8} = 0.875$$

Therefore, $\tan A = 0.875$

Using the table, or a scientific calculator, $\angle A \doteq 41°$.

The tangent ratio can be used to determine the unknown angles or sides of a right triangle.

Example 3. In right $\triangle ABC$, find
a) $\tan A$ and $\angle A$ b) $\tan C$ and $\angle C$

Solution. a) The side opposite $\angle A$ is BC. The adjacent side is AB.

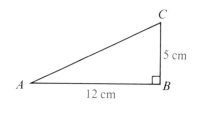

$$\tan A = \frac{BC}{AB}$$

$$= \frac{5}{12}$$

$$\doteq 0.417$$

Using the table, or a scientific calculator, $\angle A \doteq 23°$.

b) The side opposite $\angle C$ is AB. The adjacent side is BC.

$$\tan C = \frac{AB}{BC}$$

$$= \frac{12}{5}$$

$$= 2.400$$

Using the table, or a scientific calculator, $\angle C \doteq 67°$.

Check: The sum of the angles in $\triangle ABC$ should be 180°.

$$23° + 67° + 90° = 180°$$

Example 4. In right $\triangle PQR$, $\angle R = 90°$ and $PR = 7$ cm. Find QR if $\angle Q = 25°$.

Solution. Let x represent the length of QR, in centimetres.

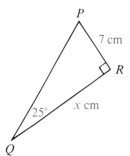

Then, $\dfrac{7}{x} = \tan 25°$

$$\frac{7}{x} \doteq 0.466$$

$$0.466x \doteq 7$$

$$x \doteq \frac{7}{0.466}$$

$$\doteq 15$$

If $\angle Q = 25°$, then $QR \doteq 15$ cm.

Example 5.   When the foot of a ladder is 2.0 m from a wall, the angle formed by the ladder and the ground is 68°.
a) How high up the wall does the ladder reach?
b) How long is the ladder?

Solution.   a) Let d represent the distance the ladder reaches up the wall in metres.

$$\text{Then, } \frac{d}{2.0} = \tan 68°$$

$$\frac{d}{2.0} \doteq 2.475$$

$$d \doteq 2.0(2.475)$$

$$\doteq 4.950$$

The ladder reaches approximately 5.0 m up the wall.

b) Let r represent the length of the ladder, in metres. Then, using the Pythagorean Theorem:

$$r^2 = (2.0)^2 + (4.950)^2$$

$$= 28.5025$$

$$r = \sqrt{28.5025}$$

$$\doteq 5.339$$

The length of the ladder is about 5.3 m.

EXERCISES 14-2

Ⓐ

1. Use the table on page 514, or a scientific calculator, to find
   a) $\tan 20°$ b) $\tan 30°$ c) $\tan 37°$ d) $\tan 45°$
   e) $\tan 55°$ f) $\tan 63°$ g) $\tan 71°$ h) $\tan 86°$

2. Find $\angle A$ to the nearest degree.
   a) $\tan A = 0.700$ b) $\tan A = 0.933$ c) $\tan A = 2.050$ d) $\tan A = 3.271$
   e) $\tan A = 0.250$ f) $\tan A = 0.549$ g) $\tan A = 1.365$ h) $\tan A = 4.556$

3. Find $\angle A$ to the nearest degree.
   a) $\tan A = \frac{1}{2}$ b) $\tan A = \frac{3}{4}$ c) $\tan A = \frac{2}{5}$ d) $\tan A = \frac{3}{5}$

   e) $\tan A = \frac{4}{3}$ f) $\tan A = \frac{5}{2}$ g) $\tan A = \frac{5}{4}$ h) $\tan A = \frac{10}{7}$

4. In each triangle, name the side
   a) opposite $\angle A$ b) adjacent to $\angle A$

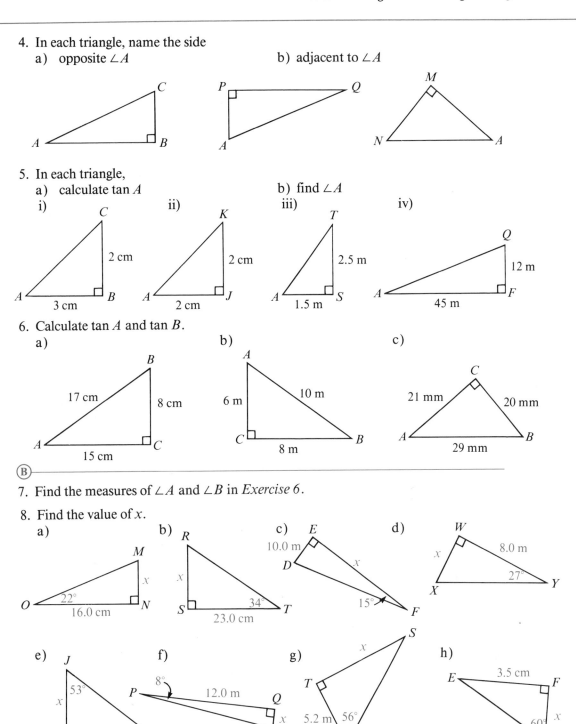

5. In each triangle,
   a) calculate tan A b) find $\angle A$
   i)   ii)   iii)   iv)

6. Calculate tan A and tan B.
   a)   b)   c)

(B)

7. Find the measures of $\angle A$ and $\angle B$ in *Exercise 6*.

8. Find the value of x.
   a)   b)   c)   d)

   e)   f)   g)   h)

9. In △*DEF*, find
   a) *DE* if ∠*F* is   i) 18°   ii) 36°   iii) 54°
   b) ∠*F* if *DE* is   i) 3.0 cm   ii) 6.0 cm   iii) 9.0 cm

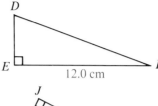

10. In △*JKL*, find
    a) *JL* if ∠*K* is   i) 20°   ii) 30°   iii) 40°
    b) ∠*K* if *JL* is   i) 8.0 m   ii) 12.0 m   iii) 16.0 m

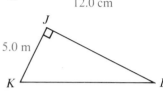

11. A guy wire fastened 40 m from the base of a television tower makes an angle of 60°
    with the ground.
    a) How high up the tower does the guy wire reach?
    b) How long is the guy wire?
    c) Repeat part (a) if the angle of the guy wire is 45°.

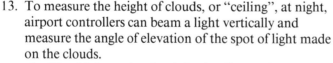

12. A communications tower is 450 m high. From a
    ship at sea, its angle of elevation is 4°.
    a) How far is the ship from the tower?
    b) What would be the angle of elevation if the ship were 25 km from the tower?

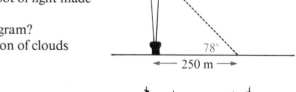

13. To measure the height of clouds, or "ceiling", at night,
    airport controllers can beam a light vertically and
    measure the angle of elevation of the spot of light made
    on the clouds.
    a) How high are the clouds in the diagram?
    b) What would be the angle of elevation of clouds
        500 m high?

14. A gorge of rectangular cross section is 65 m wide. The
    angle of depression of a bottom corner when viewed
    from the opposite edge is 70°.
    a) How deep is the gorge?
    b) What would be the angle of depression if the gorge
        were 100 m deep?

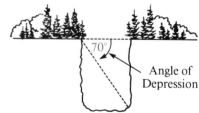

15. Rectangle *ABCD* measures 6 cm by 3 cm. Find the measures of the two acute
    angles formed at *A* by the diagonal *AC*.

16. A helicopter hovers directly over a landing pad on the top of a 125 m high
    building. The angle of elevation of the helicopter to an observer 145 m from the
    base of the building is 58°. How high is the helicopter above the landing pad?

Ⓒ

17. An isosceles $\triangle PQR$ has a base, QR, of length 10 cm and a height of 4 cm. Find the measures of the three angles of the triangle.

18. In isosceles $\triangle ABC$, $AB = AC$, $\angle B = 70°$, and $BC = 4$ cm. Find the height of the triangle to the nearest millimetre.

19. The diagram shows a cone inverted in a cylindrical can with the vertex of the cone just touching the bottom of the can. Find the vertex angle, x, of the cone.

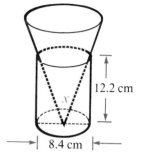

12.2 cm

8.4 cm

20. Find the acute angle formed by the line and the x-axis.
    a)   b)   c)

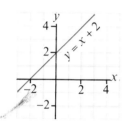
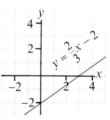
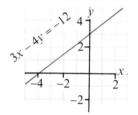

21. Find the obtuse angle formed by the line and the x-axis.
    a)   b)   c)

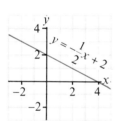
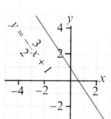
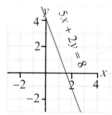

INVESTIGATE

The diagram shows squares arranged side by side to form two rectangles at right angles. The rectangles can be lengthened by adding more squares.
a) Find the angles of elevation of the diagonals shown.
b) How many squares would be needed on the vertical rectangle to have an angle of elevation greater than
    i) 80°?   ii) 85°?   iii) 88°?   iv) 89°?
c) How many squares would be needed on the horizontal rectangle to have an angle of elevation less than
    i) 10°?   ii) 5°?   iii) 2°?   iv) 1°?

14-3 THE SINE AND COSINE RATIOS IN RIGHT TRIANGLES

In the previous section, the tangent ratio was defined in a right triangle in terms of the sides opposite and adjacent to an acute angle. Since a triangle has three sides, there are additional ratios involving the hypotenuse.

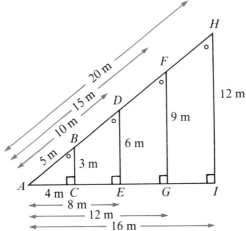

Find the ratios of sides opposite ∠*A* and the hypotenuse.

$$\frac{BC}{AB} = \frac{3 \text{ m}}{5 \text{ m}} \qquad \frac{DE}{AD} = \frac{6 \text{ m}}{10 \text{ m}}$$
$$= 0.6 \qquad\qquad = 0.6$$

$$\frac{FG}{AF} = \frac{9 \text{ m}}{15 \text{ m}} \qquad \frac{HI}{AH} = \frac{12 \text{ m}}{20 \text{ m}}$$
$$= 0.6 \qquad\qquad = 0.6$$

The ratios are all equivalent. We call this ratio the *sine* of ∠*A*, and write it as sin *A*.

Find the ratios of sides adjacent to ∠*A* and the hypotenuse.

$$\frac{AC}{AB} = \frac{4 \text{ m}}{5 \text{ m}} \qquad \frac{AE}{AD} = \frac{8 \text{ m}}{10 \text{ m}}$$
$$= 0.8 \qquad\qquad = 0.8$$

$$\frac{AG}{AF} = \frac{12 \text{ m}}{15 \text{ m}} \qquad \frac{AI}{AH} = \frac{16 \text{ m}}{20 \text{ m}}$$
$$= 0.8 \qquad\qquad = 0.8$$

The ratios are all equivalent. We call this ratio the *cosine* of ∠*A*, and write it as cos *A*.

If ∠*A* is an acute angle in a right triangle, then

$$\sin A = \frac{\text{length of side } \textit{opposite} \ \angle A}{\text{length of hypotenuse}}$$

$$\cos A = \frac{\text{length of side } \textit{adjacent} \text{ to } \angle A}{\text{length of hypotenuse}}$$

Sines and cosines of angles up to 90° can be obtained using the table on page 514, or a scientific calculator in *degree mode*.

Example 1. Find a) sin 25°　　　　　　　b) cos 75°

Solution.　　*Using the table:*　　　　　　*Using a scientific calculator:*

　　　　　　a) sin 25°　　　　　　　　Press:　25 $\boxed{\text{sin}}$
　　　　　　　= 0.423　　　　　　　　Result: 0.4226183

　　　　　　b) cos 75°　　　　　　　　Press:　75 $\boxed{\text{cos}}$
　　　　　　　= 0.259　　　　　　　　Result: 0.2588190

The table or a scientific calculator can also be used to find an angle when its sine or cosine is known.

Example 2. Find $\angle A$ to the nearest degree if

　　　　　a) $\sin A = \dfrac{3}{4}$　　　　　　　　b) $\cos A = \dfrac{1}{3}$

Solution.　　a) Express $\dfrac{3}{4}$ as a decimal:

$$\frac{3}{4} = 0.750$$

　　　　　Using the table:　　　　　　　*Using a scientific calculator:*

　　　　　Find the value in the *sin* column　　Press:　0.750 $\boxed{\text{inv}}$ $\boxed{\text{sin}}$
　　　　　closest to 0.750.
　　　　　sin 48° = 0.743　　　　　　or:　　　0.750 $\boxed{\text{sin}^{-1}}$
　　　　　sin 49° = 0.755

　　　　　　　　　　　　　　　　　Result: 48.590378

　　　　　To the nearest degree,　　　　To the nearest degree,
　　　　　$\angle A = 49°$.　　　　　　　　$\angle A = 49°$.

　　　　b) Express $\dfrac{1}{3}$ as a decimal:

$$\frac{1}{3} \doteq 0.333$$

　　　　Using the *cos* column in the table, or the $\boxed{\text{inv}}$ $\boxed{\text{cos}}$ keys
　　　　on a scientific calculator, $\angle A \doteq 71°$.

The sine and cosine ratios can be used to determine the unknown angles or sides of a right triangle, provided that the length of the hypotenuse is known.

Example 3.   In right $\triangle ABC$, find
  a) $\sin A$ and $\angle A$ b) $\cos A$ and $\angle A$

Solution.   a)   The side opposite $\angle A$ is BC. The hypotenuse is AC.

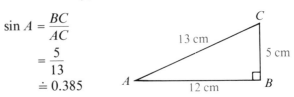

$$\sin A = \frac{BC}{AC}$$
$$= \frac{5}{13}$$
$$\doteq 0.385$$

Using the table, or a scientific calculator, $\angle A \doteq 23°$.

  b)   The side adjacent to $\angle A$ is AB. The hypotenuse is AC.

$$\cos A = \frac{AB}{AC}$$
$$= \frac{12}{13}$$
$$\doteq 0.923$$

Using the table, or a scientific calculator, $\angle A \doteq 23°$.

Example 4.   In right $\triangle PQR$, find the measures of $\angle P$ and $\angle R$ and the length of PQ, to the nearest centimetre.

Solution.   Consider $\angle P$. The 7 cm side is opposite $\angle P$, and the 18 cm side is the hypotenuse. Therefore, use the sine ratio:

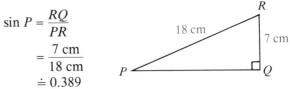

$$\sin P = \frac{RQ}{PR}$$
$$= \frac{7 \text{ cm}}{18 \text{ cm}}$$
$$\doteq 0.389$$

From the table, or a scientific calculator, $\angle P \doteq 23°$.

$$\text{Then } \angle R \doteq 180° - 90° - 23°$$
$$\doteq 67°$$

To find PQ, use $\angle P$ and the cosine ratio:

$$\frac{PQ}{PR} = \cos 23°$$
$$\frac{PQ}{18} \doteq 0.921$$
$$PQ \doteq 18(0.921)$$
$$\doteq 16.6$$

To the nearest centimetre, $PQ = 17$ cm.

Example 5. A guy wire, 20 m long, supports a tower and forms an angle of 57° with the ground. To the nearest metre,
  a) at what height is the guy wire attached to the tower?
  b) how far from the base of the tower is the guy wire attached to the ground?

Solution. a) Let y represent the length of BC.

$$\text{Then, } \frac{y}{20} = \sin 57°$$

$$\frac{y}{20} \doteq 0.839$$

$$y \doteq 20(0.839)$$

$$\doteq 16.78$$

The guy wire is attached to the tower at a height of approximately 17 m.

b) Let x represent the distance AB.

$$\frac{x}{20} = \cos 57°$$

$$\frac{x}{20} \doteq 0.545$$

$$x \doteq 20(0.545)$$

$$\doteq 10.90$$

The guy wire is attached to the ground about 11 m from the base of the tower.

EXERCISES 14-3

(A)

1. Use the table on page 514, or a scientific calculator, to find
   a) $\sin 30°$
   b) $\sin 78°$
   c) $\cos 22°$
   d) $\cos 71°$
   e) $\sin 58°$
   f) $\cos 40°$
   g) $\sin 18°$
   h) $\cos 60°$

2. Find $\angle A$ to the nearest degree.
   a) $\sin A = 0.602$
   b) $\sin A = 0.956$
   c) $\cos A = 0.777$
   d) $\cos A = 0.225$
   e) $\sin A = 0.200$
   f) $\cos A = 0.271$
   g) $\sin A = 0.930$
   h) $\cos A = 0.872$

3. Find $\angle A$ to the nearest degree.
   a) $\cos A = \frac{1}{3}$
   b) $\sin A = \frac{1}{4}$
   c) $\sin A = \frac{1}{2}$
   d) $\cos A = \frac{3}{4}$
   e) $\sin A = \frac{4}{5}$
   f) $\cos A = \frac{3}{7}$
   g) $\sin A = \frac{5}{8}$
   h) $\cos A = \frac{8}{9}$

4. In each triangle, name the side
   a) opposite ∠A   b) adjacent to ∠A   c) which is the hypotenuse

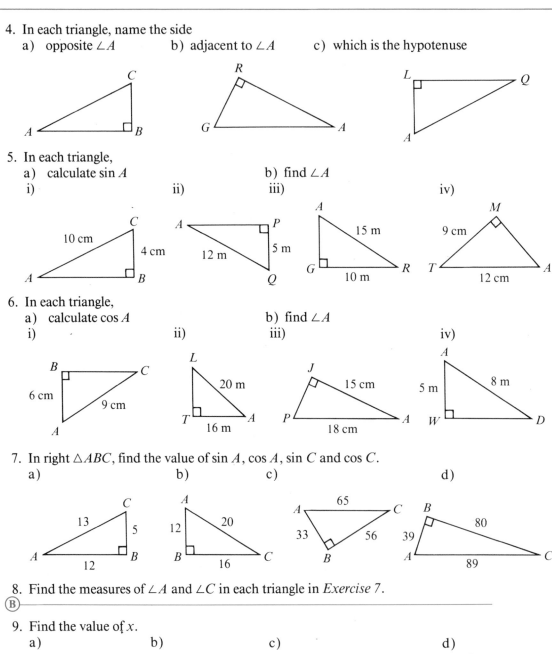

5. In each triangle,
   a) calculate sin A   b) find ∠A
   i)   ii)   iii)   iv)

6. In each triangle,
   a) calculate cos A   b) find ∠A
   i)   ii)   iii)   iv)

7. In right △ABC, find the value of sin A, cos A, sin C and cos C.
   a)   b)   c)   d)

8. Find the measures of ∠A and ∠C in each triangle in *Exercise 7*.
   (B)

9. Find the value of x.
   a)   b)   c)   d)

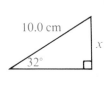

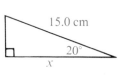

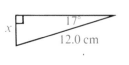

e)

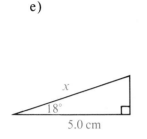

f)

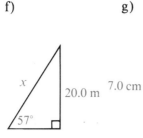

g)

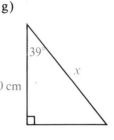

h)

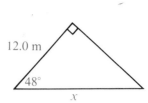

10. In △*ABC*, ∠*B* = 90° and *AC* = 25.0 m.
    a) Find *AB* and *BC* if   i) ∠*A* = 31°   ii) ∠*C* = 78°
    b) Find ∠*A* and ∠*C* if   i) *BC* = 10   ii) *AB* = 17

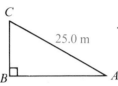

11. In △*PQR*, ∠*Q* = 90° and *PQ* = 15.0 cm.
    a) Find *PR* and *QR* if   i) ∠*P* = 58°   ii) ∠*R* = 42°
    b) Find ∠*P* and ∠*R* if   i) *PR* = 28   ii) *QR* = 25

12. A 10.0 m ladder leans against a vertical wall at an angle of 73°.
    Find the
    a) height the ladder reaches up the wall
    b) distance from the foot of the ladder to the wall

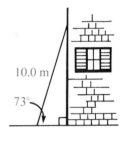

13. A storm causes some 15.0 m telephone poles to lean over.
    a) One pole leans at an angle of 72° to the ground. How high is
       the top of the pole from the ground?
    b) The top of another pole is 12.0 m above the ground. What is the pole's angle to
       the ground?

14. A wheelchair ramp is 8.2 m long and rises 0.75 m. What is the angle of elevation of
    the ramp, to the nearest degree?

15. A kite has a string 150 m long. If the string makes an angle of 41°
    with the ground, find the height of the kite.

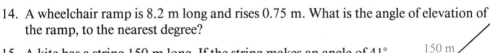

16. A mountain road rises 1 m for every 5 m along the road. Find the
    angle of inclination of the road.

17. The altitudes of an equilateral triangle are 10.0 cm long. Calculate the lengths of
    the sides, correct to the nearest millimetre.

18. Find all the angles in isosceles triangles *ABC* and *DEF*.

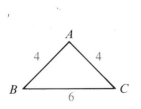

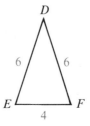

ⓒ

19. A 20 m telephone pole was broken as shown. How high above the ground is the break?

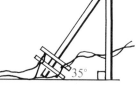

20. An equilateral triangle is inscribed in a circle. If the radius of the circle is 10 cm, calculate the length of a side of the triangle.

21. The McMath Solar Telescope in Arizona is 153 m long, and is permanently inclined at an angle of 32° above the horizontal. If ground level is 2063 m and the top of the telescope is 32 m above the ground, find the

    a) depth *DE* of the base of the telescope below ground level

    b) length *DB* of the telescope that is underground

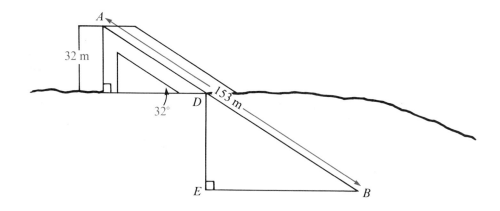

22. In △*ABC*, ∠*B* = 90° and *AC* = 1 m. Find expressions in terms of ∠*A* for *AB* and *BC*.

🕵️ **I N V E S T I G A T E**

Consider the trigonometric table on page 514.

1. Explain why none of the values in the *sin* or *cos* columns are greater than 1.

2. Compare   a) sin 30° and cos 60°   b) sin 80° and cos 10°
   Explain the relationship between the sine and cosine of angles which have a sum of 90°.

14-4 SOLVING RIGHT TRIANGLES

Finding the unknown sides and angles of a triangle is called solving the triangle. In a right triangle, this is possible if either of the following are known:

- the lengths of any two sides
- the length of one side and an acute angle

If the lengths of two sides of a right triangle are known, the Pythagorean Theorem can be used to find the length of the third side, and any trigonometric ratio can be used to find one of the acute angles.

Example 1. Solve $\triangle ABC$, given that $AB = 5.0$ cm, $BC = 2.0$ cm, and $\angle B = 90°$.

Solution. By the Pythagorean Theorem:

$$AC^2 = AB^2 + BC^2$$
$$= 5^2 + 2^2$$
$$= 29$$
$$AC = \sqrt{29}$$
$$\doteq 5.4 \text{ cm}$$

$\angle A$ can be found using the tangent ratio:

$$\tan A = \frac{2}{5}$$
$$= 0.400$$
$$\angle A \doteq 22°$$

And $\angle C \doteq 90° - 22°$
$$\doteq 68°$$

Example 2. Solve $\triangle PQR$, given that $PQ = 7.0$ m, $PR = 9.0$ m, and $\angle Q = 90°$.

Solution.

$$QR^2 = PR^2 - PQ^2$$
$$= 9^2 - 7^2$$
$$= 32$$
$$QR = \sqrt{32}$$
$$\doteq 5.7 \text{ m}$$

$\angle R$ can be found using the sine ratio:

$$\sin R = \frac{7}{9}$$
$$\doteq 0.778$$
$$\angle R \doteq 51°$$

And $\angle P \doteq 39°$

If the length of one side and one acute angle are known, a trigonometric ratio can be used to find the length of a second side. The length of the third side can then be found using either the Pythagorean Theorem or another trigonometric ratio.

Example 3.   Solve $\triangle XYZ$, given that $XY = 9.0$ m, $\angle Y = 90°$, and $\angle Z = 36°$.

Solution. $\angle X = 90° - 36°$, or $54°$. Trigonometric ratios of
either $\angle X$ or $\angle Z$ can be used to find the lengths
of YZ and XZ.

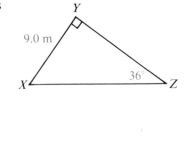

$$\frac{9}{YZ} = \tan 36°$$

$$\doteq 0.727$$

$$YZ \doteq \frac{9.0}{0.727}$$

$$\doteq 12.4 \text{ m}$$

$$\frac{9}{XZ} = \sin 36°$$

$$\doteq 0.588$$

$$XZ \doteq \frac{9.0}{0.588}$$

$$\doteq 15.3 \text{ m}$$

In applied problems, it is usually not necessary to find all the unknown
lengths and angles.

Example 4.   A truck travels 6 km up a mountain road. If the change in height is
1250 m, what is the angle of inclination of the road?

Solution.   Let $\angle A$ represent the angle of inclination of the road.

$$\text{Then, } \sin A = \frac{1250}{6000}$$

$$\doteq 0.208$$

$$A \doteq 12°$$

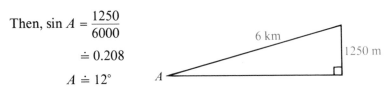

The angle of inclination of the road is approximately $12°$.

EXERCISES 14-4

Ⓐ

1. Find all unknown angles and sides.

a)

A
8.0 mm
B
5.0 mm
C

b)

6.0 cm
D   E
12.0 cm
F

c)

24.0 cm
P   Q
19.0 cm
R

d)

J
27.0 m
K
17.0 m
L

e)

29.0 m
U   T
39.0 m
V

f)

F
13.0 km   16.0 km
G   H

2. Solve each triangle.

a)

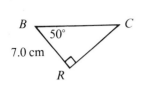

b)

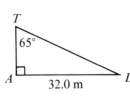

c)

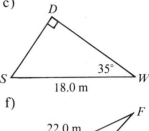

d)

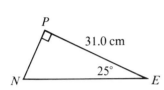

e)

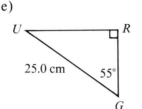

f)

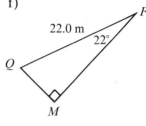

3. Solve △ABC, in which ∠B = 90°, with the data given.
   a) ∠A = 27°, AC = 10   b) ∠A = 35°, AB = 15   c) ∠C = 50°, AC = 20
   d) ∠C = 62°, BC = 100   e) AB = 40, BC = 27   f) AC = 48, AB = 35

Ⓑ

4. From a distance of 80.0 m, the angle of elevation of the top of a flagpole is 18°. Determine the height of the flagpole, to the nearest tenth of a metre.

5. A radio tower is 350 m high. If the sun's rays make an angle of 39° with the ground, determine the length of the tower's shadow.

6. Sharon is flying a kite on a string 130 m long. Determine the height of the kite if the string is at an angle of 34° to the ground. What assumptions are you making?

7. The diagonal of a rectangle is 12 cm long and makes an angle of 32° with the longer side. Find the length of the rectangle.

8. The diagonal of a rectangle is 15 cm long and makes a 20° angle with the longer side. Find the width of the rectangle.

9. An airplane is flying at an altitude of 6000 m over the ocean directly towards an island. When the angle of depression of the coastline from the airplane is 14°, how much farther does the airplane have to fly before it crosses the coast?

10. Find the measure of the acute angle formed by the intersection of the diagonals of a rectangle which measures 8 cm by 6 cm.

Ⓒ

11. The inclination of a warehouse conveyor can be set between 14° and 40°. If the length of the conveyor is 12 m, what are the minimum and maximum heights the conveyor can reach?

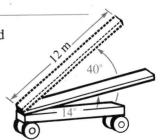

12. Determine the perimeter of a regular pentagon which is inscribed in a circle of 10 cm radius.

MATHEMATICS AROUND US

Gondola Lifts in Banff and Jasper National Parks

Gondola lifts may generally be assumed to follow the hypotenuse of a right triangle, beginning at the lower terminal and ending at the upper terminal. If the elevations of these terminals and the length of the cable, or track, are known, the average angle of inclination of the lift can be found.

Data for the three gondola lifts in Banff and Jasper National Parks are given below.

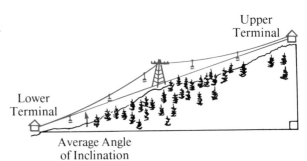

QUESTION

Calculate the average angle of inclination for each gondola lift.

Banff Sulphur Mountain Gondola Lift	Lake Louise Gondola	Jasper Tramway

Lower Terminal: 1583 m	Lower Terminal: 1532 m	Lower Terminal: 1408 m
Upper Terminal: 2286 m	Upper Terminal: 2036 m	Upper Terminal: 2500 m
Length of Track: 1561 m	Length of Track: 3353 m	Length of Track: 2000 m

14-5 APPLICATIONS OF THE TRIGONOMETRIC RATIOS

Trigonometry was originally developed to solve problems in navigation. Since then, it has been applied to a wide range of problems in mathematics, science, and industry.

Example 1.   A snow plow has a 3.2 m blade set at an angle of 25°. How wide a path will the snow plow clear?

Solution.   Let the width of the path, PQ, be x metres.

Then, $\dfrac{x}{3.2} = \cos 25°$

$x \doteq 3.2(0.906)$

$\doteq 2.90$

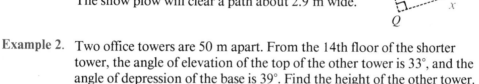

The snow plow will clear a path about 2.9 m wide.

Example 2.   Two office towers are 50 m apart. From the 14th floor of the shorter tower, the angle of elevation of the top of the other tower is 33°, and the angle of depression of the base is 39°. Find the height of the other tower.

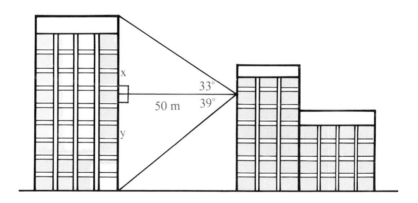

Solution.   Let the height of the taller tower be x metres above the 14th floor and y metres below the 14th floor.

Then, $\dfrac{x}{50} = \tan 33°$ and $\dfrac{y}{50} = \tan 39°$

$\quad\quad x \doteq 50(0.649)$ $y \doteq 50(0.810)$

$\quad\quad\quad \doteq 32.45$ $\doteq 40.50$

Therefore, $x + y \doteq 32.45 + 40.50$
$\quad\quad\quad\quad\quad \doteq 72.95$

The height of the other tower is approximately 73 m.

EXERCISES 14-5

1. A guy wire, supporting a TV tower 50 m tall, joins the top of the tower to an anchor point 25 m from the base. Find the length of the wire and the angle it makes with the ground.

2. A tree casts a shadow 42 m long when the sun's rays are at an angle of 38° to the ground. How tall is the tree?

3. A kite string, 140 m long, makes an angle of 40° with the ground. Determine the height of the kite.

4. In the diagram, an observer, O, is directly opposite a hydro pole, A, on the other side of a canal. A tree, B, is 30 m from O. If $\angle B = 64°$ and $\angle O = 90°$, what is the width of the canal?

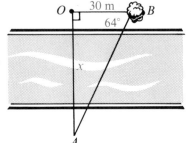

5. The diagram below shows a house designed for solar heating. Determine the length, l, of the solar collectors.

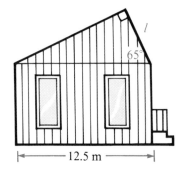

6. The diagram below shows a rod, 10.0 m long, in a well with 1.4 m of the rod protruding. How deep is the well?

Well

7. When the foot of a ladder is 2.0 m from a wall, the angle formed by the ladder and the ground is 60°.
   a) How long is the ladder?
   b) How high up the wall does the ladder reach?

8. The top of a communications tower has an angle of elevation of 6° when observed by a ship 8 km from the base of the cliff below the tower. How high is the top of the tower above sea level?

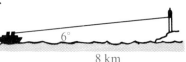

9. An airplane flying at a speed of 52.0 m/s increases its altitude at the rate of 8.0 m/s. At what angle is it climbing?

10. From an apartment window 24 m above the ground, the angle of depression of the base of a nearby building is 38° and the angle of elevation of the top is 63°. Find the height of the nearby building.

11. A 30 cm ruler rests at an angle of 20° to the horizontal in a 25 cm diameter hemispherical bowl. How far along the ruler is its point of contact with the rim of the bowl?

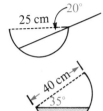

12. Water in a hemispherical bowl begins to pour out when the bowl is tilted through an angle of 35°. How deep is the water in the bowl?

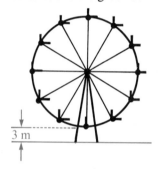

ⓒ

13. In the diagram below, how high above the ground is the child on the swing?

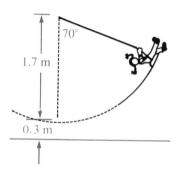

14. When a Ferris wheel, 20 m in diameter, is in the position shown, how high are its seats above the ground?

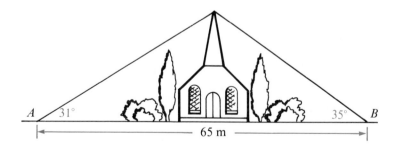

15. To an observer at *A*, the angle of elevation of a church spire is 31°. To an observer at *B*, the angle of elevation is 35°. If the observers are 65 m apart with the spire directly between them, what is the height of the spire?

16. A man whose eyes are 1.8 m above the ground notes that the angle of elevation of the top of a building is 65°. He walks 30 m farther away and finds the angle of elevation to be 55°. How tall is the building?

17. Two trees are 100 m apart. From a point midway between them, the angles of elevation of their tops are 12° and 16°. How much taller is one tree than the other?

PROBLEM SOLVING

Use a Model

The diagram shows the intersection of two corridors in a building. Determine the length of the longest ladder that can be carried around the corner from one corridor to the other.

Understand the problem

- Can you take ladders of different lengths and try to carry them around the corner?

Think of a strategy

- Make a scale diagram of the corridors.

Carry out the strategy

- Draw a scale diagram of the corridors and cut a straw to represent a ladder. Slide the straw around the corner, keeping it at all times inside the corridor. Try different lengths of straws to find the longest possible.
- Then use the scale to determine the length of the corresponding ladder.

  A 4 m ladder is too short.   An 8 m ladder is too long.

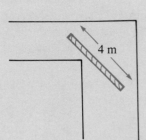

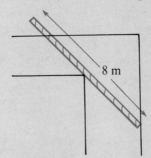

- What is the length of the longest ladder that can be carried around the corner?

Look back

- Could you obtain a more accurate result by using a larger diagram?
- The ceiling in the corridor is 3 m high. If one end of the ladder is raised to the ceiling, how does this affect the length of the longest ladder which can be carried around the corner?

Solve each problem

1. Two different views of the same cube are shown. On a copy of the third view showing two blank faces, sketch the letters as they would appear on those faces.

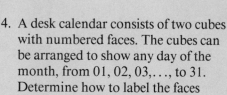

2. Determine if it is possible to place 8 checkers on an 8 by 8 checkerboard such that no two checkers are in the same row, column, or diagonal.

3. Place two quarters side by side, as shown. If the quarter on the right is rolled around the top half of the other quarter until it has been moved to the position shown, will the queen be right-side up or up-side down?

4. A desk calendar consists of two cubes with numbered faces. The cubes can be arranged to show any day of the month, from 01, 02, 03,..., to 31. Determine how to label the faces of the two cubes.

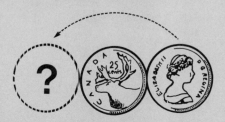

5. Place a tin can on its side on a table and hold a ruler on top, as shown. If you push the ruler sideways, while pressing it down on the can, both the ruler and the can will move in the same direction. When the can has made one complete rotation, how far has the
   a) can moved?
   b) ruler moved?

6. Assume that you have six postage stamps attached to one another, as shown. There are many ways to fold the stamps along the perforations so that stamp number 1 is on the top, and all the others are underneath.
   a) Can you do this so that the stamps are arranged in these orders?
      i) 1 5 2 6 3 4
      ii) 1 2 5 4 3 6
   b) What other arrangements can you make?

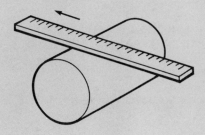

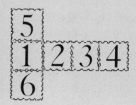

PROBLEM SOLVING

Choose the Strategy

1. Figure *ABCD* is a square. On side *BC*, an equilateral △*BEC* is drawn facing away from the square. What is the measure of ∠*BAE*?

2. A distance of 40 km was covered partly by jogging at 10 km/h and partly by cycling at 25 km/h. If the total time of travel was 2 h, find the distance covered by jogging.

3. Every natural number belongs to one of these two lists. Given any natural number, describe a simple procedure you could use to tell in which list it belongs.
   List A: 1, 4, 5, 8, 9, 12,...
   List B: 2, 3, 6, 7, 10, 11,...

4. A line segment *AB*, where *A*(0, 0) and *B*(5, 0), is the hypotenuse of a right △*ABC* which has an area of 5 units². If the coordinates of *C* are integers, find them.

5. Assume you have two different colors. In how many different ways can you paint the six faces of a cube if each face is painted with one color?

6. The diagonal of a rectangle is twice as long as the diagonal of a square. If they both have the same width, what is the ratio of their lengths? perimeters?

7. a) The numbers from 0 to 7 are marked on the vertices of this cube. Find the sums of the numbers at the ends of each edge.
   b) Can you rearrange the same numbers such that the sum of the numbers at the ends of each edge is a prime number?
   c) Can you do it such that the sums are not prime numbers?

8. Both $x^2 + 5x - 6$ and $x^2 - 6x + 5$ can be factored.
   a) Find other examples of two trinomials of the form $x^2 + bx - c$ and $x^2 - cx + b$ which can be factored.
   b) Find an example of two trinomials of the form $x^2 + bx + c$ and $x^2 + cx + b$ which can be factored.

9. Each major league baseball team plays 162 games during the regular season. After playing the first 100 games, a team has a winning percentage of 0.450. How many more wins are needed to finish the season with a winning percentage of 0.525?

10. A domino is a rectangular tile containing spots in two squares on one side. In the *double-six* set there are 0 to 6 spots in each square. All the dominoes are different.
    a) How many different dominoes are there?
    b) How many spots are there in the set?

11. Is it possible for all three angles in a triangle to be perfect squares? If it is, find one or more examples. If it is not, explain why.

Review Exercises

1. Explain why the triangles are similar and then find the values of x and y.

   a)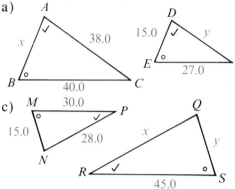

   b)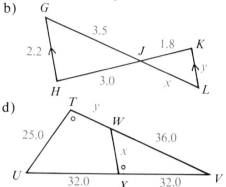

   c)

   d)

2. a) The moon is approximately 385 000 km away. When a ruler is held 56 cm from the eye, the diameter of the moon appears to be 0.5 cm. What is the diameter of the moon?

   b) During a total eclipse, the sun and moon seem to be the same size. If the sun is 150 000 000 km away, what is its diameter?

3. Find
   a) $\tan 27°$
   b) $\tan 38°$
   c) $\tan 65°$
   d) $\tan 81°$

4. Find $\angle A$.

   a) $\tan A = 1.4$
   b) $\tan A = \dfrac{7}{4}$
   c) $\tan A = 0.065$
   d) $\tan A = \dfrac{20}{7}$

5. Find the value of x.

   a)

   b)

   c)

6. In $\triangle ABC$, find $\angle B$ if AC is   a) 6   b) 12   c) 15

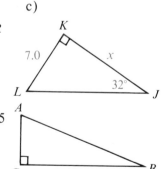

7. A rectangle measures 8 cm by 4 cm. Find the measures of the two acute angles formed at a vertex by a diagonal.

8. A guy wire fastened 50 m from the base of a television tower makes an angle of 55° with the ground. How high up the tower does the guy wire reach?

9. Find
   a) $\sin 37°$
   b) $\cos 66°$
   c) $\cos 28°$
   d) $\sin 55°$

10. Find $\angle A$.
   a) $\cos A = 0.372$
   b) $\sin A = 0.590$
   c) $\sin A = 0.805$
   d) $\cos A = 0.070$

11. a) In each triangle, calculate sin A and cos A.
    b) Find $\angle A$.

i)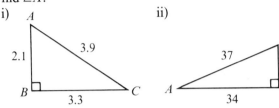

ii)

iii)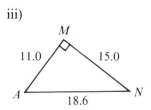

12. Determine the measures of the acute angles.

a)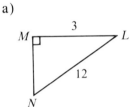

b)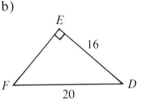

c)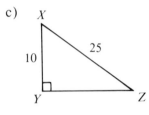

13. Determine the lengths of the sides not given.

a)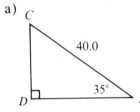

b)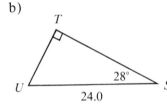

c)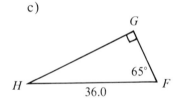

14. In $\triangle ABC$, $\angle C = 90°$ and $AC = 8.0$. Find AB and BC if
    a) $\angle A = 28°$ b) $\angle A = 54°$ c) $\angle B = 48°$

15. From a distance of 60 m at ground level, the angle of elevation of the top of a flagpole is 32°. Determine the height of the flagpole to the nearest tenth of a metre.

16. When the foot of a ladder is 1.8 m from a wall, the angle formed by the ladder and the ground is 72°.
    a) How long is the ladder?
    b) How high up the wall does the ladder reach?

17. A tree casts a shadow 40 m long when the sun's rays are at an angle of 36° to the ground. How tall is the tree?

18. From the top of a building 70 m high, the angle of depression of an automobile on a road is 27°. How far is the automobile from the foot of the building?

19. A broadcasting tower is 255 m high. How far from the base of the tower is a surveyor who observes that the angle of elevation of the top of the tower is 38°?

20. Two office towers are 30 m apart. From the 15th floor (40 m up) of the shorter tower, the angle of elevation of the top of the other tower is 70°. Find the
    a) angle of depression of the base of the taller tower from the 15th floor
    b) height of the taller tower

Table of Square Roots

n	$\sqrt{n}$	n	$\sqrt{n}$	n	$\sqrt{n}$	n	$\sqrt{n}$
1.0	1.000	5.5	2.345	10	3.162	55	7.416
1.1	1.049	5.6	2.366	11	3.317	56	7.483
1.2	1.095	5.7	2.387	12	3.464	57	7.550
1.3	1.140	5.8	2.408	13	3.606	58	7.616
1.4	1.183	5.9	2.429	14	3.742	59	7.681
1.5	1.225	6.0	2.449	15	3.873	60	7.746
1.6	1.265	6.1	2.470	16	4.000	61	7.810
1.7	1.304	6.2	2.490	17	4.123	62	7.874
1.8	1.342	6.3	2.510	18	4.243	63	7.937
1.9	1.378	6.4	2.530	19	4.359	64	8.000
2.0	1.414	6.5	2.550	20	4.472	65	8.062
2.1	1.449	6.6	2.569	21	4.583	66	8.124
2.2	1.483	6.7	2.588	22	4.690	67	8.185
2.3	1.517	6.8	2.608	23	4.796	68	8.246
2.4	1.549	6.9	2.627	24	4.899	69	8.307
2.5	1.581	7.0	2.646	25	5.000	70	8.367
2.6	1.612	7.1	2.665	26	5.099	71	8.426
2.7	1.643	7.2	2.683	27	5.196	72	8.485
2.8	1.673	7.3	2.702	28	5.292	73	8.544
2.9	1.703	7.4	2.720	29	5.385	74	8.602
3.0	1.732	7.5	2.739	30	5.477	75	8.660
3.1	1.761	7.6	2.757	31	5.568	76	8.718
3.2	1.789	7.7	2.775	32	5.657	77	8.775
3.3	1.817	7.8	2.793	33	5.745	78	8.832
3.4	1.844	7.9	2.811	34	5.831	79	8.888
3.5	1.871	8.0	2.828	35	5.916	80	8.944
3.6	1.897	8.1	2.846	36	6.000	81	9.000
3.7	1.924	8.2	2.864	37	6.083	82	9.055
3.8	1.949	8.3	2.881	38	6.164	83	9.110
3.9	1.975	8.4	2.898	39	6.245	84	9.165
4.0	2.000	8.5	2.915	40	6.325	85	9.220
4.1	2.025	8.6	2.933	41	6.403	86	9.274
4.2	2.049	8.7	2.950	42	6.481	87	9.327
4.3	2.074	8.8	2.966	43	6.557	88	9.381
4.4	2.098	8.9	2.983	44	6.633	89	9.434
4.5	2.121	9.0	3.000	45	6.708	90	9.487
4.6	2.145	9.1	3.017	46	6.782	91	9.539
4.7	2.168	9.2	3.033	47	6.856	92	9.592
4.8	2.191	9.3	3.050	48	6.928	93	9.644
4.9	2.214	9.4	3.066	49	7.000	94	9.695
5.0	2.236	9.5	3.082	50	7.071	95	9.747
5.1	2.258	9.6	3.098	51	7.141	96	9.798
5.2	2.280	9.7	3.114	52	7.211	97	9.849
5.3	2.302	9.8	3.130	53	7.280	98	9.899
5.4	2.324	9.9	3.146	54	7.348	99	9.950
		10.0	3.162			100	10.000

Table of Trigonometric Ratios

θ	$sin\ \theta$	$cos\ \theta$	$tan\ \theta$		θ	$sin\ \theta$	$cos\ \theta$	$tan\ \theta$
0	0.000	1.000	0.000		45	0.707	0.707	1.000
1	0.017	1.000	0.017		46	0.719	0.695	1.036
2	0.035	0.999	0.035		47	0.731	0.682	1.072
3	0.052	0.999	0.052		48	0.743	0.669	1.111
4	0.070	0.998	0.070		49	0.755	0.656	1.150
5	0.087	0.996	0.087		50	0.766	0.643	1.192
6	0.105	0.995	0.105		51	0.777	0.629	1.235
7	0.122	0.993	0.123		52	0.788	0.616	1.280
8	0.139	0.990	0.141		53	0.799	0.602	1.327
9	0.156	0.988	0.158		54	0.809	0.588	1.376
10	0.174	0.985	0.176		55	0.819	0.574	1.428
11	0.191	0.982	0.194		56	0.829	0.559	1.483
12	0.208	0.978	0.213		57	0.839	0.545	1.540
13	0.225	0.974	0.231		58	0.848	0.530	1.600
14	0.242	0.970	0.249		59	0.857	0.515	1.664
15	0.259	0.966	0.268		60	0.866	0.500	1.732
16	0.276	0.961	0.287		61	0.875	0.485	1.804
17	0.292	0.956	0.306		62	0.883	0.469	1.881
18	0.309	0.951	0.325		63	0.891	0.454	1.963
19	0.326	0.946	0.344		64	0.899	0.438	2.050
20	0.342	0.940	0.364		65	0.906	0.423	2.145
21	0.358	0.934	0.384		66	0.914	0.407	2.246
22	0.375	0.927	0.404		67	0.921	0.391	2.356
23	0.391	0.921	0.424		68	0.927	0.375	2.475
24	0.407	0.914	0.445		69	0.934	0.358	2.605
25	0.423	0.906	0.466		70	0.940	0.342	2.747
26	0.438	0.899	0.488		71	0.946	0.326	2.904
27	0.454	0.891	0.510		72	0.951	0.309	3.078
28	0.469	0.883	0.532		73	0.956	0.292	3.271
29	0.485	0.875	0.554		74	0.961	0.276	3.487
30	0.500	0.866	0.577		75	0.966	0.259	3.732
31	0.515	0.857	0.601		76	0.970	0.242	4.011
32	0.530	0.848	0.625		77	0.974	0.225	4.331
33	0.545	0.839	0.649		78	0.978	0.208	4.705
34	0.559	0.829	0.675		79	0.982	0.191	5.145
35	0.574	0.819	0.700		80	0.985	0.174	5.671
36	0.588	0.809	0.727		81	0.988	0.156	6.314
37	0.602	0.799	0.754		82	0.990	0.139	7.115
38	0.616	0.788	0.781		83	0.993	0.122	8.144
39	0.629	0.777	0.810		84	0.995	0.105	9.514
40	0.643	0.766	0.839		85	0.996	0.087	11.430
41	0.656	0.755	0.869		86	0.998	0.070	14.301
42	0.669	0.743	0.900		87	0.999	0.052	19.081
43	0.682	0.731	0.933		88	0.999	0.035	28.636
44	0.695	0.719	0.966		89	1.000	0.017	57.290
45	0.707	0.707	1.000		90	1.000	0.000	

Perspectives in Mathematics

Operations Revisited, page xv
1.Less than 1000: a, f; greater than 2000: d 2.Less than 10: a, f; greater than 20: b, e 3.a)15, 35 b)15, 65 c)35, 55 4.Answers may vary.

a)	356	b)	317	c)	12	d)	20	e)	43	f)	235
	× 7		× 8	× 3		× 4		× 3		× 4	
	2492		2536	36		80		129		940	

5.a)$A, X, Z, Y, B, C; A, B, Y, X, Z, C$ b)$A, W, Z, Y, X, B, C, D; A, W, X, B, C, Y, Z, D$

The Calculating Prodigies, page xvii
1.a)344 b)312 c)140 d)2500 e)1710 f)3670 g)4950 h)3563 i)711 j)1393 k)348 l)2988 2.a)1420 b)3190 c)10 300 d)21 600 e)180 f)48 g)36 h)12 3.$3.00 4.a)100 heartbeats b)about 1.3 min 5.a)i)1225, 1224, 1221, 1216, 1209 ii)5625, 5624, 5621, 5616, 5609 b)Round one number up to next larger number; round second number down to next smaller number. Multiply together. Multiply the units of the original two numbers and add to the first product. i)4225 ii)7224 iii)3016 iv)621 v)7209 vi)4221 vii)9024 viii)2009

The Ultimate Prodigy, page xix
1.368, 512, 1456 2.816, 1488, 1776 3.yes: a, b, e, f, g; no: c, d, h 4.a)Answers may vary. Because 735 is not a multiple of 16 b)15 pages c)1 page 5.a)704 b)No, reasons may vary. For example, since 704 is divisible by 32, the next multiple of 32 will be 704 + 32 or 736. 6.a)990 b)1008 7.539

The Power of Technology, page xxi
1.a)1, 2, 3, 4, 6, 9, 12, 18, 36 b)1, 2, 3, 4, 6, 7, 12, 14, 21, 28, 42, 84 c)1, 2, 4, 5, 10, 20, 25, 50, 100 d)1, 331 e)1, 19, 361 f)1, 2, 3, 4, 6, 12, 37, 74, 111, 148, 222, 444 g)1, 3, 11, 23, 33, 69, 253, 759 h)1, 797 i)1, 29, 841 j)1, 2, 4, 5, 8, 10, 20, 25, 40, 50, 100, 125, 200, 250, 500, 1000 k)1, 7, 11, 13, 77, 91, 143, 1001 l)1, 2, 11, 22, 101, 1111, 2222 2.a)1, 109, 11 881 b)1, 53, 1979, 104 887 c)1, 7, 23, 49, 97, 161, 679, 1127, 2231, 4753, 15 617, 109 319 d)1, 401, 160 801 e)1, 521, 709, 369 389 f)1, 417 577 g)1, 1009, 1 018 081 h)1, 1759, 1999, 351 624 3.a)36, 100, 361, 841, 11 881, 160 801, 1 018 081 b)perfect squares 4.401, 409 5.419 6.a)997 b)1009 7.379, 397, 739, 937

The Power of the Mind, page xxiii
1.a)317, 401, 419, 3407, 5693 b)787, 967, 1789, 2179, 3331 2.a)None of the numbers is 1 less than or 1 more than a multiple of 6 b)1, 3, 7, 9 3.593, 659, 701, 907 4.2, 5, 199 5.2, 5, 117 851 061 187

A Famous Unsolved Problem, page xxiv
1.Answers may vary a)7 + 13 b)11 + 11 c)5 + 19 d)5 + 67 e)7 + 67 f)7 + 83 g)3 + 89 h)47 + 53 i)103 + 97 j)151 + 149 2.a)Yes, for example, 9 = 2 + 7 b)No, for example, 11 cannot be expressed as the sum of two prime numbers. 3.a)Yes, for example, 5 = 2 + 3 b)No, for example, 11 cannot be expressed as the sum of two prime numbers.

Chapter 1

Exercises 1-1, page 4
1.19, 71, 97, 109, 151, 193 2.a)2×3^2 b)$2^2 \times 7$ c)$2 \times 3 \times 7$ d)$2^3 \times 7$ e)2^6 f)$2^2 \times 19$ g)7×13 h)$2 \times 5 \times 11$ i)11×13 j)11×17 k)$2^3 \times 5^2$ l)223 is prime 3.a)1, 2, 3, 4, 6, 12 b)1, 2, 4, 8, 16 c)1, 2, 3, 6, 9, 18 d)1, 5, 25 e)1, 2, 4, 8, 16, 32 f)1, 2, 3, 4, 6, 9, 12, 18, 36 g)1, 2, 3, 4, 5, 6, 10, 12, 15, 20, 30, 60 h)1, 2, 3, 4, 6, 7, 12, 14, 21, 28, 42, 84 i)1, 97 j)1, 2, 4, 5, 10, 20, 25, 50, 100 k)1, 2, 3, 4, 6, 8, 9, 12, 16, 18, 24, 36, 48, 72, 144 l)1, 2, 4, 5, 8, 10, 20, 25, 40, 50, 100, 200 4.a)12 b)15 c)14 d)5 e)12 f)13 g)48 h)16 i)8 j)18 5.a)72 b)48 c)140 d)160 e)90 f)225 g)420 h)360 i)420 j)480 6.No, examples may vary, e.g., 64 has factors 1, 2, 4, 8, 16, 32, and $\sqrt{64} = 8$ 7.The perfect squares, because one factor is multiplied by itself to give the perfect square. 8.2, 17, 19 9.a)2 + 3 + 4 b)1 + 2 + 3 + 4 + 5, 4 + 5 + 6, 7 + 8 c)4 + 5 + 6 + 7 + 8, 6 + 7 + 8 + 9, 9 + 10 + 11 10.Answers may vary, e.g., $37 = 6^2 + 1$; $101 = 10^2 + 1$; $197 = 14^2 + 1$ 11.Answers may vary, e.g., $31 = 2^5 - 1$, $127 = 2^7 - 1$, $2047 = 2^{11} - 1$ 12.a)2, 17, 19 b)2, 3, 101 c)2, 11, 101 13.80 s 14.224 pages 15.a)61 b)301 16.a)A 2, B 3 b)A 4, B 5 c)A 3, B 4 d)A 16, B 25 e)A 7, B 8 f)A 4, B 5 17.a)15 min b)12 min 18.72 19.Answers may vary. $729 = 9^3 = 27^2$, $4096 = 16^3 = 64^2$ 20.9, 90, 810, 810; 5, 140, 700, 700; 8, 240, 1920, 1920 21.a)1 b)1 c)1. The g.c.f. of consecutive numbers is 1.

Computer Power, page 6
1.a)17 b)1 c)116 2.a, e 3.a)9 b)16

Exercises 1-2, page 8
1.a)−5 b)45 c)−26 d)9 e)9 f)28 g)4 h)−20 2.a)18 b)−72 c)−300 d)−360 e)77 f)−4800 g)−4 h)−9 i)40 j)120 k)180 l)−55 3.a)4 b)−4 c)−20 d)−8 e)8 f)40 g)−24 h)0 i)1 j)−1 4.a)26 b)−32 c)−15 d)36 e)−76 f)−43 g)−34 h)−4 i)−21 j)87 k)5 l)−4

5.a)–2 **b)**–34 **c)**–37 **d)**51 **e)**25 **f)**–13 **g)**89 **h)**77 **i)**–4 **j)**–11 **k)**6 **l)**–20 **6.a)**–8 **b)**–2 **c)**5 **d)**–33 **e)**7 **f)**64 **g)**–45 **h)**–75 **i)**225 **j)**225 **k)**675 **l)**–140 625 **7.a)**21 **b)**18 **c)**–24 **d)**85 **e)**16 **f)**–33 **g)**–10 **h)**24 **8.a)**–36 **b)**–23 **c)**30 **d)**21 **e)**–22 **f)**–4 **g)**–53 **h)**–118 **i)**4

Exercises 1-3, page 10

1.a)29 **b)**11 **c)**107 **d)**15 **e)**6.7 **f)**1.8 **2.a)**4 **b)**6 **c)**8 **d)**7 **e)**5 **f)**27 **g)**10 **h)**–4 **3.a)**30 **b)**–12 **c)**–36 **d)**22 **e)**–9 **f)**–9 **4.a)**35 units² **b)**12 units² **c)** 38 units² **d)**49.5 units² **5.**45 ha **6.a)**17 **b)**–24 **c)**21 **d)**16 **e)**38 **f)**–15 **7.a)**0 **b)**–34 **c)**65 **d)**33 **e)**–20 **f)**–76 **8.a)**29 units² **b)**50 units² **c)**18 units² **d)**24 units² **9.a)**6, –8 **b)**5, –4 **c)**no solution **d)**5 **e)**all negative numbers and zero **f)**no solution

Mathematics Around Us, page 11

1.2 080 000 km²

Problem Solving, page 13

1.288 **2.a)**$1^3 = 1^2$, $1^3 + 2^3 = 3^2$, $1^3 + 2^3 + 3^3 = 6^2$ **b)**$6 \times 4 = 24$, $66 \times 34 = 2244$, $666 \times 334 = 222\ 444$ **c)**$8 \times 7 = 56$, $98 \times 67 = 6566$, $998 \times 667 = 665\ 666$ **3.a)**3rd, 8; 4th, 16; 5th, 32 **b)i)**32 **ii)**1024 **c)i)**62 **ii)**2046 **4.a)**1st, 1; 2nd, 2; 3rd, 3; 4th, 5; 5th, 8; 6th, 13 **b)i)**8 **ii)**89 **c)i)**19 **ii)**231 **5.a)**Answers may vary. For example, every 4 years, one day of the week is skipped. **b)i)**Thursday **ii)**Wednesday **iii)**Friday **iv)**Friday

Exercises 1-4, page 16

1.a)$-\frac{7}{12}$ **b)**$\frac{1}{6}$ **c)**$\frac{18}{55}$ **d)**$-\frac{22}{3}$ **e)**$-\frac{125}{8}$ **f)**$\frac{39}{8}$ **g)**$-\frac{2}{3}$ **h)**$\frac{39}{8}$
2.a)–1 **b)**$-\frac{5}{6}$ **c)**$-\frac{10}{9}$ **d)**$-\frac{5}{8}$ **e)**$-\frac{79}{63}$ **f)**$\frac{17}{12}$ **g)**$-\frac{7}{72}$ **h)**$-\frac{17}{84}$
3.a)$\frac{97}{12}$ **b)**$\frac{31}{30}$ **c)**$-\frac{307}{18}$ **d)**$-\frac{37}{12}$ **e)**$-\frac{149}{12}$ **f)**$\frac{1}{12}$ **g)**$\frac{143}{12}$ **h)**$-\frac{141}{14}$
4.a)$-\frac{1}{6}$ **b)**$-\frac{1}{3}$ **c)**$\frac{23}{12}$ **d)**$-\frac{65}{72}$ **e)**$\frac{13}{8}$ **f)**$-\frac{13}{2}$ **g)**$-\frac{1}{32}$ **h)**$\frac{1}{64}$
5.a)–0.625 **b)**$-0.\overline{4}$ **c)**$3.\overline{142\ 857}$ **d)**$-3.91\overline{6}$ **e)**5.4 **f)**$-1.\overline{54}$ **6.a)**$\frac{137}{100}$ **b)**$\frac{5}{11}$ **c)**$\frac{61}{9}$ **d)**$\frac{23}{8}$ **e)**$\frac{517}{999}$ **f)**$\frac{961}{80}$ **g)**$\frac{4091}{990}$ **h)**$\frac{662}{165}$ **i)**$\frac{10}{9}$ **j)**$\frac{15\ 697}{4995}$ **k)**$\frac{518}{999}$ **l)**$\frac{2081}{6660}$ **m)**$\frac{1}{1}$ **n)**$\frac{1}{2}$ **o)**$\frac{18}{7}$
7.a)$\frac{1}{12}$ **b)**$\frac{15}{16}$ **c)**$\frac{9}{5}$ **d)**0 **e)**$-\frac{9}{5}$ **f)**$\frac{4}{5}$ **8.a)**$-\frac{1}{8}$ **b)**–1 **c)**$-\frac{28}{27}$ **9.**\$3980/h, \$3486/h **10.**38 720 kW **11.a)**20% **b)**16% **12.a)i)**40 cm **ii)**27 cm **iii)**25 cm **b)i)**30 cm **ii)**27 cm **iii)**undefined **c)**The object is far enough away as to be considered at infinity. **13.a)**$0.\overline{5}$ **b)**$0.\overline{9}$ **c)**$0.\overline{2}$ **d)**$0.0\overline{83}$ **e)**$0.\overline{2}$ **f)**$0.\overline{148}$

INVESTIGATE, page 17

Answers may vary, e.g., $0.\overline{4}$, $0.\overline{3}$.

Exercises 1-5, page 19

1.a)±7 **b)**±9 **c)**±11 **d)**±20 **e)**±23 **f)**±25 **2.a)**8 **b)**10 **c)**12 **d)**30 **e)**40 **f)**0.5 **g)**0.2 **h)**0.1 **i)**0.04 **j)**0.005 **3.a)**1.414 **b)**1.732 **c)**7.232 **d)**11.336 **e)**21.703 **f)**21.726 **g)**21.749 **h)**21.772 **i)**1.217 **j)**0.016 **4.a)**2 **b)**–3 **c)**3 **d)**2 **e)**3 **f)**0.1 **5.a)i)**2.45 **ii)**2.449 **b)i)**3.32 **ii)**3.317 **c)i)**3.61 **ii)**3.606 **d)i)**11.14 **ii)**11.136 **e)i)**11.79 **ii)**11.790 **f)i)**12.41 **ii)**12.410 **6.a)**3.1 m, 12.4 m **b)**2.5 m, 10.1 m **7.a)**10 cm, 100 cm² **b)**5 cm, 25 cm² **8.a)**4 **b)**5 **c)**2 **d)**–1 **e)**6 **f)**–10 **g)**4 **h)**10 **i)**7 **j)**10 **9.a)**3.2 m **b)**4.5 m **10.**20 cm **11.a)**5 **b)**7 **c)**6 **d)**12 **e)**2 **f)**2 **g)**6 **h)**23 **12.a)**2.55 **b)**8.06 **c)**2.71 **d)**5.85

INVESTIGATE, page 20

The square root of the number approaches 2.

Exercises 1-6, page 23

1.a)rational **b)**irrational **c)**irrational **d)**irrational **e)**irrational **f)**rational **2.**$\sqrt{21}$, $\sqrt{200}$, $\sqrt{2.5}$ **3.**$5\sqrt{2}$, $5 + \sqrt{2}$, $5 - \sqrt{2}$, $7\sqrt{7}$, $\sqrt{5} + \sqrt{2}$, $\sqrt{7} + \sqrt{9}$, $6\sqrt{21}$, $\sqrt{17} + 12$ **4.**Answers may vary. **a)**rational 3.66, 3.67; irrational 3.653 201 3…, 3.663 201 3… **b)**rational –1.472, –1.473; irrational –1.472 123 51…, –1.471 235 14… **c)**rational 0.3978, 0.397 81; irrational 0.397 713 42…, 0.397 723 41… **d)**rational –5.3768, –5.3769; irrational –5.376 812 145…, –5.376 912 145… **e)**rational 0.89, 0.891; irrational 0.891 035 06…, 0.891 132 46… **f)**rational 2.236 068, 2.236 069; irrational 2.236 068 147…, 2.236 069 147… **5.a)**rational **b)**rational **c)**integer **d)**natural **e)**irrational **f)**rational **g)**irrational **h)**natural **6.**No, the calculator rounds an irrational number to fit its display. **7.a)**$\frac{1}{9}$, $\frac{1}{3}$, $\sqrt{\frac{1}{9}} = \frac{1}{3}$ **b)**Examples may vary. $\sqrt{0.444\ 444\ 4} = 0.\ 666\ 666\ 6$ **8.a)**The square root of an irrational number cannot be rational. **b)**Examples may vary. **9.**No, because C and d are not integers.

The Mathematical Mind, page 24

The Chinese with $\frac{355}{133}$

Exercises 1-7, page 27

1.a)8.9 **b)**10.7 **c)**12.0 **d)**1.7 **e)**4.8 **f)**9.2 **2.**30 cm **3.a)**$2\sqrt{2}$ cm **b)**$\sqrt{13}$ cm **c)**$\sqrt{10}$ cm **d)**$\sqrt{29}$ cm **5.**$2\sqrt{3}$ cm, $4\sqrt{3}$ cm² **6.**about 27 m **7.**about 246 m **8.**about 87 m **9.**$4\sqrt{2}$ cm **10.**$\sqrt{39}$ **11.**40 m **12.**23 km **13.a)**$\sqrt{38}$ **b)**$d = \sqrt{a^2 + b^2 + c^2}$ **14.a)**$\sqrt{2}$, $\sqrt{}$ **b)**12 edges, 12 face diagonals, 4 body diagonals

15.a)4 **b)**1, $\sqrt{2}$, $\frac{\sqrt{2}}{2}$, $\frac{\sqrt{6}}{2}$ **c)**12, 6, 24, 24 **16.**187 m
17.a)$\sqrt{\pi}$: 1 **b)**$\sqrt{2\pi}$: 1

Exercise 1-8, page 31

1.a)$2\sqrt{14}$ **b)**$\sqrt{154}$ **c)**-12 **d)**$6\sqrt{10}$ **e)**-48 **f)**$70\sqrt{6}$
2.a)$\sqrt{2} \times \sqrt{2} \times \sqrt{2} \times \sqrt{3}$ **b)**$\sqrt{2} \times \sqrt{3} \times \sqrt{3}$
c)$\sqrt{3} \times \sqrt{3} \times \sqrt{5}$ **d)**$\sqrt{2} \times \sqrt{2} \times \sqrt{7}$
e)$\sqrt{2} \times \sqrt{2} \times \sqrt{2} \times \sqrt{3} \times \sqrt{3}$ **f)**$\sqrt{2} \times \sqrt{2} \times \sqrt{3} \times \sqrt{5}$
g)$\sqrt{3} \times \sqrt{13}$ **h)**$\sqrt{5} \times \sqrt{13}$
i)$\sqrt{2} \times \sqrt{2} \times \sqrt{2} \times \sqrt{2} \times \sqrt{2} \times \sqrt{3}$
j)$\sqrt{2} \times \sqrt{2} \times \sqrt{2} \times \sqrt{3} \times \sqrt{5}$ **k)**$\sqrt{2} \times \sqrt{3} \times \sqrt{3} \times \sqrt{7}$
l)$\sqrt{3} \times \sqrt{5} \times \sqrt{7}$ **3.a)**$4\sqrt{2}$ **b)**$5\sqrt{2}$ **c)**$3\sqrt{3}$ **d)**$4\sqrt{6}$
e)$2\sqrt{2}$ **f)**$5\sqrt{3}$ **4.a)**$7\sqrt{3}$ **b)**$3\sqrt{6}$ **c)**$2\sqrt{19}$ **d)**$6\sqrt{5}$ **e)**$6\sqrt{5}$
f)$15\sqrt{2}$ **5.a)**$12\sqrt{3}$ **b)**$105\sqrt{2}$ **c)**$-192\sqrt{3}$ **d)**$40\sqrt{15}$
e)$84\sqrt{2}$ **f)**$165\sqrt{2}$ **6.a)**$-108\sqrt{6}$ **b)**$15\sqrt{15}$ **c)**$\frac{-2\sqrt{42}}{3}$
d)-12 **e)**$-10\sqrt{0.21}$ **f)**$132\sqrt{0.4}$ **7.a)**$12\sqrt{3}$ **b)**120 **c)**60
d)$280\sqrt{6}$ **e)**$60\sqrt{21}$ **f)**1008 **9.a)**$2\sqrt{10}$, $3\sqrt{5}$, $4\sqrt{3}$, $5\sqrt{2}$,
$2\sqrt{13}$, $3\sqrt{6}$ **b)**$-2\sqrt{21}$, $-4\sqrt{5}$, $-5\sqrt{3}$, $-6\sqrt{2}$, $-2\sqrt{17}$,
$-3\sqrt{7}$ **c)**$7\sqrt{0.05}$, $2\sqrt{0.8}$, $6\sqrt{0.1}$, $3\sqrt{0.7}$, $5\sqrt{0.3}$, $4\sqrt{0.5}$
10.a)$108\sqrt{2}$ **b)**1200 **c)**1080 **d)**$4320\sqrt{2}$ **e)**518 400
f)30 **11.**3 units² **12.**7 : 1 **13.a)**$\sqrt{15ab}$ **b)**$x\sqrt{14}$
c)$12m\sqrt{6}$ **d)**$48x\sqrt{3y}$ **e)**$90m\sqrt{2m}$ **f)**$252xy$

Exercises 1-9, page 34

1.a)$2\sqrt{7}$ **b)**$16\sqrt{6}$ **c)**$-6\sqrt{13}$ **d)**$-25\sqrt{19}$ **e)**$33\sqrt{3}$
f)$5\sqrt{15}$ **2.a)**$-4\sqrt{5}$ **b)**$3\sqrt{10}$ **c)**$18\sqrt{2}$ **d)**$13\sqrt{6} - 6\sqrt{2}$
e)$3\sqrt{5} - 6\sqrt{10}$ **f)**$8\sqrt{5} - 11\sqrt{2}$ **3.a)**$5\sqrt{10}$ **b)**$6\sqrt{2}$
c)$-3\sqrt{3}$ **d)**$-\sqrt{5}$ **e)**$2\sqrt{2}$ **f)**$-2\sqrt{6}$ **g)**$-2\sqrt{5}$ **h)**$8\sqrt{6}$
4.a)$7\sqrt{6}$ **b)**$3\sqrt{7}$ **c)**$2\sqrt{5}$ **d)**$9\sqrt{3}$ **e)**$11\sqrt{3}$ **f)**$-4\sqrt{2}$
g)$-6\sqrt{5}$ **h)**$-6\sqrt{2}$ **i)**$-8\sqrt{3}$ **5.a)**$10\sqrt{3}$ **b)**$13\sqrt{3}$ **c)**$24\sqrt{2}$
d)$-8\sqrt{2}$ **e)**$13\sqrt{6}$ **f)**$6\sqrt{5}$ **g)**$15\sqrt{2}$ **h)**$9\sqrt{7}$ **i)**$10\sqrt{6} - 2\sqrt{7}$
6.$(12\sqrt{2} - 16)$ km or about 1 km **7.a)**$-33\sqrt{3}$
b)$7\sqrt{7} + \sqrt{11}$ **c)**$\sqrt{3} - 5\sqrt{5}$ **d)**$47\sqrt{2} - \sqrt{7}$
e)$-6\sqrt{3} - 9\sqrt{2}$ **f)**$41\sqrt{6} + 36\sqrt{7}$) **g)**$-2\sqrt{2} - 16\sqrt{3}$
h)$-16\sqrt{2} - 2\sqrt{7}$ **8.a)**$4\sqrt{2}$ cm **b)**$8\sqrt{2}$ cm²
c)$(4 + 8\sqrt{2})$ cm **9.**$12\sqrt{7}$ cm², $(12 + 4\sqrt{7})$ cm
10.a)$2\sqrt{2}$ **b)**$2\sqrt{5}$ **c)**$31\sqrt{2}$ **d)**$\sqrt{5} - 4\sqrt{3}$ **e)**$-\sqrt{2} - 4\sqrt{6}$
f)$\frac{-\sqrt{6}}{2}$ **11.a)**$2\sqrt{5}$ **b)**no **c)**Answers may vary, e.g.,
$2\sqrt{3} + 2\sqrt{2} \neq 2\sqrt{5}$ **12.a)**$\sqrt{x + y}$ **b)**The sum of the
lengths of 2 sides of a triangle cannot equal the length
of the 3rd side. **13.**Yes, because the $\sqrt{}$ sign denotes a
positive value. **14.a)**$4\sqrt{x}$ **b)**$5\sqrt{2a}$ **c)**$10\sqrt{3m}$
d)$5\sqrt{5x} - 5\sqrt{6y}$ **e)**$-5\sqrt{2a} - 14\sqrt{3b}$ **f)**$4\sqrt{2x} + 7\sqrt{5y}$
15.$(8 + 8\sqrt{3})$ cm **16.a)**$AB = \sqrt{107}$, $AC = \sqrt{147}$,
$BC = \sqrt{200}$; $BC^2 \neq BA^2 + AC^2$ **b)**$4\sqrt{3}$

INVESTIGATE, page 36
Answers may vary, e.g., $a = 0$, $b = 9$

Exercises 1-10, page 37
1.a)$\sqrt{10} - \sqrt{14}$ **b)**$\sqrt{33} + \sqrt{6}$ **c)**$\sqrt{78} - \sqrt{30}$
d)$2\sqrt{15} + 6\sqrt{21}$ **e)**$\sqrt{30} - 5\sqrt{2}$ **f)**$12\sqrt{22} + 20\sqrt{26}$
2.a)$\sqrt{39} + 13$ **b)**$9 - 18\sqrt{2}$ **c)**-48 **d)**$6\sqrt{10} + 8\sqrt{15}$
e)$36\sqrt{3} - 72\sqrt{2}$ **f)**$36 - 40\sqrt{3}$ **3.a)**$10\sqrt{21} - 12 + 18\sqrt{2}$
b)$8\sqrt{21} + 12\sqrt{42} - 28$ **c)**80 **d)**$24\sqrt{15} - 216\sqrt{2} - 216$
4.a)$35 + 140\sqrt{6}$ **b)**$48\sqrt{3} - 96\sqrt{2} - 96$
c)$20\sqrt{6} + 12 - 8\sqrt{15} + 18\sqrt{2}$ **d)**$8\sqrt{10} - 24\sqrt{6} + 128$
5.a)$3\sqrt{3} + 5$ **b)**$1 - 5\sqrt{7}$ **c)**$19 - 11\sqrt{2}$ **d)**$2 + 6\sqrt{3}$ **e)**3
f)$9\sqrt{2} - 12$ **g)**$11 - 6\sqrt{2}$ **h)**$4 + 2\sqrt{3}$ **i)**$33 - 20\sqrt{2}$
6.a)$14 + 7\sqrt{2}$ **b)**$52 - 38\sqrt{2}$ **c)**$2 - 7\sqrt{3}$ **d)**$25 - 11\sqrt{7}$
e)4 **f)**18 **g)**$65 - 6\sqrt{14}$ **h)**$18 + 12\sqrt{2}$ **i)**$98 - 24\sqrt{5}$
7.a)$38 + 12\sqrt{10}$ **b)**-43 **c)**$67 - 42\sqrt{2}$ **d)**80
e)$220 - 120\sqrt{2}$ **f)**33 **g)**$197 - 70\sqrt{6}$ **h)**$24 - 10\sqrt{3}$
i)162 **j)**l **8.a)**$16 + 2\sqrt{60}$, $16 + 2\sqrt{39}$, $16 + 2\sqrt{15}$,
$16 + 2\sqrt{55}$ **b)**$\sqrt{6} + \sqrt{10}$, $\sqrt{5} + \sqrt{11}$, $\sqrt{13} + \sqrt{3}$,
$\sqrt{15} + \sqrt{1}$ **9.**$\sqrt{20} - \sqrt{6}$, $\sqrt{18} - \sqrt{8}$, $\sqrt{15} - \sqrt{11}$,
$\sqrt{14} - \sqrt{12}$

Exercises 1-11, page 41
1.a)$2\sqrt{2}$ **b)**$\sqrt{7}$ **c)**$2\sqrt{3}$ **d)**$3\sqrt{5}$ **e)**$3\sqrt{3}$ **f)**$\frac{5\sqrt{2}}{2}$ **g)**4 **h)**1
i)$\frac{\sqrt{2}}{7}$ **j)**$\frac{1}{9}$ **2.a)**2 **b)**2 **c)**$2\sqrt{2}$ **d)**$\frac{3\sqrt{2}}{2}$ **e)**$\frac{5\sqrt{3}}{3}$ **f)**$\frac{4\sqrt{14}}{15}$
g)$\sqrt{15}$ **h)**2 **i)**$\frac{2\sqrt{30}}{9}$ **j)**$\sqrt{5}$ **3.a)**$\frac{\sqrt{6}}{6}$ **b)**$\frac{3\sqrt{5}}{5}$ **c)**$\frac{12\sqrt{17}}{17}$ **d)**$2\sqrt{5}$
e)$\sqrt{3}$ **f)**$\frac{3\sqrt{7}}{14}$ **g)**$\frac{2\sqrt{2}}{5}$ **h)**$2\sqrt{2}$ **i)**$\frac{\sqrt{15}}{4}$ **j)**$\frac{8\sqrt{6}}{15}$ **4.a)**$\frac{3\sqrt{5} + 5\sqrt{3}}{15}$
b)$\frac{3\sqrt{2} - \sqrt{6}}{6}$ **c)**$\frac{2\sqrt{3} + \sqrt{6}}{6}$ **d)**$\frac{10\sqrt{7} - 21\sqrt{5}}{35}$ **e)**$\frac{20\sqrt{3} + 3\sqrt{10}}{15}$
f)$\frac{6\sqrt{7} - 21\sqrt{6}}{14}$ **g)**$\sqrt{5} - 4\sqrt{2}$ **h)**$\frac{6\sqrt{7} - 7\sqrt{3}}{7}$ **5.a)**$\frac{3\sqrt{3} + 2\sqrt{2}}{6}$
b)$\frac{15\sqrt{2} - 4\sqrt{6}}{12}$ **c)**$\frac{21\sqrt{5} - 20\sqrt{3}}{30}$ **d)**$\frac{-3\sqrt{6}}{4}$ **e)**$\frac{2\sqrt{6} - 2\sqrt{3}}{3}$ **f)**$\frac{17}{6}$
g)$\frac{1}{5}$ **h)**$\frac{10\sqrt{3} - 9}{15}$

INVESTIGATE, page 41
Answers may vary. **a)**64, 16; 3, 7 **b)** $\frac{1}{\sqrt{2}}$, $\sqrt{2}$

Mathematics Around Us, page 42
1.$1000, 18%, $180, $1180; $3000, 19.5%, $585,
$3585; $3200, 16.5%, $528, $3728; $17 500, 21.5%,
$3762.50, $21 262.50 **2.a)**$I = \frac{Pr}{100}$ **b)**$A = P + \frac{Pr}{100}$
3.a)$6.51 **b)**$331.98 **4.a)**$1.08 **b)**$2.69 **c)**$5.56

Review Exercises, page 43

1.a) 2×13 **b)** $2 \times 2 \times 11$ **c)** $2 \times 3 \times 5 \times 7$ **d)** $2 \times 7 \times 13$ **e)** $3 \times 11 \times 13$ **f)** $2^2 \times 43$ **g)** $2^3 \times 11$ **2.a)** 3 **b)** 13 **c)** 5 **d)** 7 **e)** 12 **f)** 2 **3.a)** 240 **b)** 210 **c)** 600 **d)** 504 **e)** 168 **f)** 1155 **4.** 210 s **5.a)** -7 **b)** -12 **c)** 22 **d)** -17 **e)** 71 **f)** -1 **6.a)** -18 **b)** -96 **c)** 37 **7.a)** 30 **b)** 15 **c)** -25 **8.a)** $\frac{1}{8}$

b) $\frac{65}{12}$ **c)** $-\frac{1}{24}$ **d)** $\frac{103}{30}$ **e)** $-\frac{19}{72}$ **9.a)** -2 **b)** 5 **c)** 3 **d)** 4 **e)** -2 **f)** 0.1 **10.a)** $-\frac{35}{12}$ **b)** $\frac{19}{144}$ **c)** $\frac{679}{288}$ **d)** $-\frac{55}{144}$ **11.a)** $0.\overline{2}$ **b)** $-0.5\overline{4}$

c) 3.6 **d)** $-5.1\overline{6}$ **e)** -10.25 **f)** $0.\overline{692\ 307}$ **g)** $0.\overline{72}$ **12.a)** $\frac{323}{100}$ **b)** $\frac{43}{99}$ **c)** $\frac{14}{11}$ **d)** $\frac{1541}{495}$ **e)** $\frac{2539}{1110}$ **f)** $\frac{34\ 343}{9900}$ **13.** $\sqrt{48}$,

$\sqrt{3.6}$ **14.a)** $3\sqrt{3} - 6$, irrational **b)** -4, rational **c)** -6, rational **d)** $9 - \sqrt{3}$, irrational **15.a)** 8.6 **b)** 5.2 **c)** 17.9 **16.** 16 km **17.a)** $7\sqrt{2}$ **b)** $3\sqrt{3}$ **c)** $6\sqrt{5}$ **d)** $-18\sqrt{10}$ **e)** $4\sqrt{15}$ **f)** $10\sqrt{3}$ **18.a)** $24\sqrt{2}$ **b)** 72 **c)** -100 **d)** $-150\sqrt{2}$ **e)** $30\sqrt{3}$ **f)** -144 **g)** $-6\sqrt{30}$ **h)** 52 **19.a)** $5\sqrt{5}$ **b)** $3\sqrt{2}$ **c)** $8\sqrt{2}$ **d)** $3\sqrt{3}$ **e)** $\frac{7\sqrt{2}}{12}$ **f)** $\frac{-74\sqrt{5}}{5}$ **20.a)** $4 - \sqrt{6}$ **b)** $\sqrt{6} - 27$ **c)** $2\sqrt{10} - \sqrt{15}$ **d)** $\sqrt{30} - 2\sqrt{35}$ **21.a)** $\sqrt{6}$ **b)** -19 **c)** 2 **22.a)** $2\sqrt{3}$ **b)** 12 **c)** $2\sqrt{2}$ **d)** $\frac{1}{2}$ **e)** $\frac{3}{14}$

23.a) $\sqrt{6}$ **b)** $\frac{\sqrt{3}}{3}$ **c)** $\frac{\sqrt{2}}{2}$ **d)** 2 **e)** $\frac{2}{15}$

Chapter 2

Exercises 2-1, page 47

1. Variables are: a, b; x, y; m, n; x, y, z; p, q; x.

Coefficients are: $-1, 4$; -5; 7; $\frac{1}{3}$; 6; 8. Exponents are: $1, 3$; $2, 1$; $3, 2$; $4, 2, 1$; $6, 2$; 1; 0. **2.a)** -6 **b)** 12 **c)** -18 **d)** 72 **e)** -108 **f)** $-\frac{8}{9}$ **g)** $-\frac{4}{9}$ **h)** -18 **i)** 9 **j)** 36 **3.a)** 16 **b)** 64 **c)** 2 **d)** 1 **e)** 24 **f)** 64 **4.a)** $A = lw$; $P = 2l + 2w$ **b)** 180 m² **5.a)** $C = 2\pi r$ **b)** 157 cm **6.a)** $A = \pi r^2$ **b)** 707 cm² **7.** 2.4 m³ **8.** $S = 2\pi rl$ **9.a)** 500 kg **b)** 250 kg **10.a)** 300 m **b)** 750 m **11.a)** 184 kPa **b)** 1500 kPa **12.** $\frac{x^2}{y}$

The Mathematical Mind, page 49

Answers may vary. **1.a)** $25 + 4$ **b)** $36 + 16 + 4$ **c)** $81 + 4 + 1 + 1$ **d)** $81 + 25 + 9$ **e)** $121 + 9$ **f)** $100 + 64 + 4$ **g)** $100 + 100 + 4$ **h)** $400 + 25 + 9 + 1$ **2.a)** 85 **b)** 34 **3.** 3, (50, 65, 85)

Computer Power, page 50

1. \$117.72, \$10.01, \$127.73; \$127.73, \$10.86, \$138.59; \$138.59, \$11.78, \$150.37 **3.a)** \$619.56 **b)** about 8 years; a little more than 15 years; about 23 years **4.a)** \$245.01 **b)** \$708.41 **c)** \$1103.81 **5.** See Question 4. **6.a)** about 12 years **b)** about 9 years **c)** about 7 years **d)** about 6 years

Exercises 2-2, page 54

1.a) 16 **b)** $\frac{1}{25}$ **c)** $\frac{1}{3}$ **d)** 4 **e)** $\frac{3}{2}$ **f)** $\frac{16}{9}$ **g)** 2 **h)** 1 **2.a)** 1 **b)** $\frac{1}{9}$ **c)** $-\frac{1}{8}$ **d)** $-\frac{3}{2}$ **e)** $\frac{25}{9}$ **f)** 1 **g)** 10 000 **h)** 8 **3.a)** $(-7)^3$ **b)** b^{-5} **c)** x^{-4} **d)** 3^{-2} **e)** $(1.5)^{-2}$ **f)** $(-3.5)^{-2}$ **4.a)** $x^2 y^3$ **b)** $x^3 y^2$ **c)** $x^3 z^{-2}$ **d)** $x^2 y^{-3}$ **e)** $a^4 b^{-4}$ **f)** $a^3 b^{-2}$ **5.a)** $8\frac{1}{8}$ **b)** $\frac{3}{4}$ **c)** $\frac{9}{100}$

d) $\frac{1}{25}$ **e)** 8 **f)** $-\frac{27}{100}$ **g)** $\frac{1}{2}$ **h)** $\frac{9}{8}$ **6.a)** 8, -8 **b)** $-8, 8$ **c)** $-8, 8$ **d)** $\frac{1}{8}, -\frac{1}{8}$ **e)** 8, -8 **f)** $-\frac{1}{8}, \frac{1}{8}$ **7.a)** $\frac{3}{2}$ **b)** 0 **c)** $-\frac{3}{2}$ **d)** $\frac{99}{10}$ **e)** $-\frac{3}{2}$ **f)** $-\frac{99}{10}$ **g)** $-\frac{15}{4}$ **8.a)** $\frac{3}{2}$ **b)** $\frac{99}{25}$ **c)** $\frac{25}{2}$ **d)** 400 **e)** $-\frac{1}{5}$ **f)** 576 **g)** 36 **h)** $\frac{7}{10}$ **9.a)** $-\frac{1}{16}$ **b)** $\frac{1}{4}$ **c)** -2 **d)** $-\frac{1}{8}$ **e)** $\frac{3}{4}$ **f)** -1 **g)** $-\frac{9}{8}$ **h)** $-\frac{3}{4}$ **10.a)** $-\frac{3}{16}$ **b)** $\frac{1}{36}$ **c)** 1728 **d)** 0 **e)** $-\frac{4}{9}$ **f)** $\frac{1}{36}$ **g)** $-\frac{3}{2}$ **h)** $\frac{9}{4}$ **11.a)** 4^3 **b)** 3^{-2} **c)** $(-2)^{-5}$ **d)** 10^{-3} **e)** $(-5)^{-2}$ **f)** 5^0 **g)** $\left(\frac{1}{2}\right)^{-1}$ **h)** $\left(\frac{4}{3}\right)^{-1}$ **12.a)** 10^2 **b)** $(-10)^3$ **c)** $\left(\frac{3}{4}\right)^3$ **d)** -2^5 **e)** -0.1^3 **f)** $\left(\frac{1}{7}\right)^3$ **g)** 2^6 **h)** $\left(\frac{4}{3}\right)^3$ **13.a)** 3^{-2} **b)** 6^{-2} **c)** 10^{-4} **d)** $\left(\frac{3}{2}\right)^{-3}$ **e)** 5^{-2} **f)** 2^{-3} **g)** 5^{-2} **h)** $\left(\frac{3}{2}\right)^{-3}$ **14.a)** $(1.5)^{-1}$ **b)** $\left(\frac{1}{2}\right)^2$ **c)** 2^{-3} **d)** $\left(\frac{1}{2}\right)^{-5}$ **e)** $(-5)^{-3}$ **f)** $\left(\frac{2}{7}\right)^{-3}$

15.a) 0 **b)** -1 **c)** -3 **d)** -4 **e)** -4 **f)** $\frac{2}{3}$ **g)** $\frac{1}{2}$ **h)** 5

INVESTIGATE, page 55

8; 28

Exercises 2-3, page 58

1.a) x^7 **b)** a^7 **c)** b^9 **d)** m^9 **2.a)** x^2 **b)** y^4 **c)** n **d)** a^3 **3.a)** x^9 **b)** y^6 **c)** $a^6 b^6$ **d)** $x^2 y^6$ **4.a)** x^{-3} **b)** c^{-1} **c)** y^{-5} **d)** a^{-4} **5.a)** x **b)** m^{-4} **c)** a^4 **d)** 1 **e)** x **f)** b^3 **g)** d^{-1} **h)** 1 **6.a)** x^{-6} **b)** y^5 **c)** m^{10} **d)** 1 **e)** c **f)** x^2 **g)** b^{-5} **h)** t^{11} **7.a)** x^{-6} **b)** y^2 **c)** m^{-6} **d)** c^{-9} **e)** a^{-4} **f)** xy^{-2} **g)** $x^4 y^{-6}$ **h)** $a^4 b^{-4}$ **8.a)** b^{-1} **b)** 1 **c)** $x^2 y^{-1}$ **d)** xy^{-6} **e)** $c^7 d$ **f)** $m^4 n^{-4}$ **9.a)** -32 **b)** -4 **c)** -64 **d)** $-\frac{1}{32}$ **e)** -16 **f)** 64

10. $5^{-8} = 0.000\ 002\ 56$, $5^{-7} = 0.000\ 012\ 8$, $5^{-6} = 0.000\ 064$, $5^{-5} = 0.000\ 32$, $5^{-4} = 0.0016$, $5^{-3} = 0.008$, $5^{-2} = 0.04$, $5^{-1} = 0.2$, $5^0 = 1$; $5^1 = 5$, $5^2 = 25$, $5^3 = 125$, $5^4 = 625$, $5^5 = 3125$, $5^6 = 15\ 625$, $5^7 = 78\ 125$, $5^8 = 390\ 625$, $5^9 = 1\ 953\ 125$, $5^{10} = 9\ 765\ 625$, **a)** 78 125 **b)** 390 625 **c)** 125 **d)** 390 625 **e)** 0.000 012 8 **f)** 25 **11.a)** $27x^{-15}$ **b)** $-6a^{-8}$ **c)** $2x^2$ **d)** q^2 **e)** $-\frac{27}{8}x^{-5} y^3$ **f)** $a^{11} b^{-5} c^6$

Exercises 2-4, page 61

1.a) 5.94×10^9 **b)** 7.53×10^7 **c)** 9.2×10^{-5} **d)** 7.0×10^{-12} **e)** 1.47×10^{-8} **f)** 2.956×10^{14}

2.a)2.37×10^7 km^3 **b)**1.5×10^{11} m **c)**3.0×10^{13} cells
d)1.0×10^{-4} cm **3.a)**350 000 kg
b)50 000 000 000 cells
c)43 250 000 000 000 000 000 **d)**0.000 02 mm
4.a)2.78×10^{14} **b)**4.02×10^{13} **c)**1.73×10^2
d)4.04×10^{-13} **5.a)**3.55×10^6 **b)**4.78×10^{-3}
c)3.05×10^9 **d)**1.92×10^{-14} **6.**1.6×10^{13}; 1.6×10^{17};
1.6×10^{11} **7.**5.0×10^{24} atoms **8.a)**5200 **b)**Answers
may vary. 5200 days or about 14 years. **9.**about 79
billion years

Problem Solving, page 63
1.69 km/h **2.**90 km/h **3.**131 tickets **4.**21 days
5.Assume that 90 means 90%, average is 83%.
6.$3.67 **7.**60 km/h **8.a)**14 (1 large, 9 small, and 4
squares of 4 small squares) **b)**Answers may vary.
9.2^{22}; 2^{222} **10.**lists A and B **11.a)**any real number
between 6 and 15 **b)**any real number between −9 and
0 **c)**any real number between 5 and 50 **d)**any real
number between 0.1 and 1

Mathematics Around Us, page 64
1.2.0×10^4 diatoms **2.**1.0×10^{-8} kg **3.**4.0×10^{24}
diatoms **4.a)**16 diatoms; 256 diatoms; 4096 diatoms
b)about 2.5 days; about 5 days; about 7.5 days

Exercises 2-5, page 66
1.a)4 **b)**6 **c)**10 **d)**2 **e)**12 **f)**4 **g)**3 **h)**−4 **i)**5 **j)**7
k)−3 **l)**−10 **2.a)**$5^{\frac{1}{2}}$ **b)**$2^{\frac{1}{2}}$ **c)**$17^{\frac{1}{2}}$ **d)**$100^{\frac{1}{2}}$ **e)**$27^{\frac{1}{2}}$ **f)**$156^{\frac{1}{2}}$
g)$(-55)^{\frac{1}{3}}$ **h)**$85^{\frac{1}{2}}$ **i)**$111^{\frac{1}{3}}$ **j)**$21^{\frac{1}{2}}$ **k)**$(-9)^{\frac{1}{3}}$ **l)**$25^{\frac{1}{3}}$ **3.a)**8 **b)**8
c)27 **d)**27 **e)**1000 **f)**1000 **4.a)**4 **b)**27 **c)**9 **d)**8
e)125 **f)**64 **5.a)**9 **b)**216 **c)**16 **d)**25 **e)**1000 **f)**400
6.Mercury 88 days, Venus 224 days, Earth 364 days,
Mars 689 days, Jupiter 4340 days, Saturn
10 702 days, Uranus 30 911 days, Neptune
60 777 days, Pluto 91 330 days **7.a)**$x^{\frac{3}{2}}$ **b)**$m^{\frac{4}{3}}$ **c)**y^2
d)b^4 **e)**$x^{\frac{1}{2}}$ **f)**$m^{\frac{2}{3}}$ **g)**d **h)**$p^{\frac{2}{3}}$ **8.a)**32 **b)**16 **c)**81 **d)**243
e)256 **f)**1024 **9.a)**$\frac{1}{2}$ **b)**$\frac{1}{2}$ **c)**$\frac{1}{3}$ **d)**$\frac{1}{3}$ **e)**$\frac{1}{5}$ **f)**$-\frac{1}{4}$
10.a)4 **b)**$\frac{1}{16}$ **c)**9 **d)**$\frac{1}{27}$ **e)**$\frac{4}{25}$ **f)**$\frac{64}{27}$

Review Exercises, page 68
1.a)29 **b)**9 **c)**21 **d)**49 **e)**100 **f)**−50 **g)**20 **h)**100
2.a)34 cm^3 **b)**180 cm^3 **3.a)**1 **b)**$-\frac{1}{8}$ **c)**$\frac{1}{9}$ **d)**$9\frac{1}{9}$ **e)**1
f)$\frac{1}{72}$ **g)**8 **h)**1 **4.a)**$-\frac{1}{8}$ **b)**$-\frac{1}{8}$ **c)**−4 **d)**$\frac{1}{24}$ **e)**$-\frac{5}{4}$ **f)**−1
g)$-\frac{7}{8}$ **h)**$\frac{1}{64}$ **5.a)**9.62×10^{18} **b)**1.48×10^{-11}
6.a)2.18×10^{19} m^3 **b)**1.40×10^{27} m^3 **7.a)**x^7 **b)**c^8 **c)**y^3
d)a^5 **e)**x^8 **f)**a^6b^4 **g)**x^{-1} **h)**x^5 **i)**x^{-6} **j)**x **k)**x^{-6}
l)$x^{-1}y^{-2}$ **8.a)**−32 **b)**4 **c)**16 **d)**−8

Cumulative Review, page 69
1.a)5, 180 **b)**6, 180 **c)**12, 312 **d)**6, 2730 **e)**14, 4620
2.a)4 **b)**−162 **3.a)**−37 **b)**−30 **4.a)**−11 **b)**$-\frac{39}{8}$ **c)**$\frac{47}{18}$

5.a)$4\sqrt{2}$ **b)**$6\sqrt{2}$ **c)**$-15\sqrt{3}$ **d)**$60\sqrt{2}$ **e)**$-36\sqrt{2}$ **f)**576
6.a)13.6 **b)**12.1 **c)**24.3 **7.a)**$\sqrt{6}$ **b)**$-5\sqrt{6}$ **c)**−60
d)$\sqrt{15} - 2\sqrt{6}$ **e)**12 **f)**14 **8.a)**0 **b)**$-5\sqrt{2}$ **9.a)**16 **b)**$\sqrt{2}$
c)2 **d)**3 **e)**$\frac{2}{15}$ **10.a)**64 **b)**6 **c)**4 **d)**125 **e)**13 **f)**$\frac{4}{9}$ **g)**1
h)8 **11.a)**c^6 **b)**y^9 **c)**d^{16} **d)**e^{14} **e)**x^3 **f)**y^2 **g)**b^{12} **h)**e
i)c^{10} **j)**a^9b^6 **k)**x^6y^4 **l)**x^8y^4 **m)**b^{-3} **n)**x^{-6} **o)**e^{-7} **p)**d^{-1}
12.a)5^3 **b)**$(-4)^3$ **c)**2^{-3} **d)**$(-2)^5$ **e)**3^{-3} **13.**Answers
may vary. **a)**the exponents were multiplied instead
of added **b)**the base should have remained the same
c)the exponents were divided instead of subtracted
d)the exponents were added instead of multiplied
e)the coefficient should have been squared **f)**the
exponents were subtracted, but the bases were not the
same. **14.a)**6.0×10^6 **b)**5.68×10^{-3} **c)**1.52
d)2.41×10^{-2} **15.a)**2 **b)** −2 **c)**4 **d)**3 **e)**27 **f)**4
16.a)$25^{\frac{1}{2}}$ **b)**$27^{\frac{1}{3}}$ **c)**$32^{\frac{1}{5}}$ **d)** 36^1 **e)**$49^{\frac{3}{2}}$

Chapter 3

Exercise 3-1, page 73
1.a)$2x - 3y$ **b)**$-4a + 15b$ **c)**$-5c + 7d$ **d)**$-7x - 7y$
e)$30m - 12n$ **f)**$-5b$ **2.a)**$-9r + 16s - 4t$
b)$24m + 12n - 9p$ **c)**$-5x - 27y + 14z$
d)$2h - 21k - 6l$ **e)**$-6a + 3b + 11c$ **f)**$-18x - 2y - 6z$
g)$4a^2 - 2a - 4$ **h)**$6x^2 - 9x + 5$ **i)**$-5m^2 - 7m - 7$
j)$5p^2 - 4p + 13$ **3.a)**$xy + 3xz$ **b)**$6mn + 5mp - 11np$
c)$10ab + 4ac - 6bc$ **d)**$-5de + 3df - 15ef$
e)$-5pq + 8pr + 3qr$ **f)**$25xy - 29xz$ **g)**$12ab + 2ac$
h)$58xy$ **i)**$2x^2 - 13xy$ **j)**$-7m^2 - 5mn$ **k)**$-4y^2 - xy$
l)$-18c^2 - 14cd$ **4.a)**$7x^2y - 4x^2y^2$ **b)**$-7q^2p^2 + 3p^2q^3$
c)$- y^2z^3 + y^3z^3 - 3y^3z$ **d)**$a^3b^2 - ab^3 - ba^3$
e)$- 2m^2n^2 - 7m + 2n - 2mn$ **f)**$a^2 - 3c^2 - 2ab + 2$
5.7.66 m **6.**15.71 m

INVESTIGATE, page 74
$2\pi x$

Mathematics Around Us, page 75
1.1, 3 m, 4 m, 28 m^2, 50 m^2; 2, 4 m, 5 m, 50 m^2,
79 m^2; 3, 5 m, 6 m, 79 m^2, 113 m^2; 4, 6 m, 7 m,
113 m^2, 154 m^2 **2.a)**$r = n + 2$; $r = n + 3$
b)$A = \pi(n + 2)^2$ m^2; $A = \pi(n + 3)^2$ m^2 **3.**$4\pi(2n + 5)$

Exercises 3-2, page 77
1.a)$35x^6$ **b)**$12a^2$ **c)**$-54m^5$ **d)**$10n^3$ **e)**$56y^9$ **f)**$-28b^4$
g)$6t^8$ **h)**$72p^9$ **2.a)**$18xy$ **b)**$32p^2q$ **c)**$35m^3n$ **d)**$14a^2b$
e)$-45r^2s^3$ **f)**$-44c^2d$ **g)**$6s^2t^3$ **h)**$2b^3c^5$ **3.a)**$-8ab^3$
b)$-12m^5n^7$ **c)**$21a^3b^5$ **d)**$24p^3q^7$ **e)**$24x^6y^3$ **f)**$-6a^4b^4$
4.a)$4x^3$ **b)**$9m^4$ **c)**$-9a^6$ **d)**$4b$ **e)**$4d^2$ **f)**$-4n^2$ **g)**$8b^4$
h)$10p^2q^3$ **5.a)**$\frac{9}{2}r^4s^2$ **b)**$-3x^4y^3$ **c)**$\frac{5}{2}p^6q^4$ **d)**$2a^2b$
e)$-8m^6$ **f)**$6x^5y^6$ **6.a)**$54x^{11}$ **b)**$-12a^{10}b$ **c)**$45s^{10}t^5$
d)$-100p^7q^3$ **e)**$-24m^5n^9$ **f)**$675x^{10}y^{14}$ **7.a)**$6x^6y^5$
b)$-6q^7$ **c)**$\frac{7}{2}a^2b^3$ **d)**$2x^5$ **e)**$-16m^8n^8$ **f)**$a^{12}b^{13}$

8.a) $A = \frac{\pi d^2}{4}$ **b)** $A = \pi d^2$ **c)** $V = \frac{\pi d^3}{6}$ **9.** $\pi : 4$ **10.** $2 : \pi$

11. $4 : 3$ **12.** $2 : 1$ **13.** $\frac{3}{2}x$; 10.5 units **14.** $9k^2$

15.a) $-6a^3b^3$ **b)** $-16a^5b^7$ **c)** $-80a^8b^7$ **d)** $100a^6b^6$

e) $-10ab^{-1}$ **f)** $4a^4b^5$ **16.** $\frac{2}{3}$

Exercises 3-3, page 80

1.a) $10a + 4$ **b)** $10x - 10y$ **c)** $-6m^2 - 3$ **d)** $3p + 7$
e) $11x^2 - 4x$ **f)** $-5k + 11l$ **2.a)** $11m^2 - 3m + 2$
b) $4a^3 + 4a^2 + 3a$ **c)** $-3x^2 - 20x + 17y$
d) $9t^3 - 18t^2 - 15t - 1$ **e)** $8a^3 - 18$ **f)** $-5x^2 - 8x + 5$
3.a) $P = 15.5n - 30\ 000$ **b)** $\$47\ 500; \$125\ 000; \$280\ 000$
4.a) $10x^2 - 6x^2y$; third **b)** $p^2q^2 - 3p + 2q$; fourth
c) $3m^2 - 3m - 2n^2 + 2n$; second **d)** 3; zero
e) $-3xy^2 + 2xy$; third **5.a)** $10x^2 - 8x + 16$
b) $9z^3 - 2z^2 + 1$ **6.a)** $2x^2y - 7xy + 5xy^2$
b) $4m^2n^2 - 6mn + 7mn^3$ **7.a)** $-3x^2 - y^2 - 2$; second
b) $3m^2$; second **c)** $-5x^2y^2 + 7x^2y - xy - 6xy^2$; fourth
d) $2a^2b^2 - 2a^2b - 2ab^2 - 2b^2$; fourth **8.** Answers
may vary.

INVESTIGATE, page 81
Answer is always twice the largest number chosen.

Problem Solving, page 83
1. 05 : 00 **2.** 362 880 **3.** 161 280, 201 600 **4.** 1002
5. 301 **6.a)** 2500 **b)** 5050 **7.** 50 **8.a)** 3893 **b)** 706 **c)** 345
9. 228 **10.** 245 **11.** 1480

Exercises 3-4, page 85
1.a) $20x^2 + 40$ **b)** $14a - 35$ **c)** $16k - 24k^2$
d) $24b^2 - 36b + 108$ **e)** $45m^2 - 63m + 27$
f) $24p^2 - 15p + 21$ **2.a)** $3x + 19$ **b)** $24 - 5a$ **c)** $10 - 2y$
d) $28m - 33$ **e)** $-13p^2 - 12p$ **f)** $-8x - 21y$
3.a) $60x^2 - 48x$ **b)** $6a - 21a^2$ **c)** $12p^2 - 6pq$
d) $135n^3 - 90n^2$ **e)** $21m^4n + 42m^3$ **f)** $-56x^2y - 40x^3$
4.a) $5x - 6$ **b)** $-x - 3$ **c)** $42b - 36c$ **d)** $16m - 37n + 14$
5.a) $9x^3 + 13x^2y$ **b)** $-2a^4 - 27a^3b$ **c)** $4p^3 + 51p^2q$
d) $-34a^4 + 66a^3b - 80a^3$ **6.** $2n(n - 1)$
7.a) $2a^3b^2 - 2a^2b^3 - 2ab^2$ **b)** $3x^3y^3 + 3x^3y^2 - 3x^2y^2$
c) $5m^2n^3 - 5m^3n^3 - 15m^3n^2$ **d)** $5x^2 - y^2 - 7xy + 2y$
e) $2b^3 - 2b^2c - 2c^2 + 5bc$
f) $7x^3 - 7xy^2 - 2xy - 2x^2y - 2y^3$ **8.a)** 66 **b)** $\frac{n(n - 1)}{2}$
9.a) $8a^2b - 7a^2 + 15a$; third **b)** $21mn^2 - 33m^2n$; third
c) $2xy^2 - 15x^2y$; third **d)** $43s^3 + 21s^2 - 38s$; third
e) $5x^3 - 14x^2y - 53xy^2$; third
f) $55xy - 15y^2 + 2x^2$; second
10.a) $99a^2 + 27a$ **b)** $10x - 6x^2$ **c)** $40x^2 + 30x$
d) $-20a^3 - 8a^2 + 12a$ **e)** $3.6n^2 - 8.4n$
f) $10x^3 - 30x^2 + 15x$ **11.a)** $29p - 18q + 29$
b) $-29k - 4l - 75$ **c)** $3x^2 + 5xy - 9x - 2y^2 - 14y$
d) $5a^2 - 100a$ **e)** $45x^2 - 8x^2y - 2x^3$
f) $30m^2n - m^2 - 94mn$ **12.a)** $a + 5b$ **b)** $10a + 4b$
c) $a^2 + b^2$ **d)** $a^3 - a^2b - ab^2 - b^3$ **13.** $A = 2\pi r(r + n)$
14.a) $911\ cm^2$ **b)** $8\pi r^2$ **c)** $8\pi r^2 - 10\pi r$ **d)** $3\pi r^2 + 14\pi r$

INVESTIGATE, page 87

1.

Number of sides	3	4	5	6	7
Number of diagonals	0	2	5	9	14

2.a) $n - 3$; $\frac{n(n - 3)}{2}$ **b)** $\frac{n(n - 1)}{2}$, n

Exercises 3-5, page 90
1.a) $8x^2 + 14xy + 3$ **b)** $30m^2 - 7m - 2$
c) $8c^2 - 22c + 15$ **d)** $9x^2 - 49$ **e)** $16t^2 - 12t - 40$
f) $24x^2 - 62x + 14$ **2.a)** $g^2 + 2gh + h^2$ **b)** $x^2 + 2xy + y^2$
c) $m^2 + 2mn + n^2$ **d)** $b^2 + 2bc + c^2$ **e)** $p^2 - 2pq + q^2$
f) $k^2 - 2kl + l^2$ **g)** $s^2 - 2st + t^2$ **h)** $u^2 - 2uv + v^2$
3.a) $9x^2 + 6xy + y^2$ **b)** $x^2 + 10xy + 25y^2$
c) $9a^2 + 12a + 4$ **d)** $25x^2 - 90x + 81$
e) $16m^2 - 56m + 49$ **f)** $16y^2 + 88y + 121$
g) $25t^2 - 100t + 100$ **h)** $25 + 60b + 36b^2$
4.a) $6x^2 + 5xy + y^2$ **b)** $15a^2 + 2ab - b^2$
c) $6x^2 + 5xy - 4y^2$ **d)** $x^2 + 7xy + 12y^2$
e) $35m^2 - 19mn + 2n^2$ **f)** $18x^2 - 48xy + 14y^2$
5.a) $9a^2 + 30ab + 25b^2$ **b)** $4m^2 - 28mn + 49n^2$
c) $36s^2 - 24st + 4t^2$ **d)** $16p^2 - 24pq + 9q^2$
e) $64x^2 - 48xy + 9y^2$ **f)** $9s^2 + 30st + 25t^2$
g) $25f^2 - 40fg + 16g^2$ **h)** $25y^4 + 70y^2z^2 + 49z^2$
6.a) $x^2 - y^2$ **b)** $4m^2 - 25n^2$ **c)** $81a^2 - 16b^2$
d) $36x^2 - 4y^2$ **e)** $49p^2 - 4q^2$ **f)** $144m^2 - 81$
7.a) $3x^2 - 8x - 1$ **b)** $21x^2 - 18x$ **c)** $12m^2 - 26m + 36$
d) $6cd$ **e)** $-18a^2 - 51ab + 2b^2$ **f)** $9x^2 - 26xy + 7y^2$
8.a) $7x^2 - 11x - 1$ **b)** $-3s^2 + 13st - 11t^2$
c) $3x^2 + 4xy - 5y^2$ **d)** $5m^2 + 117mn - 131n^2$ **e)** $-40xy$
f) $-7x^4 - 19x^2 - 19$ **9.a)** $6x^3 + 7x^2 - 15x + 4$
b) $4m^3 - 19m^2 + 33m - 36$ **c)** $6a^3 + a^2 - 58a + 45$
d) $15p^3 - 8p^2 - 6p + 4$ **10.a)** $6x^3 + 2x^2 - 128x - 160$
b) $40p^3 - 218p^2 + 309p - 126$ **c)** $24x^3 - 62x^2 - 7x + 30$
d) $18x^3 + 3x^2 - 88x - 80$ **e)** $50a^3 - 235a^2 + 228a - 63$
f) $125m^3 - 150m^2 + 60m - 8$ **11.a)** $10x + 2y$;
$4x^2 + 2xy - 4y^2$ **b)** $14x + 6y$; $10x^2 + 14xy + 2y^2$
c) $16x + 18$; $12x^2 + 38x + 20$ **12.a)** $3m^2 - 9m - 30$
b) $6x^2 - 4xy - 10y^2$ **c)** $30p^2 - 145p + 140$
d) $8x^3 - 68x^2y + 84xy^2$ **e)** $18a^3 - 39a^2b - 15ab^2$
f) $12x^3 + 48x^2y + 48xy^2$
13.a) $30x^2 + 108x + 70$ **b)** $6m^2 - 2m - 48$
c) $52x^2 + 107xy - 60y^2$ **d)** $-3x^2y^2 - 5xy + 28$
e) $-12a^2 + 15ab - 20b^2$ **f)** $7x^2y^2 + 14xy + 91$
14.a) $8x^2 + 57x - 69$ **b)** $-4s^2 - 39s - 11$
c) $8x^3 - 6x^2 - 26x + 40$
d) $-12m^2 + 18mn + 47m - 28n - 20$
e) $-12y^3 + 91y^2 - 39y - 70$ **f)** $42x^3 - 70x^2 + 98x - 54$
15.a) $m^2 + 11m + 26$ **b)** $3m^2 + 16m + 28$
c) $m^3 + 5m^2 + 6m - 5$ **16.a)** $4a^2 + 4ab + 4b^2$
b) $-5a^2 + 12ab - 3b^2$ **c)** $8a^2 + 6ab + 2b^2$

17.a)$l = 60 - w$ **b)**$A = w(60 - w)$ **c)**decreases by 1 cm

INVESTIGATE, page 92

2.The square of the average of any two natural numbers that differ by two is always one more than their product. **4.**Decimals, fractions, negative numbers, irrational numbers **5.a)**The area of the square is always one more than the area of the rectangle which represents the product. **b)**Natural numbers, decimals, fractions, irrational numbers

Exercises 3-6, page 94

1.a)$7x$ **b)**y^4 **c)**$4a^2b$ **d)**$8m^2n^2$ **e)**$3x^2y^2$ **f)**$18s^2t$
2.a)$3x(x + 2)$ **b)**$4y^2(2y - 1)$ **c)**$5p^2(p - 3)$
d)$8mn(3m + 2n)$ **e)**$6a^2b^2(2 + 3a)$ **f)**$-7x^2y^2(4y + 5x)$
3.a)$w(3w - 7w^2 + 4)$ **b)**$-2x(x^4 - 2x + 3 - x^2)$
c)$4(2x^2 - 3x^4 + 4)$ **d)**$5ab(b + 2 - 3a)$
e)$3xy(17x + 13y - 24)$ **f)**$3m^2n^2(3m^2 - 2mn + 4n^2)$
4.a)$5(y - 2)$ **b)**$8(m + 3)$ **c)**$6(1 + 2x^2)$ **d)**$5a(7 + 2a)$
e)$7b^2(7 - b)$ **f)**$7z^2(5 - 2z^4)$ **g)**$9d(5d^4 - 4)$
h)$13s^2(4s - 1)$ **5.a)**$3(x^2 + 4x - 2)$ **b)**$x(3x + 5x^2 + 1)$
c)$a(a^2 + 9a - 3)$ **d)**$3x(x + 2x^2 - 4)$
e)$8y(2y - 4 + 3y^2)$ **f)**$8xy(x - 4y + 2xy)$
6.a)$3(2b^7 - b + 4)$ **b)**$y(5y^2 + 6y + 3)$
c)$16x(1 + 2x + 3x^3)$ **d)**$12y^2(y^2 - 1 + 2y)$
e)$a(9a^2 + 7a + 18)$ **f)**$5z(2z^2 - 3z + 6)$
7.a)$5x(5y + 3x)$ **b)**$7mn(2m - 3n)$ **c)**$3a^2b^2(3b - 4)$
d)$4xy(x - 4y)$ **e)**$6pq(2p + 3q)$ **f)**$3m^2n^2(9m - 5n)$
8.a)$5a^2b^2(2a + 3b^2 - 1)$ **b)**$4mn(3n - 2 - 5m)$
c)$5x^2y(4 - 3y + 5xy)$ **d)**$7ab^2(a^2b + 2a - 3)$
e)$8x^2y^2(x^2y^2 - 2xy + 4)$ **f)**$6abc(3a - 1 + 5c - 4bc)$
9.a)$(a + b)(3x + 7)$ **b)**$(2x - y)(m - 5)$
c)$(x + 4)(x^2 + y^2)$ **d)**$(a + 3b)(5x - 9y)$
e)$(x - 3)(10y + 7)$ **f)**$(w + x)(7w - 10)$
10.a)$(x - 7)(3x^2 + 2x + 5)$ **b)**$(a - b)(2m + 3n - 7)$
c)$(x^2 + y)(5a^2 - 7a + 8)$ **d)**$(b - a)(6a - 4b - 3)$
e)$(2x + y)(4m^2 - 3m - 7)$ **f)**$(3a - 2b)(2x^2 + 5x + 9)$
11.a)$\frac{\pi}{4}(x^2 - y^2)$ **b)**$\pi(x^2 + 2xy)$ **12.**$x^2(1 + \frac{3\pi}{4})$
13.a)$\pi r^2(h + \frac{2r}{3})$ **b)**$2\pi r(h + r)$ **14.a)**$(x + 3)(x + y)$
b)$(x + 1)(x^2 + 1)$ **c)**$(a + 2b)(5m + 1)$
d)$(x - 2y)(3x + 5)$ **e)**$(5m - 3)(m + 2n)$
f)$(a - 3b)(2a - 3)$ **15.**Answers may vary.
a)$5ax + 5bx, 15x - 15xp, -5mx - 5nx$
b)$2a^2x - 2a^2, 2a^2p - 2a^2q, 2a^2m + 4a^2n$
16. Answers may vary. $3mn^2x + 3mn^2y + 3mn^2$

Mathematics Around Us, page 97
1.380 351 m² **2.**1 521 404 m³

Exercises 3-7, page 99

1.a)$(x + 6)(x + 4)$ **b)**$(m + 3)(m + 2)$ **c)**$(a + 8)(a + 2)$
d)$(p + 4)(p + 4)$ **e)**$(y + 7)(y + 6)$ **f)**$(d + 2)(d + 2)$
g)$(x - 4)(x - 3)$ **h)**$(c - 9)(c - 8)$ **i)**$(a - 6)(a - 1)$
j)$(b - 8)(b - 4)$ **k)**$(s - 10)(s - 2)$ **l)**$(x - 7)(x - 7)$

2.a)$(y + 5)(y - 1)$ **b)**$(b + 20)(b - 1)$ **c)**$(p + 18)(p - 3)$
d)$(x + 14)(x - 2)$ **e)**$(a - 4b)(a + 6b)$
f)$(k + 6l)(k - 3l)$ **g)**$(x - 4)(x + 2)$ **h)**$(n - 8)(n + 3)$
i)$(a - 5)(a + 4)$ **j)**$(d - 9)(d + 5)$
k)$(m - 15n)(m + 6n)$ **l)**$(y - 8z)(y + 6z)$
3.a)$(x + 12)(x + 2)$ **b)**$(m - 5)(m - 10)$
c)$(a - 6)(a - 5)$ **d)**$(x + 3)(x + 3)$ **e)**$(x + 9y)(x + 8y)$
f)$(a - 6b)(a - 6b)$ **g)**$(x - 2)(x + 10)$ **h)**$(d - 8)(d + 2)$
i)$(b + 9)(b - 2)$ **j)**$(m - 12)(m + 5)$
k)$(a - 15b)(a + 3b)$ **l)**$(y + 5z)(y - 4z)$
4.a)$(p + 13)(p + 2)$ **b)**$(x + 41)(x - 1)$
c)$(m - 9)(m + 8)$ **d)**$(t - 1)(t - 12)$ **e)**$(y + 4z)(y + 9z)$
f)$(m + 12n)(m - 8n)$ **g)**$(s + 25)(s - 4)$
h)$(c - 4)(c - 4)$ **i)**$(p - 10)(p + 9)$ **j)**$(k + 5)(k + 6)$
k)$(r - s)(r - 9s)$ **l)**$(c - 20d)(c + 4d)$
5.a)$(ab + 1)(ab + 1)$ **b)**$(mn - 9)(mn + 4)$
c)$(xy - 9)(xy - 6)$ **d)**$(pq - 17)(pq - 3)$
e)$(cd - 12)(cd + 3)$ **f)**$(xy + 3)(xy - 24)$
g)$(ab + 16)(ab + 3)$ **h)**$(mn + 2)(mn - 30)$
i)$(st - 6)(st - 12)$ **6.a)**±9, ±11, ±19 **b)**±1, ±4, ±11
c)±12, ±13, ±15, ±20, ±37
d)±4, ±7, ±11, ±17, ±28, ±59 **e)**±16, ±40 **f)**±14, ±50
7.Answers may vary. **a)**4, 6, −14, −24, −36 **b)**3, 4, −5, −12, −21 **c)**3, 8, 15, 24, 35 **d)**13, 28, 45, 64, 85
e)4, 10, 18, 28, 40 **f)**6, 10, 12, −8, −18
8.a)$2(x + 1)(x + 3)$ **b)**$5(a - 1)(a + 4)$
c)$3(y + 2)(y - 6)$ **d)**$5(y - 4)(y - 4)$
e)$2(m + 8n)(m - 7n)$ **f)**$9y(x + 1)(x + 5)$
9.a)$4(x + 3)(x + 4)$ **b)**$5(a + 2)(a - 6)$
c)$3(n - 5)(n - 4)$ **d)**$3(p - 4)(p + 9)$
e)$7(x + 2y)(x - 14y)$ **f)**$3(a - b)(a - 5b)$
10.a)$4(y + 2)(y - 7)$ **b)**$3(m + 2)(m + 4)$
c)$4(x - 3)(x + 4)$ **d)**$10(x + 2)(x + 6)$
e)$5a(m - 1)(m - 7)$ **f)**$7d(c - 3d)(c - 2d)$
11.a)$15a(a + 3b)(a + 3b)$ **b)**$6p(p + 6q)(p - 5q)$
c)$7xy(xy - 5)(xy - 4)$ **d)**$3n^2(m + 4)(m + 8)$
e)$4a(a - 4b)(a + 3b)$ **f)**$5xy^2(x + 6y)(x - 4y)$
12.a)$(x^2 + 2)(x^2 + 5)$ **b)**$(a^2 + 2b^2)(a^2 + 7b^2)$
c)$(m^2 + 4)(m^2 + 9)$ **d)**$2(b^2 + 3)(b^2 + 5)$
e)$3(c^2 + 1)(c^2 + 7)$ **f)**$5(x^2 + 3y^2)(x^2 + 2y^2)$
13.a)$(x + y + 10)(x + y - 1)$
b)$(p - 2q - 8)(p - 2q - 3)$ **c)**$3(y + 1)(3y - 13)$
d)$(x + 1)(x + 3)(x^2 + 4x + 5)$
e)$(2m - n - 5p)(2m - n + 4p)$
f)$12(x + 3y + 2)(x - y + 2)$ **14.a)**$4a^2$
b)$2(a - 3b)(a - 2b)$ **c)**$(7a - 5b)(3b - a)$
d)$(a^2 - b^2 - 2)(a^2 - b^2 + 1)$ **15.a)**Answers may vary.
$x^2 + 3x + 2, x^2 + x - 2, x^3 - 7x - 6$ **b)**Answers may vary. $x^3 + 3x^2 + 3x + 2, x^3 + 6x^2 + 10x + 4$
16.$x^4 + 2x^3$

INVESTIGATE, page 100
$b^2 = 4c; b^2 = 4ac$

Exercises 3-8, page 102
1.a)3, 2 **b)**6 , 3 **c)**−5, −3 **d)**−5, 3 **e)**−3, 10 **f)**−6, 4
2.a)$(2x + 3)(x + 2)$ **b)**$(2a + 3)(a + 4)$
c)$(3y + 1)(2y + 3)$ **d)**$(2k + 1)(k + 1)$ **e)**$(3s + 1)(s + 1)$
f)$(2x + 1)(4x + 3)$ **3.a)**$(5x − 2)(x − 1)$
b)$(3n − 2)(n − 3)$ **c)**$(2c − 1)(7c − 3)$
d)$(2x − 5)(x − 3)$ **e)**$(3x − y)(x − 7y)$
f)$(2a − b)(2a − b)$ **4.a)**$(3t − 2)(t + 3)$
b)$(3k + 4)(2k − 1)$ **c)**$(2r − 1)(4r + 3)$
d)$(4m − 5)(m + 2)$ **e)**$(5y − 1)(y + 4)$
f)$(2d + 5)(2d − 3)$ **5.a)**$(5a + 3)(a − 2)$
b)$(3x + 2)(x − 5)$ **c)**$(2m − 7)(m + 3)$
d)$(4k + 3)(k − 3)$ **e)**$(3x + 4y)(2x − 3y)$
f)$(5a − 2b)(3a + b)$ **6.a)**$(3x + 1)(x + 4)$
b)$(2m − 3)(m − 4)$ **c)**$(2s − 5)(2s − 5)$
d)$(3x + 2)(3x + 2)$ **e)**$(3y + 4z)(2y + 3z)$
f)$(4a − b)(2a − 3b)$ **7.a)**$(5x − 3)(2x + 1)$
b)$(6k − 5)(k + 1)$ **c)**$(5g + 1)(3g − 2)$
d)$(9p − 2)(p + 1)$ **e)**$(2c + 5d)(4c − d)$
f)$(5x + 2y)(3x − 2y)$ **8.a)**$(2x − 1)(2x − 1)$
b)$(2h + 1)(h + 2)$ **c)**$(4q − 3)(q − 5)$
d)$(5u − 2)(2u − 5)$ **e)**$(10m + 3n)(m − 2n)$
f)$(4c − 3d)(2c + 5d)$ **9.a)**$(3h − 4)(2h − 3)$
b)$(5r − 1)(2r + 3)$ **c)**$(2w + 3)(w + 5)$
d)$(7t + 1)(2t − 3)$ **e)**$(5x + y)(2x − 7y)$
f)$(3a − 4b)(3a − 4b)$ **10.a)**$x(3y − 2)(y − 3)$
b)$n(3m − 4)(m − 3)$ **c)**$y(x − 5)(4x + 3)$
d)$xy(2x − 3)(x + 5)$ **e)**$mn(2m − 7)(m + 3)$
f)$xy(3x + y)(2x − 3y)$ **11.a)**$10(2x + 3)(x + 2)$
b)$5(3a − 1)(a − 4)$ **c)**$3(3a − 2)(2a + 3)$
d)$2(4r − 5)(2r + 1)$ **e)**$6(2x − 3y)(2x − 3y)$
f)$4(3a + 2b)(a − 5b)$ **12.a)**$3x(2x + 5)(x + 3)$
b)$2a(3a − 2)(a + 5)$ **c)**$3y(3x − 5)(2x + 3)$
d)$5m(2m + 3)(m − 4)$ **e)**$3a(3a − 7)(a − 2)$
f)$7a(3b − 1)(2b + 3)$ **13.a)**25, 12 **b)**8, 9 **c)**12, −10
d)−22, 10 **e)**−22, −12 **f)**−22, 21
14.a)$(4x − 1)(8x − 3)$ **b)**$(8s + 1)(3s − 2)$
c)$(4a + 7)(a + 3)$ **d)**$(4x − 3y)(x + 6y)$
e)$(5a + 3b)(2a − 5b)$ **f)**$(7x − y)(3x + 4y)$
15.a)$(7x − 6)(3x + 5)$ **b)**$(9x − 2)(8x + 3)$
c)$(5x + 4)(3x − 8)$ **d)**$(8x + 3y)(6x − 5y)$
e)$(12c − 5d)(2c + 3d)$ **f)**$(5y + 2z)(8y − 3z)$

Exercises 3-9, page 105
1.a)$(x + 7)(x − 7)$ **b)**$(2b + 11)(2b − 11)$
c)$(3m + 8)(3m − 8)$ **d)**$(9f + 4)(9f − 4)$
e)$(5y + 12)(5y − 12)$ **f)**$(7x + 6)(7x − 6)$
g)$(4 + 9y)(4 − 9y)$ **h)**$(13 + 4t)(13 − 4t)$
i)$(10m + 7)(10m − 7)$ **j)**$(8b + 1)(8b − 1)$
k)$(11a + 20)(11a − 20)$ **l)**$(6b + 5)(6b − 5)$
m)$(5p + 9)(5p − 9)$ **n)**$(12m + 7)(12m − 7)$
o)$(6 + 11x)(6 − 11x)$ **p)**$(1 + 5q)(1 − 5q)$
2.a)$(2s + 3t)(2s − 3t)$ **b)**$(4x + 7y)(4x − 7y)$
c)$(9a + 8b)(9a − 8b)$ **d)**$(11c + 10d)(11c − 10d)$
e)$(p + 6q)(p − 6q)$ **f)**$9(4y + 3z)(4y − 3z)$

g)$(5m + 13n)(5m − 13n)$ **h)**$(2e + 15f)(2e − 15f)$
i)$(4m + 9n)(4m − 9n)$ **j)**$(8x + 15y)(8x − 15y)$
k)$(7a + 11b)(7a − 11b)$ **l)**$4(3b + 5c)(3b − 5c)$
3.a)$8(m + 3)(m − 3)$ **b)**$6(x + 5)(x − 5)$
c)$5(2x + y)(2x − y)$ **d)**$2(3b + 8)(3b − 8)$
e)$3(2a + 5)(2a − 5)$ **f)**$2(3p + 7)(3p − 7)$
g)$5(4s + 9)(4s − 9)$ **h)**$3(2p + 11)(2p − 11)$
i)$3x(2x + 3)(2x − 3)$ **j)**$2m(4m + 7)(4m − 7)$
k)$7b(3a + 2)(3a − 2)$ **l)**$3t^2(5s + 3)(5s − 3)$
m)$(x − y − z)(x − y + z)$ **n)**$(2a + b + 9)(2a + b − 9)$
o)$(6a − b)(12a + b)$ **p)**$(4x − 2y + 5z)(4x − 2y − 5z)$
4.a)$−5(2x + 9)$ **b)**$4(m + 1)(4m − 3)$ **c)**$24a$ **d)**$96yz$
e)$−(11p − 5)(5p + 9)$ **f)**$−15(x + 1)(3x + 1)$
g)$(x − 3)(x + 3)(x − 2)(x + 2)$
h)$(a + 4)(a − 4)(a + 1)(a − 1)$ **i)**$(y + 3)(y − 3)(y^2 + 4)$
5.About 485 000 cm^2 **6.a)**$V = \frac{4}{3}h(s^2 − h^2)$

b)2 585 173 m^3 **7.**The two pieces can be rearranged
to form a rectangle $(x + y)$ by $(x − y)$.
8.a)$x^2 − 2x^2y + x^2y^2$ **b)**$2x^2y − x^2y^2$
9.a)$8(d + 2e)(d − 2e)$ **b)**$(5m + \frac{1}{2}n)(5m − \frac{1}{2}n)$

c)$2y^2(3x + 5y)(3x − 5y)$ **d)**not possible **e)**not

possible **f)**$(p + \frac{1}{3}q)(p − \frac{1}{3}q)$ **g)**$5(x + 2)(x − 2)(x^2 + 4)$

h)$(\frac{x}{4} + \frac{y}{7})(\frac{x}{4} − \frac{y}{7})$ **10.**3, 7 **11.a)**$h = \frac{\sqrt{l^2(x^2 − 1)}}{2}$
b)6.13 cm; 7.91 cm; 8.67 cm

Review Exercises, page 107
1.a)$−5s^2 − 14s + 5$ **b)**$6g^2 − 11g − 9$ **c)**$x^2 + 9xy$
d)$−5a^2b + 3a^2b^2 − 3ab$ **2.a)**$−40xy^2$ **b)**$−6a^3b^3$
c)$24x^4y^4$ **3.a)**$−7m^3n$ **b)**$4x^4y^4$ **c)**$−a^3b^2$
4.a)$−9x^2 + 20xy$ **b)**$3m^2 − 8mn + 7n^2$ **c)**$−4x^2 + 11xy$
d)$3a^2 − 12ab$ **e)**$−5x^2y − 20xy^2$ **f)**$−12m^2n + 5mn^2$
5.a)$23x^2 − 69x$ **b)**$−14c + 12d − 57e$
c)$8m^2 − 17mn + 13m$ **d)**$8x^3 + 16x^2y − 26x^2$
6.a)$4x^3 − 24x^2 + 27x + 20$ **b)**$24y^3 + 41y^2 − 9y − 28$
7.a)$12x + 12y$; $7x^2 + 15xy + 7y^2$
b)$18x + 8y$; $16x^2 + 13xy + 2y^2$ **8.a)**$4m^2(2m − 1)$
b)$4(2y^2 − 3y^4 + 6)$ **c)**$7a^2(4 − a)$ **d)**$3a^2b^2c(2b − 5c)$
e)$10x^2y(3 − 2y + xy)$ **f)**$4mn(2n − 3 − 4m)$
9.a)$(m + 4)(m + 4)$ **b)**$(a − 4)(a − 3)$ **c)**$(y − 4)(y + 2)$
d)$(n − 9)(n + 5)$ **e)**$(s − 3)(s + 3)(s^2 − 6)$
f)$(k^2 − 15)(k^2 + 6)$ **10.a)**$(a + 12b)(a + 2b)$
b)$(m + 6n)(m + 3n)$ **c)**$(s + 18t)(s + 2t)$
d)$(x − 5y)(x + 4y)$ **e)**$(c + 25d)(c − 4d)$
f)$(p − 24q)(p + 5q)$ **11.a)**$(x − 1)(4x − 3)$
b)$(3a + 1)(2a − 5)$ **c)**$(7n − 2)(3n + 2)$
d)$(6r − 1)(r − 5)$ **e)**$3(4t + 3)(t − 2)$
f)$2(7x + 4)(4x − 1)$ **12.a)**$(b + 6)(b − 6)$
b)$(9k^2 + 1)(3k + 1)(3k − 1)$ **c)**$(6x + 7y)(6x − 7y)$
d)$(2a + 3b)(2a − 3b)$ **e)**$(5m + 9n)(5m − 9n)$
f)$(1 + 4s^2)(1 − 2s)(1 + 2s)$ **g)**$(14x + 5z)(14x − 5z)$
h)$(16p + 25q)(16p − 25q)$ **i)**$(17s + 18t)(17s − 18t)$

13.a)$8(a + 3)(a - 3)$ **b)**$6(5 + n)(5 - n)$
c)$7(x + y)(x - y)(x^2 + y^2)$ **d)**$3m(3m + 2)(3m - 2)$
e)$(\frac{a}{6} + \frac{b}{7})(\frac{a}{6} - \frac{b}{7})$ **f)**$5q^2(5p + 6)(5p - 6)$
14.a)$4(c + 3)(c - 8)$ **b)**$(x + y + z)(x - y - z)$
c)$(a + b - c)(a - b + c)$ **15.a)**$2m(4 + 7m)(4 - 7m)$
b)$5y^2(5x + 6)(5x - 6)$ **c)**$2y(8x + 5y)(8x - 5y)$
16.a)$(x - 5y)(x + 5y)(x - 2y)(x + 2y)$
b)$(m - 6n)(m + 6n)(m^2 - 2n^2)$

Chapter 4

Exercises 4-1, page 113

1.a)1 **b)**$- 4$ **c)**5 **d)**$-\frac{3}{2}$ **e)**$-\frac{1}{2}$ **f)**1 **g)**0 **h)**$\frac{15}{17}$ **2.a)**0 **b)**0
c)1 **d)**$- 3$ **e)**5 **f)**defined for all real values of x **g)**-1
h)defined for all real values of x **3.a)**$8x$ **b)**$\frac{-9x}{y}$
c)$11a^2$ **d)**$-4m^2$ **e)**$\frac{x}{3}$ **f)**$\frac{4}{7}$ **g)**$\frac{6a^2}{b}$ **h)**$\frac{-12m}{n}$ **4.a)**$3m + 2$
b)$a^2 + b$ **c)**$3x - 2$ **d)**$-2n + 4$ **e)**$\frac{3x + 4}{y}$ **f)**$3b - 4$
g)$\frac{2c + 5d}{c}$ **h)**$\frac{3x - 8y}{2}$ **i)**$\frac{4n + 7m}{2}$ **5.a)**$\frac{m}{m - 2}$ **b)**$\frac{3}{2x - 5}$
c)$\frac{b}{a + 2b}$ **d)**$\frac{3y}{2x - 5y}$ **e)**$\frac{2s}{4s + 3t}$ **f)**$\frac{2mn}{3m - 5}$ **g)**$\frac{2x}{3x - 5y}$ **h)**$\frac{2}{3 + 4y}$
i)$\frac{b}{6c - 9b^2}$ **6.a)**2 **b)**$\frac{1}{3}$ **c)**$\frac{2}{3}$ **d)**$-\frac{1}{2}$ **e)**$-\frac{3}{5}$ **f)**$\frac{1}{2}$ **g)**$\frac{1}{2}$ **h)**$\frac{7}{5}$
7.a)$\frac{2x + 6}{5}$, all real values of x except $x = 0$ **b)**$\frac{x}{2}$, all
real values of x except $x = 5$ **c)**$\frac{5x + 7}{3}$, all real values of
x except $x = 0$ **d)**$4x$, all real values of x except $x = 3$
e)$-\frac{3x}{7}$, all real values of x except $x = 2$ **f)**$\frac{9 - 3x}{-2x}$, all
real values except $x = 0$ **g)**$x + 3$, all real values of x
except $x = - 4$ **h)**$-x - 3$, all real values of x except
$x = 2$ **i)**$5 - x$, all real values of x except $x = 5$ **8.a)**$\frac{b}{2c}$
b)$\frac{3ac}{4b}$ **c)**$\frac{-6x}{y}$ **d)**$\frac{3ac^2}{4b}$ **e)**$\frac{x}{3z}$ **f)**$\frac{5c^2}{9b^2}$ **g)**$\frac{9n}{m^3}$ **h)**$\frac{-5a^2c}{8b^5}$ **9.a)**$\frac{5}{3}$
b)-1 **c)**$-\frac{2}{3}$ **d)**$-\frac{3}{2}$ **e)**$\frac{-5y}{2}$ **f)**$\frac{-3}{2}$ **10.a)**$\frac{a + 5}{a + 3}$ **b)**$\frac{x - 5}{x + 1}$ **c)**$\frac{x + 4}{x + 8}$
d)$\frac{x - 3}{x + 3}$ **e)**$\frac{r + 3}{r - 1}$ **f)**$\frac{x + 4}{x - 2}$ **g)**$\frac{x + 2y}{x - 4y}$ **h)**$\frac{m - 2n}{m + 3n}$ **i)**$\frac{a - 5b}{a + 5b}$
11.a)$\frac{x + 3y}{2x}$ **b)**$\frac{m - 4n}{3m}$ **c)**$\frac{3a + 4b}{2a}$ **d)**$\frac{a - 3b}{a}$ **e)**$\frac{3x + 2y}{x}$
f)$\frac{m - n}{3m}$ **g)**$\frac{x + 5}{x}$ **h)**$\frac{3m}{3m - 1}$ **i)**$\frac{4t - 8}{t + 4}$ **12.a)**$\frac{c - 8d}{c + 4d}$ **b)**$\frac{x - 5y}{x + 5y}$
c)$\frac{a + 4b}{a - 6b}$ **d)**$\frac{2u - 5v}{2u + 5v}$ **e)**$\frac{m + 6n}{m + 8n}$ **f)**$\frac{x - 6y}{x - 9y}$ **g)**$\frac{(x - 1)(x^2 - 4)}{x - 4}$
h)$(x - 6)(x + 5)$ **i)**$(e + 9)(e - 8)$ **13.a)**$\frac{x}{x - 1}$ **b)**$\frac{5x - 10}{x + 12}$
c)$\frac{x - 4}{x + 5}$ **d)**$\frac{a + 4}{14 - 2a}$ **e)**$\frac{x - 5}{2x}$ **f)**$\frac{x - 17}{3 - x}$ **g)**$\frac{2m - 4}{3m - 12}$ **h)**$\frac{a + 6}{2a - 8}$
i)$\frac{3b + 15}{2b + 12}$ **14.a)**$2x + 1$ **b)**2 **c)**$4x$ **d)**$4x$ **e)**1 **f)**-1
g)$\frac{x + 5}{x - 5}$ **h)**$\frac{x^2 - 1}{x^2 + 1}$ **15.a)**$\frac{1}{2x - 3}$ **b)**$\frac{1}{x + 3}$ **c)**$\frac{1}{x + 3}$ **d)**$\frac{1}{y - 4}$
e)$\frac{2x + y}{3x - y}$ **f)**$\frac{4x - 2y}{3x - y}$ **16.a)**$\frac{2a - b}{3a + 2b}$ **b)**$\frac{a}{b}$ **c)**$\frac{a + 2b}{2a + b}$ **d)**$\frac{3a + 3b - 5}{4a + 4b + 5}$

Exercise 4-2, page 117

1.a)$\frac{5a}{12}$ **b)**$\frac{m}{2}$ **c)**$\frac{-x^2}{6}$ **d)**$\frac{2c}{9}$ **e)**$\frac{-4t^2}{5}$ **f)**$6r$ **g)**$16t^2$ **h)**$10b$
2.a)$\frac{5a}{6b}$ **b)**$\frac{x}{7}$ **c)**$\frac{-y}{x}$ **d)**$\frac{3a}{2b}$ **e)**$\frac{14}{5}$ **f)**$\frac{9a^3}{10c^2}$ **g)**$\frac{4a}{3bc}$ **h)**$\frac{t^4}{20}$ **3.a)**$\frac{2t}{7s}$
b)$\frac{9x^2}{2}$ **c)**$\frac{3f^2}{7e^2}$ **d)**$-x$ **e)**$\frac{2n}{3}$ **f)**$\frac{7x}{6y}$ **g)**$\frac{a}{10b}$ **h)**$\frac{21t^4}{2}$ **4.a)**$\frac{2x}{3}$
b)$2b$ **c)**$\frac{n}{-6}$ **d)**$\frac{2x}{5}$ **e)**$\frac{20n^5}{3m^3}$ **f)**1 **5.a)**$\frac{a^5b^2}{3}$ **b)**$\frac{-5}{4xy}$ **c)**$6x^2y$
d)$\frac{8n}{9m}$ **e)**$\frac{2}{5}$ **f)**$\frac{16m^2}{15}$ **6.a)**$\frac{7}{2}$ **b)**$\frac{1}{12}$ **c)**$x - 3$ **d)**$8m$ **e)**$\frac{1}{12}$
f)$\frac{-2(a + 1)}{a}$ **7.a)**$\frac{2b}{5}$ **b)**$\frac{xy^3}{2}$ **c)**$\frac{3y}{x + 3}$ **d)**$\frac{3x + 4}{12}$ **e)**$\frac{2m}{15n}$
f)$\frac{4(a + 3b)}{3}$ **8.a)**$\frac{9}{4}$ **b)**$\frac{x + 11}{x - 2}$ **c)**$\frac{5(x - 2)^2}{3(x + 1)^2}$ **d)**1 **e)**$\frac{3x(x - 2)}{4y(x + 2)}$
f)$\frac{x - 2}{x - 1}$ **9.a)**-1 **b)**1 **c)**$\frac{x + 2}{x - 1}$ **d)**-1 **e)**$\frac{a - 3}{a - 1}$ **f)**$\frac{(x + 3)^2}{(x - 3)^2}$
10.a)$\frac{2xy(x + 4y)}{3(x + 5y)}$ **b)**$\frac{1}{2}$ **c)**$\frac{x + 2y}{x - y}$ **d)**$\frac{4m(m - 2n)}{3(m + 3n)}$
11.a)$\frac{(x - 1)(x - 6)}{2x^2}$ **b)**$\frac{x + y}{x - y}$ **c)**1 **d)**$3a + 7b$ **12.a)**$\frac{2a - b}{2b - a}$
b)$\frac{4b - 3a}{8a - 6b}$

Mathematics Around Us, page 119

1.1.2×10^6 m³ **2.a)**about 9×10^7 m³ **b)**about 57 days

Exercise 4-3, page 121

1.a)$\frac{-16}{24mn}$ **b)**$\frac{15m}{24mn}$ **c)**$\frac{-20n}{24mn}$ **d)**$\frac{-13mn}{24mn}$ **e)**$\frac{-6mn}{24mn}$ **f)**$\frac{-9mn}{24mn}$
g)$\frac{14m^2n}{24mn}$ **h)**$\frac{-21m^2}{24mn}$ **i)**$\frac{-22n^2}{24mn}$ **j)**$\frac{-20m^2n}{24mn}$ **2.a)i)**$\frac{4x}{6}$ **ii)**$\frac{8x^2}{12x}$
iii)$\frac{2x^3}{3x^2}$ **b)i)**$\frac{-9m - 3}{-12}$ **ii)**$\frac{6mx + 2x}{8x}$ **iii)**$\frac{12mx^2 + 4x^2}{16x^2}$ **c)i)**$\frac{3a - 21}{3a}$
ii)$\frac{a^2 - 7a}{a^2}$ **iii)**$\frac{5a^4 - 35a^2}{5a^4}$ **d)i)**$\frac{15y - 9}{6y}$ **ii)**$\frac{10y^3 - 6y^2}{4y^3}$
iii)$\frac{-5y^2 + 3y}{-2y^2}$ **e)i)**$\frac{-8x - 20}{-4x^2}$ **ii)**$\frac{40x^2 + 100x}{20x^3}$ **iii)**$\frac{2x + 5}{x^2}$
3.a)$\frac{3x}{6}, \frac{2x}{6}$ **b)**$\frac{10}{5x}, \frac{x^2}{5x}$ **c)**$\frac{3}{2a}, \frac{4}{2a}$ **d)**$\frac{15}{6a}, \frac{8}{6a}$ **e)**$\frac{5n}{n^2}, \frac{2}{n^2}$
f)$\frac{4}{24x}, \frac{15}{24x}$ **g)**$\frac{4x + 4}{20x^2}, \frac{5x^2 - 5x}{20x^2}$ **h)**$\frac{2x + 4}{6x^2}, \frac{3x^2 - 9x}{6x^2}$ **4.a)**$\frac{-3}{x}$
b)$\frac{2}{x}$ **c)**$\frac{7 - 5x}{4x}$ **d)**$\frac{2 - 9m}{3m^2}$ **e)**6 **f)**$\frac{x}{y^2}$ **g)**$\frac{2a}{b^2}$ **h)**$\frac{3s^2}{t^3}$ **5.a)**$\frac{-2a}{15}$
b)$\frac{-2}{15a}$ **c)**$\frac{10a^2 - 12}{15a}$ **d)**$\frac{10 - 12a^2}{15a}$ **e)**$\frac{-2}{15a}$ **f)**$\frac{10 - 12a}{15a}$ **g)**$\frac{9a^3 - 7}{6a^2}$
h)$\frac{9a - 7}{6a}$ **6.a)**$\frac{9}{2x}$ **b)**$\frac{47}{5x}$ **c)**$\frac{29}{30x}$ **d)**$\frac{13}{4a}$ **e)**$\frac{41}{24m}$ **f)**$\frac{-11}{18k}$ **g)**$\frac{43}{45t}$
h)$\frac{13}{56b}$ **7.a)**$\frac{3a}{5}$ **b)**$\frac{5m}{24}$ **c)**$\frac{11x}{18}$ **d)**$\frac{-29c}{36}$ **e)**$\frac{7e}{12}$ **f)**$\frac{13m}{24}$ **8.a)**$\frac{13}{12a}$
b)$\frac{-7}{12x}$ **c)**$\frac{13}{24mn}$ **d)**$\frac{-5}{3x}$ **e)**$\frac{7}{12y}$ **f)**$\frac{-5}{24y}$ **9.a)**$\frac{2x - 2}{x}$ **b)**$\frac{m - 9}{m}$
c)$\frac{11a + 9}{3a}$ **d)**$\frac{4x + 26}{5x^2}$ **e)**$\frac{-5m - 7}{2m}$ **f)**$\frac{-8x - 1}{4x}$ **10.a)**$\frac{k - 43}{20}$
b)$\frac{5c - 14}{6}$ **c)**$\frac{x + 10}{12}$ **d)**$\frac{5m - 9}{12}$ **e)**$\frac{-14a + 25}{24}$ **f)**$\frac{16x - 35}{18}$
11.a)$\frac{8x - 11}{6x}$ **b)**$\frac{-6n - 5}{24n}$ **c)**$\frac{9a - 29}{18a}$ **12.a)**$\frac{10a - 5}{2a}$ **b)**$\frac{4n - 3m}{6mn}$
c)$\frac{4y + 3}{xy}$ **d)**$\frac{2b + a}{2b}$ **13.a)**$\frac{3y - 2x + xy}{xy}$ **b)**$\frac{2bc - 3ac + 4ab}{abc}$
c)$\frac{6yz + 9xz - 10xy}{12xyz}$ **14.a)**$\frac{7x + 10y}{6y}$ **b)**$\frac{5m^2 - 4n^2}{3mn}$
c)$\frac{9a^2 - 20b^2}{15ab}$ **d)**$\frac{15x^2 - 8a^2}{10ax}$ **15.a)**$\frac{a^4 - 3a^2 + 2}{a^2}$ **b)**$\frac{k^4 - 2k^2 - 15}{k^2}$

c)$\dfrac{4a^4 - 12a^2 + 9}{a^2}$ **16.a)**2 **b)**7 **17.a)**$4 - \dfrac{a}{3}$ **b)**$\dfrac{1}{5} - \dfrac{1}{2x}$

c)$\dfrac{x}{y} + 1$ **d)**$7x + 1 + \dfrac{1}{x}$ **18.a)**$\dfrac{2}{3}$ **b)**$\dfrac{5}{2}$ **c)**$\dfrac{5}{3}$ **d)**5

INVESTIGATE, page 123

$x^2 + 3 + \dfrac{2}{x^2}$; $\dfrac{x^4 + 3x^2 + 2}{x^2}$; Yes. Answers may vary.

Exercise 4-4, page 127

1.a)$\dfrac{4m - 1}{m + 3}$ **b)**$\dfrac{-4s + 11}{s - 5}$ **c)**3 **d)**$\dfrac{4x + 18}{x + 6}$ **e)**$\dfrac{3m - 5}{2m + 1}$ **f)**$\dfrac{-4a - 11}{a^2 + 4}$

2.a)$\dfrac{3a + 3}{a(a - 3)}$ **b)**$\dfrac{30 - 4y}{y(y - 5)}$ **c)**$\dfrac{4m - 28}{m(m - 4)}$ **d)**$\dfrac{2c^2 - 5c + 5}{c(c - 1)}$

e)$\dfrac{3x^2 - 6x - 12}{x(x + 2)}$ **f)**$\dfrac{8x + 6}{x(x + 2)}$ **3.a)**$\dfrac{3 - 8a}{2a}$ **b)**$\dfrac{5 - 2y}{y + 1}$ **c)**$\dfrac{4n - 29}{n - 5}$

d)$\dfrac{x^2 + 4x - 2}{x + 4}$ **e)**$\dfrac{3 + 16s - 2s^2}{s - 8}$ **f)**$\dfrac{-10w - 4w^2}{w + 3}$ **g)**$\dfrac{2 + 3x - x^2}{x - 1}$

h)$\dfrac{6 - x - x^2}{x - 1}$ **i)**$\dfrac{x^2 - 8x + 17}{x - 3}$ **j)**$\dfrac{x^2 + x - 1}{x - 2}$ **k)**$\dfrac{34 - 4x - x^2}{x - 4}$

l)$\dfrac{5 + 2x - x^2}{x + 2}$ **4.a)**$\dfrac{5x + 19}{(x + 5)(x + 2)}$ **b)**$\dfrac{2x + 10}{(x - 3)(x + 1)}$

c)$\dfrac{x^2 - 3x - 2}{(x + 1)(x - 1)}$ **d)**$\dfrac{3x + 2}{x + 4}$ **e)**$\dfrac{3x^2 + 17x}{(x - 1)(x + 3)}$ **f)**$\dfrac{5x^2 + 9x}{(x + 5)(x - 3)}$

5.a)$\dfrac{-2}{(x + 1)(x - 1)}$ **b)**$\dfrac{x^2 - 5x + 7}{(x - 2)(x - 3)}$ **c)**$\dfrac{x^2 - 25x - 4}{(x + 7)(x - 3)}$

d)$\dfrac{2x^2 - 3x + 10}{(x + 2)(x - 4)}$ **e)**$\dfrac{2x^2 - 6x - 18}{(x - 3)(x - 5)}$ **f)**$\dfrac{6x}{(x - 2)(x + 2)}$

6.a)$\dfrac{2x - 4 - 3x^2}{x(x - 2)}$ **b)**$\dfrac{27}{10(x + 3)}$ **c)**$\dfrac{19y}{6(y + 9)}$ **d)**$\dfrac{3a + 19}{3(a + 1)(a - 7)}$

e)$\dfrac{4a - 2}{(a + 1)(a - 1)}$ **f)**$\dfrac{-x^2 - x}{(x - 2)(x - 3)}$ **7.a)**$\dfrac{6}{x + 2}$ **b)**$\dfrac{41}{10(x - 2)}$

c)$\dfrac{-17x}{6(x + 3)}$ **d)**$\dfrac{x}{2(2x - 3)}$ **e)**$\dfrac{8x + 5}{3(x - 4)}$ **f)**$\dfrac{5x + 6}{6(x + 4)}$

8.a)$\dfrac{2x^2 - 3x + 3}{(x - 6)(x - 3)}$ **b)**$\dfrac{-3x^2 - 8x - 7}{(x - 5)(x + 3)}$ **c)**$\dfrac{2x^2 + 4x - 3}{(x - 2)(x + 2)}$

d)$\dfrac{4x^2 - 10x - 9}{(x - 3)(x + 3)}$ **e)**$\dfrac{3x^2 + 4x}{(x - 1)(x + 2)}$ **f)**$\dfrac{-2x^2 + 13x}{(x - 3)(x - 4)}$

9.a)$\dfrac{4m - m^2}{(m - 1)(m + 1)}$ **b)**$\dfrac{3x^2 + 5x - 14}{x(x + 5)(x - 1)}$ **c)**$\dfrac{49a^2 + 17a + 10}{15(a - 2)(a + 3)}$

d)$\dfrac{-11k^2 + 28k}{4(k - 3)(k - 4)}$ **e)**$\dfrac{13x^2 + 2x - 11}{2(x - 2)(x + 7)}$ **f)**$\dfrac{18m^2 + 107m + 27}{6(2m - 1)(3m + 7)}$

10.a)$\dfrac{-x - 10}{(x + 8)(x + 6)}$ **b)**$\dfrac{4m - 7}{(m - 4)(m + 5)}$ **c)**$\dfrac{1}{x + 2}$ **d)**$\dfrac{-5}{m + 2}$

e)$\dfrac{4x^2 - 37x + 21}{(x + 7)(x - 10)}$ **f)**$\dfrac{-x + 12}{(x - 2)(x - 4)}$ **11.a)**$2x$ **b)**$-5y$

c)$\dfrac{5x^2 + 14xy - 66y^2}{6(x + y)}$ **d)**$\dfrac{2a}{(a + 3b)(a - 3b)}$ **12.a)**$\dfrac{x + y}{xy}$ **b)**$\dfrac{y + x}{y - x}$

c)$\dfrac{2xy^2}{y^2 - x^2}$ **d)**$\dfrac{x^2 + y^2}{y^2 - x^2}$ **13.a)**$\dfrac{2a + 3}{a + 2}$ **b)**$\dfrac{-2a - 3}{(a + 2)^2}$ **c)**$\dfrac{2a + 3}{a + 1}$ **d)**$\dfrac{2a + 3}{3a + 5}$

The Mathematical Mind, page 129

1.10, 9, 1, 12 **2.**50 **3.**Answers may vary.
$110 = 1^2 + 3^2 + 10^2 = 5^2 + 6^2 + 7^2$

Problem Solving, page 131

1.If n is the number of clicks in 1 min, the speed is $2.4n$ kilometres per hour. **2.a)**If t is the time in seconds to pass through the tunnel, the speed is $\dfrac{79\,920}{t}$ kilometres per hour. **b)**215 km/h **3.**63.63 m²
4.6.82 m² **5.**3 **6.a)**26 cm > perimeter > 13 cm
b)20 cm² > area > 0 **7.**1 cm, 4 cm, 1 cm **8.**$4\sqrt{5}$ cm

Exercises 4-5, page 134

1.4.8 **2.a)**12 km/h **b)**$\dfrac{2xy}{x + y}$ km/h **3.**$\dfrac{V^2 - w^2}{V}$ km/h

4.6.5 h **5.a)**2 h 52 min **b)**$\dfrac{210v - 150x}{v(v - x)}$ **6.**$\dfrac{400x}{x^2 - y^2}$ hours

7.a)$\dfrac{rs}{r + s}$ **b)**$\dfrac{Rs}{s - R}$ **c)**$\dfrac{rR}{r - R}$ **8.a)**12.5 min **b)**$\dfrac{150x}{v(v + x)}$ hours

9.a)$\dfrac{4000}{l}$ cm **b)**$\dfrac{4000x}{l(l - x)}$ cm **10.a)**2985 kg/m³, 3008 kg/m³
b)20°C

Problem Solving, page 136

1.$80\,000, $20\,000 **2.**$\dfrac{1250\,x}{33(33 - x)}$ dollars, if x students cancel **3.**7 km/h **4.a)**5 888 896 digits **b)**Answers may vary; assume 2 digits per second, 818 h; about 30 min per day **5.**5 **6.a)**6 pairs; 12 pairs; 90 pairs **b)**The product of the number of parallel lines and 1 less than the number of parallel lines **7.**About 9.5 cm
8.192, 643 **9.**$\dfrac{1}{2}$

Review Exercises, page 137

1.a)$13ab$ **b)**$3m + 2$ **c)**$5y - 2$ **d)**$\dfrac{3s - 4}{2}$ **e)**$-3b + 6$

f)$\dfrac{2y}{x + 5y}$ **g)**$\dfrac{3m}{2}$ **h)**$\dfrac{7s}{5}$ **2.a)**-3 **b)**$\dfrac{a + 5}{3a}$ **c)**$\dfrac{n - 6}{n - 2}$ **d)**$\dfrac{a - 3}{a + 3}$

e)$\dfrac{b + 4}{b - 2}$ **f)**$\dfrac{m - 3}{m + 2}$ **3.a)**$6a^2$ **b)**$\dfrac{-n}{m}$ **c)**1 **d)**$\dfrac{x^4}{y}$ **e)**$6m^2n$ **f)**$\dfrac{5x^2}{8y^2}$

4.a)$8a$ **b)**$\dfrac{-4(a + 1)}{a}$ **c)**$\dfrac{n}{m}$ **d)**$\dfrac{x^2y}{2}$ **5.a)**$\dfrac{3b(2a - b)}{2(a^2 - 9)}$ **b)**$\dfrac{m - 1}{m - 2}$

c)-1 **d)**$\dfrac{y - 3}{y - 1}$ **6.a)**$\dfrac{3}{a}$ **b)**$\dfrac{-1}{6x}$ **c)**$\dfrac{23}{4m}$ **d)**$\dfrac{5x}{24}$ **e)**$\dfrac{5}{12a}$ **f)**$\dfrac{-17}{15n}$

7.a)$\dfrac{2a - 2}{a}$ **b)**$\dfrac{x - 9}{x}$ **c)**$\dfrac{y - 33}{20}$ **d)**$\dfrac{8a - 11}{6a}$ **e)**$\dfrac{x - 5}{24x}$ **f)**$\dfrac{1 + 12x}{12x}$

g)$\dfrac{11x + 5}{12x}$ **h)**$\dfrac{11m - 13}{8m}$ **i)**$\dfrac{-8a + 17}{30a^2}$ **8.a)**$\dfrac{2b + 15a}{3ab}$ **b)**$\dfrac{9n - 10m}{12mn}$

c)$\dfrac{t + s}{t}$ **d)**$\dfrac{4c + b}{2c}$ **e)**$\dfrac{54p^2 + 49q^2}{42pq}$ **f)**$\dfrac{9x^2 - 10y^2}{15xy}$ **g)**$\dfrac{9c^2 + 35d^2}{21cd}$

h)$\dfrac{40x - 27y}{45y}$ **9.a)**3 **b)**$\dfrac{2a^2 - 5a + 5}{a(a - 1)}$ **c)**$\dfrac{5 - 2x}{x + 1}$

d)$\dfrac{m^2 - 3m - 2}{(m - 1)(m + 1)}$ **e)**$\dfrac{y^2 - 5y + 7}{(y - 2)(y - 3)}$ **f)**$\dfrac{a^2 - 25a - 4}{(a + 7)(a - 3)}$

10.a)$\dfrac{a}{2(2a - 3)}$ **b)**$\dfrac{8m + 5}{3(m - 4)}$ **c)**$\dfrac{2k^2 + 4k - 3}{(k - 2)(k + 2)}$ **d)**$\dfrac{-2b^2 + 13b}{(b - 3)(b - 4)}$

e)$\dfrac{49x^2 + 17x + 10}{15(x - 2)(x + 3)}$ **f)**$\dfrac{18x^2 + 107x + 27}{6(2x - 1)(3x + 7)}$ **11.a)**$\dfrac{x^2 - 5x - 6}{(x + 2)(x - 2)}$

b)$\dfrac{17a}{12(2a - 3)}$ **c)**$\dfrac{33a}{10(3a - 5)}$ **d)**$\dfrac{-4x + 3}{2(x - 4)}$ **e)**$\dfrac{13m^2 + 8m + 4}{6(m - 2)(m + 2)}$

f)$\dfrac{7t^2 + 3t}{5(t + 1)(t - 1)}$ **12.**220 km/h

Chapter 5

Exercises 5-1, page 142

1.a)9 **b)**-13 **c)**11 **d)**-5 **e)**7 **f)**-2 **g)**7 **h)**11 **i)**-2
2.a)8 **b)**7 **c)**2 **d)**-1 **e)**-5 **f)**-6 **g)**1 **h)**2 **i)**6 **3.a)**3
b)0 **c)**$-\dfrac{1}{2}$ **d)**8 **e)**12 **f)**$-\dfrac{3}{5}$ **g)**-3 **h)**$-\dfrac{9}{2}$ **i)**$-\dfrac{8}{7}$ **j)**5 **4.**6000
5.233 km **6.**$18.52 **7.a)**22¢ **b)**105 days **8.a)**3 **b)**-1
c)2 **d)**$-\dfrac{9}{4}$ **e)**14 **f)**$\dfrac{25}{8}$ **9.a)**-3 **b)**5 **c)**4 **d)**26 **e)**2 **f)**-2

g)8 h)5 **10.**a)–4 b)9 c)2 d)–5 e)4 f)–1 g)$-\frac{7}{2}$ h)–5
i)–4 j)$\frac{26}{11}$ **11.**a)3 b)3 c)–38 d)11 e)$-\frac{1}{2}$ f)$-\frac{5}{2}$
12.a)$\frac{7+b}{a}$ b)$\frac{e+d}{b+3}$ c)$\frac{3a}{2b-c}$ d)$\frac{d-b}{a-c}$ e)$\frac{b+c}{3a-2}$ f)$\frac{5b-2a}{2}$
g)–c h)c + b i)$\frac{4b+5c}{2a-5}$ **13.**$x = -3$ is a root for parts a)
and d); $x = -3$ is the only root for parts b) and c).
14.a)12 b)14 c)4 d)–1

INVESTIGATE, page 143
0

Exercises 5-2, page 146
1.a)0; 9 b)0; 30 c)0; 20 d)0; 8 e)0; ±6 f)0; ±12
g)0; ±10 h)0; ±15 **2.**a)0; –6 b)0; $-\frac{15}{2}$ c)0; $\frac{8}{3}$ d)0; 9
e)0; $\frac{21}{5}$ f)0; –5 **3.**a)$\frac{5}{7}$ b)12 c)$\frac{3}{4}$ d)$\frac{2}{3}$ e)4 f)$-\frac{1}{50}$
4.1600 **5.**a)144° b)15 sides **6.**a)30.7 cm b)8
7.a)2, $-\frac{1}{2}$; –13 b)–2, 1; 13 c)$-\frac{5}{3}$, $-\frac{3}{2}$; $-\frac{1}{2}$ d)2; no solution
e)$\frac{2}{5}, \frac{5}{4}, \frac{11}{2}$ f)$-\frac{7}{2}$; no solution **8.**a)5 b)–7 c)no solution
d)–8 e)–1 f)$\frac{1}{4}$ **9.**a)$-\frac{3}{5}$ b)–1 c)$\frac{1}{5}$ d)$\frac{1}{7}$ e)no solution
f)$\frac{11}{23}$ **10.**a)$\frac{8}{7}$ b)3 c)$\frac{5}{2}$ d)no solution e)$\frac{17}{3}$ f)$\frac{5}{19}$ **11.**a)$\frac{a-b}{c}$
b)$\frac{pq}{p+q}$ c)$\frac{na-mb}{mn}$ d)$\frac{t-sy}{s}$ e)$\frac{5u-y}{uy}$ f)$\frac{3c+ac}{b-2}$ **12.**The
numerators can equal zero and hence the solution is
$x = 3$.

Exercises 5-3, page 149
1.a)$x \le 4$ b)$x < 4$ c)$x < \frac{18}{5}$ d)$x \le \frac{5}{7}$ e)$x \le 4$ f)$x < \frac{5}{2}$
2.a)$x > 3$ b)$x \le 4$ c)$x \le -2$ d)$x < -2$ e)$x < -5$
f)$x \ge \frac{1}{3}$ **3.**a)$x < -4$ b)$x \le 3$ c)$x < -11$ d)$x \ge -\frac{9}{2}$
e)$x \le \frac{31}{5}$ f)$x > \frac{19}{3}$ **4.**a)$x < 2$ b)$x \le -\frac{3}{2}$ c)$x \ge \frac{7}{5}$
d)$x \ge 2$ e)$x < -5$ f)$x > -2$ **5.**a)$x > 0$ or $x < -1$
b)$0 < x \le 1$ c)$x < 0$ or $x > 2$

Exercises 5-4, page 152
1.a)$w = \frac{A}{l}$ b)$h = \frac{2A}{b}$ c)$a = g - w$ d)$s = P + e$
e)$u = v - at$ f)$t = \frac{W-R}{H}$ **2.**a)$h = \frac{V}{lw}$ b)$r = \frac{I}{pt}$ c)$r = \frac{c}{2\pi}$
d)$h = \frac{3V}{\pi r^2}$ e)$R = \frac{C-F}{n}$ f)$D = \frac{A-V}{n}$ **3.**$d = st;\ t = \frac{d}{s}$
4.$F = E + 2 - V;\ V = E + 2 - F;\ E = F + V - 2$
5.$L = 28.44 - 2D + F - \sqrt{A};\ D = \frac{28.44 - L + F - \sqrt{A}}{2};$
$F = L - 28.44 + 2D + \sqrt{A};\ A = (F - L + 28.44 - 2D)^2$
6.a)$d = \frac{C}{\pi}$ b)3.99 m c)2.72 m, 2.02 m, 0.61 m
7.a)$w = \frac{P}{2} - l$ b)6 cm, 4 cm, 1 cm **8.**$m = dv,\ v = \frac{m}{d}$
9.a)149.0 g b)1120 g **10.**a)7.46 cm³ b)2.11 cm³

11.a)$t = \frac{v-u}{a}$ b)$a = \frac{2(s-ut)}{t^2}$ c)$f = \frac{pq}{q-p}$
d)$E = \frac{C(nr+R)}{n}$ e)$a = \frac{L_2-L_1}{L_t}$ f)$b = \frac{2A-ah}{h}$
12.a)$u = \frac{2s-at^2}{2t}$ b)$x = \frac{C}{2\pi} - R$ c)$s = \frac{rR}{r-R}$ d)$n = \frac{Fd^2}{m}$
e)$W = \frac{6000-L}{L}$ f)$t = \frac{D-d}{ad}$ **13.**a)$n = \frac{C-925}{4}$ b)268,
518, 1018 **14.**a)$k = \frac{C-28d}{0.15}$ b)960 km, 773 km, 586
km **15.**a)$n = \frac{15\,000}{A-60}$ b)375, 750, 3000, 6000
16.a)$20 000 b)$53 333.33 c)$153 333.33
17.a)15 km b)1 km, 2.2 km, 3.4 km **18.**$R = \frac{rs}{r+s}$
19.a)4 Ω b)7 Ω c)9 Ω d)13 Ω **20.**$i = \frac{r^2}{d}$
21.a)144 cm b)72 cm c)48 cm d)36 cm e)29 cm
f)24 cm g)21 cm h)18 cm **22.**$r = \frac{20t}{t-20}$ **23.**a)100 Ω
b)47 Ω c)40 Ω d)33 Ω **24.**$a = \frac{br+cr}{b-r};\ b = \frac{ar+cr}{a-r};$
$c = \frac{ab - ar - br}{r}$

Mathematics Around Us, page 155
1.a)50 words/min b)30 words/min **2.**300 words; 350
words **3.**300 words **4.**Each error results in the
reduction of typing speed by 2 words/min.

Exercises 5-5, page 156
The letters used may vary. **1.**a)6x b)x – 10 c)2x + 4
d)3x – 1 **2.**a)(x + 2) years b)(x – 5) years
c)2(x – 3) years d)$\frac{1}{2}$(x + 10) years **3.**a)x b)x + 5
c)x – 4 d)2x **4.**a)a b)3a – 2 c)2a + 1 d)a + 8
5.a)n b)5n cents **6.**a)t b)10t dollars **7.**a)s
b)34s cents c)0.34s dollars **8.**2x + 1 **9.**3x + 6
10.2x² + 2x + 1 **11.**Answers may vary. a)a, 47 – a
b)a, a + 12 c)n, n + 3 d)w kilograms,
(w + 5) kilograms e)w kilograms, (w – 2) kilograms
f)x years, 4x years g)x years, 2x years h)width w,
length 5w, perimeter 12w i)width w, length 10 + w,
perimeter 20 + 4w j)width w, length $\frac{3w-5}{2}$

Exercises 5-6, page 159
1.11, 12 **2.**7, 8 **3.**10, 11 **4.**22, 24 **5.**4 years
6.25 years, 13 years **7.**36 years, 12 years **8.**8 years,
2 years **9.**10, 7 **10.**9, 14 **11.**8, 4 **12.**12, 8 **13.**55 kg,
40 kg **14.**40 kg, 50 kg **15.**45 kg, 60 kg **16.**47 kg, 54 kg
17.18, 20 **18.**17, 19, 21 **19.**19 years, 23 years,
26 years **20.**35 years, 7 years, 9 years **21.**a)16 cm,
8 cm b)10 cm, 6 cm **22.**2.5 cm **23.**3 cm
24.7 nickels, 6 dimes **25.**5 dimes, 9 quarters
26.6 nickels, 9 dimes, 12 quarters **27.**6 L **28.**12 L
29.about 1.3 L **30.**about 2.6 L **31.**0.6 L **32.**10, 12,
14, 16 **33.**19, 21, 23, 25 **34.**$6.25 **35.**–6 **36.**$\frac{4}{7}$

Mathematics Around Us, page 163
1.about 660 km/h **2.**about 1971 **3.**about 1380 km/h
5.about 410 km/h **6.**about 630 km/h **7.**interpolate
8.extrapolate

Exercises 5-7, page 166
1.Tables may vary.

a)

x	y
0	3
$-\frac{3}{2}$	0
1	5
2	7

b)

x	y
0	5
$\frac{5}{3}$	0
1	2
−1	8

c)

x	y
0	12
3	0
1	8
2	4

d)

x	y
0	−4
6	0
3	−2
−3	−6

e)

x	y
0	10
4	0
−2	15
2	5

f)

x	y
0	$-\frac{15}{2}$
5	0
1	−6
−1	9

2.Answers may vary.

a)

x	y
0	−4
1	−2
2	0
3	2

b)

x	y
−1	5
0	3
1	1
2	−1

c)

x	y
0	6
2	4
4	2
6	0

d)

x	y
0	9
1	6
2	3
3	0

e)

x	y
0	5
−2	4
−4	3
−6	2

f)

x	y
0	−8
3	−4
6	0
9	4

3. a)

n	C
0	70
1	76
5	100
10	130
20	190
50	370
80	550
100	670

c) $5.20

d) about 45

4. a)

n	C
0	300
4	380
8	460
12	540
16	620
20	700

c) about 12

5. a)

v	t
0	0
1	1.5
10	15
50	75
75	112.5
100	150

c) about 85 s d) about 35 L

8.Answers may vary. $300x + 400y = 1$, the intercepts
are too close to be able to draw the correct line
through them; $y = 3$, $x = 4$; vertical and horizontal
lines which only have one intercept; $y = 2x$, the
intercepts are the same. **9.**10, 12, 18, 20, 21, 24, 27,
30, 36, 40, 42, 45, 48, 50, 54, 60, 63, 70, 72, 80, 81,
84, 90 Graphs may vary.

INVESTIGATE, page 167
a)Answers may vary, for example, $2x + 4y = 6$,
$-10x - 7y = -4$ **b)**The lines pass through $(-1,2)$.
c)Answers may vary.

The Mathematical Mind, page 168
1. a)

x	y
0	17
1	13
2	9
3	5
4	1

b)

x	y
0	6
2	3
4	0

c)

x	y
2	1

2.2 quarters, 12 dimes; 4 quarters, 7 dimes; 6
quarters, 2 dimes **3.**1 quarter, 29 nickels; 2 quarters,
24 nickels; 3 quarters, 19 nickels; 4 quarters, 14
nickels; 5 quarters, 9 nickels; 6 quarters, 4 nickels
4.84

Computer Power, page 169
1. a)

x	y
−10	25
−8	22
−6	19
−4	16
−2	13
0	10
2	7
4	4
6	1
8	−2
10	−5

b)

x	y
−10	−4
−7	−3
−4	−2
−1	−1
2	0
5	1
8	2

c)

x	y
−7	−7
0	−3
7	1

2. 2 VCRs, 9 stereos; 4 VCRs, 6 stereos; 6 VCRs, 3 stereos; 8 VCRs, 0 stereos **3.** Answers may vary. $2x + 6y = 11, 15x + 45y = 17$

Exercises 5-8, page 172
1. Answers may vary. **a)**(1,1) **b)**(10,0) **c)**(0,-2) **d)**(2,1) **e)**(0,5) **f)**(1,1) **2.a)**(-1,0) below **b)**(1,1) below **c)**(-2,2) above **d)**(1,1) above **3.a)**$x + y > 4$ **b)**$x + 3y < 3$ **c)**$4x - y \le -2$ **d)**$3x + 5y \le -15$ **e)**$2x - y < 24$ **f)**$x - 2y + 2 > 0$ **5.**$x + y \le 400$ **6.**$x + y \le 12$

Exercises 5-9, page 175
1.a) about 1.6 m²; about 2.2 m² **b)** about 30 kg; about 75 kg **c)** no **d)** about 130 kg **2.a)** about 15 m; 30 m **b)** about 7 s, 13 s, 27 s, 33 s **c)** about 20 s **3.b)** about 3 days **c)** about 48%

6. a)

h	0	100	200	300	400
t	0	4.5	6.4	7.8	9.0

b) about 3.8 s **c)** about 35 m

7. a)

n	0	2	4	6	8	10
A	1250	1568	1967	2467	3095	3882

c) about $1967 **d)** about 6 years

8. a)

n	1000	3000	5000	8000	10 000
A	$12.00	$5.30	$4.00	$3.25	$3.00

b) about 6700; about 13 300 **9.a)** $V = x(50 - 2x)^2$ **c)** about 8.3 cm **10.b)** 8 knots

11. a)

x	±2	±1	0
y	2	1	0

b)

x	±2	±1	0
y	7	6	5

c)

x	0	±5	±1	±2
y	±5	0	±4	±3

d)

x	0	±5	±4	±3
y	±5	0	±3	±4

e)

x	0	±1	±2
y	0	±1	±2

f)

x	-5	any real number
y	any real number	5

Problem Solving, page 179
1. 103 **2.** 171 cm **3.** 35 **4.** Fill the 9 L pail and empty it twice into the 4 L pail; this leaves 1 L in the 9 L pail. Pour this into the 4 L pail. Fill the 9 L pail and pour into the 4 L pail until it's full. This will leave 6 L in the 9 L pail. **5.a)** $730 **b)** $660 **6.a)** 6 **b)** 4 **c)** 13 **d)** 5 **e)** 5, -1 **f)** -5, 3 **7.** 22 apples **8.** Answers may vary.

Exercises 5-10, page 182
1.a) ±3 **b)** ±5 **c)** ±2 **d)** ±2 **e)** ±1 **f)** $\pm\sqrt{6}$ **g)** ±7 **h)** $\pm\sqrt{7}$ **2.a)** -3, -5 **b)** 3, 4 **c)** 5, -4 **d)** -8, 3 **e)** -6, -2 **f)** 9, -4 **g)** 6, 4 **h)** -7, -8 **i)** 7, -6 **3.a)** 4, 5 **b)** 7, 9 **c)** 8, -2 **d)** -7, -3 **e)** -2, 7 **f)** 3, -5 **g)** 4 **h)** 2, 6 **i)** 11, -4 **4.** 1 s and 5 s **5.a)** -2, -3 **b)** 3, 9 **c)** -2, 5 **d)** 3, 10 **e)** 4, -6 **f)** 2 **6.a)** 12 cm by 16 cm **b)** 14 cm by 14 cm **c)** 8 cm by 20 cm **7.a)** 420 **b)** 10 **8.a)** -180 **b)** 4, 7 **c)** Answers may vary. **9.** 17 cm **10.a)** $r = \sqrt{\dfrac{A}{\pi}}$ **b)** $v = \sqrt{\dfrac{2E}{m}}$ **c)** $h = \dfrac{3V}{\pi r^2}$ **d)** $d = \sqrt{\dfrac{mn}{F}}$ **11.a)** $t = \sqrt{\dfrac{d}{4.9}}$ **b)** about 1.4 s; about 2.0 s; about 2.9 s **12.** about 2.5 m
13.a) $x = \sqrt{\dfrac{A}{0.433}}$ **b)** about 4.8 cm; about 6.8 cm; about 9.6 cm **14.a)** -3, -4 **b)** 4, 5 **c)** 3, -6 **d)** 7, -5 **e)** 5 **f)** $\frac{3}{2}$, 4 **g)** -3, $-\frac{1}{2}$ **h)** $-\frac{2}{3}$, 5 **i)** $\frac{2}{3}$, $-\frac{1}{2}$ **15.a)** $-\frac{2}{3}$, 1 **b)** -4, 1 **c)** 3, 5 **d)** 8, 0 **e)** -6, 1 **f)** 5, 1 **g)** $-\frac{3}{2}$, 3 **h)** $\frac{7}{5}$, 4 **i)** $\frac{11}{2}$, 4 **16.a)** $\frac{1}{5}$, -4 **b)** $\frac{5}{2}$, 3 **c)** $-\frac{5}{3}$, $\frac{7}{2}$ **d)** $\frac{1}{3}$, -2 **e)** -1, 6 **f)** $\frac{2}{5}$, 2 **g)** $-\frac{2}{5}$, 4 **h)** $\frac{1}{3}$, $-\frac{7}{5}$ **i)** $\frac{5}{3}$, -3 **17.a)** 3, 0 **b)** 0, -5 **c)** 3, -4 **d)** $-\frac{11}{2}$, -2 **18.** 9, 3 or -3, -9 **19.** -6, 18 or 4, 8
20. 76 **21.** 5 m wide **22.** Answers may vary. **a)** $x^2 - 7x - 18 = 0$ **b)** $x^2 - 14x + 40 = 0$ **c)** $3x^2 + 16x + 5 = 0$ **d)** $32x^2 - 20x - 7 = 0$

INVESTIGATE, page 184
Yes, for example, $x^2 + x + 1 = 0$

Review Exercises, page 185
1.a) 1 **b)** -3 **c)** 4 **d)** 2 **e)** 12 **f)** 8 **2.a)** $\dfrac{c - b}{a}$ **b)** $\dfrac{c - ab}{a}$ **c)** $\dfrac{cd - ab}{a - c}$ **d)** $\dfrac{2ac - ab}{2}$ **e)** $\dfrac{abc}{a + b}$ **f)** $\dfrac{a + b}{c}$ **3.a)** $\frac{5}{7}$ **b)** 12 **c)** 4 **d)** $-\frac{1}{50}$ **e)** $\frac{19}{3}$ **f)** $\frac{5}{2}$ **4.a)** $t = \dfrac{v - u}{a}$ **b)** $b = \dfrac{A}{h}$ **c)** $x = \dfrac{y + am}{m}$ **d)** $P = \dfrac{A}{1 + rt}$ **e)** $h = \dfrac{A - 2\pi r}{2\pi r}$ **f)** $R = \dfrac{nE - Cnr}{C}$ **5.a)** 33 cm **b)** 430 g **6.a)** $n = \dfrac{S + 360}{180}$ **b)** 6, 9, 15 **7.** 22, 23 **8.** 55, 57, 59 **9.** 27, 12 **10.** 32, 8 **11.** 11, 8 **12.** 23, 47

13. a)

x	-1	0	1	2	3
y	-12	-9	-6	-3	0

b)

x	-2	0	2	4
y	6	5	4	3

c)

x	-3	0	3
y	0	4	8

14. a)

n	C
0	500
2000	900
4000	1300
6000	1700
8000	2100
10 000	2500

c) about 6800 km
d) about 9300 km

15. a)

l	0	1	2	3	4	5	6	7	8	9
T	0	2.0	2.8	3.5	4.0	4.5	4.9	5.3	5.6	6.0

c) about 2.2 m **d)** about 6.2 m **16.a)i)** $x + y < 3$
ii) $x + 2y \geq -2$ **iii)** $x - y \leq -2$ **b)i)** $x + y > 3$
ii) $x + 2y \leq -2$ **iii)** $x - y \geq -2$ **18.a)**$-3, 7$ **b)**$7, -8$ **c)**$\frac{3}{2}$

d)$8, 1$ **e)**$1, -\frac{25}{2}$ **f)**$1, 5$

Cumulative Review, page 187
1.a)$17x^2 + 3y^2 - 19xy$ **b)**$-19x^2 - 13xy$ **2.a)**$-42x^3y^3$
b)$12a^3b^4$ **c)**$36x^6y^5$ **d)**$\frac{-a^2b}{2}$ **3.a)**$9x^2(x - 2)$
b)$7y^3(2y - 1)$ **c)**$(m + 2)(m + n)$ **d)**$(a + 4)(a + 4)$
e)$(x + 4)(x - 5)$ **f)**$(y + 3)(y - 7)$ **g)**$(m - 8)(m - 9)$
h)$(c + 4d)(c - 6d)$ **i)**$(x - 3y)(x + 8y)$
4.a)$2x^2(y + 2)(y + 4)$ **b)**$8(x + 3)(x - 3)$
c)$5mn(m - 3)(m + 7)$ **d)**$5(6 - m)(6 + m)$ **5.a)**6000
b)4800 **c)**3600 **d)**6400 **e)**-5600 **f)**11 000
6.a)$14x^2y$ **b)**$\frac{x + 6}{3x}$ **c)**$\frac{m - 4}{m - 5}$ **d)**$\frac{a - 4}{a + 4}$ **e)**$\frac{x - 6}{x - 5}$ **f)**$\frac{y + 6}{y - 5}$
7.a)$6xy$ **b)**$\frac{-3(x + 1)}{x}$ **c)**$\frac{8c^2}{3(c + 2)}$ **d)**-1 **8.a)**$\frac{19}{10x}$ **b)**$\frac{23}{12m}$
c)$\frac{-19}{30b}$ **d)**$\frac{11}{12a}$ **e)**$\frac{-2x + 29}{15}$ **f)**$\frac{2x + 31}{15}$ **9.a)**$\frac{x^2 - 5x - 6}{(x - 2)(x + 2)}$
b)$\frac{17a}{12(2a - 3)}$ **c)**$\frac{2t}{2t - 5}$ **d)**$\frac{-4x + 3}{2(x - 4)}$ **e)**$\frac{13m^2 + 8m + 4}{6(m - 2)(m + 2)}$
f)$\frac{-3b^2 + 13b + 6}{2(b - 3)(b + 3)}$ **10.a)**6; not defined for $x = 0$ **b)**$\frac{7}{3}$; not
defined for $x = 0$ **c)**2; not defined for $x = 0$ **d)**$\frac{1}{7}$, 3;
not defined for $x = 0$ **11.a)**$x = -\frac{2}{5}$ **b)**$\frac{11}{7}$ **c)**$\frac{3b + ac}{ab}$
12.a)$b = 6a - 2m.$ **b)**$h = \frac{A - 2\pi r^2}{2\pi r}$ **c)**$w = \frac{P - 2l + 5}{2}$
d)$b = \frac{a(Cn - 24)}{C}$ **13.**$x = \frac{y^2 - 4y + 4}{6}$ **14.**9, 16
15.23 cm, 8 cm **16.**9 quarters **17.**about 2.7 L
18. Wife is 30; husband is 25, daughter is 3 years old.

Chapter 6

Exercises 6-1, page 192
1.a)5 units **b)**7 units **c)**11 units **d)**12 units
e)8 units **f)**14 units **2.**AB is 7 units, CD is
$2\sqrt{10}$ units, EF is $3\sqrt{10}$ units, GH is $\sqrt{73}$ units, JK is
$\sqrt{85}$ units. **3.a)**$2\sqrt{5}$ units **b)**$2\sqrt{13}$ units **c)**$5\sqrt{2}$ units

d)$\sqrt{137}$ units **e)**$\sqrt{29}$ units **f)**$\sqrt{28.25}$ units **4.a)**HA is
5 units, HT is 12 units, AT is 13 units. DI is 4 units,
IP is 3 units, DP is 5 units. BE is 5 units, EG is
3 units, BG is $\sqrt{34}$ units. RK is $\sqrt{10}$ units, RM is
$2\sqrt{10}$ units, MK is $5\sqrt{2}$ units. SJ is $2\sqrt{5}$ units, JL is
$2\sqrt{5}$ units, SL is $2\sqrt{10}$ units. **b)**Area $\triangle HAT$ is 30
square units. Area $\triangle DIP$ is 6 square units. Area
$\triangle BEG$ is 7.5 square units. Area $\triangle MRK$ is 10
square units. Area $\triangle SJL$ is 10 square units.
5.a)$7\sqrt{2}$ units **b)**$4\sqrt{5}$ units **c)**$\sqrt{89}$ units **d)**$\sqrt{85}$ units
6.a)AB is $\sqrt{53}$ units, BC is $\sqrt{106}$ units, AC is
$\sqrt{53}$ units; $\triangle ABC$ is isosceles. **b)**PQ is $\sqrt{53}$ units, QR
is 5 units, PR is $2\sqrt{13}$ units; $\triangle PQR$ is scalene. **c)**JK is
$6\sqrt{2}$ units, KL is $2\sqrt{17}$ units, JL is $2\sqrt{17}$ units; $\triangle JKL$
is isosceles. **7.a)**AB,CD are 9 units; BC,DA are
8 units; perimeter is 34 units. **b)**JK,LM are
$3\sqrt{10}$ units; KL,MJ are $\sqrt{10}$ units; perimeter is
$8\sqrt{10}$ units. **c)**PQ,RS are $2\sqrt{13}$ units; QR,SP are
$4\sqrt{13}$ units; perimeter is $12\sqrt{13}$ units. **8.a)**AC,BD are
$\sqrt{145}$ units; area $ABCD$ is 72 square units. **b)**JL,KM
are 10 units; area $JKLM$ is 30 square units. **c)**PR,QS
are $2\sqrt{65}$ units; area $PQRS$ is 104 square units.
9.a)AB is 5 units, BC is 5 units, AC is 10 units. **b)**AB
is 10 units, BC is 5 units, AC is 15 units. **c)**AB is
$4\sqrt{5}$ units, BC is $2\sqrt{5}$ units, AC is $6\sqrt{5}$ units,
$AB + BC = AC$; A, B, C are collinear. **10.**$(6,4), (-3,1)$
11.the coastguard cutter **12.**diagonals are 526 m,
410 m; perimeter is 1365 m; area is 105 313 m².
13.$P(0,-3)$, $R(5,7)$, $S(2,1)$ **14.**$(2,0)$, $(8,0)$ **15.a)**$(0,3)$
b)$(0,2)$ **c)**$(0,1)$ **16.a)**642; 812; 1431 **b)**Washington

Computer Power, page 195
1.about 27.3 units when $x \doteq 7.1$ units and $y = 5$ units
2.120°; answers may vary. **3.**8.9%, 3.4%

Exercises 6-2, page 197
1.AB, $(1,4)$; CD, $\left(4,\frac{3}{2}\right)$; EF, $(-1,0)$; GH, $(2,-1)$;
JK, $(0,5)$ **2.a)**$(3,4)$ **b)**$(-2,2)$ **c)**$(4,5)$ **d)**$\left(1,\frac{3}{2}\right)$
e)$-\left(\frac{3}{2},\frac{3}{2}\right)$ **f)**$\left(-2,\frac{5}{2}\right)$ **g)**$\left(2,-\frac{1}{2}\right)$ **h)**$(-2,-2)$
3.JK, $(4,2)$; KL, $(7,5)$; JL, $(3,6)$ **4.a)**AC, $(6,1)$; BD,
$(6,1)$ **b)**PR, $(5,2)$; QS, $(5,2)$. The diagonals of a
rectangle intersect at their midpoints. **5.**EG, $\left(5,\frac{1}{2}\right)$;
FH, $\left(5,\frac{1}{2}\right)$ The diagonals of a parallelogram intersect
at their midpoints. **6.a)**$M(1,4)$ **b)**All lengths are 5
units. **7.a)**$M(6,5)$, $N(2,2)$ **b)**MN is 5 units; AB is 10
units; $AB = 2MN$ **8.b)**Median from P is $3\sqrt{5}$ units;
median from Q is $6\sqrt{2}$ units; median from R is 9
units. **9.**Answers may vary. $A(2,0)$, $M(0,3)$, $B(-2,6)$.

The *x*-coordinates of *A* and *B* are opposites. The *y*-coordinate of *B* is twice the *y*-coordinate of *M*.
10.a)(6,−6) **b**)(2,−9) **c**)(−6,−2) **d**)(0,0) **11.a**)(−1,0), (2,−4), (5,−8) **b**)(1.5,−4), (−2,−1), (−5.5,2)
c)(0.5,−3.5), (3,−1), (5.5,1.5) **d**)(−2.5,−1.5), (0,0), (2.5,1.5) **12.a**)(14,−4) **b**)(10,10) **c**)(−8,9) **d**)(0,0)
13.a)$\left(\frac{x_2+2x_1}{3}, \frac{y_2+2y_1}{3}\right)$, $\left(\frac{2x_2+x_1}{3}, \frac{2y_2+y_1}{3}\right)$
b)$\left(\frac{x_2+3x_1}{4}, \frac{y_2+3y_1}{4}\right)$, $\left(\frac{x_2+x_1}{2}, \frac{y_2+y_1}{2}\right)$, $\left(\frac{3x_2+x_1}{4}, \frac{3y_2+y_1}{4}\right)$
14.a)6, 8 **b**)(6,8) is the midpoint of the square.
15.(2,2)

INVESTIGATE, page 198
Answers may vary. Let the required vertices be *P, Q,* and *R*. Let *A* be the midpoint of *PQ*; *B*, the midpoint of *PR*; and *C*, the midpoint of *QR*. Find the midpoints of *AB, BC,* and *CA*. Label them *D, E,* and *F* respectively. Then *D* is the midpoint of *PC*, so the coordinate of *P* can be found (see Exercise 10). Similarly, *E* is the midpoint of *AR*, and *F* is the midpoint of *QB*.

The Mathematical Mind, page 199
1.a)*M*(2,3), *N*(7,3) **b**)*MN* = 5, *QR* = 10, *QR* = 2*MN*
2.a)*M*(a,b), *N*(a + c,b) *MN* = c *QR* = 2c *QR* = 2*MN*
b)Yes

Exercise 6-3, page 202
1.$\frac{1}{3}$ **2.**$\frac{5}{3}$ **3.a**)*AB*, $\frac{5}{8}$; *AC*, $\frac{3}{8}$; *AD*, $\frac{1}{8}$; *AE*, 0; *AF*, $-\frac{1}{4}$;
AG, $-\frac{5}{8}$ **b**)*PQ*, $-\frac{7}{5}$; *PR*, $-\frac{7}{2}$; *PS*, undefined; *PT*, $\frac{7}{2}$;
PT, $\frac{7}{4}$; *PV*, 1 **4.a**)$-\frac{11}{8}$ **b**)3 **c**)$-\frac{5}{2}$ **d**)undefined **e**)$\frac{2}{3}$ **f**)0
5.a)*AB*, −1; *BC*, $\frac{9}{2}$, *AC*, $\frac{4}{7}$ **b**)*RS*, $\frac{1}{3}$; *ST*, $\frac{5}{2}$; *RT*, $-\frac{7}{5}$
c)*LM*, $-\frac{5}{4}$; *MN*, 0; *LN*, undefined **d**)*EF*, −5;
FG, 2; *EG*, 1 **6.**2.4 **7.**0.032 **8.a**)34 m **b**)2.4 **9.a**)Yes
b)Yes, yes **10.a**)7 **b**)5 **c**)4 **d**)0 **11.a**)6 **b**)−2 **c**)−1
d)4 **12.a**)(−2,0) **b**)(1,0) **c**)(2,0) **d**)(−8,0) **e**)(7,0)
f)(16,0) **13.a**)(0,13) **b**)(0,10) **c**)(0,7) **d**)(0,$\frac{11}{2}$)
e)(0,$\frac{19}{4}$) **f**)(0,4) **g**)(0,1) **h**)(0,−2) **i**)(0,−8) **j**)(0,$\frac{5}{2}$)
14.(−2,0), (8,0) **15.**(0,6), (8,0) and (0,−6), (−8,0)

INVESTIGATE, page 204
Answers may vary.

Exercises 6-4, page 206
1.a)*AB*, $\frac{1}{2}$; *CD*, $\frac{1}{2}$; *AB* parallel to *CD* **b**)*SR*, $-\frac{2}{3}$; *QP*,
$-\frac{2}{3}$; *SR* parallel to *QP* **c**)*JK*, $\frac{7}{3}$; *LM*, $\frac{5}{3}$ **2.a**)*AB*, 2;
CD, 2; *AB* parallel to *CD* **b**)*EF*, $\frac{3}{8}$; *GH*, $\frac{2}{5}$ **c**)*RS*, $-\frac{3}{4}$;
TU, $-\frac{2}{3}$ **3.a**)slopes: *AB*, $\frac{3}{4}$; *CD*, $\frac{3}{4}$; *AB* parallel to *DC*;
BC, −5; *DA*, −5; *BC* parallel to *AD*; *ABCD* is a

parallelogram. **b**)slopes: *PQ*, $-\frac{7}{4}$; *SR*, $-\frac{7}{3}$; *QR*, $\frac{2}{3}$;
SP, $\frac{8}{13}$; *PQRS* is not a parallelogram. **c**)slopes:
JK, −3; *LM*, −3; *JK* parallel to *ML*; *KL*, $-\frac{3}{8}$; *JM*, $-\frac{3}{8}$;
KL parallel to *JM*; *JKLM* is a parallelogram.
4.a)*M*(4,1), *N*(1,−1) **b**)*MN*, $\frac{2}{3}$; *AB*, $\frac{2}{3}$; *MN* parallel to
AB **c**)*P*(−1,3); *PM*, $-\frac{2}{5}$; *BC*, $-\frac{2}{5}$; *PN*, −2; *AC*, −2; *PM*
parallel to *BC* and *PN* parallel to *AC* **5.a**)midpoint
AB, (2,1); midpoint *BC*, (5,5); midpoint *CD*, (0,6);
midpoint *DA*, (−3,2) **b**)a parallelogram **c**)Opposite
sides are parallel with slopes $\frac{4}{3}$ and $-\frac{1}{5}$. **6.**(0,5.5)
7.a)(0,6) **b**)(4,0) **8.a**)6 **b**)−6 **c**)−10 **d**)−14 **e**)8
f)−7.5 **g**)$\frac{2}{3}$ **h**)$\frac{6}{7}$ **9.a**)(−12,−3), (6,−5), (4,5)
b)(13,−11), (3,1), (−11,7) **10.a**)(0,0), (10,0), (4,6)
b)(5,10), (5,0), (−11,6)

Exercises 6-5, page 209
1.a)*AB*, $\frac{2}{3}$; *CD*, $-\frac{3}{2}$; *CD* perpendicular to *AB*
b)*SR*, $-\frac{4}{5}$; *PQ*, $\frac{4}{3}$ **c**)*GF*, −2; *EF*, $\frac{1}{2}$; *GF* perpendicular
to *EF* **2.a**)$-\frac{3}{2}$ **b**)$-\frac{8}{5}$ **c**)$\frac{4}{3}$ **d**)2 **e**)3 **3.**$\frac{3}{4}$, $-\frac{4}{3}$, −4, $\frac{1}{4}$, 2, $-\frac{1}{2}$
4.a), **b**) **5.a**)slopes: *DE*, 0; *EF*,
undefined; Δ*DEF* is a right triangle. **b**)slopes: *AC*, $\frac{1}{2}$;
BC, −2; Δ*ABC* is a right triangle. **c**)slopes: *PQ*, $-\frac{2}{3}$;
QR, $\frac{3}{2}$; Δ*PQR* is a right triangle. **d**)slopes: *KL*, $\frac{3}{8}$;
LM, $-\frac{7}{3}$; *KM*, 2 **6.a**)slopes: *AB*, $\frac{2}{3}$; *BC*, $-\frac{3}{2}$; *CD*, $\frac{2}{3}$;
AD, $-\frac{3}{2}$; *ABCD* is a rectangle. **b**)slopes: *JK*, −5;
KL, $\frac{1}{8}$; *LM*, −5; *MJ*, $\frac{1}{8}$; *JKLM* is not a rectangle.
c)slopes: *PQ*, $-\frac{1}{3}$; *QR*, 3; *RS*, $-\frac{1}{3}$; *PS*, 3; *PQRS* is a
rectangle. **7.a**)−2 **b**)$\frac{1}{2}$ **c**)−1 **d**)$\frac{2}{5}$ **e**)0 **f**)undefined
8.a)$\frac{1}{2}$ **b**)−2 **c**)1 **d**)$-\frac{5}{2}$ **e**)undefined **f**)0 **9.a**)$-\frac{1}{3}$ **b**)2
c)−1 **d**)1 **e**)1 **f**)−8 **g**)4 **h**)−10 **i**)−6 **j**)35
10. Answers may vary. **a**)*C*(−3,5) **b**)*C*(2,10)
c)*C*(2,3) **d**)*C*(−1,6) **e**)*C*(−2,7) **f**)*C*(4,5) **11.a**)*P*(9,0)
b)*P*(0,6) **12.a**)all sides $\sqrt{65}$ units **b**)rhombus **c**)both
midpoints (1,1) **d**)*AC*, −2; *BD*, $\frac{1}{2}$ **e**)The diagonals are
each other's perpendicular bisectors. **13.a**)(4,2)
b)(−2,0) **c**)(5,1) **d**)(5,2) **14.a**)*C*(4,5), *D*(5,1)
b)*C*(7,10), *D*(10,3) **c**)*C*(1,10), *D*(10,9) **d**)*C*(b,a + b),
D(a + b,a) **15.**(0,0), (5,0) **16.**(−1,0), (7,0), (2,0), (3,0)
17.a)(7,3), (5,−2) and(−5,2), (−3,7)and $\left(-\frac{3}{2},\frac{7}{2}\right)$, $\left(\frac{7}{2},\frac{3}{2}\right)$

b)(−4,2), (−1,−2) and (4,8); (7,4) and $\left(\frac{7}{2},\frac{9}{2}\right)$, $\left(-\frac{1}{2},\frac{3}{2}\right)$

18.a)P(−1,3), Q(1,−1), R(4,2) b)slopes: AP, −1; QR, 1; lengths of AP and QR, 3√2 units c)slopes: BQ, 5; PR, $\frac{1}{-5}$; lengths of BQ and PR, √26 units; OR, $\frac{1}{2}$; PQ, −2; lengths of OR and PQ, 2√5 units

INVESTIGATE, page 211
The relations are true for other right triangles.

Problem Solving, page 213
1.a)About 10.5 km b)About 2:23 pm 2.a)About 127.5 km b)About 4:04 pm 3.c)at 8 pm 4.About 133 km 5.a)3 min b)6 min c)2 min 6.18 min

Mathematics Around Us, page 214
1.Straight lines may vary. 2.a)About $10 b)About $15 c)About $38 3.a)Nearly 7 min b)About 8 min c)About 10 min 4.a)Question 2a), b), Question 3 b)Question 2c) 5.a) $10 b) $2.75

Review Exercises, page 215
1.a)15 units b)14 units c)10√2 units d)5√2 units e)4√5 units f)8√2 units 2.a)8 units, 6 units b)28 units c)10 units d)48 square units 3.a)right triangle b)right triangle 4.a)(3,2) b)(−3,−1) c)(−4,−3) d)(9,−5) e)$\left(\frac{3}{2},6\right)$ f)$\left(\frac{7}{2},\frac{5}{2}\right)$ 5.a)KL, (−1,4); LM, (1,−2); KM, (5,1) b)10 units
6.a)DE, 6√2 units; EF, 2√17 units; DF, 2√17 units b)DE, (−1,1); EF, (3,2); DF, (0,5) c)DE, −1; EF, 4; DF, $\frac{1}{4}$ 7.a)$\frac{5}{2}$ b)0 c)$-\frac{13}{7}$ d)$\frac{2}{3}$ e)$-\frac{5}{7}$ f)−3 8.a)ST, −2; PQ, −2 b)ST, $\frac{\sqrt5}{2}$ units; PQ √5 units 9.a)(1,6) b)(7,0) c)(8,7) d)(6,4) 10.midpoint BC, (6,4); 5 units 11.midpoints of sides are (4,5), (9,4), (7,−2) and (2,−1); slopes of lines joining midpoints are $-\frac{1}{5}$, 3, $-\frac{1}{5}$, and 3. 12.K(6,0), (0,4) 13.a)2 b)1 14.a)AB, $\frac{3}{8}$; AC, 4 b)$-\frac{9}{5}$ c)$-\frac{6}{13}$ 15.slopes: AB, 3; BC, $\frac{1}{6}$; CD, 6; AD, $\frac{1}{5}$; ABCD is not a parallelogram. 16.slopes: PQ, $\frac{3}{5}$ PR, $-\frac{5}{3}$ 17.a)$-\frac{3}{5}$ b)4 c)$-\frac{7}{4}$ d)0.3 e)−8 18.a)$\frac{5}{3}$ b)$-\frac{1}{4}$ c)$\frac{4}{7}$ d)$-\frac{10}{3}$ e)$\frac{1}{8}$ 19.a)15, $-\frac{20}{3}$ b)−8, 2 c)$-\frac{4}{3}$, 12 d)−3, $\frac{25}{3}$ 20.a)$-\frac{6}{7}$, $\frac{7}{6}$ b)$-\frac{2}{3}$, $\frac{3}{2}$ c)undefined, 0 21.slopes: AB, 1; BC, $\frac{5}{-6}$; CD, −5; DA, $\frac{1}{6}$; neither 22.a)S(5,0) b)S(0,−15) 23.a)S(13,0) b)$S\left(0,\frac{13}{3}\right)$ 24.a)6√5 units b)(2,0) c)12√17 units d)2√85 units e)(2,0)

Chapter 7

Exercises 7-1, page 220
1.a)2 b)$-\frac{3}{2}$ c)$\frac{1}{2}$ 8.a)All slopes are $\frac{2}{3}$. b)All slopes are $-\frac{1}{2}$. c)Slopes are $\frac{1}{3}$, $\frac{3}{7}$, and $\frac{1}{5}$. 9.a)2, $\frac{7}{4}$, $\frac{13}{7}$ b)A, B, and C are not collinear. 10.a)slopes: DE, $-\frac{1}{2}$; EF, $-\frac{1}{2}$; DF, $-\frac{1}{2}$, points are collinear. b)slopes: JK, $\frac{5}{4}$; KL, 1; JL, $\frac{8}{7}$; points are not collinear. c)slopes: RS, $\frac{4}{5}$; ST, $\frac{7}{9}$; RT, $\frac{11}{14}$; points are not collinear. 11.c)The lines are parallel. 12.0.24 13.a)(0, −3) b)(0,17) c)(0,7) or (0,1)

Exercises 7-2, page 226
1.y is doubled, y is halved.

2. i) a) 5 b) c) $y = 5x$

x	y
1	5
2	10
3	15
4	20
5	25

ii) a) −3 b) c) $y = -3x$

x	y
1	−3
2	−6
3	−9
4	−12
5	−15

iii) a) $\frac{1}{2}$ b) c) $y = \frac{1}{2}x$

x	y
2	1
4	2
6	3
8	4
10	5

iv) a) $\frac{3}{2}$ b) c) $y = \frac{3}{2}x$

x	y
2	3
4	6
6	9
8	12
10	15

3. a)

x	y
−3	−6
−2	−4
−1	−2
0	0
1	2
2	4
3	6

b) 2 c) $y = 2x$

4. i) a) b) $y = \frac{2}{3}x$

x	y
−6	−4
−3	−2
0	0
3	−2
9	−6

ii) a) b) $y = \frac{-1}{2}x$

x	y
−4	2
−2	1
0	0
4	2
6	3

iii) a)

b) $y = \frac{2}{3}x$

x	y
0	0
3	2
6	4
9	6
12	8

iv) a)

b) $y = \frac{5}{2}x$

x	y
0	0
2	5
4	10
8	20
12	30

5.a)6 **b)**30 cm **c)**7 min **d)**Letters may vary. $d = 6t$
6.a)1.6 **b)**15 m **c)**Answers may vary.
$l = \frac{8h}{5}$ or $h = \frac{5l}{8}$ **d)**Graph may vary. **7.a)**$28.00
b)29 km **c)**$a = 1.4d$ **8.a)**about 31 t **b)**about 313 t
c)2000 t **9.a)**$y = x\sqrt{2}$ **b)**Yes, for the areas to be
equal, the larger circle has a radius which is $\sqrt{2}$ times
that of the smaller circle. **10.**Pythagorean Theorem,
$r^2 = x^2 + \frac{x^2}{4}, r = \frac{\sqrt{5}x}{2}, \frac{\sqrt{5}}{2}$

Exercises 7-3, page 230
1.b)25 **c)**12 **2.a)**Tables may vary.

x	0	4	10	12
y	2	6	12	14

b)7 **c)**10 **d)**$y = x + 2$ **3.a)**Tables may vary.

n	0	4	8	12
T	200	300	400	500

b)Fixed cost is $200; variable cost is $25 for every 100
pamphlets. **c)**$825 **d)**1200 pamphlets **4.a)**Tables
may vary.

d	0	2	4	6	8
n	72	54	36	18	0

c)about 22 L **d)**about 470 km **5.a)**Tables may vary.

n	0	200	400	600	800	1000
C	2.00	3.12	4.24	5.36	6.48	7.60

c)$C = 2.00 + 0.0056n$ **d)**1200 **6.b)**$C = 3 + \frac{n}{3}$ **7.**Letters
may vary. **b)**$1200 **c)**$C = 1200 + 0.25d$ **d)**$4950
8.Letters may vary. $P = 10 + 2l$

Mathematics Around Us, page 232
1.Lines may vary. **2.**about 19°C **3.**about 28°C
4.a) Question 2 **b)**Question 3

INVESTIGATE, page 233
1.b) Answers may vary. They pass through the origin.
They have different slopes. **2.a)**1, 2, $\frac{1}{2}$, 0, −1, −2, $-\frac{1}{2}$

b)The slope is the coefficient of x. **4.b)**Answers may
vary: in part i) they pass through the same point; they
have different slopes; in part ii) they are parallel; they
cross the axes at different points. **5.a)**2, 1, $\frac{1}{2}$, 0, $-\frac{1}{2}$,
−1, −2; 2, 2, 2, 2, 2, 2 **b)**The slope is the coefficient of
x.

Exercises 7-4, page 236
1.a)3, 5 **b)**−2, 3 **c)**$\frac{2}{5}$, − 4 **d)**$-\frac{1}{2}$, 6 **e)**−4, −7 **f)**$\frac{3}{8}$, $-\frac{5}{2}$
g)$\frac{4}{3}$, − 2 **h)**$\frac{9}{5}$, 1 **2.a)**$y = 2x + 3$ **b)**$y = -x + 4$
c)$y = \frac{2}{3}x - 1$ **d)**$y = -\frac{4}{5}x + 8$ **e)**$y = -3x + \frac{5}{2}$ **f)**$y = 3$
3.a)$\frac{1}{2}$, 1, $y = \frac{1}{2}x + 1$ **b)**$\frac{3}{2}$, − 2, $y = \frac{3}{2}x - 2$ **c)**−2, 1,
$y = -2x + 1$ **4.a)**$y = -x + 2$ **b)**$y = -\frac{3}{2}x - 3$ **c)**$y = \frac{2}{3}x$
6.b)(6,0) **c)**$3\sqrt{5}$ units **d)**9 square units,
$(9 + 3\sqrt{5})$ units **7.a)**(1,6) **b)**27 square units **8.**(−2,7),
(4,4), (1,−2) **9.a)**−5 **b)**7 **c)**−11 **d)**8 **10.a)**$\frac{1}{4}$ **b)**−5
c)−2 **d)**$\frac{1}{5}$ **11.b)**(0,0) **c)**$y = 2x; y = \frac{-1}{2}x$
12.b)$y = x + 8$ or $y = x$ **13.a)**$y = \frac{2x}{3} - 1$
b)$y = \frac{-4x}{3} + 5$

Problem Solving, page 239
1.29 students **2.**10 cm by 6 cm, 8 cm by 8 cm
3.$x - 2y - 4 = 0, 2x + y + 7 = 0$ **4.**12 triangles: 6,6,6;
6,6,5; 6,6,4; 6,6,3; 6,6,2; 6,6,1; 6,5,5; 6,5,4; 6,5,3;
6,5,2; 6,4,4; 6,4,3 **5.**1.5 m **6.**466 **7.**Answers may
vary, for example, $x + y = 1$. **8.**24 units **9.a)**0.02 cm
b)0.03 cm

Exercises 7-5, page 242
1.i)a)$\frac{y - 2}{x - 1}$ **b)**$\frac{2}{3}$ **c)**$2x - 3y + 4 = 0$ **ii)a)**$\frac{y - 1}{x - 1}$ **b)**2
c)$2x - y - 1 = 0$ **iii)a)**$\frac{y - 2}{x - 3}$ **b)**$\frac{-1}{2}$
c)$x + 2y - 7 = 0$ **2.a)**$3x - y - 1 = 0$
b)$7x - y + 30 = 0$ **c)**$4x + y - 16 = 0$
d)$2x - y + 3 = 0$ **e)**$3x + 5y + 15 = 0$
f)$2x - 3y - 16 = 0$ **g)**$7x + 2y + 7 = 0$ **h)**$y = \frac{3}{4}$
3.(−4,0), (0,6), (2,9), (−2,3), (4,12) **4.**$x - y + 6 = 0$,
$3x - y + 14 = 0, x + 2y = 0, 2x + 5y - 2 = 0$
5.a)$x - 2y + 2 = 0$ **b)**$2x - 3y + 6 = 0$
c)$2x + y - 3 = 0$ **d)**$x + 3y + 6 = 0$ **e)**$x + 4y - 8 = 0$
f)$2x + 7y - 41 = 0$ **6.a)**$2x - y - 3 = 0$
b)$3x + y + 7 = 0$ **c)**$7x - 2y - 39 = 0$
d)$2x - y - 1 = 0$ **e)**$2x - 3y - 11 = 0$
f)$8x - 3y + 20 = 0$ **g)**$3x + y - 16 = 0$
h)$2x + y + 14 = 0$ **7.**$RS, 5x + 3y - 15 = 0; ST$,
$3x - y - 9 = 0; RT, x - 5y + 25 = 0$

8.a)$3x - y - 5 = 0$ **b)**$2x + 5y - 18 = 0$
c)$x + y - 2 = 0$ **d)**$2x - 3y + 11 = 0$
e)$3x - 4y - 12 = 0$ **f)**$2x + y - 5 = 0$
g)$2x - y + 4 = 0$ **h)**$x + 3y - 6 = 0$ **9.a)**AB,
$2x - 3y + 12 = 0$; BC, $3x + 2y + 18 = 0$; CD,
$2x - 3y - 14 = 0$; DA, $3x + 2y - 8 = 0$ **b)**AC,
$5x - y + 4 = 0$; BD, $x + 5y + 6 = 0$ **10.a)**-4 **b)**6
c)-19 **d)**-8 **e)**-2 **11.a)**-6 **b)**22 **c)**4
12.a)$x - 3y - 6 = 0$ **b)**$x - 3y + 24 = 0$
c)$x - 3y + 9 = 0$ **d)**$9x + 13y - 59 = 0$
13.b)AB, $2x - y = 0$; CD, $x - 2y = 0$; EF, $3x + y = 0$;
GH, $x + 3y = 0$; They pass through the origin. **c)**AI,
$x - 2y + 12 = 0$; CJ, $2x - y - 12 = 0$; KL,
$x + 3y - 48 = 0$; MN, $3x + y - 48 = 0$, $(12,12)$
14.c)$5x + 2y - 10 = 0$ **16.a)**$3x - 10y + 19 = 0$
b)$4x - y - 27 = 0$ **c)**$3x + 2y - 19 = 0$ **17.a)**PQ,
$x - 2y - 2 = 0$; QR, $3x + 4y - 26 = 0$; PR,
$3x - y + 14 = 0$ **b)**perpendicular bisector of: PQ,
$2x + y + 1 = 0$; QR $4x - 3y + 7 = 0$; PR,
$x + 3y - 2 = 0$ **c)**$(-1,1)$; $5\sqrt{2}$ units **18.a)**PR,
$x - 2y + 7 = 0$; QS, $2x + y - 6 = 0$ **b)**no **c)**yes **d)**no

Exercises 7-6, page 248
1.a)$3, 4, -\frac{4}{3}$ **b)**$4, -2, \frac{1}{2}$ **c)**$-2, -1, -\frac{1}{2}$
2.$x + 2y - 3 = 0$, $2x + 5y - 6 = 0$ **3.**$x + y + 2 = 0$,
$3x + 4y + 8 = 0$ **4.a)**$5, -5$ **b)**$3, 9$ **c)**$-4, 2$ **d)**$-6, 4$
e)$6, -8$ **f)**$3, \frac{6}{5}$ **5.a)**-2 **b)**1 **c)**$\frac{3}{2}$ **d)**$\frac{1}{3}$ **e)**2 **f)**$\frac{1}{4}$ **6.a)**$\frac{3}{4}, -3$
b)$\frac{5}{2}, -5$ **c)**$-2, 3$ **d)**$-\frac{3}{5}, -4$ **e)**$-\frac{1}{2}, \frac{5}{2}$ **f)**$\frac{4}{7}, \frac{15}{7}$
9.$2x - 3y + 12 = 0$ and $4x - 6y - 9 = 0$ have same
slope. **10.**$2x - y - 8 = 0$ and $5x - 7y - 20 = 0$
have same x-intercept; $x - y + 2 = 0$ and
$4x - 3y + 6 = 0$ have same y-intercept;
$3x + 6y + 5 = 0$ and $2x + 4y - 9 = 0$ have same
slope. **11.b)**$x - 2y + 6 = 0$, $2x + y + 2 = 0$
12.b)$3x + 2y - 8 = 0$, $x + 6y - 8 = 0$ **13.a)**$(6,2)$,
$(-3,8)$, $(0,-7)$ **b)**$3\sqrt{13}$ units, $3\sqrt{26}$ units, $3\sqrt{13}$ units
c)$-\frac{2}{3}, \frac{3}{2}, -5$ **d)**right-isosceles triangle **e)**58.5 square
units, $3\sqrt{13}(2 + \sqrt{2})$ units

INVESTIGATE, page 249
$-\dfrac{A}{B}, -\dfrac{C}{B}, -\dfrac{C}{A}$

Exercises 7-7, page 251
1.$3x + y + 9 = 0$, $6x + 2y - 9 = 0$, $9x + 3y + 20 = 0$
2.$3x + 2y - 6 = 0$, $6x + 4y + 15 = 0$
3.$5x - 2y + 8 = 0$, $10x - 4y + 15 = 0$ are parallel;
$2x + 5y - 12 = 0$, $4x + 10y + 5 = 0$ are perpendicular.

4.a)slopes $2, -\frac{1}{2}, -\frac{3}{2}$; yes **b)**slopes $\frac{3}{5}, -2, \frac{5}{3}$; no **c)**slopes
$-\frac{4}{7}, \frac{1}{2}, -2$; yes **5.a)**$2x - y + 3 = 0$ **b)**$x + 4y - 12 = 0$
c)$x - 2y + 6 = 0$ **6.a)**$2x - 3y + 9 = 0$
b)$2x + y - 3 = 0$ **c)**$3x - y + 3 = 0$
7.a)$4x - 3y - 6 = 0$ **b)**$4x - 3y - 18 = 0$
c)$4x - 3y + 24 = 0$ **d)**$4x - 3y + 6 = 0$
8.a)$3x - y - 11 = 0$ **b)**$3x + 4y - 16 = 0$
c)$4x - 3y - 13 = 0$ **d)**$2x + y - 9 = 0$
e)$3x + 5y - 17 = 0$ **f)**$8x - 3y - 29 = 0$
9.$2x + y - 14 = 0$, $x - 2y - 2 = 0$ **10.**$2x - 3y - 7 = 0$,
$3x + 2y - 17 = 0$ **11.a)**$3x - 5y + 13 = 0$
b)$x - 3y + 7 = 0$

INVESTIGATE, page 252
a)$\dfrac{A_1}{B_1} = \dfrac{A_2}{B_2}$ but $\dfrac{C_1}{B_1} \neq \dfrac{C_2}{B_2}$ **b)**$\dfrac{A_1}{B_1} = \dfrac{A_2}{B_2}$ and $\dfrac{C_1}{B_1} = \dfrac{C_2}{B_2}$
c)$\dfrac{A_1}{B_1} = \dfrac{-B_2}{A_2}$

Review Exercises, page 253
1.$l_1, -\frac{3}{2}, l_2, -3; l_3, \frac{4}{3}; l_4, \frac{l}{4}$ **4.**The points are collinear.
5.a)$y = \frac{3}{4}x$ **b)**80 **c)**22.5 **d)**$\frac{3}{4}$ **6.**165 km, 5.5 h
7.a)77 **b)**20 **8.a)**Letters may vary. **b)**$\$450$
c)$C = 450 + 0.04d$ **d)**$\$1170$ **9.a)**$4, -3$ **b)**$-\frac{5}{3}, 7$
c)$-\frac{9}{4}, -3$ **10.a)**$y = -\frac{1}{2}x - 4$ **b)**$y = \frac{4}{3}x - 6$
c)$y = -\frac{3}{2}x + \frac{3}{4}$ **12.a)**$1, 5$ **b)**$8, \frac{3}{4}$ **13.**$(3,2), (8,4), \left(\frac{1}{2}, 1\right)$
14.$3x - 2y + 17 = 0$, $5x + 2y + 7 = 0$
15.a)$x - y + 2 = 0$ **b)**$11x + 9y - 19 = 0$
c)$4x - y + 2 = 0$ **d)**$4x + 7y + 11 = 0$
16.a)$3x + 4y - 35 = 0$ **b)**$2x - 5y + 15 = 0$
17.a)PQ, $x - 3y = 0$; QR, $2x + 3y - 27 = 0$; PR,
$4x - 3y + 9 = 0$ **b)**$x - 3y + 18 = 0$ **c)**$3x + y - 16 = 0$
d)$y = 3$ **18.a)**$-5, 2, \frac{2}{5}$ **b)**$3, 12, -4$ **c)**$\frac{14}{3}, -2, \frac{3}{7}$
20. $-\frac{14}{3}, \frac{7}{6}$ **21.**right triangle

Cumulative Review, page 255
1.a)10 units **b)**18 units **c)**$12\sqrt{2}$ units **d)**$7\sqrt{2}$ units
e)7 units **f)**5 units **2.**$(6 + 6\sqrt{2})$ units; isosceles
triangle **3.**The points are collinear. **4.a)**$(7,-4)$
b)$(2,-2)$ **c)**$\left(-1, \frac{1}{2}\right)$ **d)**$\left(\frac{3}{2}, \frac{5}{2}\right)$ **e)**$\left(\frac{11}{2}, \frac{1}{2}\right)$ **f)**$\left(-1, \frac{3}{2}\right)$ **5.a)**-1
b)$\frac{1}{2}$ **c)**$-\frac{8}{9}$ **d)**$\frac{3}{5}$ **e)**$\frac{1}{2}$ **f)**-4 **6.a)**6 **b)**10 **c)**-2 **d)**20 **e)**8
7.a)$\frac{11}{2}$ **b)**$(-2, -1)$ **c)**$\sqrt{61}$ units **8.** Midpoints are:
$AB, (-1,2)$; $BC, (2,-2)$; $CD, (6,0)$; $DA, (3,4)$; slopes of
lines joining adjacent midpoints: $-\frac{4}{3}, \frac{1}{2}, -\frac{4}{3}, \frac{1}{2}$.

9.a)$\frac{6}{5}$, $-\frac{5}{6}$ **b)**$-\frac{7}{6}$, $\frac{6}{7}$ **c)**$\frac{7}{5}$, $-\frac{5}{7}$ **10.a)**$\frac{14}{3}$ **b)**$\frac{1}{2}$ **11.a)**8, $-\frac{9}{2}$
b)$-\frac{25}{2}$, 2 **c)**6, $-\frac{8}{3}$ **d)**9, -4 **e)**$\frac{1}{2}$, -8 **12.a)**$y = \frac{-2x}{5}$
b)$y = 7 + 2x$ **13.a)**-2, 7 **b)**$\frac{3}{4}$, -3 **c)**-1, -2 **d)**$-\frac{5}{2}$, -3
e)-2, $\frac{5}{2}$ **f)**-2, 3 **14.a)**$y = \frac{-2x}{3} + 4$ **b)**$y = \frac{6x}{5} - 3$
15.a)$2x - 7y + 48 = 0$ **b)**$16x + 9y - 10 = 0$
c)$x + 5y + 10 = 0$ **16.a)**$2x + 5y - 8 = 0$
b)$5x + 3y - 1 = 0$ **17.a)**$3x + 5y - 1 = 0$ **b)**$y = 5$
c)$x + 3y - 12 = 0$ **d)**$x = 5$ **19.**Parallel lines are
$x - 2y - 10 = 0$, $2x - 4y - 12 = 0$, and
$x - 2y - 5 = 0$; the line $2x + y - 4 = 0$ is
perpendicular to the parallel lines listed;
perpendicular lines are $4x - 3y - 12 = 0$ and
$6x + 8y - 24 = 0$.

Chapter 8

Exercises 8-1, page 260
1.a)$(2,3)$ **b)**$(2,4)$ **c)**$(4,3)$ **d)**$(-3,-5)$ **e)**$(0,-4)$ **f)**$(4,5)$
g)$(-3,1)$ **h)**$(-4,2)$ **2.a)**$(-2,-6)$ **b)**$(-2.5,-2.3)$
c)$(-0.7,0.8)$ **d)**$(-1.8,-8.5)$ **3.a)**$(30,-30)$ **b)**$(0,30)$
c)$(25,-30)$ **d)**$(-14,4)$ **4.a)**$(\frac{5}{2},\frac{3}{2})$ **b)**$(\frac{7}{2},\frac{3}{4})$
c)$(\frac{10}{3},-\frac{4}{3})$ **d)**$(\frac{3}{4},\frac{1}{2})$ **e)**$(34,-13)$ **f)**$(\frac{1}{2},\frac{1}{3})$ **g)**$(-2.3,3.4)$
h)$(4.7,-2.2)$ **5.a)**$(2,3)$ **b)**$4x + y = 11$. Line passes
through $(2,3)$. **c)**$2x - 3y = -5$. Line passes through $(2,3)$.
6.a)$(2,4)$ **b)**$(1,0)$ **c)**$(-3,-5)$ **d)**$(\frac{19}{3},\frac{1}{3})$

INVESTIGATE
No. The lines may be parallel and have no points of
intersection or the lines may coincide and have an
infinite number of points of intersection.

Exercises 8-2, page 264
1.a)$6x + 3y = 14$; $4x + y = 6$
b)$5x + 2y = 27$; $x + 8y = 3$
c)$4x + 3y = 2$; $2x - 7y = -16$
d)$2x + 2y = 20$; $16x - 6y = 4$
2.a)i)$3x = 9$; $x - 2y = -1$
ii)$7x - 2y = -16$; $5x + 4y = -6$ **b)i)**Lines pass
through $(3,2)$. **ii)**Lines pass through $(-2,1)$ **3.a)**$(1,3)$
b)Answers may vary. $3x - 2y = -3$; $x + 4y = 13$
c)Lines pass through $(1,3)$. **4.**Answers may vary.
a)$8x + 6y = 14$ **b)**$6x + 3y = 12$ **c)**$5x + 6y = -9$
   $4x - 8y = -4$ $4x - 5y = 22$ $3x + 12y = 13$
d)$9x + 4y = 42$ **5.a)i)**$6x - 2y = -14$
   $3x + 8y = 18$ $3x + 12y = 6$
ii) $3x + 6y = 24$
    $10x - 6y = 2$
b)i)$9x + 10y = -8$ **ii)**$13x = 26$
c)i)$3x - 14y = -20$ **ii)**$7x - 12y = -22$

Exercises 8-3, page 267
1.b) **2.a)**$(3,4)$ **b)**$(-1,3)$ **c)**$(2,-3)$ **d)**$(4,3)$ **e)**$(-2,3)$
f)$(2,-4)$ **g)**$(3,-1)$ **h)**$(3,7)$ **3.a)**$(2,-3)$ **b)**$(-1,5)$
c)$(3,-1)$ **d)**$(4,3)$ **e)**$(-4,2)$ **f)**$(-2,-3)$ **g)**$(3,4)$ **h)**$(2,-1)$

4.a)$(4,-2)$ **b)**$(3,5)$ **c)**$(\frac{1}{2},\frac{1}{3})$ **d)**$(2,3)$ **e)**$(-3,-7)$ **f)**$(-2,1)$
g)$(\frac{5}{2},-3)$ **h)**$(-6,3)$ **5.a)**$(\frac{4}{5},\frac{-3}{5})$ **b)**$(\frac{23}{11},\frac{8}{11})$ **c)**$(\frac{3}{14},\frac{15}{14})$ **d)**$(2,1)$
e)$(\frac{25}{11},\frac{20}{11})$ **f)**$(-3,5)$ **g)**$(2,-1)$ **h)**$(4,-6)$ **6.a)**$(3,-4)$
b)$(2,0)$ **c)**$(-6,10)$ **d)**$(4,-2)$ **e)**$(12,-9)$ **f)**$(6,3)$
7.a)$(2,3)$ **b)**$(11,3)$ **c)**$(3,2)$ **d)**$(10,4)$ **e)**$(3,8)$ **f)**$(4,\frac{1}{2})$
g)$(8,2)$ **h)**$(\frac{116}{13},\frac{106}{13})$ **8.a)**$(3,4)$ **b)**$(3.07,3.95)$ **c)**The
results are very similar but b) is more accurate.
9.Answers may vary. **a)**yes **b)**$(11,4)$, $(-1,-4)$
c)equations for the same line **10.a)**no solution
b)equations of parallel lines **11.a)**$m = 4$, $n = 3$
b)$m = 3$, $n = 1$ **c)**$m = -1$, $n = 2$ **d)**$m = 2$, $n = 0$

12.a)$\left(\frac{r + s}{2p}, \frac{r - s}{2q}\right)$ **b)**$\left(\frac{c - b^2}{a - b}, \frac{c - ab}{b - a}\right)$ **c)**$\left(\frac{p + l}{m + n}, \frac{pn - ml}{m + n}\right)$
d)$(0,1)$ **e)**$\left(\frac{r}{p - q}, \frac{r}{q - p}\right)$ **f)**(a,b) **13.a)**$(2a,b)$
b)$(a + b, a - b)$

Exercises 8-4, page 270
1.c), **d) 2.a)**$(2,7)$ **b)**$(3,-2)$ **c)**$(-1,-8)$ **d)**$(1,4)$
e)$(-2,5)$ **f)**$(-2,3)$ **g)**$(3,5)$ **h)**$(4,-2)$ **3.a)**$(-1,3)$
b)$(2,-2)$ **c)**$(2,1)$ **d)**$(3,1)$ **e)**$(-2,-3)$ **f)**$(4,-3)$
g)$(20,-6)$ **h)**$(4,-3)$ **4.a)**$(\frac{7}{6},\frac{1}{12})$ **b)**$(2,-1)$ **c)**$(\frac{23}{2},\frac{-15}{2})$
d)$(19,-30)$ **e)**$(0,1)$ **f)**$(-\frac{1}{6},\frac{7}{12})$ **g)**$(2,-\frac{7}{3})$ **h)**$(\frac{1}{6},\frac{1}{12})$
5.a)$(5,-1)$ **b)**$(-1,1)$ **c)**$(3,2)$ **d)**$(-2,1)$

Exercises 8-5, page 273
1.a)no solution **b)**infinitely many solutions **c)**one
solution **d)**infinitely many solutions **e)**one solution
f)one solution **g)**no solution **h)**infinitely many
solutions **2.**Infinitely many solutions:
$4x + 2y = 20$, $x - 3y = 12$, $2x + y = 10$, $2x - 6y = 24$
No solution: $2x + y = 10$, $x - 3y = 12$, $6x + 3y = 15$,
$15x - 15y = -60$ Answers may vary for one solution.
One solution: $4x + 2y = 20$, $6x + 3y = 5$,
$x - 3y = 12$, $2x - 6y = 24$ **3.**Answers may vary.
a)$6x - 8y = 24$ **b)**$3x - 4y = 24$ **c)**$x - 2y = 12$ **4.a)**,
c), **d) 5.a)**, **d) 6.a)**Answers may vary.
$x + 4y = 7$, $3x + 6y = 9$ **b)**$(-1,2)$ **c)**The solution is
always $(-1,2)$

INVESTIGATE
a)Answers may vary, $x + y = 1$, $2x + 2y = 4$. The
lines are parallel. **b)**$x + y = 1$, $2x + 2y = 2$. The lines
coincide.

The Mathematical Mind, page 275
1.a)$y = -1$, $z = 2$ **b)**$(4,-1,2)$ **2.a)**$(3,4,1)$ **b)**$(2,1,-1)$
c)$(5,-2,3)$ **3.a)**$(1,2,3)$ **b)**$(-4,3,-1)$ **c)**$(5,-2,-2)$
4.8, 2, 5

Exercises 8-6, page 277
1.a)$x + y$ **b)**$2x + 3y$ **c)**$5x - 4y$ **d)**$\frac{1}{2}x + \frac{1}{3}y$
2.a)$2x + 5y$ **b)**$x + y$ **3.a)**$5n$ **b)**$10d$ **c)**$5n + 10d$
d)$n + d$ **4.a)**$a + s$ **b)**$4a + 2s$ **5.a)**$10x + y$ **b)**$10y + x$
c)$x + y$ **d)**$11x + 11y$ **6.a)**w **b)**$w + 10$ **c)**$4w + 20$
d)$w^2 + 10w$ **7.a)**$2w - 3$ **b)**$6w - 6$ **c)**$2w^2 - 3w$

8.a)$x + 2y$ **b)**$x + 6y$ **9.a)**$0.06x$ **b)**$0.09y$
c)$0.06x + 0.09y$ **10.**$x + y = 50$ **11.**$5x + 4y = 40$
12.$4x + 3y = 250$ **13.**$6a + 4s = 1800$
14.$5n + 10d = 200$ **15.**$x + y = 10$ **16.**$x - y = 15$
17.$2x - 5y = 10$ **18.**$x - 2y = -7$ **19.**$\frac{1}{4}x - \frac{1}{2}y = 3$
20.$x - 7y = 5$

INVESTIGATE, page 278

The quotient is always 11. Let the digits be x and y.
The two numbers that can be formed from these
digits are $10x + y$, $10y + x$. Their sum is $11x + 11y$.
Divide the sum of the digits. $\dfrac{11x + 11y}{x + y} = \dfrac{11(x + y)}{x + y}$
$= 11$

Exercises 8-7, page 280

1.16, 9 **2.**37, 16 **3.**115, 67 **4.**3, 7 **5.**8 – \$2, 3 – \$5
6.3 quarters, 4 dimes **7.**20 quarters, 12 dimes
8.\$3, \$2 **9.**\$0.75, \$2.00 **10.**$\frac{11}{2}, \frac{3}{2}$ **11.**4, 15 **12.**$\frac{43}{5}, \frac{13}{5}$
13.15, 10 **14.**15 nickels, 12 dimes **15.**21 nickels, 15
quarters **16.**\$2.75/L, \$0.63/L **17.**\$28/day, \$0.25/km
18.$w = 12$ cm; $l = 20$ cm **19.**$w = 9$ cm; $l = 14$ cm
20.2, 8 **21.**6, 9 **22.**8, 5 **23.**$\frac{5}{3}, \frac{41}{3}$ **24.**scientist, \$80;
assistant, \$60 **25.**\$6, \$2.50 **26.**$\frac{3}{2}$ **27.**$\frac{14}{20}$ **28.**$\frac{3}{4}$ **29.**Day 1,
7; Day 2, 3 **30.**-7, -11

Mathematics Around Us, page 283

1.a)about 145 years **b)**answers may vary **c)**answers
may vary **2.a)**answers may vary **b)**answers may vary
c)442 years **3.**48.5 m/year **4.**Answers may vary.
Example: snowfall and temperature are consistent
and no other factors are an influence.

Exercises 8-8, page 286

1.59 **2.**58 **3.**61 **4.**\$45 **5.**\$150, \$6 **6.**\$200, \$300 **7.**71
8.25 **9.**40 g, 15 g **10.**1 kg, 0.083 kg **11.**\$550, \$250
12.\$1500, \$1000 **13.**\$555.55, \$444.45 **14.**18, 38
15.61, 39 **16.**100 **17.**7 **18.**27 **19.**51 **20.**\$35, \$50
21.150, 300 **22.**100 **23.**\$15/d; \$0.10/km
24.\$1400, \$600 **25.**\$175, \$325 **26.**\$6.40, \$9.60
27.331 **28.a)**$10x + y = 7(x + y)$, $x = 2y$
b)L.S. $= 10y + 2y = 12y$R.S. $= 4y + 4x = 4y + 8y$
$= 12y$

Problem Solving, page 291

1.18 h, 4 h **2.**3 h, 1 h **3.**30 min **4.**60 km
5.about 5 h 42 min, about 34.2 km **6.a)**25 km/h
b)5 km/h **7.**62.5 km/h, 562.5 km/h **8.**1 h 20 min
9.3 min 45 s **10.**24 min **11.**44.1 kg, 5.9 kg

Exercises 8-9, page 294

1.10 kg standard, 30 kg prime **2.**32 kg grade one,
48 kg second grade **3.**40 m³ **4.**750 barrels of \$22.50
oil, 500 barrels of \$35.00 oil **5.a)**200 km **b)**10 L
6.1000 mL **7.a)**400 km **b)**36 L **8.a)**250 km
b)15.75 L **9.**11.67 L, 23.33 L **10.**480 L of 16%, 720 L of
36% **11.**1929 mL of 60%, 771 mL of 95% **12.**36, 12

13.8, 5 **14.**300 km **15.**810 km **16.**2 kg, 1 kg **17.a)**\$9
b)\$9 **18.**24 **19.**74 **20.**40 **21.**\$3000 **22.**Terri,
\$19 500; Tammy, \$17 000 **23.**12.5 kg of \$2.25
ju-jubes, 12.5 kg of \$3.75 ju-jubes **24.**150 t of \$150
feed, 75 t of \$195 feed **25.a)**470 km, **b)**415.8 L
26.24 t of Brand A, 32 t of Brand B **27.**canoe,
5.83 km/h; current, 0.83 km/h **28.**15 km **29.**12 min
30.8.18 h **31.**1.875 h **32.**72, 76
33.$10x + y = 4(x + y)$, $y = 2x$;
L.S. $= 10x + 2x = 12x$R.S. $= 12|x - 2x| = 12|-x|$
34.17.5 km **35.**\$8.75 **36.**6.6 d

Computer Power, page 297

1.a)(10,5) **b)**(–4,9) **c)**(–0.66,–1.3) **d)**(2.3,–1.3)
e)(1.75,0.659) **f)**(–0.950,–2.69)

Problem Solving, page 298

1.8 **2.a)**0.47 m **b)**8 **3.**2001 **4.**Divide the prime
numbers by 4. If the remainder is 1, it goes in List B.
If the remainder is 3, it goes in List A.
5.$2x + y - 8 = 0$ **6.**100 km **7.**6 or 7 **8.**Answers may
vary. **a)**7 **b)**8 **c)**7 **9.**0 or –6

Review Exercises, page 299

1.a)(–3,–5) **b)**$(\frac{7}{2},1)$ **c)**$(\frac{-14}{5}, \frac{2}{5})$ **d)**$(\frac{-3}{5}, \frac{11}{5})$ **2.**Answers may
vary. $4x + 10y = 16$, $2x - 6y = -14$; $6x + 15y = 24$,
$3x - 9y = -21$ **3.a)**(–1,–1) **b)**$(\frac{5}{3},0)$ **c)**(–2,–1) **d)**(0,2)
e)(3,–2) **f)**(4,0) **g)**(2,–1) **h)**(4,–2) **4.a)**(–2,3) **b)**(4,1)
c)$(\frac{18}{5}, \frac{3}{5})$ **d)**(5,–3) **e)**(–3,6) **f)**(–4,–3) **g)**$(\frac{3}{4}, -4)$
h)(0,–3) **5.a)**$\left(\dfrac{c(3a - 2b)}{a^2 - b^2}, \dfrac{c(3b - 2a)}{b^2 - a^2}\right)$ **b)**$\left(\dfrac{r(p + q)}{p^2 + q^2},\right.$
$\left.\dfrac{r(q - p)}{p^2 + q^2}\right)$ **c)**$\left(\dfrac{-2n^2}{m - n}, \dfrac{2m^2}{m - n}\right)$ **6.a)**one solution
b)infinitely many **c)**no solution **7.**Answers may
vary. **a)**$7x + y = 14$, $4x - y = 8$; $x - 3y = 2$,
$3x + 2y = 6$ **b)**$8x + 3y = 11$, $x + 5y = 6$;
$6x - 7y = -1$, $x + 5y = 6$ **c)**$3x + 2y = 1$, $2x + 5y = 8$;
$x + 8y = 15$, $x - 3y = -7$ **d)**$-3x + 5y = 28$,
$-6x + 7y = 23$; $-9x + 9y = 18$, $3x - 2y = 5$
8.a)$x + y = 80$ **b)**$x - y = 7$ **c)**$3x + 4y = 30$
d)$5n + 10d = 300$ **e)**$4w + 10 = 40$ **9.**20, 16 **10.**57
11.24, 39 **12.**18 **13.**41 **14.**38 **15.**80 kg at \$2; 20 kg at
\$2.40 **16.**Train going west, 35 km/h; train going east,
50 km/h **17.**14 km/h, 4 km/h **18.**80 g sterling;
20 g silver **19.**skilled, \$37.50; unskilled, \$18.75
20.8:15 p.m.

Chapter 9

Exercises 9-1, page 304

1.a)(8,0) **b)**(–5,2) **c)**(10,2) **d)**(3,6) **e)**(5,2)
f)(–15,–1) **g)**(11,3) **h)**(11,11) **i)**(–23,1)
2.c)translation 5 units to the right and 2 units up
3.c)reflection in the x-axis **4.b)**rotation about (0,0)
5.a)(3,–1) **b)**(3,2) **c)**(4,–3) **d)**(1,7) **e)**(6,–1) **f)**(2,3)

6.a)$(0,-6)$ **b)**$(2,8)$ **c)**$(0,6)$ **d)**$(0,3)$ **e)**$(0,7)$ **f)**$(-4,2)$
9.a)$(-6,11)$ **b)**$(-2,4)$ **c)**$(-4,2)$ **d)**$(8,-4)$ **e)**$(-8,-4)$
f)$(9,8)$

Exercises 9-2, page 307

1.a)$(3,-1)$, $(-2,4)$, $(3,2)$, $(1,3)$, $(0,1)$
b)$(x,y) \rightarrow (x + 4, y - 1)$, $(9,-2)$,
$(x,y) \rightarrow (x + 5, y - 2)$, $(-3, 2)$,
$(x,y) \rightarrow (x - 3, y + 3)$ **2.b)**, **d)**, **f) 4.a)**$(0,0) \rightarrow (-2,5)$,
$(3,1) \rightarrow (1,6)$, $(2,-6) \rightarrow (0,-1)$ **b)**$(2,-2) \rightarrow (0,3)$,
$(3,2) \rightarrow (1,7)$, $(-1,-4) \rightarrow (-3,1)$ **d)**Length of each
segment $\sqrt{29}$ units. Slope of each segment $\frac{-5}{2}$.
7.b)$(x,y) \rightarrow (x + 3, y + 1)$ **8.a)**$(x,y) \rightarrow (x + 2, y + 4)$
b)$(x,y) \rightarrow (x - 1, y + 3)$ **9.b)**$PQ = 4\sqrt{5}$ units, slope $\frac{1}{2}$;
$P'Q' = 4\sqrt{5}$ units, slope $\frac{1}{2}$. $PR = \sqrt{29}$ units, slope $\frac{-2}{5}$;
$P'R' = \sqrt{29}$ units, slope $\frac{-2}{5}$; $QR = 3\sqrt{5}$ units, slope 2;
$Q'R' = 3\sqrt{5}$ units, slope 2. Area of $\triangle PQR$ is 18 units².
Area of $\triangle P'Q'R'$ is 18 units². The side lengths, slopes
of sides, and areas are invariant. **10.b)**$MJ = \sqrt{26}$ units,
slope $\frac{1}{5}$; $M'J' = \sqrt{26}$ units, slope $\frac{1}{5}$. $ML = 6$ units, slope
undefined; $M'L' = 6$ units, slope undefined.
$KL = \sqrt{10}$ units, slope $\frac{-1}{3}$; $K'L' = \sqrt{10}$ units, slope $\frac{-1}{3}$.
$JK = 2\sqrt{5}$ units, -2; $J'K' = 2\sqrt{5}$ units, -2. Area of
$JKLM$ is 20 units². Area of $J'K'L'M'$ is 20 units². The
side lengths, slopes of sides and areas are invariant.
11.b)$AB = \sqrt{26}$ units, slope $\frac{-1}{5}$; $A'B' = \sqrt{26}$ units, slope
$\frac{-1}{5}$. $BC = 3\sqrt{5}$ units, slope $\frac{1}{2}$; $B'C' = 3\sqrt{5}$ units, slope $\frac{1}{2}$.
$CD = \sqrt{26}$ units, slope $\frac{-1}{5}$; $C'D' = \sqrt{26}$ units, slope $\frac{-1}{5}$.
$AD = 3\sqrt{5}$ units, slope $\frac{1}{2}$; $A'D' = 3\sqrt{5}$ units, slope $\frac{1}{2}$.
Area of $ABCD$ is 24 units². Area of $A'B'C'D'$ is
24 units². **12.b)**Answers may vary.
$(x,y) \rightarrow (x + 1, y + 4)$. **13.b)**Answers may vary.
$(x,y) \rightarrow (x - 1, y + 1)$, $(x,y) \rightarrow (x + 2, y - 2)$ **14.a)**4
b)$(x,y) \rightarrow (x + 1, y + 2)$, $(x,y) \rightarrow (x - 2, y + 1)$,
$(x,y) \rightarrow (x - 1, y - 2)$, $(x,y) \rightarrow (x + 2, y - 1)$

INVESTIGATE, page 309

$PP' = 3\sqrt{5}$ units, slope $\frac{1}{2}$; $QQ' = 3\sqrt{5}$ units, slope $\frac{1}{2}$.
$RR' = 3\sqrt{5}$ units, slope $\frac{1}{2}$. The segments joining all
points to their corresponding image points have the
same length and slope.

Exercises 9-3, page 312

1.

2	2	2	2	2
3	3	3	3	3
4	4	4	4	4
5	5	5	5	5
6	6	9	6	6

2.a)$(-1,4)$, $(-5,0)$, $(-2,-3)$ **b)**$(6,-2)$, $(0,-3)$, $(-4,1)$
3.a), **c)**, **d)**, **f) 7.b)**$PQ = 2$ units, slope 0;
$P'Q' = 2$ units, slope undefined. $QR = 4$ units, slope
undefined; $Q'R' = 4$ units, slope 0. $PR = 2\sqrt{5}$ units,
slope -2; $P'R' = 2\sqrt{5}$ units, slope $\frac{1}{2}$. Area of $\triangle PQR$ is
4 units². Area of $\triangle P'Q'R'$ is 4 units². The sides of the
triangle have the same length as their images.
The sides of the triangle are perpendicular to their
images. The area of $\triangle PQR$ is the same as the area
$\triangle P'Q'R'$. **8.b)**$AB = 4\sqrt{5}$ units, slope $\frac{1}{2}$;
$A'B' = 4\sqrt{5}$ units, slope -2. $BC = 2\sqrt{5}$ units, slope -2;
$B'C' = 2\sqrt{5}$ units, slope $\frac{1}{2}$. $CD = 4\sqrt{5}$ units, slope $\frac{1}{2}$;
$C'D' = 4\sqrt{5}$ units, slope -2. $AD = 2\sqrt{5}$ units, slope
-2; $A'D' = 2\sqrt{5}$ units, slope $\frac{1}{2}$. Area of $ABCD$ is
40 units². Area of $A'B'C'D'$ is 40 units². The sides of
the rectangle have the same length as their images.
The sides of the rectangle are perpendicular to their
images. The area of $ABCD$ is the same as the area of
$A'B'C'D'$. **9.b)**$\frac{1}{4}$-turn about $(3,0)$ **10.a)**$\frac{1}{4}$-turn about
$(3,3)$ **b)**$\frac{1}{2}$-turn about $(3,3)$ **c)**$\frac{1}{4}$-turn about $(3,3)$
13. Answers may vary. $(x,y) \rightarrow (-x,-y)$

INVESTIGATE, page 314

1.b) The perpendicular bisector of the segments
joining the vertices and their images pass through the
rotation centre. **2.b)**The angle between JK and $J'K'$
JL and $J'L'$, and KL and $K'L'$ is 90°. **c)**Sides of the
figure are perpendicular to the corresponding sides of
the image.

Exercises 9-4, page 318

3.a), **b)**, **d)**, **4.a)**$(-1,3)$, $(-4,-2)$, $(1,5)$ **b)**$(-2,-3)$,
$(1,2)$, $(-3,0)$ **7.b)**$JK = 4\sqrt{5}$ units, slope $\frac{1}{2}$;
$J'K' = 4\sqrt{5}$ units, slope $\frac{-1}{2}$. $KL = 10$ units, slope 0;
$K'L' = 10$ units, slope 0. $JL = 2\sqrt{5}$ units, slope -2;
$J'L' = 2\sqrt{5}$ units, slope 2. Area of $\triangle JKL$ is 20 units².
Area of $\triangle J'K'L'$ is 20 units². The sides of the triangle
have the same lengths as their images. The slopes of
the sides of the triangle are not the same as the slopes
of their images. The area of $\triangle JKL$ is the same as the
area of $\triangle J'K'L'$. **8.b)**$AB = \sqrt{29}$ units, slope $\frac{2}{5}$;
$A'B' = \sqrt{29}$ units, slope $\frac{1}{2}$. $BC = \sqrt{29}$ units, slope $\frac{-5}{2}$;
$B'C' = \sqrt{29}$ units, slope $\frac{-2}{5}$. $CD = \sqrt{29}$ units, slope $\frac{2}{5}$;
$C'D' = \sqrt{29}$ units, slope $\frac{5}{2}$. $AD = \sqrt{29}$ units, slope $\frac{-5}{2}$;
$A'D' = \sqrt{29}$ units, slope $\frac{-2}{5}$. Area of $ABCD$ is 29 units².
Area of $A'B'C'D'$ is 29 units². The sides of the
square have the same lengths as their images. The
slopes of the sides of the square are not the same as
the slopes of their images. The area of the square is
the same as the area of its image. **9.b)**reflection in the
line $x - 3 = 0$ **10.b)**reflection in the line $x - y - 3 = 0$
11.b)reflection in the line $x + y + 1 = 0$ **13.b)**Slope

AB is -4. Slope $A'B'$ is 4. Slope is not preserved; it is not a translation. Rotation centre is not preserved; it is not a rotation. Location of points on the reflection line are not preserved, it is not a reflection. **c)**Length of sides and area are preserved; slopes are reversed. **16.b)**$3x - y - 3 = 0$ **c)**$(3,-4)$ **17.a)**$(-3,1)$, $(3,0)$, $(4,-2)$ **b)**$(0,-1)$, $(-4,6)$, $(5,3)$ **c)**$x + y - 2 = 0$

INVESTIGATE, page 320
1.b)slope of PP' is $\frac{1}{2}$. Slope of QQ' is $\frac{1}{2}$. Slope of reflection line is -2. Reflection line is perpendicular to both PP' and QQ'. Length of PP' is $4\sqrt{5}$ units. Distance from P to reflection line is $2\sqrt{5}$ units. Length of QQ' is $2\sqrt{5}$ units. Distance from Q to reflection line is $\sqrt{5}$ units. **c)**The reflection line is perpendicular to the segments joining matching points. The reflection line bisects the segments joining matching points. **2.c)**If a side is extended, it meets its image on the reflection line.

Exercises 9-5, page 324
1.b)$AB = 5$ units, slope 0; $A'B' = 10$ units, slope 0. $BC = \sqrt{10}$ units, slope -3; $B'C' = 2\sqrt{10}$ units, slope -3. $AC = 5$ units, slope $\frac{3}{4}$. $A'C' = 10$ units, slope $\frac{3}{4}$.
Area of ABC is $7\frac{1}{2}$ units^2. Area of $A'B'C'$ is 30 units^2.
The length of each side of the image is twice the length of the triangle. The slopes of the sides of the triangle are the same as the slopes of the sides of the image. The area of the image is 4 times the area of the triangle. **c)**The scale factor is 2. The dilatation centre is $(0, 0)$. **2.c)**$OA' = 6\sqrt{2}$ units, $OA = 2\sqrt{2}$ units; $\frac{OA'}{OA} = \frac{3}{1}$. $OB' = 6\sqrt{5}$ units, $OB = 2\sqrt{5}$ units; $\frac{OB'}{OB} = \frac{3}{1}$. $OC' = 6\sqrt{2}$ units, $OC = 2\sqrt{2}$ units, $\frac{OC'}{OC} = \frac{3}{1}$.
d)$A'B' = 6$ units, $AB = 2$ units; $\frac{A'B'}{AB} = \frac{3}{1}$. $B'C' = 6\sqrt{5}$ units, $BC = 2\sqrt{5}$ units, $\frac{B'C'}{BC} = \frac{3}{1}$. $A'C' = 4$ units, $AC = 12$ units; $\frac{A'C'}{AC} = \frac{3}{1}$. **e)**3
3.b) The triangles are similar, but not congruent. **c)**$OP' = \sqrt{5}$ units, $OP = 3\sqrt{5}$ units; $\frac{OP'}{OP} = \frac{1}{3}$. $OQ' = 2\sqrt{5}$ units, $OQ = 6\sqrt{5}$ units; $\frac{OQ'}{OQ} = \frac{1}{3}$. $OR' = 5$ units, $OR = 15$ units; $\frac{OR'}{OR} = \frac{1}{3}$. **d)**$PQ = 9$ units, slope 0. $P'Q' = 3$ units, slope 0. $QR = 3\sqrt{5}$ units, slope -2. $Q'R' = \sqrt{5}$ units, slope -2. $PR = 6\sqrt{2}$ units, slope 1. $P'R' = 2\sqrt{2}$ units, slope 1. The length of each side of the image is $\frac{1}{3}$ the length of the

corresponding side of the triangle. The slope of each side of the image is the same as the slope of the corresponding side of the triangle. **e)**$\frac{1}{3}$

4.b) The rectangles are similar, but not congruent. **c)**Lengths may vary. Examples for $\frac{1}{2}$ cm grid paper: $OB' = 5.7$ cm, $OB = 1.9$ cm; $\frac{OB'}{OB} = \frac{3}{1}$. $OC' = 7.8$ cm, $OC = 2.6$ cm; $\frac{OC'}{OC} = \frac{3}{1}$. **d)**$AB = 3$ units, $A'B' = 9$ units; $BC = 2$ units, $B'C' = 6$ units; $CD = 3$ units, $C'D' = 9$ units; $AD = 2$ units, $A'D' = 6$ units; Area of $ABCD$ is a 6 units^2. Area of $A'B'C'D'$ is 54 units^2. **6.a)**$\frac{3}{2}$ **b)** $\frac{5}{2}$ **c)** $\frac{5}{3}$ **d)** $\frac{2}{5}$ **e)** $\frac{3}{5}$ **f)** $\frac{2}{3}$
8.b) The trapezoid and the image are similar, but not congruent. **c)**$\frac{1}{4}$ **9.b)**$4 : 1$ **11.a)**The perimeter of each successive image is 2 times the perimeter of the next smaller trapezoid. The area of each successive image is 4 times the area of the next smaller trapezoid. **b)** The slopes of the images are preserved. The location of the dilatation centre is preserved. The length and the area are not preserved. Lines joining matching points pass through the dilatation centre.

Mathematics Around Us, page 327
2.Move C away from M. **3.**Move C toward M. **4.**The image would be congruent to the figure. **5.**Dilatation about the point 0 with a scale determined by the position of C.

Exercises 9-6, page 330
1.b)$2x + y - 10 = 0$ **2.a)**$3x - 4y - 26 = 0$ **b)**$3x - 4y - 33 = 0$ **c)**$3x - 4y + 8 = 0$ **d)**$3x - 4y - 19 = 0$ **3.a)**$3x - 5y - 1 = 0$ **b)**$3x - 5y + 3 = 0$ **c)**$3x - 5y = 0$ **d)**$3x - 5y - 11 = 0$ **4.a)**$2x + 7y - 4 = 0$ **b)**$3x - y - 4 = 0$ **c)**$4x - 9y - 12 = 0$ **d)**$2x + 5y - 16 = 0$ **5.b)**$2x - y - 12 = 0$; $2x - y + 12 = 0$ **6.a)**$3x + y - 6 = 0$; $3x - y + 6 = 0$ **b)**$2x - 5y - 10 = 0$; $2x - 5y + 10 = 0$ **c)**$4x - 7y + 28 = 0$; $4x - 7y - 28 = 0$ **d)**$5x + 8y + 20 = 0$; $5x + 8y - 20 = 0$ **7.a)**$x + 2y - 10 = 0$ **b)**$x + 2y - 10 = 0$ **c)**$x + 2y - 10 = 0$ **8.b)**$x - 2y - 3 = 0$ **9.a)**$x + 5y - 1 = 0$ **b)**$3x - 2y + 3 = 0$ **c)**$4x + y - 8 = 0$ **d)**$3x - 7y + 6 = 0$ **e)**$x + y - 7 = 0$ **f)**$x - y + 5 = 0$ **10.a)**$x + y + 5 = 0$ **b)**$x + y - 5 = 0$ **c)**$x - y - 5 = 0$ **d)**$x - y + 5 = 0$ **11.a)**$x + 3y + 6 = 0$ **b)**$3x - y - 6 = 0$ **c)**$x + 3y - 6 = 0$ **12.b)**Answers may vary. $(x, y) \rightarrow (x + 2, y)$, $(x, y) \rightarrow (x, y - 3)$, $(x, y) \rightarrow (x + 4, y + 3)$ **13.**$x + y = 0$ **14.a)**$(x, y) \rightarrow (x, y + 4)$ **b)**reflection in the line $2x - 5y = 0$ **c)**$180°$ about $(0, 0)$

Investigate, page 331
a)Infinitely many b)Infinitely many c)Infinitely many

Computer Power, page 332
1.a)$-3x + y + 8 = 0$; $-3x + y - 17 = 0$
b)$3x + y + 6 = 0$; $3x + y - 6 = 0$; $-x + 3y + 6 = 0$; $-x + 3y - 6 = 0$ **c**)$x + 3y + 6 = 0$; $-3x + y + 6 = 0$; $x + 3y - 6 = 0$ **d**)$-3x + y - 30 = 0$; $-3x + y + 18 = 0$

Exercises 9-7, page 334
2.a)$N(8, 0)$ **b**)$5\sqrt{13}$ units **4.a**)$3\sqrt{10}$ units
b)$3\sqrt{10}$ units **c**)$9\sqrt{2}$ units **5.a**)Fence B **b**)106 m
7.a)D **b**)1070 m **8.b**)8 **c**)$(2 + 5\sqrt{5})$ units

Problem Solving, page 337
1.a)$(x, y) \rightarrow (-x, -y + 6)$ **b**)$A'(0, 4)$, $B'(4, 3)$, $C'(0,1)$
2.a)ii) **b**)$(x, y) \rightarrow (-x + 4, y)$ **c**)$A'(1, -2)$, $B'(-2, 0)$,
$C'(-1, 3)$ **3.b**)Reflection in the line $x - y + 3 = 0$
c)$(x, y) \rightarrow (y - 3, x + 3)$ **d**)$P(5, 2) \rightarrow P'(-1, 8)$,
$Q(4, 5) \rightarrow Q'(2, 7)$, $R(1, 4) \rightarrow R'(1, 4)$
4.a)$(x, y) \rightarrow (2x, 2y - 6)$ **b**)$A(0, 2) \rightarrow A'(0, -2)$,
$B(3, 3) \rightarrow B'(6, 0)$, $C(4, 6) \rightarrow C'(8, 6)$,
$D(1, 5) \rightarrow D'(2, 4)$ **5.b**)$(5, -2)$
c)$(x, y) \rightarrow (3x - 10, 3y + 4)$ **d**)$A(7, 0) \rightarrow A'(11, 4)$,
$B(7, 2) \rightarrow B'(11, 10)$, $C(3, 2) \rightarrow C'(-1, 10)$,
$D(3, 0) \rightarrow D'(-1, 4)$

Review Exercises, page 338
1.a)$(8, 3)$ **b**)$(-6, -4)$ **c**)$(4, 6)$ **d**)$(9, 1)$ **2.a**)$(6, 11)$
b)$(1\frac{1}{2}, 13)$ **c**)$(6, 7)$ **d**)$(-5, 2)$ **4.**$2x - y - 2 = 0$
5.a)$\frac{1}{4}$-turn about $(0, 0)$ **b**)$\frac{1}{2}$-turn about $(0, 0)$
6.$2x + y + 3 = 0$ **7.a**)Reflection in the x-axis
b)Reflection in the line $x + y = 0$ **8.**$x + y + 4 = 0$
12.$2x + 3y - 2 = 0$ **13.**15 units

Cumulative Review, page 339
1.a)$(4, 1)$ **b**)$(\frac{5}{2}, -\frac{3}{2})$ **c**)$(-\frac{7}{3}, \frac{3}{2})$ **2.a**)$(2, 1)$ **b**)$(-5, 3)$
c)$(3, -2)$ **3.a**)$(3, 1)$ **b**)$(-4, 3)$ **c**)$(-2, -5)$ **4.a**)1 **b**)0
c)infinite **5.a**)$x - y = 12$ **b**)$3x + y = 10$ **c**)$x = 2y - 4$
d)$10x + 25y = 350$ **e**)$11x + 11y = 77$ **6.**3 at \$8.50; 4
at \$6.00 **7.**11, 15 **8.**16 cm, 4 cm **9.**37 **10.**\$1500,
\$3000 **11.**683.3 km **13.a**)1, 3 **b**)4, 7 **c**)2, 6, 8 **d**)5, 9
14.a)dilatation **b**)translation **c**)reflection **d**)rotation
e)translation **f**)reflection **16.**$6\sqrt{2}$ units

Chapter 10

Mathematics Around Us, page 342
2.Answers may vary. **3.**Answers may vary.

Exercises 10-1, page 345
1.b)The products of two 2-digit numbers are 3-digit
or 4-digit numbers. **2.a**)$1 + 3 + 5 + 7 + 9 = 25 = 5^2$,

$1 + 3 + 5 + 7 + 9 + 11 = 36 = 6^2$, $1 + 3 + 5 + 7 + 9 + 11 + 13 = 49 = 7^2$ **b**)The sums of consecutive odd numbers starting at 1 are perfect squares. **3.d**)The angle at the circumference is always 90°.
4.a)$MN = \frac{1}{2}BC$; $MN||BC$ **b**)For any $\triangle ABC$, if M and N are the midpoints of AB and AC, $MN = \frac{1}{2}BC$ and $MN||BC$. **5.b**)parallelogram **d**)The figure formed by joining the midpoints of the 4 sides of any quadrilateral is a parallelogram.

Problem Solving, page 347
1.Answers may vary. **a**)25 cannot be written as the sum of 3 perfect squares **b**)A triangle with angles 120°, 30°, 30° is possible **c**)A baseball diamond viewed from any of the bases is a square that does not have two horizontal and vertical sides. **2.a**), **b**) **3.a**)false; 0 **b**)true **c**)false; $1^2 = 1$ **d**)true **e**)false; the altitude of an obtuse triangle lies outside it **f**)false; any rectangle in which its length is not equal to its width is not a square **g**)true

The Mathematical Mind, page 348
1.5¢ **2.**No **3.**69 km/h

Exercises 10-2, page 350
1.a)teenager **b**)long hair **c**)wet **d**)melt **e**)four right angles **f**)never meet **2.a**)Manuel will be fit **b**)Jennifer's writing will improve **c**)some rectangles have equal sides **d**)$\angle ABC$ measures 90° **3.a**)yes **b**)no **c**)yes **d**)no **8.**Eddie, Ahmad, Alec, Dan, Carlos

Exercises 10-3, page 353
1.a)$\angle DEC$, $\angle AEB$; $\angle BEC$, $\angle AED$ **b**)$\angle TQR$, $\angle PQS$; $\angle PQT$, $\angle SQR$ **2.a**)90°, 90° **b**)45°, 135° **3.a**)50°, 70° **b**)115°, 115° **c**)75°, 75°

Exercises 10-4, page 355
1.a)yes **b**)no **c**)yes **d**)yes **e**)yes **f**)no **2.a**)120° **b**)105° **c**)30° **d**)128° **e**)90° **3.**30°, 150°; 55°, 125°; 80°, 100° **7.a**)90° **b**)60°; 120° **8.**$\dfrac{180}{n + 1}$, $\dfrac{180n}{n + 1}$ **9.**270°

Exercises 10-5, page 358
4.a)axiom **b**)theorem **c**)theorem **d**)axiom **5.**An axiom is a self-evident or universally recognized truth. A theorem is a statement proven by deductive reasoning.

Exercises 10-6, page 361
1.$\angle 3 = \angle 5$, $\angle 4 = \angle 6$; $\angle 2 = \angle 6$, $\angle 1 = \angle 5$, $\angle 3 = \angle 7$, $\angle 4 = \angle 8$ **2.a**)38°, 142° **b**)55°, 125° **c**)120°, 60° **3.**40° **4.**135° **5.a**)130°, 50°, 130° **b**)58°, 128°, 128° **c**)115°, 65°, 115° **d**)30°, 80°, 80° **e**)40°, 40°, 320° **f**)50°, 60°, 70° **8.a**)120°, 70°, 70°, 50° **b**)56°, 56°, 89°
9.$\angle QBC = \angle RCB$, $\angle ABC = \angle DCB$ **11.**The tops are farther apart than the bases due to the curvature of the earth.

Exercises 10-7, page 366
1.a)77° **b)**110° **c)**25° **d)**33° **e)**62° **f)**135° **2.a)**150°,
70° **b)**25°, 115° **c)**70°, 50° **d)**35°, 80° **5.**360° **6.**130°
7.∠*BAC* = 30°, ∠*CAE* = 150° **11.**360°; the sum of the
3 exterior angles of triangle is 360°.

Review Exercises, page 368
1.b) All numbers ending in 5 can be expressed as the
sum or difference of two perfect squares. **2.a)**Jeffery
is poor **b)**the opposite angles of *PQRS* are equal
c)Δ*ABC* is isosceles **4.**inductive, deductive,
deductive **5.a)**140° **b)**105° **c)**90° **d)**60° **e)**15°
10.a)65° **b)**150° **c)**130°

Chapter 11

Exercises 11-1, page 372
1.a)*JK* = *PQ*, ∠*JKL* = ∠*PQR*, *KL* = *QR* (SAS)
b)∠*J* = ∠*P*, ∠*K* = ∠*Q*, ∠*L* = ∠*R*; *JK* = *PQ*, *JL* = *PR*,
KL = *QR* **2.a)***DE* = *EF* = *FG*; *AD* = *BE* = *CF*;
AE = *BF* = *CG* (SSS) **b)**the triangles are congruent
3.a)∠*BAC* = ∠*CAD*, *AC* = *AC*, ∠*ACB* = ∠*ACD*
(ASA); *AC* = *AC*, *AB* = *AD*, *BC* = *DC*;
∠*BAC* = ∠*DAC*, ∠*BCA* = ∠*DCA*, ∠*B* = ∠*D*
b)*PQ* = *PS*, ∠*QPR* = ∠*SPR*, *PR* = *PR* (SAS);
PQ = *PS*, *PR* = *PR*, *QR* = *SR*; ∠*QPR* = ∠*SPR*,
∠*PRQ* = ∠*PRS*, ∠*Q* = ∠*S* **c)***XZ* = *XY*,
∠*YXW* = ∠*ZXW*, *XW* = *XW* (SAS); *XZ* = *XY*,
XW =*XW*, *ZW* = *YW*; ∠*YXW* = ∠*ZXW*,
∠*XWY* = ∠*XWZ*, ∠*Z* = ∠*Y* **4.a)**i), iii)(ASA) **b)**i),
ii)(SAS) **5.a)**∠*J* = ∠*B* or *CR* = *YP* **b)***SM* = *PX* or
∠*O* = ∠*Q* **29.**Δ*DEF* is a counterexample to AAA.
30.Δ *DEF* is a counterexample to SSA.

Exercises 11-2, page 379
1.a)65° **b)**100° **c)**145° **2.**60°
3.∠*CBD* = ∠*CDB* (ITT). Therefore, ∠*CDE* = ∠*ABC*
(SAT). **5.a)**35° **b)**40° **c)**90° **6.a)**60° **b)**120° **c)**30°
7.150° **8.a)**75°, 15° **b)**15°, 105° **16.**22.5°
18.36°, 36°, 72°

Exercises 11-3, page 384
1.a)60°, 120° **b)**70°, 110° **2.a)**50°, 130°, 130°
b)70°, 110°, 110° **c)**90°, 90°, 90° **3.a)**55°, 65°, 6 cm
b)60°, 120°, 120° **c)**120°, 60°, 5 cm **d)**60°, 120°,
12 cm **e)**55°, 125°, 35° **f)**70°, 110°, 8 cm
4.16 cm, 10 cm **6.**50°, 5.3 m **7.**40° **15.**yes

INVESTIGATE, page 386
All are possible.

Exercises 11-4, page 390
2.a)4.70 **b)**26.66 **c)**26.83 **3.a)**19.4 **b)**24.6 **c)**48.8
4.a)10.0 **b)**7.2 **c)**6.3 **5.**4$\sqrt{2}$ cm **6.**$\sqrt{10}$ cm **7.a)***a* − *b*
b)*b*²; *c*² − *a*² **c)***b*² = *c*² − *a*²

Problem Solving, page 393
1.Assume *PQ* = *PR*. Then ∠*Q* = ∠*R*. But ∠*Q* = 50°
and ∠*R* = *60°*. Therefore, ∠*Q* ≠ ∠*R* and *PQ* ≠ *PR*.
2.For angles 1, 2, and 3 in any triangle,
a)if ∠2 = ∠3 = 90°, then ∠1 + 90° + 90° = 180°
and ∠1 = 0° **b)**if ∠2 > 90° and ∠3 > 90°, then ∠1 + ∠2
+ ∠3 = 180°, but ∠2 + ∠3 > 180°.

Review Exercises, page 399
1.a)60°, 110° **b)**90°, 120° **c)**45°, 150° **6.**20 cm
12.a)65°, 115°, 65° **b)**110°, 70°, 13° **c)**105°, 75°, 150°
13.a)10.2 **b)**14.8 **c)**8.0

Chapter 12

Exercises 12-1, page 404
2.a)18.8 cm **4.b)**3 cm, 5 cm **5.a)**3 cm **b)**464 cm²
6.a)$\dfrac{x}{2\pi}$ **b)**$\dfrac{x^2(2\pi + 1)}{2\pi}$ **7.**393 cm² **8.**$\dfrac{5\pi x^2}{16}$ cm²

INVESTIGATE, page 405
1.c)*d* = 4.5 cm, *h* = 14.0 cm; *d* = 6.3 cm, *h* = 9.9 cm
2.a) Yes **b)**Any rhombus

Exercises 12-2, page 408
1.a)301 cm² **b)**37.7 cm² **c)**2355 mm² **2.a)**534 cm²
b)94.2 m² **c)**5652 cm² **3.a)**204 cm² **b)**322.5 m²
c)3385 cm² **4.a)**53.4 m² **b)**3391 cm² **c)**24 417 cm²
5.278.8 cm² **6.a)**yes **b)**3:4 **7.a)**No; the one with base
radius 4 has greater area. **b)**2:3 **8.a)**$\pi r\sqrt{r^2 + h^2}$
b)$\pi r(\sqrt{r^2 + h^2} + r)$ **9.a)**$\dfrac{3\pi x^2}{2}$ cm² **b)**π:4

10.a)$\dfrac{\pi x^2(1 + \sqrt{5})}{4}$ cm² **b)**π(1 + $\sqrt{5}$):24 **c)**$\dfrac{1 + \sqrt{5}}{2}$:3

INVESTIGATE, page 410
The volume of a cone is ⅓ the volume of a cylinder
with the same height and base radius.

Exercises 12-3, page 413
1.a)18 086 cm³ **b)**904.3 m³ **c)**127 563 cm³
2.a)2721 cm³ **b)**2.3 cm³ **c)**164 117 cm³ **3.a)**73.2 m³
b)170 cm³ **c)**294 375 cm³ **4.a)**5 cm, 78.5 cm²,
785 cm³ **b)**8 cm, 50.2 cm², 402 cm³ **c)**0.6 cm,
1.1 m², 0.7 m³ **5.**24.6 m³ **6.**20.6 m³ **7.a)**1060 m³
b)580.3 m² **8.**1236 mm³ **9.**6 **10.a)**4 521 600 m²
b)81 389 m³ **c)**$16 074 327 **11.**13 cm **12.a)**15.7 cm³
b)5.2 cm³ **13.a)**52.3 cm³ **b)**20.9 cm³ **14.**813 888 m³
15.a)6167 **b)**4 182 480 m³ **c)**1 394 160 m³
16.a)doubled **b)**multiplied by 4 **c)**multiplied by 8
17.a)3 cm **b)**3$\sqrt{3}$ cm **c)**9$\sqrt{3\pi}$ or 49 cm³ **18.a)**small:
2 cm; large: 6 cm **b)**small: 2$\sqrt{15}$ cm; large: 2$\sqrt{7}$ cm

c)small: $\dfrac{8\sqrt{15}\pi}{3}$ or 32 cm³; large: 24$\sqrt{7}\pi$ or 199 cm³

19.a)34 901 mm³ **b)**0.18 mm **c)**$\dfrac{\pi(D^2 - d^2)}{4l}$ **20.**30 m
21.4 m³

INVESTIGATE, page 415
The one with the short side of the rectangle as its height.

Problem Solving, page 417
1.three times the length of one edge of a small cube
2.72 **3.**13 cm by 13 cm **4.**91 cm **5.a)**2400 cm **b)**12

INVESTIGATE, page 418
The area of a sphere is slightly more than 3 times the square of the diameter.

INVESTIGATE, page 419
1.$\frac{2}{3}$ **2.**The volume of a sphere is $\frac{2}{3}$ the volume of the cylinder in which it fits.

Exercise 12-4, page 422
1.a)1256 cm², 4187 cm³ **b)**314 cm², 523 cm³
c)2902 cm², 14 703 cm³ **2.**Baseball: 171.9 cm²,
212.1 cm³ Golf: 58.1 cm², 41.6 cm³ Table Tennis:
43.0 cm², 26.5 cm³ Volleyball: 1371.6 cm²,
4777.7 cm³ **3.**1256 cm², 4187 cm³ **4.a)**6 : π **b)**6 : π
5.a)12 cm **b)**1809 cm² **c)**7235 cm³
6.a)3.8 × 10⁷ km², 2.2 × 10¹⁰ km³ **b)**6.1 × 10¹² km²,
1.4 × 10¹⁸ km³ **7.**sphere **8.a)**9 **b)**27 **9.**Radius
doubled, surface area multiplied by 4 or 2², volume
multiplied by 8 or 2³; radius tripled, surface area
multiplied by 9 or 3², volume multiplied by 27 or 3³;
radius multiplied by n, surface area multiplied by n^2,
volume multiplied by n^3. **10.**$A = \pi d^2$, $V = \dfrac{\pi d^3}{6}$
11.a)4302.3 m³ **b)**1378.1 m² **12.a)**$\sqrt[3]{2}$: 1 **b)**$\sqrt[3]{4}$: 2
13.a)343 : 1 **b)**3.7 × 10¹⁰ : 1

The Mathematical Mind, page 425
2.$V = \pi r^3$, $V = \frac{2}{3}\pi r^3$, $V = \frac{1}{3}\pi r^3$
$V_{cylinder} : V_{hemisphere} : V_{cone} = 3 : 2 : 1$ **3.**3.1428571…,
3.140845. $3\frac{10}{71}$ is closer to π. **4.**Answers may vary.
a)$r = 0.25$ mm, $V = 0.065$ mm³ **b)**1.4 × 10²⁵ km³
c)2.2 × 10⁴⁴ **d)**8.0 × 10⁹³

Computer Power, page 427
1.a)$h = 8.6$ cm, $r = 4.3$ cm **b)**$h = 10.8$ cm,
$r = 5.4$ cm **c)**$h = 12.4$ cm, $r = 6.2$ cm
2.a)$h = 5.4$ cm, $r = 5.4$ cm **b)**$h = 6.8$ cm, $r = 6.8$ cm
c)$h = 7.8$ cm, $r = 7.8$ cm **3.a)**$h = 2r$ **b)**$h = r$

Mathematics Around Us, page 428
1.1.99 × 10⁻⁷ cm, 1.99 × 10⁻⁹ m **2.a)**1.13 × 10⁻⁷ cm
b)15.0 cm

Review Exercises, page 429
1.a)75.4 cm by 35 cm **b)**125.6 cm by 36 cm
c)533.8 mm by 425 mm **d)**18.8 cm by 20 cm

2.a)16.2 cm, 133° **b)**31.2 cm, 277° **c)**260 mm, 139°
d)172 mm, 178° **3.a)**3542 cm² **b)**7034 cm²
c)272 238 mm² **d)**433 cm² **4.a)**304 cm² **b)**2354 cm²
c)81 640 mm² **d)**46 016 mm² **5.a)**7.5 cm **b)**13 cm
6.a)4.8 cm; 2.5 cm **b)**627 cm², 510 cm²
7.$A = 133.4$ cm², $V = 93.6$ cm² **8.a)**276 cm², 352 cm³
b)353 mm², 509 mm³ **c)**22.9 m², 7.4 m³
9.a)105 cm², 83 cm³ **b)**141.6 cm², 124.6 cm³
c)178 cm², 166 cm³ **10.a)**90 cm², 57 cm³ **b)**106 cm²,
71 cm³ **c)**122 cm², 85 cm³ **11.**134 m³ **12.**2120 cm³,
918 cm² **13.**No, cylinder with radius of 4 cm has a
greater volume. **14.**No, cone with radius of 4 cm has
a greater volume. **15.a)**1017 cm², 3052 cm³
b)196 250 mm², 8 177 083 mm³ **c)**530.7 cm²,
1149.8 cm³ **16.**1838.9 cm²; 7416.9 cm³
17.a)124.8 cm³ **b)**142.5 cm³ **c)**approximately 1 : 2
18.a)306.3 cm³ **b)**193.9 cm³ **c)**3 : 5 **19.a)**18.1 m²,
5.0 m³ **b)**16 880 mm², 176 887 mm² **c)**6029 cm²,
31 082 cm³

Cumulative Review, page 431
1.b) The sum of the cubes of consecutive numbers is
always a perfect square. **3.a)**34, 55 **b)**41, 58
4.a) Maria did not register in time. **b)**A square is a
rhombus. **5.a)**$x = 65°$, $y = 115°$ **b)**$x = 40°$, $y = 80°$
c)$x = 60°$, $y = 85°$ **d)**$x = 125°$, $y = 55°$ **e)**$x = 50°$,
$y = 62°$ **f)**$x = 68°$, $y = 63°$ **6.a)**138° **b)**102° **c)**120°
7.a)$x = 40°$, $y = 140°$ **b)**$x = 100°$, $y = 40°$ **14.a)**3.07
b)10.3 **17.**$r = 3.8$ cm, $A = 573$ cm² **18.a)**1254.4 cm²,
687.0 cm² **b)**3232.4 cm², 1734.6 cm² **19.**4616 cm²,
48 466 cm³ **20.**2625 cm², 11 144 cm³ **21.**about 154
22.25 434 cm², 381 510 cm³

Chapter 13

Exercises 13-1, page 436
1.a)1500 km **b)**3000 km **2.a)**30 **b)**57% **3.a)**−25°C,
−32°C **b)**43 km/h **4.a)**153, women; 163, men; 140,
women; 150, men; 130, women; 140, men **b)**40
years, women; 52 years, men; 52 years, women; 64
years, men **5.**Saskatchewan, 13.68 million tonnes;
Alberta, 6 million tonnes; Manitoba, 2.88 million
tonnes **6.a)**7.25 kg **b)**2.75 kg **7.**$2500, $500 **8.a)**+3,
−5 **b)**1982 – 1983 **c)**99.0, 94.0, 92.0, 92.0

Exercises 13-2, page 441
1.a)1, 3, 2 **b)**12 **c)**25 **2.a)**1, 0, 2 **b)**6 **c)**3 **d)**20
3.a)2, 3, 1 **b)**5, 8 **4.a)**235 s **b)**1, 2 **c)**9

Exercises 13-3, page 446
1.a)5.6, 6, 6 **b)**31, 32, 25 **c)**5.3, 5.3, 6.3 **d)**100.5, 99,
no mode **e)**65.7, 65, 58 **2.**179 cm, 178 cm, 182 cm
3.$245.24, $200, $200 **4.a)**52, 53.5, 55 **b)**188, 188.5,
192 **5.a)**0.283 **b)**0.276 **c)**no **6.a)**322.5, 319
b)296.9, 308 **7.a)**$700 000 **b)**770 **c)**$909.09

8.a)$52.93 **b**)$25 **c**)$25 **9.**21 **10.a**)0.394 **b**)0.390
c)5 **d**)0.406 **11.**Answers may vary. **a**)3, 11, 12, 13,
14, 15, 16 **b**)41, 63, 64, 65, 66, 67, 68 **c**)0, 5, 5, 10,
11, 12, 13 **d**)9, 10, 11, 12, 15, 15, 33

INVESTIGATE, page 447
The seesaw will balance at 5.5, if 5.5 is the mean of
the numbers where the masses are placed. A seesaw
balances at the point which is the mean of the
positions of the masses when the masses are equal.

Exercises 13-4, page 449
Answers may vary.

Exercises 13-5, page 451
1.a)Median x-coordinates are 2 and 8. Median
y-coordinates are 2 and 4. **c**)Through (2,2) and (8,4)
2.a)Through (1955,387) and (1980,932) **b**)1150
(thousand) **3.a**)Through (1977,8.5) and (1984,14.2)
b)19% **4.a**)Through (1.4,6.7) and (5.2,10.1)
b)12 L/100 km **5.a**)Through (45.1,32.9) and
(62.1,50.4) **b**)70 m **6.b**)Through (1973,24) and
(1984,30) **c**)33 **7.a**)Through (1972,81) and
(1982,94). No. **b**)Through (1945,34.72) and
(1980,363.51). No.

Exercises 13-6, page 453
1.a)3, 6, 6, 6, 8 **b**)2, 6, 6, 5, 5 **c**)12, 18, 18, 18, 27, 27
d)39, 35, 27, 24, 24, 17 **2.a**)24, 22, 22, 24, 33, 33, 25,
25, 25, 27, 28, 30, 30, 30, 25, 23 **b**)Answers may
vary. **3.a**)325, 387, 448, 640, 709, 932, 843
b)Answers may vary. **4.a**)8.6, 8.5, 8.3, 7.6, 6.8, 6.8,
12.1, 13.8, 14.2, 14.2 **b**)Answers may vary.

Computer Power, page 454
1.b)Through (12.5,5.4) and (72.5,12.17) **c**)21.2
million tonnes **2.**Answers may vary. **3.b**)11, 11, 15,
15, 14, 14, 21, 21, 18, 18, 21, 21, 21, 25, 25, 35, 25,
35, 56, 56, 36, 34, 34, 29, 56, 45, 55, 55, 55, 81, 59, 59
d)Answers may vary.

Exercises 13-7, page 460
1.b) **2.c**) **3.b**) **4.a**), **b**)Answers may vary. **5.a**),
b)Answers may vary. **c**)76, 74, 78 **6.a**), **b**)Answers
may vary. **c**)5667.5, 5679, 5535 **7.a**), **b**)Answers
may vary. **8.a**), **b**)Answer may vary. **c**)$48.91, $25,
$25

INVESTIGATE, page 461
Answers may vary. **a**)farther from the results for the
population **b**)closer to the results for the poplulation

Mathematics Around Us, page 462
1.a)The tagged buffaloes become thoroughly mixed
with the untagged buffaloes and the population
remains constant. **b**)1275 **2.**1250 **3.**3800

Exercises 13-8, page 464
1.0.49

2.

1	2	3	4	5	6
0.163	0.170	0.159	0.162	0.177	0.169

It was fair because the relative frequencies of the
outcomes are close **3.**0.026 **4.**0.38 **5.a**), **b**),
c)Answers may vary. **d**)It approximates 0.5 more
and more closely **6.**Answers may vary. **7.a**), **b**), **c**),
d)Answers may vary **e**)200, 400, 40 **8.a**), **b**)Answers
may vary. **c**)Answers may vary, but should
approximate: 125, 42, 83 **9.**621 **10.**0 : 889, A : 700,
B : 166, AB : 95 **11.**A, A **12.**red : 391 blue : 234
yellow : 625 **13.a**), **b**), **c**)Answers may vary.

Exercises 13-9, page 467
1.a)0.25 **b**)0.5 **c**)0.077 **d**)0.038 **e**)0.077 **f**)0.115
2.a)0.182 **b**)0.091 **c**)0.364 **d**)0.636 **e**)0 **f**)0.273
3.a)0.008 **b**)0.005 **c**)0.003 **4.a**)0.000 01 **b**)0.0001
c)0.0012 **d**)0 **e**)1 **5.a**)0.167 **b**)0.5 **c**)0.333 **d**)0.5
6.a)0.125 **b**)0.5 **c**)0.5 **d**)0.25 **e**)0.375 **f**)0.875 **g**)0
h)1 **7.a**)0.333 **b**)0.5 **c**)0.083 **d**)0.042 **8.a**)8 **b**)83
c)833 **9.a**)7 **b**)6 **c**)2 **10.** No, reasons may vary.
Passing a test depends on reasons other than chance.
For example, the amount of preparation for the test
and the difficulty of the test are factors. **11.a**)0.3
b)0.25 **c**)0.45 **d**)0.55 **e**)0.75 **f**)0 **12.** B **13.** 0.4
14.a)500 **b**)77 **c**)250 **d**)19 **15.a**)0.24 **b**)0.462 **c**)0
d)0.08 **16.a**)i)0.04 ii)0.51 iii)0.15 **b**)11 000 **c**)350
17.a)0.85 **b**)0.56 **18.a**)0.1433 **b**)greater **c**)0.1433

Exercises 13-10, page 471
1.a)0.125 **b**)0.25 **2.**0.028 **3.**0.0625 **4.a**)0.125
b)0.0156 **5.a**)0.300 **b**)0.008, 0.240 **6.a**)0.64 **b**)0.04
7.0.0016 **8.a**)0.391 **b**)0.357 **9.a**)0.36, 0.333
b)0.198, 0.167 **c**)0.36, 0.347 **10.a**)0.333 **b**)0.167
c)0.056 **11.a**)0.0625, 0.0059, 0.0533 **b**)0.0588,
0.0045, 0.0498 **12.a**)0.0002 **b**)0.013 **c**)0.174
13.0.109, 0.382, 0.018 **14.a**)0.25 **b**)0.1875 **c**)0.5625
15.0.0833; 0.0769. All months are equally
probable. **16.a**)0.0001 **b**)0.402 **c**)0.132 **d**)0.0008
17.a)0.072 **b**)0.068 **18.a**)0.191 **b**)0.145 **19.**0.0625
20.0.000 03

Problem Solving, page 475
1.yes **2.**Answers may vary. $123 - 45 - 67 + 89 = 100$
3.Answers may vary. **a**)$1 + 23 + 45 + 6 + 7 + 8 + 9 =$
99 **b**)$9 + 8 + 7 + 65 + 4 + 3 + 2 + 1 = 99$ **4.a**)1. is
false. 2. is true. 3. is false. **b**)1. and 2. are neither true
nor false. **5.**sides 5.6 cm, 9.1 cm, or 10.4 cm **6.**white
7.a)27 **b**)21 **c**)45 **8.a**)3 **b**)1 unit, $\sqrt{2}$ units, $\sqrt{3}$ units

Review Exercises, page 476

1.a)24 **b**)28 **c**)152 **2.a**)175 **b**)85 **c**)45 **3.a**)11.25 h
b)16.875 h **c**)13.275 h **d**)16.875 h **4.a**)2, 3, 0 **b**)10
c)67 **d**)30 **7.**64.2, 63, 62 **8.b**)Through (1973, 184)
and (1983, 89); 13 000 **10.a**), **b**), Answers may vary.
c)171.9, 174, 176 **11.**0.027 **12.**390 **13.a**)0.25 **b**)0.5
c)0.077 **d**)0.038 **e**)0.231 **f**)0.115 **14.a**)0.2 **b**)0.3
c)0.5 **d**)0.7 **e**)0.8 **f**)0 **15.a**)0.167 **b**)0.333 **c**)0.5
d)0.333 **16.a**)0.340 **b**)0.318 **17.a**)0.0625, 0.0059,
0.0133 **b**)0.0588, 0.0045, 0.0113 **18.a**)0.2143
b)0.2143 **c**)0.036 **19.**0.001 **20.a**)0.25 **b**)0.1875
c)0.375 **d**)0

Chapter 14

Exercises 14–1 page 482

1.a)$\dfrac{AB}{DE} = \dfrac{BC}{EF} = \dfrac{AC}{DF}$ **b**)$\dfrac{RK}{CP} = \dfrac{KA}{PE} = \dfrac{RA}{CE}$

c)$\dfrac{PQ}{JK} = \dfrac{QR}{KL} = \dfrac{PR}{JL}$ **d**)$\dfrac{MS}{NR} = \dfrac{SA}{RA} = \dfrac{MA}{NA}$

2.a)$\dfrac{RS}{JK} = \dfrac{ST}{KL} = \dfrac{RT}{JL}$, $x = 6.0$

b)$\dfrac{WN}{BT} = \dfrac{NC}{TL} = \dfrac{WC}{BL}$, $x = 6.7$

c)$\dfrac{XY}{PQ} = \dfrac{YZ}{QR} = \dfrac{XZ}{PR}$, $x = 7.3$

d)$\dfrac{QE}{NT} = \dfrac{ES}{TC} = \dfrac{QS}{NC}$, $x = 17.1$ **5.a**)$x = 7.2$, $y = 7.8$
b)$x = 6.0$, $y = 7.5$ **c**)$x = 5.3$, $y = 8.0$ **d**)$x = 9.0$,
$y = 5.0$ **6.a**)$x = 4.8$, $y = 6.7$ **b**)$x = 6.4$, $y = 9.3$
c)$x = 15$, $y = 2$ **d**)$x = 10.5$, $y = 5.5$ **7.a**)5.4 m
b)5.2 m **8.**22.4 m **9.**18.7 m **10.**70 m **11.**$h_1 = 4.3$ m,
$h_2 = 9.6$ m **12.a**)$AB = 7.2$, $BC = 8.2$, $AC = 5.7$,
$DE = 10.8$, $EF = 12.4$, $DF = 8.5$
b)$\dfrac{AB}{DE} \doteq 0.67$ $\dfrac{BC}{EF} \doteq 0.66$ $\dfrac{AC}{DF} \doteq 0.67$,
$\triangle ABC \sim \triangle DEF$ **c**)yes **14.a**)75, 90, 105, 120, 135
b)2535

Exercises 14-2, page 490

1.a)0.364 **b**)0.577 **c**)0.754 **d**)1.000 **e**)1.428 **f**)1.963
g)2.904 **h**)14.300 **2.a**)35° **b**)43° **c**)64° **d**)73° **e**)14°
f)29° **g**)54° **h**)78° **3.a**)27° **b**)37° **c**)22° **d**)31° **e**)53°
f)68° **g**)51° **h**)55° **4.a**)CB, PQ, NM **b**)AB, AP, AM
5.a)i)0.667 ii)1.000 iii)1.667 iv)0.267 **b**)i)34° ii)45°
iii)59° iv)15° **6.a**)$\tan A = 0.533$, $\tan B = 1.875$
b)$\tan A = 1.333$, $\tan B = 0.750$ **c**)$\tan A = 0.952$,
$\tan B = 1.050$ **7.a**)$\angle A = 28°$, $\angle B = 62°$ **b**)$\angle A = 53°$,
$\angle B = 37°$ **c**)$\angle A = 44°$, $\angle B = 46°$ **8.a**)6.5 cm
b)15.5 cm **c**)37.3 m **d**)4.1 m **e**)3.5 cm **f**)1.7 m
g)7.7 m **h**)2.0 cm **9.a**)i)3.9 m ii)8.7 cm iii)16.5 cm
b)i)14° ii)27° iii)37° **10.a**)i)1.8 m ii)2.9 m iii)4.2 m
b)i)58° ii)67.4° iii)72.6° **11.a**)69 m **b**)80 m **c**)40 m

12.a)6435 m **b**)1° **13.a**)1176 m **b**)64° **14.a**)179 m
b)57° **15.**26.6°, 63.4° **16.**107 m **17.** $\angle P = 102.6°$,
$\angle Q = \angle R = 38.7°$ **18.** 55 mm **19.**38° **20.a**)45°
b)33.7° **c**)36.9° **21.a**)153° **b**)124° **c**)112°

INVESTIGATE, page 493

a)78.7°, 76.0°, 71.6°, 63.4°, 45.0°, 26.6°, 18.4°, 14.0°,
11.3° **b**)i)6 ii)12 iii)29 iv)58 **c**)i)6 ii)12 iii)29 iv)58

Exercises 14-3, page 497

1.a)0.500 **b**)0.978 **c**)0.927 **d**)0.326 **e**)0.848 **f**)0.766
g)0.309 **h**)0.500 **2.a**)37° **b**)73° **c**)39° **d**)77° **e**)12°
f)74° **g**)68° **h**)29° **3.a**)71° **b**)14° **c**)30° **d**)41° **e**)53°
f)65° **g**)39° **h**)27° **4.a**)BC, GR, LQ **b**)AB, AR, AL
c)AC, AG, AQ **5.a**)i)0.400 ii)0.417 iii)0.667
iv)0.750 **b**)i)24° ii)25° iii)42° iv)49° **6.a**)i)0.667
ii)0.800 iii)0.833 iv)0.625 **b**)i)48° ii)37° iii)34°
iv)51° **7.a**)0.385, 0.923, 0.923, 0.385 **b**)0.800, 0.600,
0.600, 0.800 **c**)0.862, 0.508, 0.508, 0.862 **d**)0.899,
0.438, 0438, 0.899 **8.a**)23°, 67° **b**)53°, 37° **c**)59°, 31°
d)64°, 26° **9.a**)5.3 cm **b**)14.1 cm **c**)3.5 cm **d**)13.4 m
e)5.3 cm **f**)23.8 m **g**)9.0 cm **h**)17.9 m
10.a)i)$AB = 21.4$ m, $BC = 12.9$ m ii)$AB = 24.4$ m,
$AC = 5.2$ m **b**)i)$\angle A = 24°$, $\angle C = 66°$ ii)$\angle A = 47°$,
$\angle C = 43°$ **11.a**)i)$PR = 28.3$ cm, $QR = 24.0$ cm
ii)$PR = 22.4$ cm, $QR = 16.7$ cm **b**)i)$\angle P = 58°$,
$\angle Q = 32°$ ii)$\angle P = 53°$, $\angle R = 37°$ **12.a**)9.6 m **b**)2.9 m
13.a)14.3 m **b**)53° **14.**5° **15.**98 m **16.**11°
17.115 mm **18.**$\angle A = 98°$, $\angle B = 41°$, $\angle B = 41°$,
$\angle D = 38°$, $\angle E = 71°$, $\angle F = 71°$ **19.**7.3 m **20.**17 cm
21.a)49 m **b**)92.6 m **22.**$AB = \cos A$, $BC = \sin A$

INVESTIGATE, page 500

1.$\sin A = \dfrac{\text{length of side opposite } \angle A}{\text{length of hypotenuse}}$

$\cos A = \dfrac{\text{length of side adjacent to } \angle A}{\text{length of hypotenuse}}$

and the hypotenuse is longer than either of the other 2
sides. Therefore, the sine and cosine for a triangle
must be less than 1. **2.a**)$\sin 30° = \cos 60°$ **b**)$\sin$
$80° = \cos 10°$ The sine of an angle equals the cosine of
an angle which is 90° minus that angle. The cosine of
an angle equals the sine of an angle which is 90°
minus that angle.

Exercises 14-4, page 502

1.a)$AC = 9.4$ mm, $\angle A = 32°$, $\angle C = 58°$
b)$EF = 10.4$ cm, $\angle D = 60°$, $\angle F = 30°$
c)$PR = 14.7$ cm, $\angle P = 52°$, $\angle Q = 38°$ **d**)$JL = 21.0$ m,
$\angle K = 51°$, $\angle J = 39°$ **e**)$UV = 26.1$ m, $\angle T = 42°$,
$\angle V = 48°$ **f**)$GH = 20.6$ km, $\angle G = 51°$, $\angle H = 39°$
2.a)$\angle C = 40°$, $CR = 8.3$ cm, $BC = 10.9$ cm
b)$\angle L = 25°$, $TA = 14.9$ m, $TL = 35.3$ m **c**)$\angle S = 55°$,
$DS = 10.3$ m, $DW = 14.7$ m **d**)$\angle N = 65°$,
$PN = 14.5$ cm, $NE = 34.2$ cm **e**)$\angle U = 35°$,

$RG = 14.3$ cm, $UR = 20.5$ cm **f)**$\angle Q = 68°$,
$QM = 8.2$ m, $MF = 20.4$ m **3.a)**$\angle C = 63°$, $AB = 9$,
$BC = 5$ **b)**$\angle C = 55°$, $AC = 18$, $BC = 11$ **c)**$\angle A = 40°$,
$AB = 13$, $BC = 15$ **d)**$\angle A = 28°$, $AB = 188$, $AC = 213$
e)$\angle A = 34°$, $\angle C = 56°$, $AC = 48$ **f)**$\angle A = 43°$,
$\angle C = 47°$, $BC = 33$ **4.**26.0 m **5.**432 m **6.**73 m. The
assumption is that the string is straight. **7.**10 cm
8.5 cm **9.**24 065 m **10.**74° **11.**2.9 m, 7.7 m
12.59 cm

9.a)0.602 **b)**0.407 **c)**0.883 **d)**0.819 **10.a)**68° **b)**36°
c)54° **d)**86° **11.a)i)**0.846, 0.538 **ii)**0.405, 0.919
iii)0.806, 0.591 **b)i)**58° **ii)**24° **iii)**54° **12.a)**14°, 76°
b)53°, 37° **c)**24°, 66° **13.a)**23.0, 32.8 **b)**11.3, 21.2
c)15.2, 32.6 **14.a)**$AB = 9.1$, $BC = 4.3$ **b)**$AB = 13.6$,
$BC = 11.0$ **c)**$AB = 10.8$, $BC = 7.2$ **15.**37.5 m
16.a)5.8 m **b)**5.5 m **17.**29 m **18.**137.4 m **19.**327 m
20.a)53° **b)**122.4 m

Mathematics Around Us, page 504
Banff: 27°, Lake Louise: 9°, Jasper: 33°

Exercises 14-5 page 506
1.56 m, 63° **2.**33 m **3.**90 m **4.**62 m **5.**5.3 m
6.8.57 m **7.a)**4.0 m **b)**3.5 m **8.**0.841 km **9.**9°
10.84 m **11.**23.5 cm **12.**8.5 cm **13.**1.4 m **14.**1 seat
3 m above, 1 seat 23 m above, 2 seats at each; 4.4 m,
8 m, 13 m, 18 m, 21.6 m **15.**21 m **16.**130.1 m
17.3.7 m

Problem Solving, page 509
2.Answers may vary. **3.**Right-side up **4.**Answers may
vary. 0, 1, 2, 3, 4, 5; 0, 1, 2, 6, 7, 8 with the 6 written
so that is also an up-side down 9. **5.a)**a distance equal
to its circumference. **b)**a distance equal to twice the
circumference of the can. **6.a)i)**yes **ii)**no **b)**Answers
may vary. For example,
1 6 5 2 3 4; 1 2 3 4 5 6; 1 2 3 6 5 4

Problem Solving, page 510
1.15° **2.**6.7 km **3.**Dive the numbers by 4. If the
remainder is 0 or 1, the number is in List A. If the
remainder is 2 or 3, the number is in List B. **4.**(1,2),
(1,–2), (4,2), or (4,–2) **5.**64 **6.**length of rectangle:
length of square = $\sqrt{7} : 1$
perimeter of rectangle: perimeter of square = $\sqrt{7}+1 : 2$
7.a)1, 3, 5, 3, 4, 6, 8, 10, 9, 11, 13, 11
b)Answers may vary. For example, replace the
numbers 0, 1, 2, 3, 4, 5, 6, 7 with 0, 3, 2, 5, 7, 4, 1, 6.
c)Answers may vary. For example, replace the
numbers 0, 1, 2, 3, 4, 5, 6, 7 with 0, 1, 3, 6, 2, 7, 5, 4.
8.a) Answers may vary. If $c = d + 1$, the binomials can
be factored. **b)**$x^2 + 5x + 6$ and $x^2 + 6x + 5$. **9.**40
10.28, 168 **11.**Yes. 100°, 64°, 16°

Review Exercises, page 511
1.a)$x = 22.2$, $y = 25.7$ **b)**$x = 2.1$, $y = 1.3$ **c)**$x = 42.0$,
$y = 22.5$ **d)**$x = 14.1$, $y = 20.9$ **2.a)**about 3400 km
b)about 1 340 000 km **3.a)**0.510 **b)**0.781 **c)**2.145
d)6.314 **4.a)**55° **b)**60° **c)**4° **d)**71° **5.a)**5.5 **b)**15.0
c)11.2 **6.a)**31° **b)**50° **c)**56° **7.**27°, 63° **8.**71.4 m

Absolute value, 9, 190
Alternate angles, 359
Altitude, 244
Angle (s),
    alternate, 136, 359
    corresponding, 359
    opposite, 352
    sum in a polygon, 185
    supplementary, 354
Angle sum theorem, 364
Area,
    of a circle, 78
    of a triangle, 9
Average, 444
Axioms, 357
    ASA, 372
    Congruence, 370-372
    Parallel lines, 359
    SAS, 371
    SSS, 370

Bar graph, 434
Base,
    of a power, 52
Bermuda Triangle, 11
Binomial(s), 88, 93
    differences of squares, 104-106
    product of, 88-91, 98, 101
Bisector,
    perpendicular, 244
Byte, 61

Calculator
    use of, 3, 18-20, 23-24, 60-61, 65,
      179
Cartesian coordinate system, 190
Centroid, 198
Circle,
    area of, 78, 227
    circumference, 402
Circle graph, 436
Clusters, 448
Coefficient, 46
    literal, 141
Coincident lines, 272
Collinear, 222
Composite number, 3-4
Compound interest, 50-51
Computer Power, 50-51, 169, 194-195,
    297, 332, 454-455
Computer programs, 6, 50-51, 169,
    195, 297, 332, 454-455
Cone,
    constructing a, 403
    slant height of, 403
    surface area, 408
    volume of, 47, 412

Congruence Axioms, 370-372
    ASA, 372
    SAS, 371
    SSS, 370
Congruent triangles, 370-376
Constant of proportionality, 224
Constant slope property, 218, 240-241
Coordinate(s),
    and calculation of slope, 201
    and midpoint of a line segment, 196
Coordinate geometry, 189-256
Copernicus, Nicolas, 65
Corresponding,
    angles, 359
    points, 302
    sides, 370
    vertices, 303
Cosine ratio, 494
Counterexample, 346, 351
Cube,
    types of diagonals, 29
Cube root, 19, 65
Cylinder,
    constructing a, 402
    surface area, 406
    volume of, 48

Decimal(s),
    form, 14-17
    patterns in, 15, 21
    repeating, 15-17, 21, 22
    terminating, 15-17, 22
Deductive Reasoning, 349-351
Degree,
    of a polynomial, 79
Denominator,
    common, 120
    lowest common, 120
    rationalizing the, 39-41
Density, 152
Dilatations, 321-326
    centre, 323
    enlargement, 322
    image, 321
    mapping rules, 322
    properties, 323
    reduction, 322
    scale factor, 321
Diophantine equation(s), 168-169
Diophantus, 168
Direct variation, 224
Distance formula, 191
Distributive law, 37, 84, 93, 140

Enlargement, 322
Equation(s),
    containing fractions, 141-147, 165,
     185

in one variable, 140-147
in two variables, 164-169, 174-177,
    180-188, 223-237, 240-256
involving rational expressions,
    144-147, 181-185, 187, 188
linear, 164-169, 185-186, 188,
    223-237, 239-256
non-linear, 174-177, 180-184, 186
of a straight line, 164-167, 186,
    217-237, 239-254
quadratic, 176-177, 180-184, 186,
    188
roots of, 140, 142-143
slope y-intercept form of, 234-237,
    247
solving by inspection, 55
solving in one variable, 140-147, 185,
    188
solving in three variables, 274-275
solving in two variables, 265-270
solving problems with, 140-142,
    158-161, 184-186, 188, 279-287,
    292-296
solving quadratic, 180-184, 186
standard form of, 240-252
writing, 224, 226-231, 235-237,
    239-244, 251-254, 256
Equilateral triangle, 28
    area of, 183
Euclid, 387
Euclidean algorithm, 6
Euclidean geometry, 387
Euler, Leonhard, 49, 152
Exponent(s), 45-70, 72, 76, 79
    in formulas, 46-49, 51, 65, 67, 76-78
    fractional, 65-67
    integral, 52-58
    laws, 56-58, 65, 66, 76
Extrapolating, 163, 214, 232

Factor,
    common, 2, 6, 93-96, 99, 104, 111
    greatest common (g.c.f.), 2, 4-6, 43,
     69, 93, 94, 169
    perfect-square, 30, 31
    prime, 3, 4, 43
    scale, 321
Factoring, 93-96, 98-106
    by decomposition, 101
    difference of squares, 104-106
    perfect-square trinomials, 98
    quadratic equations, 180-184
    trinomials, 98-106, 187
Fibonacci sequence, 12
Formula(s), 9, 17, 62, 76, 94, 150-154,
    185-186, 223, 225, 227
    exponents in, 46-49, 51, 65, 67, 68,
     76-78, 106, 134, 181, 183

substituting in, 9, 10, 17, 46-48, 51, 62, 65, 67, 68, 77, 78, 80, 81, 106, 132-135, 140, 142, 145, 146, 150-155, 164, 166, 177, 181, 183, 185, 186, 188, 225, 229, 230, 231
writing, 42, 47, 48, 80, 81, 86, 87, 96, 106, 133-135, 177
Four square problem, 49
Frequency,
  polygon, 441
  table, 440

Geometry, Euclidean, 387
Graphing
  linear equations in two variables, 164-167, 186, 188, 223-237, 240-254
  linear inequalities in one variable, 148-149
  linear inequalities in two variables, 170-173, 186, 188
  non-linear relations, 174-177, 186, 188
Gwennap Pit, 75

Half-plane, 170
Hemisphere, 78, 96
Histogram, 435
Hypotenuse, 25, 26, 36, 196, 197

Image,
  reflection, 316
  rotation, 311
  translation, 303
Indirect proof, 392-393
Inductive reasoning, 344-345
Inequality(ies), 148, 149
  in one variable, 148-149
  in two variables, 170-173, 186, 188
Inscribed circle, 154
Integer(s), 5-8, 14, 21, 23, 52, 98, 100, 102, 103, 110, 156, 159, 160 168, 169, 239, 246
Intercepts, 246
  x-, 239, 245, 248, 249, 254
  y-, 234-237, 239, 245-249, 251-254, 256
Interest
  compound, 50-51
  rate, 42, 50-51
  simple, 42
Interpolating, 163, 174, 214, 232
Intersecting lines,
  number of solutions, 272
Invariant,
  length, 312, 317

point, 311
  properties, 306
Irrational numbers, 21-24, 26, 30-41, 43, 44, 92
Isosceles triangle, 26, 211
Isosceles Triangle Theorem, 377

Kepler, Johann, 65
Kilopascal (unit of pressure), 48

Lagrange, Joseph, 49
Lambert, Johann, 24
Line(s),
  coincident, 272
  equation of, 165
  equation of image, 328-331
  intersecting, 272
  parallel, 136, 190, 205-208, 210, 216, 219-222, 237, 243, 250-252, 254-256
  perpendicular, 196, 208-211, 216, 219-222, 237, 243, 250-252, 254-256
  property of equations of, 241
Line graph, 435
Linear relation(s), 164-173, 223-237, 239-254, 256
Linear Systems
  number of solutions, 271-272
  properties of, 261-262
  solving by addition or subtraction, 265-266
  solving by graphing, 259
  solving by substitution, 269
Line of best fit, 162-163, 214, 232
Literal coefficients, 141

Maclaurin, Colin, 274
Mathematical Mind, The, 24, 49, 129, 168, 199, 274, 348, 387, 424-425
Mathematics Around Us, 11, 42, 64, 75, 97, 119, 155, 162-163, 214, 232, 283, 327, 342-343, 398, 428, 462, 504
Mean, 198, 444
  measure of central tendency, 445
Measures of central tendency, 444-445
Median,
  as a measure of central tendency, 444-445
  fit line, 450, 454
  of a triangle, 198, 215, 216, 244, 254, 255
Midpoint, 196-199
  coordinates of, 196-199, 215, 216, 254, 255

Mode, 445
Monomials, 72-78, 84, 98, 102
  adding and subtracting, 72-74, 79
  factoring, 93-96
  multiplying and dividing, 76-78, 187
  product of a polynomial and, 84-87, 187
Multiple, 2
  least common (l.c.m.), 2, 4, 5, 43, 69

Negative reciprocals, 208, 219, 250
Networks, 194
  shortest, 194-195
Nomogram, 155
Non-linear relation(s), 174-177
Number line, 148-149
Numbers,
  composite, 3
  irrational, 21-24, 26, 30-41, 43, 44, 92
  natural, 2, 3, 4, 49, 92, 131, 136
  negative, 7, 9, 19, 92
  positive, 6, 9, 19, 20
  rational, 14-17, 21-23, 41, 44
  real, 22, 30, 36, 202, 221, 255
Numerator, 15, 39, 111, 116, 126, 147, 161

Operations, 52, 66
Opposite Angle Theorem, 352-353
Ordered pair(s), 164, 165, 170
Orientation,
  in reflections, 317

Pantograph, 327
Parallel lines, 136, 190, 205-208, 210, 216, 219-222, 237, 243, 250-252, 254-256
  axiom, 360
  theorem, 359
Parallelogram 197, 205, 207, 215, 216, 244, 249, 255, 382
  area of 10,
  properties of, 383
Partial variation, 228-231, 253, 256
Percent, 213, 238, 239
Perfect cube, 5
Perfect square, 5, 22, 30, 31, 49, 98, 100, 131, 136
Perpendicular bisector, 244
Perpendicular lines, 196, 208-211, 216, 219-222, 237, 243, 250-252, 254-256
Point, invariant, 311
Polygon,
  number of diagonals, 87

regular, 146
sum of angles, 185
Polyhedron, 152
Polynomials, 71-108, 110
adding and subtracting, 78-81, 187
degree of, 79
evaluating, 187
factoring, 93-96, 98-106, 108
multiplying, 88-91
multiplying by monomials, 84-87, 187
simplifying, 79-81, 84-91, 107, 187
Population, 456
Power(s), 52-55, 57-59, 65, 66, 70, 76
Prediction, 463
Prime,
factor, 3, 4, 43
factorization property, 3
number, 2, 3, 4, 106, 121
relatively, 6
Principal, 42
Prism rectangular, 29, 76, 97
Probability, 466
Problem solving,
Check for Hidden Assumptions, 62-63
Choose the Strategy, 136, 298, 510
Consider All Cases, 474-475
Draw a Diagram 238-239
Introduce a Variable, 130-131
Look for a Counterexample, 346-347
Look for a Pattern, 12-13
Solve a Simpler Problem, 82-83
Transform, Solve, Transform, 336-337
Use a Graph, 212-213
Use a Model, 508-509
Use a Table, 288-289
Use Indirect Proof, 392-393
Use Spatial Visualization, 416-417
Work Backwards, 178-179
Proofs, transformational, 394-397
Properties,
invariant, 306
Pyramid, 28, 106
Pythagoras, 25
Pythagorean Theorem, 25-29, 190, 388

Quadrant, 171
Quadratic relation(s), 176, 177, 180-184, 186, 188

Radical(s), 18, 19
adding and subtracting, 33-36
combined operations, 37, 38
dividing, 39-42

entire, 30, 31
like and unlike, 33
mixed, 30, 31, 44
multiplying, 30-32
sign, 18
simplifying, 30-41
Ramanujan, Srinivasa, 129
Random number table, 459
Rational expression(s), 109-138, 144, 145
adding and subtracting, 122-130, 187
applications of, 132-135
dividing and multiplying, 116-118, 187
equations involving, 144-147, 181-185, 187
equivalent, 122, 123
evaluating, 110, 113
simplifying, 110-118, 122, 124-130, 137, 138, 187
Ratio(s)
cosine, 494
sine, 494
tangent, 487
Rational numbers, 41, 44
in decimal form, 14-17, 21-23, 43
in fraction form, 14-17, 22, 23, 43
Real numbers, 1-44, 202, 221, 255
Reasoning,
deductive, 349-351
inductive, 344-345
Reciprocal, 57, 116, 136
negative, 208, 219, 250
Rectangle graph, 436
Rectangular prism, 29, 76, 97
Reduction, 322
Reflection,
image, 316
mapping rules, 316
properties of, 317
reflection line, 316
Relation(s),
linear, 164-173, 223-237, 239-254, 256
non-linear, 174-177
quadratic, 175, 177, 180-184, 186, 188
Rhombus, 322
Right triangle, 25-29, 36, 191, 196, 197, 208, 210, 211, 222, 252
Roots
cube, 18-20, 65, 66
fourth, 19, 20
fifth, 19, 20
of an equation, 140, 142, 143, 184
square, 18-20, 65, 66, 180
Rotation,
centre, 310

image, 311
mapping rule, 311
properties of, 312

Sample,
random, 456
Scale factor, 321
Scatterplots 448-455
clusters, 448
median fit line, 450, 454
smoothing, 452, 455
Scientific notation, 59-61, 70
Shanks, William, 21
Similar triangles, 480
Simple interest, 42
Sine ratio, 494
Slant height, 403
Slope(s), 200-21, 215, 216, 218-222, 233-237, 240-243, 246-256
of parallel lines, 205-208, 210, 216, 219, 222, 237, 243, 250-252, 254-256
of perpendicular lines, 208-211, 216, 219, 222, 237, 243, 250-252, 254-256
property of constant, 218, 240, 241
Slope y-intercept form, 234-237, 247
Smoothing graphs, 452, 455
Speed,
average, 62-63, 212-213
Sphere,
surface area of, 420
volume of, 421
Square, 350, 386
Square root, 18-20, 22, 23
exact, 18
principal, 18, 25, 65
Stem-and-Leaf table, 440
Supplementary Angle Theorem, 354
Surface area,
of a cone, 407
of a cylinder, 87, 96, 406
of a sphere, 78, 420

Tangent ratio, 487
Term(s), 46, 48, 72, 88, 180
like, 33, 72, 79
Theorem,
angle sum, 364
isosceles triangle, 377
opposite angle, 352
parallel lines, 360
Pythagorean, 388
supplementary angle, 354
Transformations, 302
applications, 333-335
mapping rule, 302

Translating words into symbols, 156, 157, 276-278
Translation(s), 305-309
  image, 303
  mapping rule, 306
  properties of, 307
Transversal, 136, 359
Tree diagram, 470
Triangle(s),
  area of, 9-11, 183
  congruent, 370-376
  equilateral, 28
  isosceles, 26, 191, 211
  right, 25-29, 36, 191, 196, 197, 208, 210, 211, 222, 252
  similar, 480
Trigonometric ratios, 487, 494
  applications of, 505-507
Trinomials, 88
  factoring, 92-96, 98-106

Variable, 46-48, 72, 93, 110-113, 120, 144, 145, 152-154, 156, 181, 185
  isolating the, 140, 180
  solving in one, 140-147, 185, 188
  solving in three, 274-275
  solving in two, 265-270
Variation,
  direct, 223-227, 253, 256
  partial, 228-231, 253, 256
Volume,
  of a cone, 47, 76, 412
  of a cylinder, 48, 76, 77, 96, 411
  of a rectangular prism, 76, 97
  of a sphere, 68, 76-78, 421
  of a square-based pyramid, 106